Staci Harrison

W9-APD-726

PEARSON   ALWAYS LEARNING

Student Workbook with Procedures

to accompany

Pearson's Comprehensive Medical Assisting: Administrative and Clinical Competencies

Custom Edition

Sig endoscopy

Taken from:
Student Workbook for Pearson's Comprehensive Medical Assisting,
Second Edition
by Nina Beaman, Lorraine Fleming-McPhillips, Kristiana Sue Routh,
Robyn Gohsman, and Stacia Reagan with Lori Tyler

Cover Image: Courtesy of Photodisc/Getty Images

Taken from:

Student Workbook for Pearson's Comprehensive Medical Assisting, Second Edition
by Nina Beaman, Lorraine Fleming-McPhillips, Kristiana Sue Routh, Robyn Gohsman, and Stacia Reagan with
Lori Tyler
Copyright © 2011 by Pearson Education, Inc.
Published by Pearson
Upper Saddle River, NJ 07458

Copyright © 2013 by Pearson Learning Solutions
All rights reserved.

Permission in writing must be obtained from the publisher before any part of this work may be reproduced or
transmitted in any form or by any means, electronic or mechanical, including photocopying and recording, or
by any information storage or retrieval system.

All trademarks, service marks, registered trademarks, and registered service marks are the property of their
respective owners and are used herein for identification purposes only.

Pearson Learning Solutions, 501 Boylston Street, Suite 900, Boston, MA 02116
A Pearson Education Company
www.pearsoned.com

Printed in the United States of America

8 9 10 11 12 V011 18 17 16 15

000200010271769339

JL

PEARSON

ISBN 10: 1-269-31172-7
ISBN 13: 978-1-269-31172-4

Contents

© 2011 Pearson Education, Inc.

INTRODUCTION

This student workbook is designed as a study guide and practice tool to accompany the student text, *Pearson's Comprehensive Medical Assisting, Second Edition*. Read the chapter outlines and use the study guide to reinforce what you have learned. Test your knowledge of medical terminology by completing the variety of activities in the Key Terminology Review section. Measure whether you have achieved the learning objectives in each chapter by completing the exercises in the Applied Practice and Learning Activities sections of the workbook. Apply your knowledge to real life situations by answering the Critical Thinking Questions. Use outside resources to complete the research activity at the end of each chapter.

Each chapter of this student workbook includes the following:

Chapter Outline: This is a list of the major content areas in the chapter. Review each of the topics and refer to your textbook for any topics that remain unclear to you.

Student Study Guide: This is of material presented in the chapter. Fill in the blanks, or answer the questions by following PowerPoint presentations in class, or reading through your text.

Applied Practice: Use the knowledge you learned in the chapter to complete these activities.

Learning Activities: These questions/tasks allow you to measure whether or not you have achieved the learning objectives for the chapter.

Key Terminology Review: This section tests your knowledge of the medical terminology presented in the chapter.

Critical Thinking Questions: These challenging questions allow you to apply your knowledge to real-life situations.

Research Activity: Use outside sources to complete these activities and go beyond the classroom.

© 2011 Pearson Education, Inc.

CHAPTER 1
Medical Assisting: The Profession

CHAPTER OUTLINE

General review of the chapter:

History of Medical Assisting
Education and Training for the Medical Assistant
Role of the Medical Assistant
Characteristics of a Good Medical Assistant
Certifying Professional Organizations
Career Opportunities

STUDENT STUDY GUIDE

Use the following guide to assist in your learning of the concepts from the chapter.

I. The History and Training of Medical Assistants

   1. Steps in the History of Trained Medical Assistants

      A. Originally MAs received their training

      _____.

      B. The increase in responsibility and _____ issues led to the need for medical assistants to be more formally trained.

      C. Prior to the formal training of medical assistants, _____ were in higher demand to assist physicians.

   2. The AAMA

      A. The AAMA as the acronym for the

      _____.

      B. The AAMA was founded by _____.

      C. In the year _____, the AAMA was organized.

   3. AAMA Definition of a Medical Assistant

      A. According to the AAMA's definition of medical assistants, MAs work primarily in _____ settings.

      B. Medical assistants perform both _____ and _____ procedures.

   4. Formal Training for the Medical Assistant

      A. Certificate training varies from _____ weeks to a yearlong program and focuses typically on _____ skills.

      B. Diploma MA programs are similar to certificate programs but focus on both _____ skills.

      C. Medical assistant degree programs are approximately _____ years in length.

5. Accreditation

   A. Accreditation is a _____ process.

   B. Accreditation ensures that a program in a school meets or exceeds _____.

6. Accrediting Agencies for MA Programs

   i. _____

   ii. _____

7. Units, Modules, and/or Courses of Instruction Typically Found in an MA Program

   i. _____

   ii. _____

   iii. _____

   iv. _____

   v. _____

   vi. _____

   vii. _____

   viii. _____

   ix. _____

   x. _____

   xi. _____

8. The Medical Assistant Externship

   A. Is a _____ component of an MA program.

   B. Externships take place in _____, _____, or _____ settings.

II. Role and Responsibilities of the Medical Assistant

   1. Role of the Medical Assistant

      A. The role of the MA is to _____ the physician.

   2. Places of Employment for MAs

      i. _____

      ii. _____

      iii. _____

      iv. _____

      v. _____

   3. Duties of the Medical Assistant

      A. Duties typically _____ from office to office.

      B. _____ and _____ of setting determine the types of duties the medical assistant will perform.

      C. Duties vary due to _____ and _____ regulations and guidelines.

   4. Administrative Duties

      A. _____ nonpatients and visitors is one example of the MA's administrative duties.

      B. During the physician's absence it is up to the medical assistant to _____ the office.

   5. Clinical Responsibilities

      A. Clinical responsibilities of the MA include _____ patients in preparation for physical exams and procedures.

      B. Prior to a physical exam, the MA may need to obtain a patient's _____ history.

      C. Inventory control may involve the _____ and _____ of supplies.

   6. The Occupational Analysis of the CMA (AAMA) 2007–2008

      A. Defines _____ for medical assisting.

      B. Study used a document called the _____.

      C. Study was revised in the year _____ and again in _____.

© 2011 Pearson Education, Inc.

7. General, Clinical, and Administrative Skills of the CMA (AAMA)
    A. Identifies three major categories of competences of entry-level MAs
        i. _____
        ii. _____
        iii. _____

8. General Characteristics of a Good MA
    A. Ability to perform _____ and _____ skills.
    B. _____ cares about others.
    C. Ability to _____ and get along with others.

9. How to Present a Professional Image
    A. Develop a basic _____ of human behavior.
    B. Exhibit good daily personal _____ and _____ habits.
    C. Provide _____ care.

III. Certification and Career Opportunities for the MA
    1. MA Certifying Organizations
        i. _____
        ii. _____
        iii. _____
        iv. _____

    2. American Association of Medical Assistants
        A. Headquarters are located in _____.
        B. Key association in the field of _____.
        C. Offers _____ credential.

    3. AAMA Certification Exam
        A. Offered to graduates of programs accredited by _____ or _____.
        B. Computerized exams are available _____ the year.
        C. _____ indicates that the candidate has met the standards of the AAMA for being an MA.

    4. American Medical Technologists
        A. Provides a _____ certification exam for MAs.
        B. _____ is awarded to candidates who pass the AMT certification exam.
        C. RMA certification exam focuses on three areas:
            i. _____
            ii. _____
            iii. _____

    5. AMT Certification Requirements for Applicants
        A. Be of good _____ character.
        B. Graduate must have graduated from an _____ program/organization.
        C. Applicant must have completed a minimum of _____ clock-hours or _____.

    6. General Medical Assisting Knowledge
        i. _____
        ii. _____
        iii. _____
        iv. _____
        v. _____
        vi. _____

© 2011 Pearson Education, Inc.   *Medical Assisting: The Profession*

7. National Center for Competency Testing
   A. Issues the _____ credential.
   B. Candidate must be a _____ graduate and have completed an _____ program or provide documentation of 2 years of _____ experience.
   C. Continuation of certification requires _____ hours per year of continuing education.

8. National Certified Medical Office Assistant
   A. Offered by the _____.
   B. To qualify a candidate must have a _____ diploma and must have completed a medical assisting program.
   C. Those who are not graduates of a MA program but are able to provide documentation of _____ years experience working as an MA are eligible to sit for the NCMA exam.

9. National Healthcareer Association
   A. Founded in the year _____.
   B. Grants the following two credentials: _____, _____.
   C. Qualified applicants must pass a _____ examination.

KEY TERMINOLOGY REVIEW

Complete the sentences below using the correct key terms found at the beginning of the chapter.

1. One of Juan's greatest qualities as a medical assistant was his ability to show _____ to his patients at the oncology clinic where he was employed.

2. The _____ was previously known as the Kansas Medical Assistant Society.

3. _____ is the process in which an institution voluntarily completes a process of determining whether or not their school meets or exceeds standards set forth by an accrediting body.

4. Malcolm was scheduled to take a Medical Assistant Review class that would prepare him to enter his _____; which was necessary to complete his medical assistant training.

5. Someone with _____ is honest, dependable, dedicated to high standards, and adheres to a code of values.

6. _____ is the issuance by an official body or professional organization of a certificate and credentials to one who has met the education and experience standards of the organization.

7. _____ provides oversight for the registration and testing of medical assistants, medical technologists, and phlebotomists.

8. _____ is awarded to candidates who pass the AMT certification examination.

9. After becoming certified as an RMA and acquiring additional administrative experience, a medical assistant can apply for the _____ credential.

10. Credential issued by the National Center for Competency Testing is the _____.

APPLIED PRACTICE

Give two examples of each positive quality that a medical assistant should possess.

© 2011 Pearson Education, Inc.

Quality	Example
Integrity	
Empathy	
Discretion	
Confidentiality	
Thoroughness	
Punctuality	
Congeniality	
Proactivity	
Competence	
Appearance	

LEARNING ACTIVITY: TRUE/FALSE

Indicate whether the following statements are true or false by placing a T or an F on the line that precedes each statement.

_____ 1. Historically, medical assistants were trained on the job by physicians.

_____ 2. An externship is typically a paid position for a period of 160 hours.

_____ 3. A medical assistant can only call him- or herself a nurse if certified by either an ABHES- or a CAAHEP-accredited medical assisting program.

_____ 4. Membership in the AAMA is not necessary to take the certification examination.

_____ 5. For the MA credential to remain current, it must be revalidated every 3 years.

_____ 6. The RMT is a nonprofit certifying body.

_____ 7. Entry-level medical assistants may find work as office managers, medical records managers, hospital unit secretaries, and instructors for medical assistant programs.

_____ 8. A rehabilitation center provides care to patients who need immediate medical treatment.

_____ 9. If you witness behaviors that are unsafe to workers, you must notify OSHA.

_____ 10. As a medical assistant, it is a crime to perform procedures that only nurses or physicians are licensed to do.

CRITICAL THINKING

Answer the following questions to the best of your ability. Utilize the textbook as a reference.

1. Sara Dunn is taking an administrative medical assisting class as part of her training toward earning a medical assisting certificate. She has been assigned the task of writing a paper that outlines the history of medical assisting. Part of the assignment is to include the milestones reached by this profession over the past 50 years. How should Sara outline this paper?

_____

_____

_____

_____

2. Diane Luder, CMA (AAMA), has been working as an administrative medical assistant in a busy pediatric office for 5 years. Diane's job has been in the billing and coding department. Helga, a colleague of Diane's in the billing and coding department, tells Diane about the benefits of joining a professional organization of coders. How might Diane benefit from joining such a group?

_____

_____

_____

_____

_____

RESEARCH ACTIVITY

Utilize Internet search engines to research the following topics and write a brief description of what is found. It is important to utilize reputable websites.

1. Research your state and local chapters of the American Association of Medical Assistants. What information is available? When and where are meetings located? If a chapter does not exist in your area, what are the requirements for starting a chapter?

_____

_____

_____

_____

_____

_____

_____

_____

_____

© 2011 Pearson Education, Inc.

CHAPTER 2
Medical Science: History and Practice

CHAPTER OUTLINE

General review of the chapter:

History of Medicine
Medical Practitioners
Medical Practice Acts
Health Care Costs and Payments
Types of Medical Practices
Medical and Surgical Specialties
Health Care Institutions
Allied Health Professionals
Centers for Disease Control and Prevention (CDC)

STUDENT STUDY GUIDE

Use the following guide to assist in your learning of the concepts from the chapter.

I. The History of Medicine

1. Code of Hammurabi

    A. Used by _____ physicians in 3000 B.C.
    B. Laws related to the _____.
    C. Hammurabi was _____.

2. Early Contributions

    A. Personal hygiene, the sanitary preparation of food, and other matters of public health were pioneered by the practices of the _____ culture.
    B. Some records of early _____ practitioners depict them using nonpoisonous snakes to treat the wounds of patients.

3. The Caduceus

    A. The Caduceus is the recognized symbol for _____.

4. Other Early Contributions to Medicine

    A. Herbal medical remedies originating from ancient _____ are recorded as early as 800 B.C.
    B. The _____ culture wrote about human blood pulses around the time of 250 B.C.

5. Early Medicinal Remedies Still Used Today

    A. _____ used to treat heart patients.
    B. _____ from the foxglove plant to regulate and strengthen the heartbeat.
    C. _____ to treat urinary tract infections.

6. Fifth Century to 16th Century

    A. During this time frame _____ progress was made in medical practices.

    B. _____ epidemics occurred during this medieval period.

    C. Wealthy individuals were treated by surgeons, others were treated by _____.

7. Hippocrates

    A. Known as the _____.

    B. Shifted medicine from _____ to science.

    C. Stressed the body's _____ nature.

8. The Hippocratic Oath

    A. The oath serves as a widely used _____ guide for physicians.

    B. When taking the oath, physicians pledge to work for the _____ of patients, to _____ no deadly drugs, and to do no _____ to patients.

9. Galen

    A. Stressed the value of _____.

    B. Founded _____.

    C. Known as the _____.

10. Other Influential Individuals of Early Medicine

    A. _____ was the first individual to use a telescope to study the skies, leading to the invention of the microscope.

    B. John Hunter is known as the Founder of _____.

    C. The first individual to perform the first vaccination using the smallpox vaccine was _____.

11. Advancements made in Medicine During the 19th Century

    A. Discovered that certain diseases and wound infections were caused by _____.

    B. Use of _____ microscopes.

    C. Improved knowledge of the _____ body through accurate documentation.

12. Influential Individuals in Medicine During the 19th Century

    A. _____ established the science of bacteriology.

    B. Joseph Lister introduced the _____ system in surgery.

    C. _____ traced the cause of puerperal sepsis.

    D. One of the original "microbe hunters" was _____.

13. Other Major Advancements During the 19th Century

    A. _____ discovered x-rays.

    B. The discovery of radium by _____ and _____.

    C. _____ worked in the field of psychiatry.

14. Contributions from Americans in the 19th Century

    A. Both _____ and _____ discovered the use of ether.

    B. _____ helped to conquer yellow fever.

15. Influential Women in Medicine

    A. _____ is known as the founder of modern nursing.

    B. _____ established the American Red Cross.

II. The Practice of Medicine

  1. Title of Doctor

    A. Designates a person who holds a _____ degree.

    B. Practicing medicine requires a minimum of _____ years of education and training.

© 2011 Pearson Education, Inc.

2. Doctor of Osteopathy
   A. Learns the skill of _____ therapy.
   B. Places greater emphasis on the relationship between the _____ and the
      _____.
   C. Attends school of _____.
3. Medical Practice Acts
   A. Indicates who must be _____ to perform certain procedures.
   B. Designates reports that must be made to the _____.
   C. Denotes _____ associated with a license.
4. Ways a Medical License May Be Granted
   i. _____
   ii. _____
   iii. _____
5. Causes for Suspension or Revoking of a Medical License
   i. _____
   ii. _____
   iii. _____
6. Types of Medical Practices
   i. _____
   ii. _____
   iii. _____
   iv. _____
   v. _____
   vi. _____
7. Categories of Hospitals
   i. _____
   ii. _____
   iii. _____
   iv. _____
8. Outpatient Surgical Centers
   A. Facility where _____ procedures are performed.
   B. Also known as _____ surgical centers.
   C. Surgeries typically require _____ recovery time.
9. Urgent Care Centers
   A. Offer quick care for non-_____ situations.
   B. In some managed care systems, these centers may be designated as a _____ facility.
10. Types of Long-Term Care Institutions
   i. _____
   ii. _____
   iii. _____
   iv. _____
11. Hospice
   A. Emphasizes improved quality of care for the _____.
   B. Most hospice care is provided at _____.
12. National Health Care Skill Standards
   A. Developed to define the body of knowledge and _____ _____ health care workers
      should possess for entry-level and technical-level positions.

B. _____ standards are used by schools, colleges, and health care facilities to establish curriculum and competencies.

C. _____ cluster careers include those that involve the health care status of the patient.

13. Diagnostic Career Cluster

    A. Careers that involve _____, _____, and reporting patient information.

    B. Laboratory technicians are skilled in _____ blood, urine, lymph, and body tissue.

    C. Phlebotomists are skilled in _____ blood.

14. Information Services Career Cluster

    A. Careers involved with _____ patient information.

    B. Health information technologists _____ the permanent records relating to patient's condition and treatment.

    C. The job that entails being responsible for clerical duties and other communications duties in hospitals are those of a _____.

15. Environmental Services Career Cluster

    A. Careers involved with the patient's _____ _____ environment.

    B. Career examples in this cluster include _____, _____, _____, and _____.

16. Centers for Disease Control and Prevention (CDC)

    A. Division of the _____.

    B. Purpose is to safeguard public health by _____ and _____ disease.

    C. Act as a resource for the _____ _____.

KEY TERMINOLOGY REVIEW

Complete the sentences below using the correct key terms found at the beginning of the chapter.

1. The medical specialty _____ treats patients who are obese.

2. _____ is a medical specialty that treats abnormal responses to acquired hypersensitivity to substances with medical methods, including testing and desensitization.

3. _____ shows that an individual has met the educational/experience standards in their profession.

4. Malcolm is dying of cancer and is now receiving _____ care.

5. A disease that affects many people in different countries at the same time is called a _____.

6. _____ provides proof that the individual has been authorized by a government agency to perform work in their profession.

7. To numb the pain, Dr. Antolik gave his patient local _____ prior to the removal of an in-grown toenail.

8. Mrs. Krichko took her anatomy and physiology class to the local morgue to view a _____ and witness its dissection for pathological study.

9. Rates of disease or illness are called _____.

10. _____ is a hospital payment system that classifies each Medicare patient according to his or her illness.

APPLIED PRACTICE

Match the early contributor of medicine with his or her accomplishment.

© 2011 Pearson Education, Inc.

a. Hippocrates
b. Galen
c. Laennec
d. Franklin
e. Koch

f. Leeuwenhoek
g. Fleming
h. Salk
i. Semmelweiss
j. Blackwell

1. _____ Discovered that colds could be passed from one person to another.
2. _____ First to study bacteria and protozoa using a microscope.
3. _____ His experiment with hand washing reduced the death rate of women who delivered babies in hospitals.
4. _____ He practiced and taught medicine on the island of Kos, Greece. He is known as the "Father of Medicine."
5. _____ Discovered penicillin.
6. _____ Invented the stethoscope.
7. _____ Discovered the cause of tuberculosis.
8. _____ Developed vaccines.
9. _____ Founded experimental physiology.
10. _____ First female physician in the United States.

LEARNING ACTIVITY: TRUE/FALSE

Indicate whether the following statements are true or false by placing a T or an F on the line that precedes each statement.

_____ 1. The Hippocratic Oath is no longer used, but it was around for nearly 2,000 years.

_____ 2. During the early part of the 20th century, the main form of medical practice was solo practice.

_____ 3. In a partnership practice, each partner is responsible for the actions of all partners.

_____ 4. Many early and historic plant remedies are still used today for heart conditions, indigestion, bleeding, and urinary tract infections.

_____ 5. An associate practice consists of three or more physicians who share the same facility and practice medicine together.

_____ 6. A group practice is managed by a board of directors.

_____ 7. A technician typically has an associate's degree from a 2-year community college or vocational program.

_____ 8. Registered nurses have more training than nurse practitioners.

_____ 9. Physical therapists develop programs that help restore the patient's ability to manage the activities of daily living.

_____ 10. In nearly every state, a physician's assistant can prescribe medications.

CRITICAL THINKING

Answer the following questions to the best of your ability. Utilize the textbook as a reference.

1. Michelle Manwiller, CMA (AAMA), is working with Harold Chan, a 55-year-old patient. Mr. Chan tells Michelle that he would like to try Chinese medicine treatments instead of taking the

© 2011 Pearson Education, Inc.

medication the physician has prescribed. He asks Michelle if she is familiar with the philosophy behind Chinese medicine. How might Michelle answer?

_____

_____

_____

_____

2. Robert Bautista is taking an administrative medical assisting course as part of his training to earn a certificate in medical assisting. He has been asked to write a paragraph outlining the contributions the Greek physician Galen made to medicine. Robert has been told to include the reasons why Galen's findings were not completely accurate. What could Robert write on this topic?

_____

_____

_____

3. Willie Harrison is creating a presentation for a history class he is enrolled in. Since he is in a medical assisting program, he wants his history paper to revolve around a medical topic. Willie has chosen to write about the history of the use of anesthesia in medicine. How should he start his outline for this presentation?

_____

_____

_____

_____

_____

4. Marian Reiman, CMA (AAMA), is teaching a night class to medical assisting students. Marian wants to lecture on the different types of hospitals that currently exist in the United States. What are the four categories of hospitals she should talk about and how should Marian describe one of these categories?

_____

_____

_____

_____

_____

RESEARCH ACTIVITY

Utilize Internet search engines to research the following topics and write a brief description of what is found. It is important to utilize reputable websites.

1. Using the Internet, choose and research one of the early contributors to medicine and write a two- to three-paragraph summary regarding your findings.

_____

_____

© 2011 Pearson Education, Inc.

CHAPTER 3
Medical Law and Ethics

CHAPTER OUTLINE

General review of the chapter:

Classification of the Law
Professional Liability
Patient and Physician Relationship
Documentation
Public Duties of Physicians
Drug Regulations
Role of the Medical Assistant
Code of Ethics
Medical Ethics
Medical Assistant's Principles of Medical Ethics
Medical Assistant's Standard of Care
The Patient's Bill of Rights
HIPAA and Confidentiality
Ethical Issues and Personal Choice

STUDENT STUDY GUIDE

Fill in the study guide below using both your textbook and notes from your instructor's lecture.

I. Law and Liability

  1. Classification of Law

    A. _____ law is made to protect the public as a whole from the harmful acts of others.
    B. _____ law concerns relationships between individuals or between individuals and the government.
    C. _____ law is concerned with a breach or neglect of an understanding between two parties.

  2. Civil Law

    A. _____ law falls under civil law and covers acts that result in harm to another.
    B. _____ occurs when the patient is injured as a result of the health care professional not exercising the ordinary standard of care.
    C. When an individual is being threatened with imminent bodily harm, the person doing the act could be charged with _____.
    D. A violation of the personal liberty of another person through unlawful restraint is known as _____ _____.

  3. The Four Ds of Unintentional Torts

    i. _____
    ii. _____

© 2011 Pearson Education, Inc.

iii. _____

iv. _____

4. Laws Governing Collection

    i. _____

    ii. _____

    iii. _____

    iv. _____

    v. _____

5. Standard of Care

    A. Asserts that the physician must provide the same _____, _____, and _____ that a similarly trained physician would provide under the same circumstances in the same locality.

    B. Physicians are expected to perform the same acts that _____ and _____ physicians would perform.

    C. If the physician violates the standard of care he or she is liable for _____.

II. Patient–Physician Relationship

1. Physician Rights

    A. Both the physician and the patient must agree to _____ if there is to be a contract for service and treatment. The patient must confide _____ to the physician in order to receive proper treatment.

    B. Physicians have the right to _____ payment for the treatment given.

2. Patient Rights

    i. _____

    ii. _____

    iii. _____

    iv. _____

3. Patient Obligations

    i. _____

    ii. _____

    iii. _____

4. Common Exceptions to Informed Consent

    A. A physician does not have to inform a patient about risks that are _____ known.

    B. If the physician feels that the disclosure of risks may be _____ to the patient, then he or she is not responsible for disclosing them.

    C. If the patient requests that the physician _____ disclose the risks.

5. Categories of Minors Who Can Give Consent

    i. _____

    ii. _____

6. Legal Implications to Consider When Treating a Minor

    i. _____

    ii. _____

    iii. _____

7. Durable Power of Attorney (DPOA)

    A. Allows an agent or _____ to act on behalf of the patient.

    B. Agent may be a _____, _____, _____, or an _____.

    C. Used when a patient becomes physically or _____ _____.

8. Uniform Anatomical Gift Act

    A. Allows a person _____ years or older and of sound mind to make a gift of any or all parts of his or her body for the purposes of organ transplantation or medical research.

    B. A physician who is not involved in the transplant will determine the _____.

    C. No _____ is allowed to change hands for organ donations.

III. Documentation and Regulations

  1. When a Medical Record Is Subpoenaed for Court

    A. Copy only the parts of the record that are _____.

    B. Send a _____ _____ unless the original record is subpoenaed.

    C. Place a _____ for the subpoenaed record in the patient's file.

  2. Considerations for Testifying in Court

    i. _____

    ii. _____

    iii. _____

    iv. _____

    v. _____

    vi. _____

  3. Childhood Vaccines and Toxoids Required by Law

    i. _____

    ii. _____

    iii. _____

    iv. _____

    v. _____

    vi. _____

  4. Drug Regulation Agencies

    A. The _____ has jurisdiction over testing and approving drugs for public use.

    B. The _____ is a branch of the U.S. Department of Justice.

    C. The _____ regulates the sale and use of scheduled drugs.

  5. Requirements for Controlled Substances

    A. Controlled drugs must be kept in a _____ cabinet.

    B. Any theft must be immediately reported to both the regional _____ office and local police.

    C. Federal regulations require a _____ inventory of drug supplies.

  6. Role of the Medical Assistant as Related to Controlled Substances

    A. Does not _____ controlled substances.

    B. Must be knowledgeable about the _____ governing the documentation and control of drugs.

    C. Must always _____ any unusual patient behavior indicating addictive drug use.

  7. MA's Role Related to Drug Administration

    A. May administer medication only under the _____ supervision of a physician.

    B. When preparing medications for administration, check the medication _____ times.

      i. _____

      ii. _____

      iii. _____

IV. Medical Ethics

  1. Ethics and Medical Ethics

    A. Branch of philosophy related to _____ or _____ principles.

    B. Medical ethics refers to the _____ conduct of people in medical professions.

    C. The members of the medical profession set _____ and _____ for themselves.

© 2011 Pearson Education, Inc.

2. Areas Covered in the AMA Principles of Medical Ethics

    i. _____

    ii. _____

    iii. _____

    iv. _____

    v. _____

3. Pledge Made Under the AAMA Code of Ethics

    A. Render service with full _____ for the _____ of humanity.

    B. Uphold the honor and high _____ of the profession and accept its _____.

    C. Seek to continually improve the _____ and _____ of medical assistants for the benefit of patients and professional colleagues.

4. As a medical assistant, you are NOT expected to:

    i. _____

    ii. _____

    iii. _____

5. The Patient's Bill of Rights

    A. Developed by the _____.

    B. Describes the _____ relationship.

6. HIPAA

    A. Defined as the _____.

    B. Regulates the _____ of patient health information.

KEY TERMINOLOGY REVIEW

Write a sentence using the selected key terms in the correct context.

1. **Defamation of character:**

    _____

    _____

2. **Bioethics:**

    _____

    _____

3. **Breach of contract:**

    _____

    _____

4. **Contributory negligence:**

    _____

    _____

5. **Informed consent:**

    _____

    _____

6. **Living Will:**

    _____

    _____

© 2011 Pearson Education, Inc.

7. *Practice of medicine:*

_____

_____

8. *Reasonable person standard:*

_____

_____

9. *Tort:*

_____

_____

10. *Statute of limitations:*

_____

_____

APPLIED PRACTICE

Provide answers to the following questions.

1. Considering the Latin terms discussed throughout the text, identify which of the Latin terms pertain to the situations below and then translate the term:

   A. A physician is sued because he amputates the wrong leg during surgery.

   _____

   _____

   B. Dr. Lin is being sued because his medical assistant injured a patient while suturing a 3-mm incision on the patient's lower leg, a procedure that is clearly outside the MA's scope of practice.

   _____

   _____

   C. Due to possible negligence by a physician, a child has been injured. When the case goes to court, an individual is appointed to represent the child.

   _____

   _____

LEARNING ACTIVITY: TRUE/FALSE

Indicate whether the following statements are true or false by placing a T or an F on the line that precedes each statement.

_____ 1. Although less serious in nature, misdemeanors may carry a punishment of jail time.

_____ 2. Tort law is an example of contract law.

_____ 3. Libel is the name for an oral defamatory statement.

_____ 4. In the case of unintentional tort, the plantiff must prove proximate cause.

_____ 5. It is harder to prevent negligence than it is to defend it.

© 2011 Pearson Education, Inc.

6. Medical malpractice can include medical errors but every mistake or error is not considered malpractice.

7. Breach of contract can only occur when both parties fail to comply with the terms of the agreement.

8. Physicians have a duty to issue a legal certificate of death for natural and unnatural deaths.

9. Physicians have a duty to report all injuries of children.

10. The requirements of reporting elderly abuse vary by state.

CRITICAL THINKING

Answer the following questions to the best of your ability. Utilize the textbook as a reference.

1. Beth Clark is taking an administrative medical assisting course as part of her medical assisting training. She has been given the assignment of writing a paper that outlines the current ethical standpoints of the AMA. What points should Beth include?

_____

_____

_____

2. Mary Alice Durfey, RMA is the administrative manager for Shepard Valley Out-Patient Surgery Clinic. She has been asked to create a checklist for surgeons that will cover the vital information of the Doctrine of Informed Consent. Surgeons will use this as they explain to patients the procedure or surgery that will be performed. What should Mary Alice include on this check list?

_____

_____

_____

_____

_____

3. Create a medical malpractice scenario in which the statute of limitations defense would apply.

_____

_____

_____

_____

4. Create a scenario, different from the one listed in the textbook, in which a health care worker would utilize the Good Samaritan Act as a defense in a lawsuit.

_____

_____

_____

_____

RESEARCH ACTIVITY

Utilize Internet search engines to research the following topics and write a brief description of what is found. It is important to utilize reputable websites.

1. Using the Internet as a research source, search for a medical malpractice case. Describe the case you find and include whether the patient or the physician won the case. Did you feel the case was decided fairly? Why or why not?

_____

_____

_____

_____

_____

_____

_____

_____

_____

_____

_____

_____

_____

_____

_____

_____

_____

_____

_____

_____

_____

© 2011 Pearson Education, Inc.

CHAPTER 4
Medical Terminology

CHAPTER OUTLINE

General review of the chapter:

Word Parts
Grammar and Medical Terms
Gross Anatomy
Body Structure and Function
Surgical and Diagnostic Terms

STUDENT STUDY GUIDE

Fill in the study guide below using both your textbook and notes from your instructor's lecture.

I. Word Parts and Combining Forms

   1. Words for Forming Medical Terms

      A. Medical terms also will often contain prefixes and suffixes, both of which add further _____ to the given term. If a word root is used, to prepare the word root for combining with another part, a _____ is sometimes added.

   2. Combining Vowels

      A. If the suffix begins with a vowel, _____ the combining vowel from the combining form and _____ the suffix. If the suffix begins with a consonant, *keep* the combining vowel and _____ the suffix to the combining.

   3. Prefix

      A. A prefix is a word element that is placed _____, or is _____ to the beginning of the word root.

      B. Prefixes are always placed at the _____ of words to alter or modify their meanings or to create new words.

   4. Suffix

      A. In medical terminology usage, a suffix is a word element that is affixed to the _____ of the word.

      B. A suffix could be a _____ or group of _____ attached to the _____ of a word to alter or modify its meaning or to create a new word.

II. Anatomy and Physiology

   1. Anatomical Position

      A. Used when describing the _____ and _____ of a structure in the human body.

      B. Describes the position of the body standing _____ with arms _____ of the body, palms facing _____, eyes looking _____ ahead.

      C. Legs are _____ with feet and toes are pointing _____.

© 2011 Pearson Education, Inc.

2. Body Planes (indicate the position of each of the body planes)

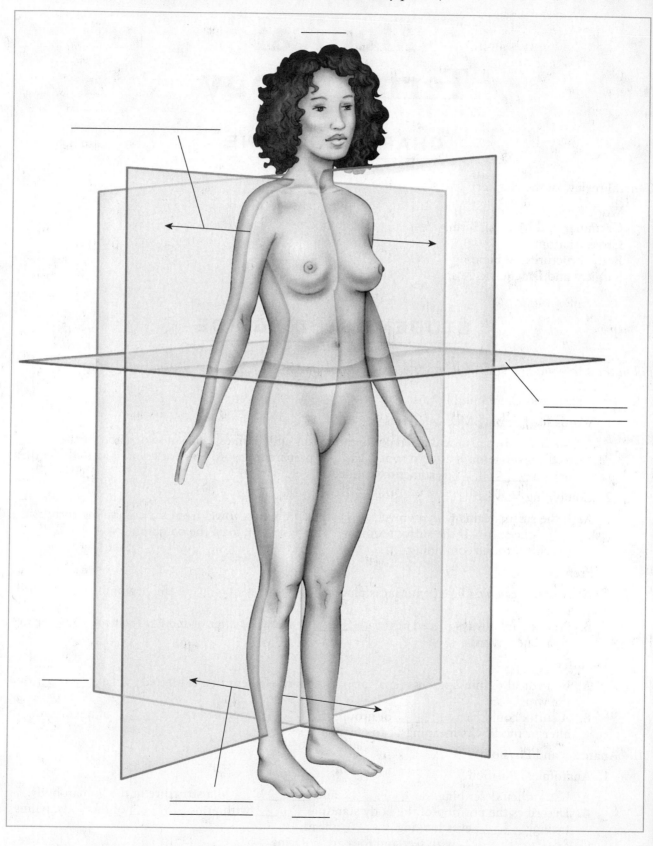

© 2011 Pearson Education, Inc.

3. Terms for Describing Body Position (explain each)

   A. Superior or cephalic: _____

   B. Inferior or caudal: _____

   C. Anterior or ventral: _____

   D. Posterior or dorsal: _____

   E. Medial: _____

   F. Lateral: _____

   G. Apex: _____

   H. Base: _____

   I. Proximal: _____

   J. Distal: _____

   K. Superficial: _____

   L. Deep: _____

   M. Supine: _____

   N. Prone: _____

4. Positions

   A. One of the main tasks of the medical assistant is to _____ the patient in the correct _____ for whatever procedure is to be performed.

   B. The vast majority of examinations require positioning patients on their _____.

   C. For a pelvic examination, the _____ position is used, with legs flexed in stirrups.

   D. For a proctological examination, the _____ position is favored.

   E. If a patient has low blood pressure, as is the case when a patient is in shock, the medical assistant should place the patient in the _____ position.

5. Body Cavities (explain each)

   A. The body's _____ are contained in cavities.

   B. The cranial cavity houses the _____.

   C. The chest, or _____, cavity holds the lungs and heart.

   D. Under the diaphragm, the _____ cavity holds other vital organs including the intestines, stomach, reproductive organs.

6. Anatomical Divisions of the Abdomen (on the figure provided label each region of the abdomen)

© 2011 Pearson Education, Inc.

7. The Integumentary System

  A. The integumentary system includes various parts that aid in the protection, exchange of heat and fluids, and absorption. List these components:

   i. _____

   ii. _____

   iii. _____

   iv. _____

   v. _____

   vi. _____

8. The Skeletal System

  A. The skeletal system consists of bones that are used to store _____, to give the body height and movement, and to _____ and _____ the body organs.

  B. The combining form for bone is _____.

  C. –clast is the combining form for _____.

  D. cost/o is the combining form for _____.

  E. Physician specializing in (straightening) bones is an _____.

9. The Muscular System

  A. Muscles aid bones in _____.

  B. The combining forms for muscles are _____ and _____.

  C. The word part –trophy means _____.

  D. tax/o is the combining form for _____.

  E. A medical assistant or physician may perform _____ activities to assess a muscle's ability to extend, flex, or rotate as necessary.

10. The Nervous System

  A. The nervous system helps the body to sense changes in the _____ and _____ environments.

  B. Pain is referred to with the suffixes _____ and _____.

  C. A frequently used medication that reduces pain is referred to as an _____.

  D. Pain in the diaphragm is known as _____.

  E. cephal/o means the _____, and encephal/o is _____.

11. Special Senses

  A. Special senses include _____, _____, taste, touch, and _____.

  B. The combining forms for eye are _____, _____, and _____.

  C. The combining forms for the ear are _____ and _____.

  D. _____ measures the acuity of hearing.

12. The Circulatory System

  A. The circulatory system consists of the heart, the blood vessels, the blood, and the structures that make up the _____ system.

  B. The cardiovascular system is a subsystem of the _____ system and is comprised of the heart and its vessels.

  C. The combining form for the heart is _____.

  D. Fatty plaque in the arteries is referred to as _____.

13. The Immune System

  A. The immune system protects the body from _____.

  B. White blood cells called _____ defend the body.

  C. Word part bas/o means _____.

  D. The combining form –phage means _____.

© 2011 Pearson Education, Inc.

14. The Respiratory System
    A. The respiratory system exchanges oxygen (O_2) in the environment for _____ in the body.
    B. The main organs of respiration are the _____.
    C. A specialist in the respiratory system is a _____.
    D. _____ is a combining form that means "lung."

15. The Digestive System
    A. The digestive system either _____ or _____ food and drugs for the body.
    B. The _____ is another term for the mouth.
    C. Key organs of this system are the _____ and _____.
    D. A physician with specialized training in the digestive system is a _____.

16. The Urinary System
    A. The urinary system rids the body of the toxic byproducts of _____.
    B. The combining form for the kidney is _____.
    C. A physician with specialized training related to the kidney is a _____.
    D. The _____ go toward the bladder, and the _____ goes toward the outside of the body.

17. The Endocrine System
    A. The endocrine system is the ductless glandular system that controls other body systems by secreting _____ within the bloodstream.
    B. *Endo-* means _____ and *–crine* means _____.
    C. The _____ is the master gland of this system.
    D. The word part estr/o means _____.

18. The Reproductive System
    A. The reproductive system aids in reproducing _____.
    B. The physician with specialized training in women's health is a _____.
    C. The combining forms for the uterus are _____ and _____.
    D. A common abbreviation related to the male reproductive system is _____.

19. Surgical and Diagnostic Terms (define each of the following word parts)
    A. –graphy: _____
    B. –scopy: _____
    C. –tome: _____
    D. –stomy: _____
    E. –tomy: _____

KEY TERMINOLOGY REVIEW

Write a sentence using each of the word parts listed. Note the word part by underlining it in your sentence.

1. *combining form:*

    _____
    _____

2. *combining vowel:*

    _____
    _____

3. *prefix:*

    _____
    _____

© 2011 Pearson Education, Inc.

4. *suffix:*

_____

_____

5. *word root:*

_____

_____

APPLIED PRACTICE

For each of the following rules related to forming plurals, write a sentence without the use of the plural ending and then rewrite the sentence using the word with a plural ending.

1. Words ending in *on* will drop *on* and add *a.*

_____

_____

2. Words ending in *us* will drop *us* and add *l.*

_____

_____

3. Words ending in *um* will drop *um* and add *a.*

_____

_____

4. Words ending in *y* will drop *y* and add *ies.*

_____

_____

5. Words ending in *nx* will change the *x* to *g* and add *es.*

_____

_____

LEARNING ACTIVITY: TRUE/FALSE

Indicate whether the following statements are true or false by placing a T or an F on the line that precedes each statement.

_____ 1. When identifying medical words, if the suffix begins with a consonant, drop the combining vowel from the combining form and add the suffix.

_____ 2. The abbreviation for anterioposterior is AP.

_____ 3. The root word *ankyl* means stiff or bent.

_____ 4. The combining form for vein would be *vein/o.*

_____ 5. The prefix *de* means through or apart.

_____ 6. Prefixes used in medical terminology have only one meaning.

_____ 7. The suffix *drome* means to lead or pull.

_____ 8. In a court of law, misspelling and improperly used medical terminology can imply sloppy patient care.

© 2011 Pearson Education, Inc.

_____ 9. The frontal plane divides the body and its parts into left and right positions.

_____ 10. The transverse plane is a crosswise plane that runs parallel to the ground.

CRITICAL THINKING

Answer the following questions to the best of your ability. Utilize the textbook as a reference.

1. Andrea Natal has been working as an MA for Dr. Smith for about a month. Andrea has just finished assisting with a patient examination. As Dr. Smith leaves the examination room, he hands Andrea the patient's chart and indicates that he has written down some instructions that need to be given to the patient. After the physician leaves the room, Andrea looks at the patient's chart and discovers that she is unable to decipher some of the information. What should Andrea say to the patient and do to ensure that the patient receives the correct information? What should Andrea not do?

_____

_____

_____

_____

_____

_____

_____

_____

RESEARCH ACTIVITY

Utilize Internet search engines to research the following topics and write a brief description of what you find. It is important to utilize reputable websites.

1. Select one of the organs of the body described in your textbook. Using your school's library and/or information obtained on the Internet, conduct research on the various conditions that can occur in that system. Prepare a one- to two-page paper on what you learned about the system and the conditions that can occur within the system. Be sure to cite your sources at the end of your paper.

_____

_____

_____

_____

_____

_____

_____

_____

_____

_____

© 2011 Pearson Education, Inc.

CHAPTER 5

Communication: Verbal and Nonverbal

CHAPTER OUTLINE

General review of the chapter:

Interpersonal Dynamics
The Communication Process
Verbal and Nonverbal Communication
Communication Techniques
Assertive versus Aggressive Behavior
Barriers to Communication
Communication in Special Circumstances
Intraoffice Communication
Staff Arrangements
Communication and Patients' Rights

STUDENT STUDY GUIDE

Use the following guide to assist in your learning of the concepts from the chapter.

I. The Communication Process

1. The Holistic Approach to Medicine

    A. Means caring for the _____ patient.
    B. Addresses the social, _____, and _____ needs, as well as the physical treatment of the patient.
    C. Means treating everyone with _____ and _____.

2. Importance of Self-Awarenss

    A. Leads to more effective _____.
    B. Terms to self-awareness include:
        i. _____
        ii. _____
        iii. _____
        iv. _____
        v. _____

3. The Learning Styles of Our Patients (list and explain each)

        i. _____
        ii. _____
        iii. _____

© 2011 Pearson Education, Inc.

4. Units of the Communication Process (Fill in the blanks)

5. Factors Affecting Verbal Communication

    i. _____
    ii. _____
    iii. _____
    iv. _____
    v. _____
    vi. _____

6. Factors in Nonverbal Communication

    i. _____
    ii. _____
    iii. _____
    iv. _____
    v. _____
    vi. _____

II. Communication Techniques

    1. Considerations When Communicating

        A. _____ of the communication.
        B. _____ to be given.
        C. _____ skills to be used.
        D. _____ clarification and feedback.
        E. _____ if goal was met.

    2. Barriers to Communication

        i. _____
        ii. _____
        iii. _____

© 2011 Pearson Education, Inc.

iv. _____

v. _____

vi. _____

vii. _____

viii. _____

ix. _____

3. Avoiding Prejudging and Stereotyping (list the ways to avoid)

i. _____

ii. _____

iii. _____

iv. _____

v. _____

vi. _____

III. Communicating with Patients and Staff

1. Fears that Can Cause Patient Anger

i. _____

ii. _____

iii. _____

iv. _____

2. The "White Coat" Syndrome

A. Patients who are fearful of anyone in a _____ _____.

B. Patients with this syndrome experience _____ _____.

3. Methods for Communicating with Anxious Patients

i. _____

ii. _____

iii. _____

iv. _____

v. _____

4. Communicating with the Mentally Ill

A. Determine the level of _____ that is possible.

B. Speak _____ and _____.

C. Keep messages _____.

5. Steps for Addressing Conflict

A. Communicate your needs in _____ terms.

B. Know when to express your _____.

C. Do not _____ you know the other person's feelings.

D. Look at the issue from the other person's _____.

6. Elements of Critical Thinking

A. _____ questions.

B. _____ the problem.

C. _____ the evidence.

D. _____ emotional reasoning.

E. _____ assumptions and bias.

F. _____ oversimplification.

G. _____ other interpretations.

H. _____ ambiguity.

I. _____ about one's own thinking.

7. Staff Meetings
    A. Should be _____ scheduled.
    B. The success of staff meetings is due to:
        i. Presence of an _____.
        ii. Adhering to _____ and _____ times.
        iii. Avoiding _____ sessions.
IV. Patient Education
    1. HIPAA Privacy Rule
        A. Protects _____ _____.
        B. Allows patients to have better access to _____ _____.
        C. Provides patients with _____ control over who can release medical information and how it will be done.
    2. The MA's Role in Advising Patients
        A. _____ empathetically and establish rapport.
        B. Ask _____ or _____ questions.
        C. _____ the information the physician has related to the patient.
        D. Keep all matters related to the patient's personal health information _____.

KEY TERMINOLOGY REVIEW

Choose the term that best represents each statement below.

a. kinesthetic

b. active listening

c. risk management

d. close-ended question

e. character

f. empathy

g. leading questions

h. feedback

i. values

j. open-ended question

k. bias

l. prejudice

m. ethnocentric

n. passive listening

o. stereotyping

p. sympathy

1. _____ Identification with another person's feelings.

2. _____ Questions that contain part of the answer.

3. _____ Unfair preference or dislike of something.

4. _____ Involves completely paying attention to the speaker, concentrating on the verbal message, watching for nonverbal cues, and offering a response.

5. _____ Feeling sorry for or pitying someone.

6. _____ "Do you have a headache?"

7. _____ A set of standards a person uses to measure the worth or importance of someone or something.

8. _____ An opinion that is based on race, gender, or economic status.

9. _____ Refers to planning and implementing strategies for reducing the physician's risk of a lawsuit in the medical setting.

10. _____ The sum of the values, attitudes, and behaviors.

11. _____ The belief which some individuals have that their cultural background is better than any other.

© 2011 Pearson Education, Inc.

12. _____ "Can you describe your headache?"

13. _____ Listening to someone without offering a reply.

14. _____ Learner assimilates knowledge better through hands-on activities.

15. _____ A preformed and unfavorable belief or attitude toward a certain culture or group with little or no information about the culture or group.

16. _____ Information that is reflected in an interpersonal exchange.

APPLIED PRACTICE

1. *Without using the examples in the textbook, for each of the following defensive behaviors provide your own example of how a patient may exhibit this behavior.*

   i. Compensation

   _____
   _____

   ii. Denial

   _____
   _____

   iii. Displaced anger

   _____
   _____

   iv. Introjection

   _____
   _____

   v. Projection

   _____
   _____

   vi. Rationalization

   _____
   _____

   vii. Regression

   _____
   _____

   viii. Repression

   _____
   _____

   ix. Sublimation

   _____
   _____

2. A patient has arrived at the office for a yearly physical. After reviewing the steps for listening to obtain a patient's chief complaint, write a script that outlines your interactions with the patient and how the steps illustrate your understanding of how to demonstrate effective listening skills when obtaining the patient's chief complaint.

   _____
   _____

_____

_____

_____

_____

_____

_____

_____

_____

_____

_____

_____

_____

_____

_____

_____

_____

_____

_____

_____

LEARNING ACTIVITY: MULTIPLE CHOICE

Circle the correct answer to each of the questions below.

1. Assertive behavior:
   a. Is imposing one's viewpoint on another.
   b. Can result in resentment by others.
   c. Is trusting one's own ideas or instincts.
   d. All of the above.

2. Which of the following would be an open-ended question?
   a. Mrs. Knight, would you explain to me how you are feeling today?
   b. Mrs. Knight, how are you feeling today?
   c. Mrs. Knight, do you need help?
   d. None of the above.

3. Which of the following would be a barrier to communication?
   a. Eye contact
   b. Use of meaningful statements
   c. Noise
   d. None of the above

© 2011 Pearson Education, Inc.

4. An example of a probing question would include:
   a. "You say your head hurts?"
   b. "Where on your head do you feel pain?"
   c. "Do you have pain anywhere else?"
   d. All of the above.

5. Mr. Marlon Jones has come to the office due to an ear infection. Which of the following would be an example of the use of reflecting to ensure good communication?
   a. Mr. Jones states that he hurts. You ask him where it hurts.
   b. Mr. Jones states that he is feeling very scared. You ask him what he is scared about.
   c. Mr. Jones states that he has recently been feeling very tired. You repeat back to him that recently he has been feeling very tired.
   d. Any of the above.

CRITICAL THINKING

Answer the following questions to the best of your ability. Utilize the textbook as a reference.

1. Mrs. Jean Smith has come into the office to address a concern that she has. How can you make sure that you are actively listening to what Mrs. Smith is saying?

2. A patient has just walked into the office and begins to yell at the front desk medical assistant about the bill. Consider and outline the methods that the MA should use to communicate with the angry patient.

3. A hearing-impaired patient has come into the office. What methods might you use to communicate with this patient?

4. Now consider a visually impaired patient. What methods might you use to communicate with this patient?

_____

5. As an MA, you may encounter patients who are terminally ill. What skills might you employ when communicating with a terminally ill patient?

_____

_____

_____

_____

6. Write a scenario (either real or imagined) where a problem occurs with a patient or staff member and the steps that you would take to solve the problem. If you choose to describe a real-life situation, you do not have to use real names or any personal information.

_____

_____

_____

_____

_____

RESEARCH ACTIVITY

Utilize Internet search engines to research the following topics. It is important to utilize reputable websites.

1. Use the Internet to find information regarding the aspects of a professional, well-developed policy and procedures manual. Answer the following questions:

   a. What website would you recommend to an office manager that may help guide him or her in the development of the manual?
   b. What did you learn from your research about what makes a successful policy and procedures manual?

_____

_____

_____

_____

_____

_____

_____

_____

_____

_____

_____

© 2011 Pearson Education, Inc.

CHAPTER 6

The Office Environment

CHAPTER OUTLINE

General review of the chapter:

> General Safety Measures
> Employee Safety
> Proper Body Mechanics
> Office Security
> Quality Medical Care
> What Is Quality Assurance?

STUDENT STUDY GUIDE

Use the following guide to assist in your learning of the concepts from the chapter.

I. Safety in the Medical Office

   1. Occupational Safety and Health Administration

      A. Concerned with any _____ hazard.
      B. Sets _____ standards for workplaces.
      C. _____ are levied against employers who fail to comply with regulations.

   2. General Safety Guidelines

      A. _____, don't run, during an emergency.
      B. Walk on the _____ side of the hallway.
      C. Use _____ when using stairways.
      D. Never carry _____ syringes or sharp objects.
      E. Report _____ any unsafe conditions.
      F. Use different _____ for lab specimens and medications.
      G. Store _____ substances in locked cabinets.

   3. Disasters in a Medical Office

      i. _____
      ii. _____
      iii. _____
      iv. _____
      v. _____
      vi. _____

   4. Disaster Plan in the Medical Office

      A. All employee training on the disaster plan must be _____ to demonstrate OSHA compliance.
      B. Further regulations are required for sites with _____ equipment.
      C. All employees must be _____ on the steps to follow in any emergency.

© 2011 Pearson Education, Inc.

5. Guidelines for Fire Safety
   A. Floor plans should indicate _____, _____, and _____.
   B. Portable _____ fire extinguishers should be placed no more than _____ feet from any employee area.
   C. Fire drills should be conducted at least _____.
   D. _____ cabinets should be used to protect records.
   E. Emergency numbers should be placed in _____ areas.

6. Steps for Handling a Fire
   i. _____
   ii. _____
   iii. _____
   iv. _____
   v. _____
   vi. _____
   vii. _____

7. Necessary Items in Case of a Fire
   A. Fire extinguishers with proper documentation of _____.
   B. Clearly marked _____ and _____ that are free of debris.
   C. _____ of all exits.

8. Guidelines for Electrical Safety
   A. All equipment should be _____.
   B. _____ protectors should be used for all electronic equipment.
   C. Use of _____ outlets for "wet" areas.

9. Material Safety Data Sheets
   A. Written materials on _____ chemicals.
   B. Provides information on the _____ of the _____ and what to do in order to be protected.
   C. Must be filed in a _____ binder.

10. Types of Medical Waste
    i. _____
    ii. _____
    iii. _____
    iv. _____

11. Exposure Control Plan
    A. A written document required by _____.
    B. Assists in _____ employee exposure to infectious materials.
    C. Reviewed by all employees, with _____ kept for _____ years after termination of employment.
    D. Updated _____.

12. Universal Precautions
    A. Issued by the _____.
    B. Treats all blood and body fluids as contaminated with _____ pathogens.
    C. Emphasizes the use of a _____ _____ when infectious material has been spilled.

13. OSHA Guidelines Regarding the Use of PPE
    A. Employer must supply the PPE and provide _____ or _____.
    B. PPE must be of a strength to act as a _____ to infectious materials.
    C. _____ gloves may not be reused.

© 2011 Pearson Education, Inc.

D. Protective eye equipment must have _____ sides to prevent infectious material from entering the area.

E. All PPE must be _____ and placed in a _____ container before leaving the office.

14. Guidelines for Housekeeping Department Personnel

A. Must be _____ trained.

B. Housekeeping should only empty _____, NOT _____ and _____ containers.

15. Housekeeping Guidelines for Medical Personnel

A. Wear appropriate _____.

B. For wet spills, use prepared _____ according to package directions.

C. Immediately clean and disinfect contaminated surfaces with _____ bleach/water solution after exposure to infectious materials.

D. _____ all surfaces on a regular schedule.

E. Properly bag contaminated clothing and laundry in _____, labeled biohazard bags.

F. Have biohazardous waste removed by a _____ waste disposal service.

G. Use _____, _____, biohazardous sharps containers for all needles and sharps.

H. Replace the sharps container when _____ full.

I. _____ and _____ the sharps container before placing with the biohazardous waste.

J. Perform hand hygiene _____ and _____ using gloves.

16. Steps for Securing the Medical Office

A. Ensure that doors and windows have _____ _____.

B. Provide only a few keys to _____ personnel for opening and closing the office.

C. Change _____ _____ if a key is missing.

D. _____ the electronic security system after the last person leaves the office.

17. Incident Reports

A. Protect _____ and _____ against lawsuits.

B. Must be written in _____ ink.

C. Should contain only _____ information.

II. Quality Assurance

1. The AMA's Eight Essentials of Quality Care

A. Emphasize _____ detection and treatment.

B. Encourage the patient's _____ in the decision-making process regarding his or her treatment.

C. Demonstrate _____ for the patient and the patient's family.

D. Achieve the _____ goal through the wise use of technology and other resources.

E. Provide adequate _____ in the patient's medical record to facilitate _____ evaluation and _____ of care.

2. Major Areas of Health Care Regularly Examined to Determine Quality

i. _____

ii. _____

iii. _____

iv. _____

v. _____

3. Components of a Quality Assurance Program

A. Review of all _____ and _____ services and procedures.

B. Structure set up to _____ items for review.

© 2011 Pearson Education, Inc.

C. _____ all issues such as number of errors and "needle sticks."

D. Emphasis is placed on areas where _____ actions should be taken.

4. Medical Assistant's Role in Quality Assurance

A. _____ patient complaints.

B. _____ patient education.

C. _____ laboratory tests done in the office.

D. _____ with the physician regarding patient complaints.

5. CLIA

A. CLIA stands for _____.

B. Mandates _____ control of _____ tests by category and documentation.

C. Categories include _____, _____, and _____.

KEY TERMINOLOGY REVIEW

Choose the term that best represents each statement below.

a. incident

b. quality assurance (QA)

c. National Committee for Quality Assurance (NCQA)

d. ground fault circuit interrupter (GFCI)

e. ergonomics

f. body mechanics

g. personal protective equipment (PPE)

h. OSHA

i. biohazards

j. MSDS

1. _____ Process of gathering and evaluating information about the services provided.

2. _____ Contains printed material concerning a hazardous chemical.

3. _____ Gloves, fluid-resistant lab coats, safety glasses, and a surgical mask, shield, or respirator.

4. _____ Evaluates the quality of health plans.

5. _____ Provides very specific regulations regarding chemical hazards and hazardous waste.

6. _____ A prescription pad is missing.

7. _____ Coordination of body alignment, balance, and movement.

8. _____ Biological substances, such as medical waste and samples of a virus or bacterium, that pose a threat to human beings and are potentially infectious.

9. _____ Applies scientific information and data regarding human body mechanics to the design of objects and overall environment for human use.

10. _____ Designed to protect people from severe or fatal electrical shocks.

APPLIED PRACTICE

1. *Provide two examples of when the use of each of the following PPEs would be important:*

i. Gloves

_____

_____

ii. Mask

_____

_____

iii. Eye and face shield

_____

_____

iv. Gowns or lab coats

_____

_____

LEARNING ACTIVITY: TRUE/FALSE

Indicate whether the following statements are true or false by placing a T or an F on the line that precedes each statement.

_____ 1. The proper way to clean up a wet spill is to use the closest item, which is usually paper towels or wash rags.

_____ 2. Front office equipment to be considered biohazards in a medical office includes printer and copier ink.

_____ 3. All back office equipment is considered to be a biohazard.

_____ 4. Employees cannot refuse to get the Hepatitis B vaccine if they choose to work in a clinical environment.

_____ 5. The best way to prevent exposure to bloodborne pathogens is to wear personal protective equipment.

_____ 6. To be safe, gloves must be worn at all times when working with a patient.

_____ 7. Face masks are typically not worn if eye shields are being used.

_____ 8. When moving an object, be sure to create a base of support by keeping your feet 6 to 8 inches apart.

_____ 9. When moving heavy objects, keep your back and knees slightly bent.

_____ 10. An incident report should be completed if a patient has misplaced or lost personal property while at the office.

CRITICAL THINKING

Answer the following questions to the best of your ability. Utilize the textbook as a reference.

1. What is the main premise of Standard/Universal Precautions? What impact on patient discrimination do you think this could have?

_____

_____

_____

_____

_____

2. In your clinic, one of the laundry receptacles has a biohazardous label and another is for regular laundry without visible blood or body fluids. Your manager tells you that the laundry services will

© 2011 Pearson Education, Inc.

be a day late due to snow and asks you to wash the regular laundry at home and bring it back tomorrow. Would you do this? Explain why or why not.

_____

_____

_____

_____

_____

_____

_____

RESEARCH ACTIVITY

Utilize Internet search engines to research the following topics and write a brief description of what you find. It is important to utilize reputable websites.

1. Research the website for the Occupational Safety and Health Administration, *www.osha.gov*.

   What information can be found for health care facilities?
   List some facts found within the website:

   _____

   _____

   _____

   _____

   _____

   _____

   _____

   _____

   _____

   _____

   _____

   _____

   _____

   _____

   _____

   _____

   _____

   _____

   _____

   _____

   _____

   _____

   _____

© 2011 Pearson Education, Inc.

CHAPTER 7
Telephone Techniques

CHAPTER OUTLINE

General review of the chapter:

Telephone Techniques
Typical Incoming Calls
Prescription Refill Requests
Telephone Triage
Handling Difficult Calls
Using a Telephone Directory
Telephones Used for Patient Education
Long Distance Calls
Using an Answering Service
Handling an Emergency Telephone Call

STUDENT STUDY GUIDE

Use the following guide to assist in your learning of the concepts from the chapter.

I. Telephone Techniques

   1. Guidelines for Answering the Office Telephone

      i. _____

      ii. _____

      iii. _____

      iv. _____

      v. _____

   2. Elements of a Professional Greeting

      i. _____

      ii. _____

      iii. _____

   3. Guidelines for Making Calls

    A. Access _____ line as required.
    B. Dial _____ code if necessary.
    C. Identify the _____ to ensure that you are speaking with the intended person.
    D. Do not disclose _____ information to an unauthorized person.
    E. Know the _____ of the office with regard to personal calls.

   4. Guidelines for Using the Hold Button

    A. An individual should not be left on hold for more than about _____ seconds.
    B. When taking a second call, ask the _____ caller if he or she may be placed on hold. Ensure that the _____ caller is not an emergency, and then return to finish

© 2011 Pearson Education, Inc.

the call with the _____ caller prior to handling issues with the _____ caller.

C. If information must be retrieved for the caller, _____ to place the caller on hold.

5. Steps for Transferring Calls

    i. _____
    ii. _____
    _____.
    iii. _____
    iv. _____
    v. _____

6. Items Required When Taking a Message

    i. _____
    ii. _____
    iii. _____
    iv. _____

7. Guidelines for Taking a Message

A. Have _____ and _____ ready.
B. Obtain the necessary _____.
C. _____ the message with the caller.
D. _____ the telephone number for a return call.
E. Pull the patient's medical record, if required, for the return call. Attach the message to the front of the _____.
F. Ensure that the telephone message is placed in the patient's chart as _____ of the call.
G. Follow _____ rules with regard to patient information.

8. Pagers and Cell Phones

A. Know the office policy with regard to _____ use.
B. Obtain the necessary _____ and codes for contacting the physician by pager and/or cell phone.
C. Follow hospital building policies on _____ of pagers and cell phones.

9. Prescription Refill Requests

A. Due to a high volume of calls, _____ _____ systems are often used.
B. The MA is often responsible for _____ and _____ to messages.
C. Messages should be checked at least _____ a day.
D. A prescription refill request must be _____ on by a physician.
E. A message may need to be attached to the _____ prior to obtaining a physician's approval.

10. Steps for Taking a Prescription Refill Message

    i. _____
    ii. _____
    iii. _____
    iv. _____
    v. _____
    vi. _____
    vii. _____
    viii. _____
    ix. _____

11. Purposes for Using a Telephone Log

A. Typically used to keep track of _____ _____ calls.
B. Helps to identify any _____ _____ calls that are not _____ related.

© 2011 Pearson Education, Inc.

12. Purposes for Using an Answering Service

    i. _____

    ii. _____

    iii. _____

13. Handling Emergency Calls

    A. Every office should have a _____ protocol.

    B. Immediately get caller's _____ and _____.

    C. If it is an emergency, alert the _____ and/or _____.

    D. Try to _____ the individual.

KEY TERMINOLOGY REVIEW

Use the key terms found at the beginning of the chapter to finish the sentences below. Key terms may be more than one word in length.

1. Dr. Adamson at the local hospital would like to conduct a meeting by phone with his patient and the referring physician. The best way to facility this would be to set up a _____.

2. _____ refers to the changes in pitch and tone of your voice and the way you utter your words and phrases.

3. Before seeing a specialist, Mrs. Smith has been told that she must get a _____.

4. When the office is closed, the _____ will typically handle all emergency calls.

5. A _____ allows messages (voice mail) to be left or recorded when the medical assistant is unavailable to answer the telephone.

6. Most medical offices will use some form of a multi-line telephone. Some may have separate lines, where you must press a particular line's button to answer it, or a system that will feed calls to you from a _____ or waiting line.

7. _____ refers to the quality or state of being understandable.

8. Being careful not to speak too rapidly will help with word _____.

9. When calling a patient, it is important for the medical office to set up a system to block the office number from showing up on the patient's _____.

10. A medical assistant is on the phone with a patient; the process she uses to determine the order in which patients should be treated is called _____.

11. Have you ever noticed that when you ask a question your voice tends to rise at the end of the phrase? This is an example of the _____ of your voice.

12. When calling the office, Ms. Perez encounters an _____ that helps direct her call to the appropriate person with whom she should speak regarding her concerns.

APPLIED PRACTICE

Using your textbook, complete the activity or answer the questions below.

1. Using the box below, create a message pad template that could be used in a medical office to take telephone messages. Consider the important information to be obtained from callers when they call the office.

© 2011 Pearson Education, Inc.

2. Manuel Vargas is an administrative medical assistant. He receives a phone call from a patient requesting a refill for one of her prescription medications. How should Manuel handle this call? What information must Manuel obtain from the patient? What should he do with the message after the call has ended?

_____

_____

_____

_____

_____

LEARNING ACTIVITY: MULTIPLE CHOICE

Circle the correct answer to each of the questions below.

1. Which of the following would be appropriate to play for callers who are on hold?

   a. A local radio station
   b. Prerecorded music
   c. A message about seasonal allergies
   d. All of the above

2. Which of the following might be offensive or irritating for callers to listen to while they are on hold?

   a. Religious music
   b. Prerecorded music
   c. A message about seasonal allergies
   d. A local radio station

3. How long is an acceptable period of time to leave a caller on hold?

    a. Less than 10 seconds
    b. 20–30 seconds
    c. 45–60 seconds
    d. 1–2 minutes

4. What items should a medical assistant have available before answering the office telephone?

    a. Pen or pencil
    b. Paper
    c. Telephone message pad
    d. All of the above

5. The medical office telephone should be answered within how many rings?

    a. On the first ring
    b. By the second ring
    c. By the third ring
    d. No more than five rings

6. What rule are you violating if a patient's private information is thrown into the trash?

    a. OSHA's privacy rule
    b. HIPAA's privacy rule
    c. HIPPA's privacy rule
    d. AMA's privacy rule

7. Which of the following telephone calls should be taken care of first?

    a. A patient who says she needs to schedule her yearly mammogram
    b. An angry patient who is calling about her bill
    c. A patient who says he is having chest pains
    d. A patient who is calling to find out his laboratory results

8. What information would you expect to find in a telephone triage notebook?

    a. Driving directions to the medical office
    b. The hours the clinic is open
    c. The questions to ask a patient who complains of chest pains
    d. All of the above

9. In the event of a medical emergency in the office, what information should the medical assistant have available before calling for emergency services?

    a. The patient's name
    b. The patient's age
    c. The patient's gender
    d. All of the above

10. Which of the following emergency telephone numbers should the medical assistant have readily available at the front desk?

    a. Poison control
    b. The local police department
    c. The local fire department
    d. All of the above

© 2011 Pearson Education, Inc.

CRITICAL THINKING

Answer the following questions to the best of your ability. Utilize the textbook and other resources such as the Internet in considering the following questions.

1. Rosie Sanchez, CMA (AAMA), has been working as an administrative medical assistant in an internal medicine clinic for the past year. A large part of her day is spent answering the office telephone and scheduling appointments. She would like the office to provide her with a hands-free headset for the telephone system. The clinic director has asked Rosie to create a list that outlines the benefits of having a hands-free headset over a conventional telephone headset. What should Rosie list?

   _____

   _____

   _____

2. Ron Douglas is a student in an administrative medical assisting class. He has been given an assignment to create an office policy that discusses how the speakerphone function of the front desk telephone system can be used without violating patient confidentiality. What should Ron write?

   _____

   _____

   _____

3. Martin Taylor, RMA, is working in an audiology clinic. The clinic is researching the possibility of purchasing a new telephone system that will include an automatic routing unit where callers can dial an extension to reach the desired party. Martin has been asked to create a list of pros and cons for this type of system. What should Martin include on his list?

   _____

   _____

   _____

   _____

RESEARCH ACTIVITY

Utilize Internet search engines to research the following topics. It is important to utilize reputable websites.

1. Search the Internet for on-call, after-hours answering services that are provided for medical offices. What types of services are offered by these companies? What is the general cost for on-call answering services?

   _____

   _____

   _____

   _____

   _____

   _____

© 2011 Pearson Education, Inc.

CHAPTER 8
Patient Reception

CHAPTER OUTLINE

General review of the chapter:

Duties of a Receptionist
Personal Characteristics and Physical Appearance
Opening the Office
Collating Records
Greeting the Patient upon Arrival
Registering New Patients
Charge Slips
Consideration for the Patient's Time
Escorting the Patient into the Examination Room
Patient Education
Managing Disturbances
No-Shows
Closing the Office

STUDENT STUDY GUIDE

Use the following guide to assist in your learning of the concepts from the chapter.

I. Opening the Office and Receiving Patients

   1. The Duties of a Receptionist

      A. _____ patients upon arrival.
      B. Assisting new patients with _____ of proper forms.
      C. _____ copayments.
      D. Maintaining a _____ and _____ environment in the reception area.
      E. _____ any disturbances in the reception room.
      F. _____ return appointments.
      G. Making _____ calls for upcoming appointments.

   2. The Reception Room

      A. The term _____ is to be avoided.
      B. Often, it is the MA's job to keep the reception room _____ and _____ of hazards.
      C. The reception room provides the _____ impression of the office.

   3. The Image of the Medical Assistant

      A. Image is important because the MA is often the _____ person the patient meets.
      B. Attention should be paid to good _____ and _____ habits.
      C. Make-up, hairstyle, and jewelry should reflect _____.
      D. Name _____ should always be visible.

© 2011 Pearson Education, Inc.

4. Responsibilities in Opening the Office

   A. Arrive _____ minutes prior to office hours.
   B. Ensure that the day's charts have been _____ and _____.
   C. Ensure that _____ slips have been printed in advance for each patient.
   D. Print out _____ lists of patient appointments and distribute them.

5. The Task of Collating Records

   A. This is usually done the day _____ patients are seen.
   B. All necessary information should be received and in the record _____ to the patient's visit.
   C. In some offices, patients' records are organized in the _____ in which patients will be seen.
   D. A _____ appointment list is placed on top of the collated records.
   E. As patients arrive, the _____ should be verified on the schedule.

6. Steps for Collating Records

   i. _____
   ii. _____
   iii. _____
   iv. _____
   v. _____
   vi. _____

7. General Guidelines for Greeting Patients

   A. Make a good impression by being _____ and _____.
   B. If possible, have emergency or _____ patients enter through a private entrance.
   C. Place _____ ahead of other visitors.
   D. Follow _____ guidelines.

8. Patient Sign-in Sheet

   A. The sheet is maintained at the _____ desk.
   B. The sheet provides a _____ record of all patients who come to the office.
   C. The sheet should be checked for _____ and _____ of information.
   D. In order to be HIPAA compliant, all efforts should be made to protect _____ _____.

9. Patient Registration Forms

   A. Forms are sometimes sent to patients _____ to their first appointment.
   B. Some offices request that patients arrive _____ minutes early to complete the forms.
   C. Forms contain _____ information.
   D. Forms should be _____ marked to indicate areas that patients need to complete.
   E. Patients should be provided _____ as needed to ensure the completeness of the forms.

10. Registering New Patients

   A. Office billing and payments policies should be _____ explained to new patients.
   B. Obtain the patient's signature on an _____ form.
   C. Ensure that forms are filled out _____ and _____, including signatures.
   D. Verify information with the patient's _____ card.
   E. Photocopy _____ _____ of the insurance card.
   F. Determine if a _____ is required.

11. Payment for Services

   A. Should be documented on the _____ slip.
   B. The charge slip contains a list of the most common _____ for procedures and diagnoses at that office.
   C. Payment or _____ should be made prior to the patient leaving the office.

12. Consideration for the Patient's Time

   A. Inform the patient when the wait for his or her appointment will be longer than _____ minutes.

© 2011 Pearson Education, Inc.

B. Listen and do not _____ to a patient's anger.

C. Remain calm and be _____.

D. Tell the patient if a longer wait time is due to an _____ emergency.

E. Addressing both the patient's and the physician's time issues is _____ to successful scheduling.

II. Completing a Patient Visit

  1. Escorting the Patient to the Examination Room

    A. When calling the patient, verify the patient's _____ with the record and with the patient.

    B. Offer _____ to those who need it.

    C. Walk at a _____ pace.

  2. The Patient and the Examination Room

    A. Enter the room with the patient and _____ explain what clothing the patient should remove.

    B. _____ patients in disrobing if necessary.

    C. Make every effort to protect the patient's _____.

    D. Once the physician has completed the exam, return to the examination room and _____ before entering.

    E. _____ ask the patient if he or she has any additional questions.

  3. Ensuring Effective Patient Education

    A. Ensure that patient education is adapted and provided at a _____ that the patient understands.

    B. Assess the patient's level of understanding by asking the patient to _____ what he or she heard.

    C. If a misunderstanding is apparent, _____ the information to an appropriate level and ask the patient to repeat again.

    D. Provide _____ information to which the patient can refer.

    E. Do not _____ to ask the physician or another individual in the office to help clarify information for the patient.

  4. Electronic Educational Materials

    A. Education is easily accomplished if the office has _____ medical records.

    B. Software can target patients with certain conditions and then provide _____ with educational materials that are related to those conditions.

    C. E-mail can be a _____ -effective way to inform patients of various treatment options and procedures.

  5. Guidelines for Dealing with Disturbances

    A. If possible, move angry or loud patients into a _____ office area.

    B. Handle the situation as _____ and _____ as possible.

    C. Using a quiet, calm manner, _____ respond to the patient's complaint.

    D. Ask the patient to _____ the issue.

    E. Discuss _____ with the patient.

    F. Know office policy regarding when the _____ must be called.

  6. Dealing with Children

    A. The children of adult patients are allowed in the examination room unless _____ is required.

    B. If a child does not follow the adult to the examination room, the MA must ensure the child's _____ while left alone.

    C. Rarely are children seen by physicians without the presence of a _____.

  7. Handling Medical Emergencies in the Reception Room (list the steps)

    i. _____

    ii. _____

© 2011 Pearson Education, Inc.

iii. _____

iv. _____

v. _____

vi. _____

8. Steps for Closing the Office

A. Allow for _____ minutes at the end of the day to close the office.

B. Check records for any missing _____ and ensure that visits have been posted for billing.

C. _____, _____, and _____ all records for patients who will be seen the next day.

D. Place the collated records with _____ _____ attached and the _____ _____ of the next day's scheduled patients together in the appropriate place.

E. Make a copy of the _____ _____ of patients for each physician.

F. Deposit in the bank or place in the office safe, all money received from _____ payments.

G. Lock all _____ and file rooms, as well as _____ offices and any other individual offices within the medical practice.

H. Turn off all _____ equipment and appliances.

I. Ensure that all _____ rooms are clean and ready for the next day.

J. Straighten and _____ the reception room.

K. _____ the answering service.

L. Double-check to ensure that _____ are locked and the alarm system is activated.

KEY TERMINOLOGY REVIEW

Choose the term that best represents each statement below.

a. Receptionist

b. Copayments

c. Demographic

d. Medical emergency

e. Overbooking

f. Collating

g. Fax

h. No-show

1. _____ Machine used to send reports between facilities.

2. _____ When more than one patient is scheduled for the same time slot.

3. _____ Designated amounts that some medical insurance plans require patients to pay for medical services.

4. _____ May be responsible for providing and explaining instructions regarding tests and procedures such as fasting before a particular blood test.

5. _____ Information, such as age, gender, ethnic background, education, and Social Security number.

6. _____ Patient condition that requires the immediate attention of a physician.

7. _____ Patients who do not keep their appointment and do not call to cancel.

8. _____ Refers to collecting all records, test results, and information pertaining to a patient who is scheduled to be seen by the physician.

APPLIED PRACTICE

Using information from your textbook and other sources you may find on the topic, complete the following applied practice.

1. Aubrey Cody is a CMA (AAMA) who has been hired as a medical assistant for a new pediatric practice that is being built. The physicians within the practice have asked her to design and decorate

© 2011 Pearson Education, Inc.

the reception area. In the practice, there are three physicians who can see up to four patients each hour. How could Aubrey design the medical office reception area? What is the minimum amount of seating that should be in the reception area? What theme, toys, and reading materials would be appropriate for the reception area? Explain your answer after you have designed the reception area.

_____

_____

_____

_____

_____

LEARNING ACTIVITY: MULTIPLE CHOICE

Circle the correct answer to each of the questions below.

1. If the medical assistant is on the telephone when a patient arrives at the office what should she do to let the patient know that she is aware of their presence?

   a. Continue looking down at the desk so that the patient realizes that she is on the telephone and will not be able to offer help right away.

b. Make eye contact with the patient, smile, and hold up an index finger to indicate that she'll be with them in just a moment.

c. Turn her back to the patient in order to keep the telephone conversation more private.

d. Any of the above

2. When mentioning another patient's name over the telephone or to another staff member within hearing distance of any patients in the reception room

a. use caution and speak in a low voice.

b. be sure that the glass partition at the reception desk is closed so that others in the reception room are not able to hear the conversation.

c. step into a private area where other patient's are unable to hear the conversation.

d. Any of the above

3. When established patients check in at the front desk, what information should the receptionist first confirm with the patient?

a. That the patient's marital status has not changed since their last visit

b. The type of medications that the patient is taking

c. Current contact information

d. All of the above

4. When using a sign-in sheet, HIPAA allows the following information to be requested:

a. Patient's name

b. Time of arrival

c. Physician's name

d. All of the above

5. Patient information forms should contain which of the following pieces of information?

a. Patient's home address

b. Patient's insurance information

c. Patient's contact telephone numbers

d. All of the above

6. A charge slip is also known as

a. a checklist.

b. superbills or encounter forms.

c. a patient booklet.

d. Any of the above

7. In general, patients should not be made to wait longer than _____ minutes for their appointment.

a. 10

b. 15

c. 20

d. None of the above

8. Overbooking

a. is when more than one patient is scheduled for the same time slot.

b. should only be done in an emergency.

c. is an acceptable practice as long as patients are informed ahead of time.

d. All of the above

© 2011 Pearson Education, Inc.

9. When escorting a patient into the examination room,

    a. the receptionist will typically escort the person.
    b. the patient should be called by his or her first name unless instructed otherwise.
    c. making pleasant conversation with the patient may help ease the patient's anxieties.
    d. All of the above

10. How should the receptionist respond when confronted with an angry patient?

    a. Move the patient out of the front desk area.
    b. Ask the patient to sit down in the reception room until they have calmed down.
    c. Walk away from the front desk until the patient calms down.
    d. Any of the above

CRITICAL THINKING

Answer the following questions to the best of your ability. Utilize the textbook as a reference.

1. Marcus Winston, RMA, has been hired to work as an administrative medical assistant at the front desk in a small, one-physician medical office. Dr. Quan has been using a paper sign-in sheet for his patients for many years. Marcus has recently completed his medical assisting education and remembers learning that sign-in sheets must be HIPAA compliant. What can Marcus tell Dr. Quan about the paper sign-in system that he is currently using?

    _____

    _____

    _____

2. Sara Womack, CMA (AAMA), is the medical office manager in a women's clinic. She has two employees who share the job of front desk receptionist. Aaron Shelley, CMA (AAMA), doesn't like to work at the front desk. He is often short with the patients, some of whom have complained to the physician. Michael Sulley, RMA, is the other front desk receptionist. Michael has a sunny personality and thoroughly enjoys the fast pace at the front desk. Would Sara be better serving the patients at the women's clinic if she moved Aaron out of that position and had Michael work there full-time? Why or why not? What sort of ramifications might occur if Sara leaves Aaron in the front desk position?

    _____

    _____

    _____

    _____

3. Marjorie Sorensen, CMA (AAMA), has just been hired to work as the office manager for Dr. Rodriguez. The doctor tells Marjorie that she has noticed that many tasks are being skipped by the front desk staff when opening the office in the morning. Dr. Rodriguez believes that the front desk staff is forgetting these tasks and has asked Marjorie to come up with a solution to this problem. What might Marjorie suggest?

    _____

    _____

    _____

    _____

© 2011 Pearson Education, Inc.

4. Isaiah Chung is taking an administrative medical assisting course as part of his training to become a medical assistant. His instructor has assigned the task of creating an office policy for opening the medical office. How might Isaiah's policy read?

_____

_____

_____

_____

RESEARCH ACTIVITY

Utilize Internet search engines to research the following topics and write a brief description of what you find. It is important to utilize reputable websites.

1. Using the information and décor theme of the reception area that you designed in the applied practice activity, search the Internet and obtain figures and estimates regarding the cost of decorating a reception area. Take into consideration paint, accessories, seating, tables, and so forth. Be sure to cite the websites that you use to find your information.

_____

_____

_____

_____

_____

_____

_____

_____

_____

_____

_____

_____

_____

_____

_____

_____

_____

_____

_____

_____

© 2011 Pearson Education, Inc.

CHAPTER 9
Appointment Scheduling

CHAPTER OUTLINE

General review of the chapter:

Appointment Schedules
Scheduling Systems
Patient Scheduling Process
Established Patient Appointments
New Patient Appointments
Maintaining the Schedule
Future Appointments
Patient Referrals
Hospital Admission Scheduling
Scheduling Surgery and Outpatient Procedures
Appointment Exceptions
Telephone and E-mail Scheduling
Scheduling Other Types of Appointments

STUDENT STUDY GUIDE

Use the following guide to assist in your learning of the concepts from the chapter.

I. Scheduling Systems

   1. Factors to Be Considered in Selecting a Scheduling System

      i. _____

      ii. _____

      iii. _____

      iv. _____

      v. _____

      vi. _____

      vii. _____

   2. Purpose of a Scheduling System

     A. Assists in the _____ of the office.

     B. Provides _____ management.

     C. _____ efficiency.

     D. Helps to ensure the _____ of patient care.

   3. Variations in Appointment Schedules

      i. _____

      ii. _____

      iii. _____

      iv. _____

v. _____

vi. _____

4. Specified Times

   A. Length of appointment is determined by _____ needs.

   B. Up to each staff member to reduce _____ time.

   C. Important for office to build in _____ time.

5. Wave Scheduling

   A. Provides _____ for unforeseen events.

   B. Purpose is to _____ and _____ each hour on time.

   C. Each hour is divided into _____ amounts of time.

   D. Three _____ -minute or four _____ -minute appointments could be seen in an hour.

   E. Patients are seen in the _____ in which they arrive.

6. Open Office Hours

   A. _____ structured of all systems.

   B. Patients may arrive at _____ during business hours.

   C. This method is _____ by some because it avoids the disruption caused by missed appointments.

7. Advantages of Computerized Scheduling Systems

   A. Completed in a _____ -time environment.

   B. Provides the ability to _____ appointment information with ease.

   C. Maximizes office process _____ and patient _____.

   D. Provides the ability to track _____ in the medical practice.

8. Manual Scheduling Systems

   A. Consists of a _____ schedule book.

   B. Book is selected based on practice _____ and _____.

9. Requirements for Both Computerized and Manual Systems

   A. The appointment book is a legal document that can be _____ by the court.

   B. Appointment books should be _____ for future reference and kept for several years in the event of a court case.

   C. If there are any changes in the scheduled patients in the appointment book, these should be noted both in the _____ and in the _____.

II. Patient Scheduling Process

   1. Steps for Scheduling the Patient

     i. _____

     ii. _____

     iii. _____

     iv. _____

     v. _____

     vi. _____

     vii. _____

     viii. _____

   2. Steps for Manually Scheduling Established Patients

     A. Use a _____ so that appointments can be erased to make changes as needed.

     B. Set up a _____ by blocking out all time periods when the physician is not available for appointments.

     C. Print the patient's _____ first and last names next to the appropriate time on the schedule.

     D. Add _____ for *junior* and _____ for *senior* if there are two patients with the same name in a family.

© 2011 Pearson Education, Inc.

E. Ask the patient for _____ work and home telephone numbers, including the area codes.

F. Write these numbers next to the _____.

G. Record the _____ for the visit on the schedule.

3. Additional Steps Related to Scheduling Patients Electronically

A. Ensure that the scheduling system is _____.

B. Search for the _____ patient.

C. _____ that the telephone numbers in the system are correct.

4. Steps for Scheduling New Patients

A. _____ the necessary appointment scheduling equipment.

B. Obtain the patients full _____ name.

C. Record the patient's chief _____ and _____ .

D. Request the name of the patient's insurance _____ and policy _____.

E. Attempt to _____ the new patient's request for his or her preferred appointment time.

F. Provide the new patient with _____ to the office.

G. Welcome and thank the new patient by _____ for selecting your medical office.

H. _____ new patient information in a new medical record.

5. Addressing Missed Appointments and No-Shows

A. Charge the patient according to office _____.

B. _____ the patient and reschedule.

C. _____ the missed appointment and rescheduled date.

D. Write _____ or _____ on the appointment schedule and in the patient chart.

6. Advance Bookings and Follow-up

A. Advance bookings are done for _____ scheduled appointments.

B. Ensure that the patient receives an _____ card.

C. Follow-ups can be made in _____, by _____, or via _____.

7. Issues Related to Arranging a Referral Appointment

A. Information required for an outgoing or incoming referral includes

   i. _____

   ii. _____

   iii. _____

   iv. _____

   v. _____

   vi. _____

   vii. _____

B. Depending on the insurance, _____ may be necessary before scheduling the appointment.

8. Steps for Arranging a Referral Appointment

A. Before providing the patient's name, etc., _____ that the practice accepts the patient's medical insurance.

B. Record the referral appointment information in the _____, as well as on an appointment _____ for the patient.

C. Record the name of the individual with whom you spoke in the _____, as well as on the _____.

D. Notify the patient of the _____ and _____ of the appointment.

9. Considerations for Scheduling a Direct Admission to a Hospital

A. Contact the patient's _____ for pre-admissions approval.

B. Verify the _____ of the patient's first and last names.

C. Obtain the patient's social security number from the _____.

D. Ask patient for _____ phone number and area code.

E. Give the physician's statement from the _____ as the reason for the admission.

F. Document the patient's name with the insurance company that gave _____.

10. Steps for Scheduling an Inpatient Surgical Procedure

    i. _____

    ii. _____

    iii. _____

    iv. _____

    v. _____

    vi. _____

    vii. _____

    viii. _____

    ix. _____

    x. _____

11. Steps for Scheduling an Outpatient Procedure

    i. _____

    ii. _____

    iii. _____

    iv. _____

    v. _____

    vi. _____

    vii. _____

    viii. _____

    ix. _____

    x. _____

    xi. _____

    xii. _____

12. Considerations for Handling Nonscheduled Patients

A. Determine the _____ of the patient's condition.

B. Ask the patient for his or her telephone number and where he or she is calling from, and determine whether the patient is _____.

C. Follow office _____ and _____ regarding handling emergency situations.

D. Inform the _____ immediately regarding a potential emergency.

KEY TERMINOLOGY REVIEW

Match the correct medical term with the definition listed below.

a. Acute conditions

b. Advance bookings

c. Archived

d. Catch-up

e. Cycle time

f. Double-booking

g. Established patient

h. Matrix

i. Modified wave scheduling

j. Open-ended questions

k. Privacy screen

l. Real time

m. Scheduling system

n. Subpoena

o. Time patterns

p. Triage

q. Wave scheduling

1. _____ Block others from viewing the computer screen.

2. _____ Also known as assigning priority.

© 2011 Pearson Education, Inc.

3. _____ Allows patients to book their next appointment 3 to 6 months ahead of time.

4. _____ Requires more than a *yes* or *no* answer and are used to gather pertinent information.

5. _____ A time when appointments are not scheduled.

6. _____ Facilitates the coordination of appropriate time segments for staff, patients, and the practice's available equipment.

7. _____ Illnesses or injuries that patients suddenly experience and that require treatment but may not be life threatening.

8. _____ A patient who has been seen by a practitioner within the past 3 years.

9. _____ Process of blocking out times in the appointment schedule when the provider is unavailable or out of the office.

10. _____ Information requested by the courts.

11. _____ The length of time the average patient spends in the medical office.

12. _____ Another term for "stored."

13. _____ To have three patients scheduled at intervals during the first half hour with none scheduled for the second half hour.

14. _____ Refers to automatically placing the appointment, patient needs, and information within the appropriate areas of the computer program versus the manual system.

15. _____ Patients are scheduled only during the first half hour and are served on a first come, first served basis.

16. _____ Similar to matrixing off time within the schedule to allow for catch-up time or unscheduled appointments.

17. _____ Scheduling more than one patient for the same appointment time.

APPLIED PRACTICE

Follow the directions as instructed for each question below.

1. Using the information below and the manual schedule on the following pages, create a matrix for the medical office. *(Remember to use a pencil.)*

   a. The medical offices open at 8:30 A.M. every day.
   b. The last appointment for the day is scheduled no later than 3:30 P.M.
   c. The office is closed for appointments for lunch starting at 12:00 P.M.; it reopens at 1:15 P.M.
   d. Dr. Cho has hospital rounds every Wednesday from 7:30 A.M.–10:00 A.M.
   e. Dr. Jackson has hospital rounds every Thursday from 7:45 A.M.–10:15 A.M.
   f. On February 3, Dr. Cho has a meeting at Alliance Assisted Living that starts at 3:30 P.M.
   g. On February 2, Dr. Jackson has a meeting with a pharmaceutical representative that is scheduled for 12:45–1:30 P.M.

2. Schedule the following patients on the appointment schedule.

   a. LaToya Atwater is a new patient to see Dr. Cho. Wednesdays work best for LaToya.
   b. Sujin Dalywhal wants to see Dr. Jackson on Thursday afternoon for an abdominal suture removal.
   c. Jose Alvarez calls on Wednesday morning because he has had a terrible headache for the past 2 days.
   d. Anna Maria DeCamillo is a diabetic patient who wants to see Dr. Jackson for her 3-month diabetic check-up on Wednesday afternoon.
   e. Mark Tomlinson wants to see Dr. Cho for his annual check-up on Thursday.
   f. Aiden Taylor needs to be seen on Thursday morning for his 3-year well-child visit with Dr. Jackson.
   g. Dr. Cho requests that an appointment be made on Wednesday morning with her patient, Lydia Pazmino, regarding her blood test results.

Pearson Family Clinic

Wednesday, February 2, 20xx

	Dr. S. Cho	Dr. A. Jackson
7:30		
7:45		
8:00		
8:15		
8:30		
8:45		
9:00		
9:15		
9:30		
9:45		
10:00		
10:15		
10:30		
10:45		
11:00		
11:15		
11:30		
11:45		
12:00		
12:15		
12:30		
12:45		
1:00		
1:15		
1:30		
1:45		
2:00		
2:15		
2:30		
2:45		
3:00		
3:15		
3:30		
3:45		
4:00		

© 2011 Pearson Education, Inc.

Thursday, February 3, 20xx

	Dr. S. Cho	Dr. A. Jackson
7:30		
7:45		
8:00		
8:15		
8:30		
8:45		
9:00		
9:15		
9:30		
9:45		
10:00		
10:15		
10:30		
10:45		
11:00		
11:15		
11:30		
11:45		
12:00		
12:15		
12:30		
12:45		
1:00		
1:15		
1:30		
1:45		
2:00		
2:15		
2:30		
2:45		
3:00		
3:15		
3:30		
3:45		
4:00		

© 2011 Pearson Education, Inc.

LEARNING ACTIVITY: MULTIPLE CHOICE

Circle the correct answer to each of the questions below.

1. How many minutes do most patients consider to be an acceptable wait time prior to seeing the doctor?
   a. 10
   b. 15
   c. 20
   d. None of the above

2. Which of the following is an acceptable way to note a missed appointment in a hardcopy appointment book?
   a. Use white correction fluid to cover the patient's name.
   b. Use a black marker to obliterate the patient's name.
   c. Use an eraser to remove the patient's name.
   d. Write no-show (NS) both on the appointment schedule and in the patient's chart.

3. What is one way to remind patients of their upcoming appointment in the medical office?
   a. Send out a reminder card to the patient just prior to the appointment.
   b. Call the patient to remind him or her of the appointment.
   c. Send an e-mail to the patient to remind him or her of the appointment.
   d. Any of the above.

4. The _____ method of scheduling is where two or three patients are scheduled at the beginning of each hour, followed by single patient appointments every 10 to 20 minutes for the rest of that hour.
   a. wave
   b. modified wave
   c. open hours
   d. fixed appointment

5. The _____ method of scheduling is where patients are scheduled only for the first half of each hour. The first patient to arrive is seen first.
   a. wave
   b. modified wave
   c. open hours
   d. fixed appointment

6. The _____ method of scheduling is most commonly used in walk-in clinics, laboratories, and x-ray facilities where patients are typically seen on a first come, first served basis.
   a. wave
   b. modified wave
   c. open hours
   d. fixed appointment

7. To eliminate the need to "squeeze in" an emergency or unscheduled appointment, the medical assistant should integrate _____ into the office schedule, if office policy allows.
   a. more time
   b. time patterns
   c. wave scheduling
   d. None of the above

© 2011 Pearson Education, Inc.

8. Examples of emergency conditions that require patients to be seen immediately include
   a. Skin rash
   b. Pain or burning on urination
   c. Chest pain
   d. All of the above

9. When confirming an appointment with a patient on the telephone, the patient should be asked to repeat the following information:
   a. Location of the appointment
   b. Date of the appointment
   c. Time of the appointment
   d. All of the above

10. Triage
    a. Becomes necessary when more than one seriously ill patient is waiting to see the patient.
    b. Takes place each time a patient visits the office.
    c. Is only done in a hospital setting.
    d. A skill performed only by the physician.

CRITICAL THINKING

Answer the following questions to the best of your ability. Utilize the textbook as a reference.

1. Dylan Reilly, CMA (AAMA), is working in a busy family practice office. The physicians and staff all agree that the appointment scheduling system is not working and patients are frequently waiting long periods of time for appointments. How should Dylan go about creating a new scheduling procedure for this office?

   _____
   _____
   _____
   _____

2. Armando Alonso is taking an administrative medical assisting course as part of his medical assisting training. He has been given an assignment to create a list of the information patients should be given when scheduling the patient in order to help prepare the patient for medical procedures. What sort of information should Armando list?

   _____
   _____
   _____
   _____

3. Anna Simonenko, CMA (AAMA), is working at the front desk in a family practice clinic. Anna has been asked to schedule Roger Edetsberger for a procedure to be performed in the hospital. Anna tells Roger that she will need to call his insurance company before she can schedule the procedure. Roger asks, "Why do you need to do that? Can't you just schedule the procedure now and call the insurance company some other time?" What can Anna say to Roger?

   _____
   _____
   _____
   _____

RESEARCH ACTIVITY

Utilize Internet search engines to research the following topics and write a brief description of what you find. It is important to utilize reputable websites.

1. Research various appointment scheduling software programs for medical offices.

    What products are available?
    What must be considered prior to purchasing medical office software?
    What type of technical support is available?

    _____

    _____

    _____

    _____

    _____

    _____

    _____

    _____

    _____

    _____

    _____

    _____

    _____

© 2011 Pearson Education, Inc.

CHAPTER 10
Office Facilities, Equipment, and Supplies

CHAPTER OUTLINE

General review of the chapter:

Medical Office Facility
Office Layout
Office Equipment
Supplies

STUDENT STUDY GUIDE

Use the following guide to assist in your learning of the concepts from the chapter.

I. Medical Office Facility and Equipment

    1. Desirable Characteristics of a Medical Facility

        A. Presents a _____ and _____ environment.
        B. Is clean, neat, and well _____.
        C. Makes a good _____ impression.
        D. Generates positive employee _____.

    2. Aspects to Be Considered in the Medical Office

        i. _____
        ii. _____
        iii. _____
        iv. _____
        v. _____
        vi. _____
        vii. _____
        viii. _____
        ix. _____
        x. _____
        xi. _____

    3. Americans with Disabilities Act

        A. Protects the rights of the disabled regarding access to _____, _____, _____, _____, _____, and _____.

    4. Lighting and Colors

        A. _____ colors are typically used.
        B. _____ art should hang on the walls.
        C. Fish tanks are _____ for children and adults.

5. Reception Room Safety

   A. Prevent fires by eliminating sparks from _____, and _____ and _____ equipment.

   B. Ensure that staff members understand their _____ during a fire.

   C. Post _____ plans in a central location within the office.

6. Equipment Typically Found in Administrative Areas

   i. _____

   ii. _____

   iii. _____

   iv. _____

   v. _____

   vi. _____

   vii. _____

   viii. _____

   ix. _____

7. Factors Promoted by an Effective Office Flow

   i. _____

   ii. _____

   iii. _____

   iv. _____

   v. _____

8. Considerations for the Patient Entrance

   A. It provides the _____ impression.

   B. High steps should be _____.

   C. Push and pull indicators should be placed on _____.

9. Considerations for the Reception Area

   A. Desk area should provide _____ and the confidentiality of information.

   B. Desk area should allow for ease of _____ to patient records but at the same time protect patient privacy.

   C. Waiting area should contain seats that can be _____ and that provide good _____.

   D. Toys in the waiting area should be _____ and _____.

10. Assisting Patients in Understanding the Office Layout

    A. Provide _____ that indicate the location of the various areas in the office.

    B. The use of _____ indicators on the floor or walls may be helpful.

    C. Ensure that _____ and _____ are clear of obstructions.

11. Considerations for Office Bathrooms

    i. _____

    ii. _____

    iii. _____

    iv. _____

    v. _____

    vi. _____

    vii. _____

12. Uses of Word Processing in the Medical Office

    A. Makes creating and retrieving documents more _____.

    B. Allows the ability to _____ and _____ text without having to cut and paste a paper document.

    C. Allows for making _____ copies.

© 2011 Pearson Education, Inc.

13. Use of Voice Recognition Software
    A. Allows the physician to speak into a _____ connected to a computer program that transcribes the physician's dictated office notes into a _____ report.
    B. Due to the set-up _____, few physicians have adopted this system.
    C. It is used in some hospital _____ _____ departments.

14. Electronic Postage
    A. Requires the user to apply for and receive approval from the _____ prior to use.
    B. User is required to determine the _____ of postage required for letters and packages and then a computer interfaces with the postal system to print the appropriate postage.
    C. Method may be used in offices with a lot of _____ mail.

15. Considerations for Purchasing Equipment
    i. _____
    ii. _____
    iii. _____
    iv. _____

16. Purposes of an Equipment Log
    A. Used to _____ pieces of equipment that require regular maintenance.
    B. Helps prove that the _____ has been well maintained.
    C. May be a required document for _____ purposes.

II. Supplies and Inventory
    1. Factors Affecting the Selection of Vendors
        i. _____
        ii. _____
        iii. _____
        iv. _____
        v. _____
        vi. _____
        vii. _____
        viii. _____
        ix. _____
        x. _____

    2. Considerations for Supply Inventory Control
        A. Mark the _____ sheet whenever an item is removed from the supply cabinet.
        B. Assign a staff member the responsibility for _____ all supplies.
        C. Ensure that reordering occurs in a _____ manner so that the supply is never totally depleted.
        D. Consider the _____ with which supplies are used and the amount of _____ necessary for having the order processed and delivered when reordering supplies.

    3. Establishing an Ordering System
        A. It is important to determine when _____ of the supply will have been used and how long an order takes to arrive.
        B. Use of _____ reminders or _____ reminder cards may be useful.
        C. _____ scanning systems can be purchased as an ordering system.

    4. Drug Samples
        A. These are small packages of drug samples for physicians to distribute to _____.
        B. The are provided by _____ representatives.
        C. The discarding of samples must be done according to _____ and _____ regulations.

KEY TERMINOLOGY REVIEW

Use the key terms found at the beginning of the chapter to complete the sentences below.

1. The _____ is the legislation that protects the rights of the disabled regarding access to employment, public buildings, transportation, housing, schools, and health care facilities.

2. Dr. Sabol chose to purchase an extended _____ that would cover repair and maintenance for an additional 7 years.

3. Supplies that are used up quickly and have a relatively inexpensive unit cost are called _____ supplies.

4. The distinguishing factor between capital equipment and general office supplies is the _____ of the product.

5. _____ equipment refers to items that require a large dollar amount to purchase (generally more than $500) and have a relatively long life.

6. The medical facility generally has a flow that lends itself easily to teamwork, time management, organized and efficient office equipment usage, and patient flow. This is known as _____.

7. Dr. Linn asked his clinical manager to create a/an _____ of all the supplies located in the supply closet.

8. _____ is the length of time that the average patient spends in the medical office.

9. _____ refers to the positive or negative state of mind of employees with regard to their work or work environment.

10. An _____ can be purchased to cover some period of time after the warranty has expired.

11. Capital equipment also has a _____, which is referred to as depreciation.

12. _____ is a loss in the value of the product resulting from normal aging, use, or deterioration.

13. In general, it takes multiple _____ to provide all of the supplies for a medical practice.

APPLIED PRACTICE

Read the scenario and answer the questions that follow.

> ### Scenario
> Javier Gomez, CMA (AAMA), is working in the front office of a busy family practice. His manager, Chris, has asked him to create a detailed inventory list of all of the supplies needed for his station at the patient check-out desk. Below is a list that Javier has started.

Item Name	Company	Amount on Hand
Pens	Office Supplies R Us	14
Message pad	Office Supplies R Us	2 tablets
Ink pad	Office Supplies R Us	2 pads

© 2011 Pearson Education, Inc.

1. Based on the inventory list, what additional important information should Javier include before submitting his list to Chris?

   _____

   _____

   _____

2. Considering that Javier is working at a patient check-out desk, where patients pay co-payments and schedule follow-up appointments as needed, what additional items would Javier be likely to add to his inventory list? Name at least five additional items.

   _____

   _____

   _____

   _____

   _____

LEARNING ACTIVITY: MULTIPLE CHOICE

Circle the correct answer to each of the questions below.

1. ADA regulations ensure that every public facility

   a. is made easily accessible to the handicapped.
   b. provides unrestricted hallways.
   c. has elevators or ramps available.
   d. All of the above

2. When addressing safety issues in the medical office, concerns noted may include

   a. the use of throw rugs.
   b. the culture of the office.
   c. the tone of the office.
   d. All of the above

3. Issues to be considered when setting up a medical office include the

   a. employees who work in the office.
   b. office design and layout.
   c. other offices in the building.
   d. None of the above

4. The first element of office flow is the

   a. restrooms.
   b. patient entrance.
   c. placement of examination rooms.
   d. staff offices.

5. Which of the following is considered to be capital equipment?

   a. Copy machine
   b. EKG paper
   c. Medications
   d. All of the above

6. Uses and advantages of using a postal meter include which of the following?

   a. Metered mail does not have to be stamped when it arrives at the post office.

   b. A postal meter will calculate the exact postage required and either print it directly onto the letter or print out a strip to be affixed to the package.

   c. A postal meter allows for postage to be printed directly onto an envelope or onto an adhesive-backed strip that is placed directly on an envelope or package.

   d. All of the above

7. Examples of expendable supplies include

   a. scanners.

   b. the telephone system.

   c. clinical supplies such as catheters.

   d. All of the above

8. An inventory list of all sample drugs must be maintained to adhere to _____ regulations.

   a. Drug Enforcement Administration (DEA)

   b. Americans with Disabilities Act (ADA)

   c. Food and Drug Administration (FDA)

   d. None of the above

9. Which of the following guidelines should be followed with regard to drug samples?

   a. Must be placed in a secure location.

   b. Should be kept all together by category.

   c. All samples should be rotated like other supplies, with newer samples placed in the back behind samples of the same medication and strength with earlier expiration dates.

   d. All of the above

10. A warranty

   a. is a manufacturer's guarantee in writing that its product will perform correctly under normal conditions.

   b. can be purchased to cover a period of time after the original warranty has expired.

   c. will state in detail what is actually covered by the contract.

   d. provides for replacement of defective parts but for an additional charge.

CRITICAL THINKING

Answer the following questions to the best of your ability. Utilize the textbook as a reference.

1. Corey Steinberg, CMA (AAMA), has recently been hired to work as an administrative medical assistant in a busy cardiology practice. Corey has been given the task of creating a manual that outlines the warranty information, as well as the maintenance schedule for each piece of medical office equipment. How should Corey go about beginning this task?

_____

_____

_____

_____

2. Monte Beaton, RMA, is the office manager in a gastroenterology practice. Monte has recently hired three new medical assistants and wants to ensure that they are properly trained to use each piece of equipment in the medical office. How can Monte ensure that the training is done properly?

© 2011 Pearson Education, Inc.

_____

_____

_____

3. Krystle Shawger is taking an administrative class as part of her medical assisting training. She has been given an assignment to write an essay describing how an equipment maintenance log would be useful in the medical office. What might Krystle include in her paper?

_____

_____

_____

4. Marian Harrison, RMA, is the administrative office manager in a family practice clinic. She is writing an office policy for the inventory of administrative office equipment. What might her policy include?

_____

_____

_____

5. Joanne Felmer, CMA (AAMA), works in a walk-in clinic. At the weekly office staff meeting, the office manager mentioned the need for purchasing a new EKG machine. The office manager has asked Joanne to research the various options available. How should Joanne handle this task?

_____

_____

_____

_____

RESEARCH ACTIVITY

Utilize Internet search engines to research the following topics and write a brief description of what you find. It is important to utilize reputable websites.

1. Conduct an Internet search for office and medical supply companies. Which companies supply products at competitive prices? What are the shipping charges? Which company seems to have the best variety of products? How could this information be useful for medical offices?

_____

_____

_____

_____

_____

_____

_____

_____
_____
_____
_____
_____
_____
_____
_____
_____
_____
_____
_____
_____
_____
_____
_____

© 2011 Pearson Education, Inc.

CHAPTER 11
Written Communication

CHAPTER OUTLINE

General review of the chapter:

Letter Writing
Word Choice
Composing Letters
Letter Styles
Interoffice Memoranda
Proofreading
Editing
Abbreviations
Reference Materials
Preparing Outgoing Mail
Classifications of Mail
Size Requirements for Mail
Mail Handling Tips
Electronic Mail
Reflection on the Medical Practice

STUDENT STUDY GUIDE

Use the following guide to assist in your learning of the concepts from the chapter.

I. Written Communication in the Medical Office

  1. How Professionalism Is Reflected in Written Communication

    A. Physical _____ of the letter.
    B. _____ of the message being sent.
    C. Use of grammar and _____.

  2. Elements to Be Included in a Professional Letter

    A. Message should be _____ and to the point.
    B. Expected outcome should be _____.
    C. Threats or derogatory comments should _____ be made.
    D. Negative _____ should be avoided.

  3. Usage to Be Avoided

    i. _____
    ii. _____
    iii. _____
    iv. _____
    v. _____
    vi. _____

4. Ways to Improve Sentences and Paragraphs

    A. Ensure that the sentence length never exceeds _____ words.
    B. Eliminate all words that are _____.
    C. Cover _____ point in each paragraph.
    D. Avoid use of the _____ pronoun.
    E. Avoid redundancy and _____.
    F. Eliminate inflated _____.

5. Active vs. Passive Voice

    A. When using the active voice, the subject of the sentence does the _____.
    B. The use of the active voice is considered to be more effective because it is _____ and more _____ than the use of the passive voice.
    C. When using the passive voice, the _____ receives the action.

6. Rules for Writing Numbers

    A. Numbers _____ through _____ are spelled out.
    B. Only Arabic _____ are used in tables, statistical data, dates, measurements, money, percentages, and time.
    C. When placing numbers in columns, align them as follows: Arabic integers are aligned on the _____. Decimal numbers are aligned on the _____ point. Roman numerals are aligned on the _____.
    D. Do not use _____ when writing on-the-hour time.

7. Eight Parts of Speech

    i. _____
    ii. _____
    iii. _____
    iv. _____
    v. _____
    vi. _____
    vii. _____
    viii. _____

8. Standard Components of a Business Letter

    i. _____
    ii. _____
    iii. _____
    iv. _____
    v. _____
    vi. _____
    vii. _____
    viii. _____
    ix. _____
    x. _____

9. Address of the Recipient

    A. Address is typed along the _____ margin and is _____-spaced.
    B. Company name is typed exactly as shown on the company's own _____.
    C. Name of the city is followed by a _____.
    D. Two-letter state abbreviation is followed by _____ spaces and then the ZIP code.

10. Guidelines for Using Courtesy Titles

    A. _____ is always an appropriate title for men.
    B. If there is a professional title, such as MD or PhD, this is used instead of the _____ title.
    C. _____ is used when the marital status of a woman is unknown.

© 2011 Pearson Education, Inc.

D. _____ is appropriate for unmarried women who prefer that title and is also used for young girls.

11. Body of the Letter

    A. Contains the _____ of the letter.
    B. Begins _____ lines below the salutation.
    C. The body is _____-spaced, with _____-spacing between each paragraph.
    D. Paragraphs are either _____ or indented on the first line.
    E. Most letters bearing a single message are usually _____ or _____ paragraphs in length and are confined to a _____ page.

12. Signature Line

    A. Typed _____ lines below the complimentary close.
    B. If the name and title are on the same line, they are separated by a _____.

13. Steps for Composing a Business Letter

    i. _____
    ii. _____
    iii. _____
    iv. _____
    v. _____
    vi. _____

14. Developing a Two-Page Letter

    A. _____ stationary is used only for the top sheet.
    B. A _____-inch margin is used at the bottom of the page.
    C. All pages following the first page must begin with the _____ and the _____ _____ of the letter.

15. Letter Styles

    i. _____
    ii. _____
    iii. _____
    iv. _____
    v. _____

16. Editing

    A. When editing medical reports, do not change the _____ of the report or _____ the meaning in any way.
    B. If the meaning seems to be unclear, check with the writer of the report before any _____ changes are made.
    C. When editing material that you have composed, changes can be made to increase _____.

17. Medical Abbreviations

    A. _____ medical abbreviations can be used in medical reports and when filing insurance documents.
    B. The _____ has released a list of abbreviations that should never be used.

18. Reference Tools for Writing

    i. _____
    ii. _____
    iii. _____
    iv. _____

II. Handing Mail in the Medical Office

1. Tasks Related to the Handling of Incoming Mail

    i. _____

    ii. _____

    iii. _____

2. Sizes of Letterhead Stationary

A. _____ letterhead is used for most office correspondence.

B. _____ or _____ style is used by some physicians for their social correspondence.

C. _____ letterhead is a half-sheet used for brief letters and memoranda.

3. Folding and Inserting Letters into a No. 10 Envelope

A. Fold the bottom _____ of the letter upward and crease the fold.

B. Fold the top of the letter downward to _____ inch from the previous crease and crease this fold.

C. Place this edge into the envelope _____.

4. Folding and Inserting Letters into a No. 6¾ Envelope

A. Bring the bottom edge up to _____ inch from the top edge.

B. Fold the right edge _____ _____ the width of the paper and crease this fold.

C. Fold the left edge to _____ inch from the previous crease and insert this edge into the envelope first.

5. Guidelines for Optimal Efficiency of OCR Scanning

A. The address must be typed on the envelope using _____-spacing and capital letters with no _____.

B. The last line in the address must include the city, the two-digit state code, and the ZIP code. The line must not exceed _____ characters.

6. Considerations When Typing an Envelope

A. The bottom margin of the No. 10 envelope should be _____ inch with _____ -inch margins on the left and right sides.

B. No. 6¾ envelopes should have a _____-inch margin on the left side, with the address _____ lines from the top of the envelope.

C. The return address for the sender should always be placed in the upper-_____ corner of the envelope.

7. ZIP Codes

A. ZIP codes start on the East Coast with the number _____, increasing to the number _____ on the West Coast and in Hawaii.

B. The first _____ numbers identify the city and all five digits combine to identify the individual post office and _____ within the city.

C. _____ additional digits have been added to the ZIP code by the USPS. These represent the addressee's _____ location.

8. Common Types of Mail

    i. _____

    ii. _____

    iii. _____

    iv. _____

    v. _____

    vi. _____

© 2011 Pearson Education, Inc.

9. Size Requirements for Mail

   A. Domestic mail must be at least _____ inch thick.
   B. Mail that is _____ inch or less in thickness must be _____ inches in height and at least _____ inches long. All mail not meeting this requirement is considered to be _____.
   C. Items that are bulky and lightweight require a _____-pound balloon rate surcharge.

10. Guidelines for Preparing Mail That Is to Be Metered

    A. Separate all _____ mail from the _____ mail.
    B. Separate all mail destined to either _____ or _____ from the rest of the international mail.
    C. When mailing letter size envelopes, flaps must be _____, _____, or _____.
    D. Envelopes larger than a _____ size envelope must be sealed before being sent.

11. Issues Related to Electronic Mail

    A. Electronic mail cannot be used if the original _____ on the document must be sent.
    B. The _____ of the message should remain as professional as if you were typing a letter to be sent through the USPS.
    C. E-mail is not efficient for use in _____.
    D. It is imperative to adhere strictly to all _____ confidentiality laws when using e-mail.

12. Issues Related to Instant Messaging

    A. Instant Messaging is a way to communicate with another person in _____ _____.
    B. Instant messages are not _____ documents and cannot be attached to a person's _____ records or be used in a court of law.
    C. Abbreviating words when instant messaging is not acceptable for electronic messages sent from within the _____ .

13. Steps in Opening and Sorting Mail

    i. _____
    ii. _____
    iii. _____
    iv. _____
    v. _____
    vi. _____
    vii. _____
    viii. _____
    ix. _____
    x. _____
    xi. _____
    xii. _____

14. Guidelines for Sending a Fax

    A. _____ document is inserted into the fax machine.
    B. _____ sheet should be sent first.
    C. All fax cover sheets must be _____ compliant.

15. Contents of a Fax Cover Sheet

    i. _____
    ii. _____
    iii. _____
    iv. _____
    v. _____

© 2011 Pearson Education, Inc.

KEY TERMINOLOGY REVIEW

Without using your textbook, write a sentence using the selected key terms in the correct context.

1. *active voice*

_____

_____

2. *block letter style*

_____

_____

3. *complimentary close*

_____

_____

4. *constant information*

_____

_____

5. *electronic mail*

_____

_____

6. *enclosure*

_____

_____

7. *gender bias*

_____

_____

8. *homophones*

_____

_____

9. *letterhead*

_____

_____

10. *memos*

_____

_____

11. *modified block letter style*

_____

_____

12. *optical character recognition*

_____

_____

© 2011 Pearson Education, Inc.

13. *passive voice*

_____

_____

14. *proofreading*

_____

_____

15. *redundant*

_____

_____

16. *reference initials*

_____

_____

17. *salutation*

_____

_____

18. *signature line*

_____

_____

19. *thesaurus*

_____

_____

20. *variables*

_____

_____

APPLIED PRACTICE

Follow the directions for each assignment below.

1. Using proofreader's marks, make the necessary corrections to the body of the business letter. (Refer to Figure 11-5 in your textbook.)

> Mr. SUSAN Rowe (8-12-1877 was seen in my office today. She presents with complaints of uper right quadrant pain times too weeks. Mrs. rowe states that alon g with the pain, she is experiencing nausea and vomitting. Upon palpation the abdomen appears bloted and is sensitive to the touch

2. Using word processing software, create an interoffice memo. Andrew Edwards, CMA (AAMA), is the sender of the memo and all clinical staff members are intended to be the recipients. The purpose of the memo is to inform the clinical staff that a pharmaceutical sales representative will be presenting information on a new cardiac drug that Dr. Sheila Tyrone is considering using for patient therapy. The presentation will occur on Friday during the lunch hour.

LEARNING ACTIVITY: MULTIPLE CHOICE

Circle the correct answer to each of the questions below.

1. Which of the following is the size of a standard business envelope?
   a. 3½" × 8½"
   b. 4⅛" × 9½"
   c. 4¼" × 9¼"
   d. None of the above

2. How much postage is required to mail an interoffice memo?
   a. $0.31
   b. $0.23
   c. $0.20
   d. None of the above

3. In order to catch all of the errors in a written document, how many times should the medical assistant read a letter before sending it out?
   a. Once
   b. Twice
   c. Three times
   d. Four times

4. The _____ of a professional letter typically appears two lines down from the ending portion of the body.
   a. closing
   b. subject line
   c. salutation
   d. letterhead

5. Which of the following pieces of information are typically included in the office letterhead?
   a. Office name
   b. Office address
   c. Office e-mail address
   d. All of the above

6. Which of the following statements is written correctly?
   a. The patient is taking five milligrams of the medication every hour.
   b. The patient is taking 5 milligrams of the medication every hour.
   c. The patient is taking five (5) milligrams of the medication every hour.
   d. All of the above are correct.

7. Which of the following words is misspelled?
   a. foriegn
   b. occurrance
   c. liason
   d. All of the above are misspelled

8. The closing appears _____ spaces below the end of the body of the letter.
   a. one
   b. two

© 2011 Pearson Education, Inc.

c. three
d. four

9. Which of the following parts of speech modifies a noun or a pronoun?

   a. Verb
   b. Adverb
   c. Adjective
   d. Preposition

10. Which of the following style of letters is spaced with all lines flush with the left margin except for the first line of each paragraph?

    a. Modified block
    b. Simplified letter block
    c. Semi-simplified letter block
    d. None of the above

CRITICAL THINKING

Answer the following questions to the best of your ability. Utilize the textbook as a reference.

1. Missy Hurst, RMA, is working as an administrative medical assistant with a gastroenterology practice. Dr. Brown has asked Missy to annotate the laboratory reports that come back from the lab. What is he asking Missy to do?

   _____

   _____

   _____

   _____

2. Henry Connelly, CMA (AAMA), has just been hired to work at the front desk in a family practice clinic. Part of his job is to open and sort the mail. There is no written office policy about this task currently on file in the office so Henry decides to create one. How should Henry proceed and what might his policy look like?

   _____

   _____

   _____

   _____

3. Willie Rachenko, RMA, has been working with Dr. Stuart for several years. Dr. Stuart asks Willie to contact Mr. Brocheer regarding his lab results from earlier this week. Willie looks into Mr. Brocheer's chart and sees that the patient has listed his work e-mail address. Willie isn't able to reach Mr. Brocheer by telephone and instead of leaving a voice mail message asking the patient to return his call, Willie decides to e-mail the patient with his lab results. Later that day, Mr. Brocheer calls the office very upset. He tells Willie that his boss intercepted the e-mail and now knows that his employee was screened for a possible sexually transmitted disease. What did Willie do wrong?

   _____

   _____

   _____

4. Mallory Valdez is taking an administrative medical assisting class. She has been given the assignment of writing a short paper that outlines the various mailing services offered by the U.S. Postal Service. What should Mallory include in her paper?

_____

_____

_____

_____

RESEARCH ACTIVITY

Utilize Internet search engines to research the following topics and write a brief description of what you find. It is important to utilize reputable websites.

1. Visit www.usps.com and research information regarding certified mail, rates, and extra services available. When could some of the "extra services" be useful when dealing with written correspondence between the medical office and patients?

_____

_____

_____

_____

_____

_____

_____

_____

_____

_____

_____

_____

_____

_____

_____

_____

_____

_____

_____

_____

© 2011 Pearson Education, Inc.

CHAPTER 12

Computers in the Medical Office

CHAPTER OUTLINE

General review of the chapter:

Use of Computers in Medicine
Types of Computers
Basic Computer Components
Security for the Computer System
Selecting a Computer System
The Internet
Electronic Signatures
Computers and Ergonomics

STUDENT STUDY GUIDE

Use the following guide to assist in your learning of the concepts from the chapter.

I. Computers in the Medical Office

   1. Functions of Computers in the Medical Office (List six general functions.)

      i. _____

      ii. _____

      iii. _____

      iv. _____

      v. _____

      vi. _____

   2. Microcomputers

     A. Contains a small piece of electronic hardware called a _____.

     B. Allows the _____ of information in a very small amount of space.

   3. Central Processing Unit

     A. The CPU contains the main _____ of a computer.

     B. The CPU acts as a traffic controller, directing the computer's _____ and sending electronic signals to the right place at the right time.

     C. The transmission speed of these electronic signals is measured in _____.

     D. One _____ equals one _____ cycles per second.

     E. The higher the _____, the faster the _____.

   4. Random Access Memory (RAM)

     A. RAM is available only as long as the computer is _____.

     B. Once the computer is turned off, or powered down, all information stored in RAM is _____.

© 2011 Pearson Education, Inc.

5. Read-Only Memory (ROM)

   A. Once data is recorded, it cannot be removed, only _____.
   B. ROM is used to _____ information that is not actively being used by the computer.
   C. ROM is used primarily to _____ permanent data.

6. The Computer Monitor

   A. Allows the user to _____ what the computer has been told to do.
   B. Monitors are available in a variety of _____ and _____.
   C. The screen size is measured in _____ inches.

7. Types of Monitors

   A. A _____ monitor displays two colors—one for the background and one for the foreground.
   B. A _____ monitor is a special type of monochrome monitor that is capable of displaying different shades of gray.
   C. A _____ monitor displays anywhere from 16 to more than 1 million different colors.

8. Hard-Disk Drive

   A. A hard-disk drive is the _____ storage media inside the computer.
   B. It is controlled by the _____.
   C. _____ and information can be stored on a hard-disk drive.
   D. The more visual the software, the _____ the amount of storage space that is required.

9. CD-ROM

   A. Stands for _____.
   B. Computer programs, databases, and other large amounts of information on CD-ROM are _____ encoded and may not be changed by the user.
   C. It is capable of holding or storing more information than _____ floppy disks.

10. DVD

   A. Stands for _____ or _____.
   B. Used most often to record presentations that combine _____ and _____.

11. Removable Disk Drive

   A. Uses disks mounted in _____.
   B. Comes in a variety of sizes ranging from _____ megabytes to _____ gigabytes.

12. Portable Universal Serial Bus Drive

   A. Also known as a _____ drive, a _____ drive, or a _____ drive.
   B. This small portable storage device can hold up to _____ GB of data.

13. Microsoft Office Application Programs (List three commonly used applications.)

   i. _____
   ii. _____
   iii. _____

14. Computer Office Security Considerations

   A. Position the computer _____ so that it cannot be easily seen by patients.
   B. Use a _____ screen around the computer workstation.
   C. Use a screen _____.
   D. Use computer _____.

15. Uses of the Internet in the Medical Office (List three common uses.)

   i. _____
   ii. _____
   iii. _____

© 2011 Pearson Education, Inc.

16. Chair Ergonomics When Working on the Computer
    A. Push your hips as _____ back in the chair as possible.
    B. Adjust the seat height so that your feet are _____ on the floor and your knees are _____, or _____ than, your hips.
    C. Adjust the back of the chair to a _____ to _____ reclined angle.
    D. Make sure that your upper and lower back are _____.

17. Ergonomics When Working on the Keyboard
    A. If possible, adjust the keyboard height so that your shoulders are _____, your elbows are in a slightly _____ position, and your wrists and hands are _____.
    B. Wrist rests can help maintain a _____ posture and pad hard surfaces.
    C. Wrist rests should only be used to rest the _____ of the hands between keystrokes.

18. The Monitor and Ergonomics
    A. Adjust the monitor and source documents so that your _____ is in a neutral, relaxed position.
    B. Position the top of the monitor approximately _____ to _____ inches above your seated eye level.
    C. To reduce glare, place the screen at a _____ angle to windows and adjust curtains or blinds.

19. Body Ergonomics When Working on the Computer
    A. Take short _____ or _____ -minute stretch breaks every _____ to _____ minutes.
    B. After each hour of work, take a break or change tasks for at least _____ to _____ minutes.
    C. Avoid eye fatigue by resting and _____ your eyes periodically.
    D. Rest your eyes by covering them with your palms for _____ to _____ seconds.

KEY TERMINOLOGY REVIEW

Match the term to the correct definition below.

a. bandwidth
b. central processing unit (CPU)
c. clock speed
d. computer
e. input devices
f. Internet
g. Internet service provider (ISP)
h. kilobytes (KB)
i. main memory
j. mass storage device
k. memory
l. output devices
m. random access memory (RAM)
n. read-only memory (ROM)
o. software
p. universal serial bus (USB)
q. World Wide Web (WWW)

1. _____ A programmable machine or system of hardware that responds to a specific set of instructions and performs a list of instructions in programmed language.

2. _____ Provides access to the Internet.

3. _____ Set of instructions by means of which the computer performs its functions.

4. _____ Makes it possible for a computer to temporarily store data and programs.

5. _____ Internal storage area in the computer that can be accessed randomly.

6. _____ The amount of data that can be transmitted in a fixed amount of time.

7. _____ The speed at which the CPU can process instructions.

8. _____ Makes it possible for a computer to permanently retain large amounts of data even when the computer is off.

9. _____ Allow the user to see what the computer has accomplished.

10. _____ The brain of the computer, which executes the specific set of instructions.

11. _____ An internal storage area in the computer where data have been recorded.

12. _____ Computer network of thousands of interfacing networks worldwide.

13. _____ Acts as a traffic controller, directing the computer's activities and sending electronic signals to the right place at the right time.

14. _____ Feed data and instructions into a computer.

15. _____ A system of Internet servers.

16. _____ One thousand units of storage or memory

17. _____ A small portable storage device that can hold up to 64 GB or more of data.

APPLIED PRACTICE

Read the scenario and answer the questions that follow.

> **Scenario**
>
> Shane Eiler, RMA, is an office manager for Inner Harbor Sports Medicine. His office computer has had a recent attack from a malware program. This attack has left his computer unusable.

1. Shane has been asked to research the cost of purchasing a new computer for the medical office. Create a list of the steps he should take to determine the type of system that is best for the office.

   _____

   _____

   _____

   _____

2. The physicians have also asked Shane to create a list of suggestions for securing the office computers from unauthorized access. What suggestions should Shane make?

   _____

   _____

   _____

   _____

LEARNING ACTIVITY: MULTIPLE CHOICE

Circle the correct answer to each of the questions below.

1. _____ are devices that allow documents to be copied and transferred to the computer.
   a. Thumb drives
   b. Personal digital assistants

© 2011 Pearson Education, Inc.

    c.   Printers

    d.   Scanners

2. _____ is the computer equipment.

    a.   The hardware

    b.   The software

    c.   The peripheral

    d.   The USB

3. _____ are typically used in a medical office.

    a.   Supercomputers

    b.   Mainframe computers

    c.   Minicomputers

    d.   Microcomputers

4. The computer's CPU is considered to be the computer's _____.

    a.   brain

    b.   memory

    c.   keyboard

    d.   mouse

5. An articulating keyboard is used to _____.

    a.   connect to the computer via a wireless connection

    b.   reduce typing stress by supporting the hands and wrists comfortably

    c.   type faster than when using a conventional keyboard

    d.   maintain patient privacy when using the keyboard

6. As computer technology advances, _____ are becoming obsolete.

    a.   floppy disk drives

    b.   CD drives

    c.   DVD drives

    d.   Thumb drives

7. _____ makes it possible for a computer to temporarily store data and programs.

    a.   Mass storage device

    b.   Memory

    c.   Software

    d.   CPU

8. Laptops are also known as _____.

    a.   Palm pilots

    b.   PDAs

    c.   Notebooks

    d.   CPUs

9. The hard-disk drive, a magnetic storage media inside the computer, is usually called the _____.

    a.   A drive

    b.   B drive

c. C drive

d. D drive

10. An/A _____ printer works by forming dots when the ink is blown onto the paper.

a. dot matrix

b. laser

c. deskjet

d. inkjet

CRITICAL THINKING

Answer the following questions to the best of your ability. Utilize the textbook and other resources such as the Internet in considering the following questions.

1. Marcia Dukat is taking a computer applications class in the medical assisting program. She has been given an assignment to create a list of steps that medical office staff can take in order to protect the office computers from viruses. What should Marcia's list include?

    _____

    _____

    _____

2. Rolf Von Trapp, RMA, is discussing the need for a new computer system with the physician. Dr. Nyrse has asked Rolf to describe the difference between the hardware, the software, and the peripherals that go with the various computer systems. How might Rolf define these three components?

    _____

    _____

    _____

3. George El Fashir, CMA (AAMA), has been asked to describe the various computer drives that might be used to store information from the computer systems in his office. What information should George prepare?

    _____

    _____

    _____

4. Riley Gaddum is taking a computer class as part of his medical assistant training. He has been given an assignment to describe the difference between ROM and RAM. What might Riley write for this assignment?

    _____

    _____

    _____

© 2011 Pearson Education, Inc.

RESEARCH ACTIVITY

Utilize Internet search engines to research the following topics and write a brief description of what you find. It is important to utilize reputable websites.

1. Use the Internet to research medical office software programs. What software program do you like the most? What features does it have? Why would you recommend its use?

    _____

    _____

    _____

    _____

    _____

    _____

    _____

    _____

    _____

    _____

    _____

    _____

    _____

    _____

    _____

    _____

    _____

    _____

CHAPTER 13

Managing Medical Records

CHAPTER OUTLINE

General review of the chapter:

The Medical Record
Documentation of Patient Medical Information
Components of the Medical Record
Filing
Quality Assurance for Quality Medical Care
Releasing Medical Records
Storing Medical Records
Medical Transcription
Ownership of the Medical Record
Retention and Destruction of Medical Records

STUDENT STUDY GUIDE

Use the following guide to assist in your learning of the concepts from the chapter.

I. Managing Medical Records

   1. Categories and Reports Found in a Medical Record

     i. _____

     ii. _____

     iii. _____

     iv. _____

     v. _____

     vi. _____

     vii. _____

     viii. _____

     ix. _____

     x. _____

     xi. _____

     xii. _____

     xiii. _____

     xiv. _____

     xv. _____

     xvi. _____

   2. The Chronological Medical Record

     A. Follows the patient _____.

     B. Each visit consists of a new entry by _____ rather than by _____ or _____.

     C. This record can sometimes makes it more difficult to "catch" _____.

© 2011 Pearson Education, Inc.

3. The Problem-Oriented Medical Record
   A. Used to identify patient problems and chart by those _____.
   B. The functional aspect of this type of charting is that the patient _____ list is found at the _____ of the chart.
   C. As new problems and diagnoses are identified, they are noted on the _____ list.
   D. Helps health care providers who do not already know a specific patient to obtain a _____ regarding previous visits and problems at a glance.

4. Sections of the Problems-Oriented Medical Record
   i. _____
   ii. _____
   iii. _____
   iv. _____

5. SOAP Charting
   A. "S" identifies the _____ information gathered from the patient.
   B. "O" stands for _____, the data gathered during the visit.
   C. "A" is for _____, the physician's _____ diagnosis.
   D. "P" indicates the _____ of the chart where _____ for the care of this patient are discussed.

6. The Source-Oriented Medical Record
   A. Patient information is placed in the medical record in _____ _____ order and is organized in different sections.
   B. Each office determines which _____ to be used and in what order they are to appear in the medical chart.
   C. The sections commonly include medical history and physical, insurance, _____ notes, _____, laboratory reports, and _____.

7. Information that SHOULD NOT BE INCLUDED in a Patient's Chart
   i. _____
   ii. _____
   iii. _____

8. Information that SHOULD BE INCLUDED in the Medical Record
   A. _____ statements.
   B. Everything that is done during a _____ _____ visit.
   C. Legible writing in _____ ink.

9. Correcting Errors Made When Documenting Care in an Electronic Medical Record
   A. When documenting care in an EMR, prior to saving the entry, errors may be corrected by _____ as you would with any other type of computer program.
   B. If an error is discovered after the entry is saved, an _____ entry, called an _____, will be required.
   C. When using an EMR, the entry will be automatically _____ and _____ electronically when saved.

10. Steps for Adding Items to a Patient's Record
   i. _____
   ii. _____
   iii. _____
   iv. _____
   v. _____
   vi. _____
   vii. _____

11. Guidelines for Changing Items in a Patient's Record
    i. _____
    ii. _____
    iii. _____
    iv. _____
    v. _____
    vi. _____
    vii. _____

12. Responsibilities of the MA

    A. Document information _____ in the medical record.
    B. Ensure that the information added to the medical record is _____.
    C. _____ that patients' records are kept up to date.
    D. Make files as easily _____ as possible.

13. Contents of Medical Records
    i. _____
    ii. _____
    iii. _____
    iv. _____
    v. _____
    vi. _____
    vii. _____
    viii. _____
    ix. _____
    x. _____
    xi. _____
    xii. _____
    xiii. _____
    xiv. _____
    xv. _____
    xvi. _____

II. Filing

    1. Categories of Medical Records
       i. _____
       ii. _____
       iii. _____

    2. The Vertical File Cabinet

       A. Set up _____ to _____ stacked pull-out drawers holding up to _____ files per drawer.
       B. A drawback of this method is that the files are _____ and consume _____ .

    3. The Lateral File Cabinet

       A. Set up with _____ allowing for easy access to files by pulling them off the
          _____.
       B. Use a _____ method for visual recognition of files.

    4. The Movable File Cabinet

       A. Set up with _____ powered or _____ controlled file units that move on
          tracks in the floor.
       B. This method is a type of _____ filing system.
       C. This method is _____ saving since the file units can be moved close together when
          they are not in use.
       D. Useful for _____ and _____ since the floor can be reinforced when the track is installed.

© 2011 Pearson Education, Inc.

5. Traditional Hard-copy Patient Record
    A. The patient's file typically has tabs on the _____ or _____ edge.
    B. These tabs are marked with _____ labels.
    C. It is easier to read the labels in the file drawer if the files have _____ tab cuts.
    D. File folders may be _____ to indicate the primary care physician.

6. Outguide
    A. Inserted where a file has been _____ to indicate the place to which the file should be _____.
    B. Can be used to indicate who has _____ the file and when it was _____.
    C. Especially helpful in a large office when trying to _____ charts.
    D. Usually a distinctive color, such as _____, to indicate that a file is missing.

7. The Purposes of Labels on File Folders
    A. The main purpose is to _____ what is in the file.
    B. The label can include a _____ stripe that can be used for other purposes, such as identifying the _____ _____ physician.
    C. Offices use special labels on charts to bring attention to patient _____, required _____, and the year of the last visit.
    D. Special labels help the staff find _____ information at a glance.

8. Rules for an Alphabetical Filing System
    A. A name with only an _____ in place of the first name is filed before a _____ name.
    B. Hyphenated names are treated as _____ unit.
    C. Apostrophes are _____.
    D. Titles and initials are _____, but placed in _____ after the name.
    E. Married women are to be indexed using their _____ name.
    F. Seniority units are filed _____.

9. Numerical Filing or Patient Identification System
    A. Used in _____ and many larger clinics.
    B. A number is assigned to each patient's _____ _____.
    C. The number is generally a _____ -digit number divided into _____ sections of _____ digits each.

10. Straight Numerical Filing
    A. This is the _____ numerical method.
    B. Each record is filed _____ based on its assigned number.
    C. Numbers used in this system begin at _____ and continue upward.

11. Terminal Digit Filing
    A. Based on the last digits of the _____ number.
    B. Evenly distributes the files within the entire filing system, eliminating the need for frequent _____ of files.
    C. Requires dividing the files into _____ primary sections, starting with _____ and ending with _____.
    D. Three sections of numbers assigned to each file are designated as _____, _____, and _____ sections, respectively.

12. Unit Numbering
    A. Assigns a number to patients the _____ time that they are seen or admitted to a hospital.
    B. All other hospitalizations or hospital visits use the _____ number.
    C. Requires that all of the records be kept at the _____ location.

13. Serial Numbering

   A. With this system, the patient receives a different medical record number for each _____ visit.
   B. The patient acquires _____ records that are stored at _____ locations.
   C. The assigned numbers are kept in an _____ record in which numbers in sequential order have a _____ placed next to them as each new _____ is entered.

14. Subject Matter Filing

   A. Used for _____ files.
   B. The method is adequate as long as the files are relatively _____.

15. Color-Coding Systems

   A. Assigns a _____ for each number from _____.
   B. _____ bars on files correspond to the medical record number.
   C. Typically, the _____ primary digits are color-coded.
   D. The system allows for misfiles to be _____ seen.

16. The Alpha-Z System

   A. The system is based on _____ colors using _____ letters on a _____ background for the first half of the alphabet, with the addition of a white stripe on the _____ background for the second half of the alphabet.
   B. Uses _____ _____ to denote the patient's name and a colored label with the letter of the alphabet to indicate the _____ unit.
   C. In large practices with several physicians, each physician may have a _____ assigned to him or her.

17. Advantages of Cross-Referencing Files

   i. _____
   ii. _____
   iii. _____

18. Guidelines for Locating Missing Files

   i. _____
   ii. _____
   iii. _____
   iv. _____
   v. _____
   vi. _____
   vii. _____

19. Tickler Files

   A. A tickler file is a _____ for future events
   B. Should be reviewed _____.
   C. Contents may include _____, _____, _____, and _____.

III. Releasing, Retaining, and Storing Medical Records

   1. Quality Assurance Programs

      A. The _____ is to improve the quality of care.
      B. Implementation requires developing _____ criteria.
      C. One method for documenting problem areas is the use of _____ reports.

   2. The Incident Report

      A. A report should be completed whenever there is an _____ occurrence.
      B. The purpose is to document exactly what happened, with the goal of _____ another similar episode.

© 2011 Pearson Education, Inc.

C. Details on completing an incident report are usually included in every office's _____ _____.

3. The Joint Commission
   A. The Commission is a private, _____ agency.
   B. Establishes guidelines to address the _____ of care provided by _____ and _____ agencies.
   C. Conducts _____ and _____ programs to ensure that institutions are following the guidelines for _____.
   D. Works with facilities to correct _____.

4. The Occupational Safety and Health Administration
   A. OSHA's purpose is to ensure a _____ _____ environment for employees.
   B. Sets basic _____ standards that all institutions must follow.
   C. Violators of OSHA standards must _____ _____.

5. Authorizing the Release of Records
   A. The _____ owns the medical record.
   B. The patient has the _____ right to access the record.
   C. A _____ _____ must be signed to authorize the release of a patient's record.

6. The Skills of a Medical Transcriptionist
   i.   _____
   ii. _____
   iii. _____
   iv. _____
   v.   _____
   vi. _____

7. Ownership of X-rays
   A. X-rays are the property of the _____.
   B. Physicians are able to loan their films to other physicians for further examination; however, the _____ must sign a _____.
   C. The films should always be returned to the _____.

8. Ownership of Medical Records
   A. If a patient requests to view his or her own medical records, access must be allowed, unless the physician determines that it may be _____ to the patient.
   B. Prior to allowing the patients to view their records, the MA must first check with the _____ or _____ for approval.
   C. Never leave patients _____ with their records.

9. Guidelines for Retaining Medical Records
   A. To be absolutely safe, medical records should be retained _____.
   B. The standard set by most states is to keep records _____ to _____ years after the last treatment or _____ years after the patient reaches the age of _____.
   C. The AMA recommends keeping the records for _____ years.

KEY TERMINOLOGY REVIEW

Match the correct medical term with the definition listed below.

a. active records
b. addendum
c. alphabetical filing

d. chronological medical records
e. closed records
f. electronic medical records

g. inactive records

h. medical record

i. microfiche

j. microfilm

k. numerical filing

l. POMR

m. SOMR

n. SOAP

o. terminal-digit filing

1. _____ The key to this type of filing is to divide the names and titles into units (first, second, and third).

2. _____ Source of all documentation related to the patient.

3. _____ Used to identify patient problems and chart by those problems.

4. _____ Miniaturized photographs of records.

5. _____ Patients who have been seen within the past 3 years and are currently being treated.

6. _____ Based on the last digits of the ID number; evenly distributes the files within the entire filing system.

7. _____ A computerized means of gathering, documenting, and storing information about the patient and the care received in the medical setting.

8. _____ A charting method that is distinct because of the four parts of the approach.

9. _____ Follows the patient over a period of time, with each visit consisting of a new entry by date, rather than by symptoms or diagnosis.

10. _____ Patients who have not been seen within the past 3 years or another period determined by office policy.

11. _____ Organizes patient information in the medical record in reverse chronological order.

12. _____ Patients who have actively terminated their contact with the physician.

13. _____ Patient identification system used in hospitals and many larger clinics.

14. _____ Sheets of microfilm.

15. _____ An addition to an original document.

APPLIED PRACTICE

Follow the instructions with each question below.

1. Indicate if the following patients would be considered active, inactive, or closed patient files?

   a. Lori Hughes, a patient who has moved out of the state
   Patient file status: _____

   b. Quin Tao, a patient who has not been seen in the office for 5 years
   Patient file status: _____

   c. Gloria Sanchez, a patient who was in the office for care last week
   Patient file status: _____

   d. Sara Womack, a patient who died last year
   Patient file status: _____

2. Using the progress note below, accurately place the statements below into SOAP format. Mario Reynolds, born August 12, 1990, presents to the office with the following:

   - T: 100.3°
   - Positive Rapid Strep Test
   - "My throat is sore."
   - Pharyngitis and Strep Throat
   - Throat appears red and white spots present on tonsils.

© 2011 Pearson Education, Inc.

- Penicillin V 250mg BID × 10 days
- BP: 118/86
- Wt: 192#
- Patient has been sick with a fever for 3 days.

PROGRESS NOTE

Patient: _____ **DOB:** _____

	S	O	A	P

LEARNING ACTIVITY: MULTIPLE CHOICE

Circle the correct answer to each of the questions below.

1. Which of the following techniques is the appropriate way to correct an error in the patient's medical record?

   a. Use white correction fluid to obliterate the error.
   b. Use a black marker to obliterate the error.
   c. Draw a single line through the error; initial and date the correction.
   d. Any of the above

2. Under which of the following circumstances can the patient's medical record be copied and released?

   a. When the patient's spouse comes to the office to request a copy
   b. When the patient's employer calls the office to request a copy
   c. When the patient has signed a release form
   d. When the patient's brother sends a letter asking for a copy

3. The American Medical Association recommends keeping medical records for _____.

   a. 2 years
   b. 5 years
   c. 10 years
   d. Indefinitely

4. Once an office is out of room for storing patient medical records, which of the following is an appropriate way to store records?

   a. On a separate backup system
   b. In computer database files
   c. On microfilm
   d. Any of the above

5. Which of the following is true about retaining patient medical records?

   a. The record should be kept for 3 years from the date of the last service.
   b. The length of time that the record is kept is determined by the statute of limitations in any particular state.
   c. The record should be kept until the patient reaches age 18.
   d. All of the above are true.

6. _____ patient files are the files of patients who have moved and will not be continuing to receive treatment by the physician or facility.

   a. Open
   b. Closed
   c. Inactive
   d. None of the above

7. _____ patient files are the files of patients who have not been seen within the past 3 years or another period determined by office policy.

   a. Open
   b. Closed
   c. Inactive
   d. None of the above

8. _____ patient files are the files of patients who have been in to see the physician recently.

   a. Open
   b. Closed
   c. Inactive
   d. None of the above

9. The simplest numerical method of filing is _____.

   a. straight numerical filing
   b. terminal-digit filing
   c. middle-digit filing
   d. unit-number filing

10. _____ is a type of medical charting that tracks a patient's problems throughout medical care by assigning a number to each of the patient's medical problems.

   a. Narrative notes
   b. SOAP notes
   c. POMR notes
   d. None of the above

CRITICAL THINKING

Answer the following questions to the best of your ability. Utilize the textbook and other resources such as the Internet in considering the following questions.

1. Chris Nichols, CMA (AAMA), has been given the task of deciding which patient files to purge from the clinic in order to create more storage space. How should Chris proceed with this project?

   _____

   _____

© 2011 Pearson Education, Inc.

2. Michael Manson, RMA, has just been hired to work in a family practice clinic. On his first day in the office, he notices that many patients' records have words such as "problem" and "talker" listed on them. He asks the MA who is training him about these words and is told that it is the office's way of noting those patients who are difficult to work with or who talk excessively during their visit. What kinds of problems might this facility encounter when using these notations?

_____

_____

_____

3. Susan Haufe, RMA, is working with a small, one-doctor internal medicine clinic. The physician, Dr. Chentow, is unable to retain his patient records indefinitely. What considerations must Susan give to the method of destruction?

_____

_____

_____

_____

RESEARCH ACTIVITY

Utilize Internet search engines to research the following topics and write a brief description of what you find. It is important to utilize reputable websites.

1. Using the Internet as a research source, research the types of filing systems that may be found in a medical setting. Describe the pros and cons of each system.

_____

_____

_____

_____

_____

_____

_____

_____

_____

_____

_____

_____

_____

_____

CHAPTER 14
Electronic Medical Records

CHAPTER OUTLINE

General review of the chapter:

Electronic Medical Records Are Easily Accessible
How Does Paper Charting Differ from Electronic Charting?
Making the Conversion from Paper to Electronic Medical Records
Electronic Medical Records and HIPAA Compliance
Using Personal Digital Assistants with Electronic Medical Records
Benefits of Electronic Medical Records
Making Corrections in the Medical Record

STUDENT STUDY GUIDE

Use the following guide to assist in your learning of the concepts from the chapter.

I. Electronic Medical Records

1. Electronic Medical Records (EMRs)

   A. EMRs are sometimes called _____ _____ _____.
   B. The EMR is a means of _____, _____, and _____ information about the patient and the care received in the medical setting.

2. Advantages of the EMR—Accessibility!

   i. _____
   ii. _____
   iii. _____
   iv. _____
   v. _____
   vi. _____
   vii. _____
   viii. _____

3. Converting from Paper to Electronic Medical Records

   A. Some clinics are able to use a _____ to _____ the patient's paper medical record for use in the EMR system.
   B. Other clinics may need to enter information from the paper medical record to the EMR _____.
   C. Once the information from the paper medical record has been transferred to the EMR, the clinic staff may choose to _____ the paper record by _____ the documents.
   D. Some offices may choose to _____ the paper record in a secure location rather than _____ it.

© 2011 Pearson Education, Inc.

4. Training Staff on the EMR

    A. Training should be attended by _____ in the office who will be using the software.

    B. A training _____ should be supplied for use in training future staff members.

    C. A technical support person from the _____ should be available to answer questions or concerns related to the software.

5. Ensuring Patient Privacy with the EMR

    A. All computer users must have their own _____ to access patient medical records.

    B. With each person having login information, the software can _____ each entry or deletion and who made it.

    C. Each station must be _____ _____ when the user is away from the desk.

    D. Computer screens must not be _____ by other patients while private patient information is displayed on the screen.

6. Data Backup System

    A. Mandated by _____.

    B. Must be used on a _____ basis.

7. Personal Digital Assistants in the Medical Office

    A. A PDA is a lightweight, _____, usually pen- or stylus-based computer that is used as a personal _____.

    B. A PDA offers the benefit of being _____ enough for physicians to carry with them from patient to patient.

    C. Most EMR systems can be _____ to work according to an office's specific needs.

8. Benefits Gained Through Using the EMR

    i. _____

    ii. _____

    iii. _____

    iv. _____

    v. _____

    vi. _____

9. Electronic Signatures

    A. Most electronic medical records provide an electronic signature component that is based on the individual's _____ via his or her user name and _____.

    B. Once the entry is made into the patient's chart, the staff member or physician clicks _____ and the entry is electronically _____.

10. Avoiding Medical Errors

    A. EMR software typically has a _____ mechanism built in that alerts the prescribing physician to any _____ medications that a particular patient may be taking.

    B. Studies have found that medical errors are caused by _____ or _____ handwriting, a problem that would be eliminated if providers made their entries electronically.

11. Saving Time

    A. Time saved by the use of an EMR system may be better invested in _____ .

    B. Many EMR systems include lists of possible _____ for the physician to choose from based on the symptoms that the patient lists.

    C. EMRs allow medical staff to easily transmit _____ information to a patient's health insurance provider when requested.

12. Availability of Medical Records Online

    A. Some clinics allow patients to look up portions of their EMR via the _____.

    B. Using a _____-_____ system, patients can access a company's network or intranet for their laboratory results, dates of immunization, or history of medications prescribed.

© 2011 Pearson Education, Inc.

13. Steps for Correcting an Error in the EMR

    i. _____

    ii. _____

    iii. _____

    iv. _____

    v. _____

    vi. _____

KEY TERMINOLOGY REVIEW

Without using your textbook, write a sentence using the selected key terms in the correct context.

1. *Electronic medical record:*

_____

_____

2. *Electronic signature:*

_____

_____

3. *Indecipherable:*

_____

_____

4. *Electronic health record:*

_____

_____

5. *Health Insurance Portability and Accountability Act (HIPAA):*

_____

_____

6. *Personal digital assistant (PDA):*

_____

_____

APPLIED PRACTICE

Read the scenario and then answer the questions that follow.

Scenario

Jeffery Cody, RMA, is the office manager for Foothills Family Medicine. The office has slowly been transferring from paper medical records to electronic medical records.

1. In the final stages of this process, how will the medical office include written reports and consultations from other facilities?

_____

_____

© 2011 Pearson Education, Inc.

2. Jeffery is writing a memo to the office staff regarding making corrections to medical records. What information should he include in his memo?

_____

_____

_____

_____

LEARNING ACTIVITY: TRUE/FALSE

Indicate whether the following statements are true or false by placing a T or an F on the line that precedes each statement.

_____ 1. Electronic medical records offer enhanced ease, efficiency, and accessibility.

_____ 2. Using electronic medical records, a medical office can send reminder postcards to patients more easily than performing this task using paper medical records.

_____ 3. Using electronic medical records, a medical office is able to perform many tests in the office and have the results shown immediately in the electronic medical record.

_____ 4. It is much more difficult to remain HIPAA-compliant with patient medical records if the office is using electronic medical records instead of paper medical records.

_____ 5. Once a paper medical record has been converted to an electronic version, the paper record may be kept in secure storage or may be shredded.

_____ 6. Most electronic medical records programs have drop-down menus that allow the user to choose information from a list.

_____ 7. As a result of a study released in 1999, the Institute of Medicine suggested that some medical errors are caused by indecipherable handwriting.

_____ 8. Using electronic medical records, health care providers may be alerted to possible medication errors.

_____ 9. In medical offices where electronic signatures are used, an original version of the user's signature does not need to be kept on file in the office.

_____ 10. All medical facilities use the same software for electronic medical records.

CRITICAL THINKING

Answer the following questions to the best of your ability. Utilize the textbook as a reference.

1. Rosa Valdez, CMA (AAMA), is working in the billing office of a urology practice. The office uses electronic medical records for patient charting. Rosa frequently finds that she needs to alert other staff members of her need to speak with a patient about their account. How might Rosa devise a way to alert her coworkers of her need to see a patient when that patient comes into the office?

_____

_____

_____

2. Chris Hernandez, RMA, is the office manager of a busy family practice clinic. Chris has been asked by the physicians to come up with some ideas for using the electronic medical records

software to create a marketing program. What kinds of ideas could Chris suggest for this project?

_____

_____

_____

_____

3. Mickey Cape is taking a course on electronic medical records. Mickey has been given an assignment to write a policy on how to dispose of paper medical records once the record has been converted to electronic form. What might Mickey come up with?

_____

_____

_____

_____

4. Barret Risenhour, RMA, is the office manager in a women's clinic. The physicians in the clinic are considering moving to electronic medical records from the paper records that they have been using for years. Barret has been asked to create a list of the pros and cons of using electronic medical records versus paper records. What might Barret's list contain?

_____

_____

_____

_____

5. Dr. Shawn Hagen has been using paper medical records in his practice for more than 20 years. He is reluctant to change to electronic medical records because he feels that his computer skills are poor. What sort of information can his office manager give him about the ease of converting from paper to electronic medical records?

_____

_____

_____

_____

_____

RESEARCH ACTIVITY

Utilize Internet search engines to research the following topics and write a brief description of what you find. It is important to utilize reputable websites.

1. Using the Internet as a research source, locate three companies that sell electronic medical records software. Create a list of the pros and cons of each system.

_____

_____

_____

_____

© 2011 Pearson Education, Inc.

CHAPTER 15
Fees, Billing, Collections, and Credit

CHAPTER OUTLINE

General review of the chapter:

Professional Fees
Billing
Credit Policy
Collections
Accounting Systems
Bookkeeping Systems
Computerized Systems
Professional Courtesy

STUDENT STUDY GUIDE

Use the following guide to assist in your learning of the concepts from the chapter.

I. Fees, Billing, Collections, and Credit

   1. Factors Used to Determine Physician's Fees

      i. _____

      ii. _____

      iii. _____

   2. Informing Patients of Fees and Payment Policies

     A. Information should include _____ , _____ , and _____ procedures.

     B. Information can be conveyed during the _____ phone call with the patient and then a _____ can be mailed to the patient.

     C. Fees and payment _____ should be posted in the office.

   3. Methods for Securing Payment

     A. Collect payment at the time that the _____ is provided.

     B. _____ the patient.

     C. Use an outside _____ _____.

   4. Truth in Lending Form

     A. The form clearly states the _____ of the _____ charge and the _____ payments.

     B. Where there are no finance charges, this is to be stated on the _____ form.

     C. The original form is given to the _____ and a copy is retained by the _____.

   5. Consent Form for Billing

     A. Allows the medical office to bill the _____ on behalf of the patient for the services provided.

© 2011 Pearson Education, Inc.

B. Grants the office permission to forward information regarding the patient's visit, including _____ and _____, to the insurance carrier if requested.

C. Should be placed in the file and updated _____.

6. Billing Methods

A. _____ internally.

B. Generated by the _____ _____.

C. Generated externally through the use of a _____ service.

7. Superbill

A. Also known as an _____ form.

B. Can be used as a _____ slip, statement, and insurance reporting form.

C. Provides a _____ list of patient services with _____ and _____.

8. Ledger Card and Mailing Statements

A. _____ ledger card is created for each patient.

B. Used to record _____, _____, and _____ for the patient.

C. When mailing a statement to the patient, the ledger card can be _____ and used as the _____.

9. Information Required for Billing

i. _____

ii. _____

iii. _____

iv. _____

v. _____

vi. _____

vii. _____

10. Billing Third-Party Payers and Minors

A. Third-party payers are individuals other than the patient who have agreed to pay the _____ _____.

B. Assignment of benefits ensures _____ payment to the _____ .

C. _____ minors can be billed.

11. Steps for Preparing a Ledger Card

i. _____

ii. _____

iii. _____

iv. _____

v. _____

12. Making Credit Arrangements with Patients

A. Remind patients during the _____ reminder call about their obligation to pay.

B. Try to obtain payment at the time of _____.

C. Provide a billing statement to patients when they leave the office with a _____ for payment.

D. If credit arrangements are necessary, make them during the patient's _____ visit.

13. Guidelines for Collections

i. _____

ii. _____

iii. _____

iv. _____

v. _____

vi. _____

vii. _____

viii. _____

ix. _____

14. Reasons for Outstanding Bills

    A. The patient does not feel that the bill is _____.
    B. The patient is _____ to pay.
    C. The patient does not _____ the bill.

15. Effects of Having Delinquent Accounts

    A. Patients stay away from the office because they are _____ about their financial situation.
    B. There is a possible implication of _____ on the part of the physician as to the _____ of care that the patient received.
    C. Loss of _____.

16. Account Age Analysis

    A. Computerized systems provide reports that indicate accounts which are _____, _____, and _____ days overdue.
    B. The collection step needed is determined by the _____ of the account.
    C. Manual systems utilize _____ systems with various colors or flags attached to _____ cards to indicate the age of the accounts.

17. Collection Techniques

    i. _____
    ii. _____
    iii. _____
    iv. _____
    v. _____

18. Guidelines for Making Collection Calls

    A. Avoid placing calls earlier than _____ A.M. or later than _____ P.M. and on Sundays and holidays.
    B. Do not call the patient's _____.
    C. _____ the person prior to discussing the account.
    D. Be _____ regarding who you are and the intent of the call.
    E. Do not _____ or intimidate the patient.
    F. Ask the patient when payment should be expected and _____ this information in the patient's record.
    G. Politely _____ the patient for his or her time and repeat back to the patient the terms agreed upon.

19. Guidelines for Sending a Personalized Letter

    A. Insert the letter with the _____ statement.
    B. The letter should inquire _____ the bill has not been paid.
    C. In the letter, an offer should be made to assist the patient with making payment _____.
    D. The letter must convey the message that _____ will be taken to resolve the payment obligation.

20. Basic Guidelines for Drafting a Collection Letter

    i. _____
    ii. _____
    iii. _____
    iv. _____
    v. _____
    vi. _____

© 2011 Pearson Education, Inc.

vii. _____

viii. _____

ix. _____

x. _____

xi. _____

21. "Skips"

    A. Steps for finding skips:
        i. Check the _____ form to confirm the information.
        ii. Call the telephone numbers and _____ to try to locate the individual.
        iii. Ensure that _____ has been indicated on the billing envelope.

22. Claims Against Estates

    A. When a patient dies, a bill should be sent to the _____ of the deceased.

    B. Contact the next of kin to obtain information regarding who is the _____ of the estate.

    C. It is important to follow up on the collection of bills to prevent any impression that the physician was at _____ with regard to the medical care of the deceased patient.

23. Posting a Payment from a Collection Agency

    A. After verifying the correct patient account to which the payment is to be applied, _____ the patient's ledger card to the next line on the _____ sheet.

    B. Enter the _____ name and previous balance in the appropriate _____.

    C. Enter the _____ of the payment, the _____ of the collection agency, and the _____ of the payment in the appropriate _____.

    D. Enter the amount of the payment on the _____ portion of the _____ sheet in the check's _____.

    E. Subtract the payment from the _____ patient balance and record the new balance on the patient's _____ card.

    F. If an adjustment is to be made to the account because of the collection agency's fee, record the amount in _____ in the _____ column of the _____ card. Enter the description _____.

    G. Subtract the amount of the adjustment from the previous patient _____ and record the new _____ on the patient's _____ card.

II. Accounting Systems

    1. Key Points for Bookkeeping

        A. Use _____ ink and write clearly. Do not use a _____ .

        B. Keep the _____ straight with the decimal points aligned.

        C. Check all arithmetic carefully for errors such as _____ decimal points and errors in _____ and _____ .

        D. Do not _____ , write over, or use _____ _____ fluid.

        E. _____-check every entry.

    2. Steps for Performing Accounts Receivable

        i. _____

        ii. _____

        iii. _____

        iv. _____

    3. Defining Credit

        A. To credit an account means to _____ the payment from the account.

        B. A patient has a credit balance when an _____ occurs.

        C. A credit balance may be noted on the patient's account either in _____ or by enclosing the amount in _____ .

© 2011 Pearson Education, Inc.

4. Single-Entry Bookkeeping

   A. Information is entered _____.
   B. The tools required include a _____ sheet, a cash payment _____, and an accounts receivable _____.
   C. A payroll record and _____ _____ voucher may also be included.

5. Double-Entry Bookkeeping

   A. This system requires financial transactions to be recorded in _____ places.
   B. A _____ bookkeeper is required for this system.
   C. The _____ system forces a balance.

6. The Philosophy of Accounting

   A. Accounting is based on the premise that the _____ of the business, less the _____ of the business, equal the net worth of that business.
   B. This concept is expressed by the following standard accounting equation: _____ = _____ + _____ .
   C. Assets include everything owned by the medical practice, such as _____, bank accounts, and _____ .
   D. Liabilities are _____ that the medical practice owes to its _____ .

7. The Pegboard System

   A. Used to document patient _____ and _____ .
   B. Also called the _____ method.

8. Components of the Pegboard System

      i. _____
     ii. _____
    iii. _____

9. The Receipt Form

   A. Used when a patient's payment is made but _____ _____ is provided on that day.
   B. Use carbonless paper to allow the entering of _____, _____ , and _____ onto the master day sheet, the superbill, and the patient's _____ card at the same time.

10. Recording Payments

    A. When the superbill is received at the front desk, the MA or the receptionist will enter the correct charge next to every _____ or _____ and place the total on the front of the superbill.
    B. The superbill is then placed back on the _____, using care to line it up on top of the correct patient's name.
    C. The ledger card is then placed under the last page of the _____ slip, aligning the first blank line of the ledger card with the carbonized entry strip on the _____.

11. Posting Adjustments

    A. When an adjustment is made, the MA or the receptionist enters the correct _____ amount into the computer system or _____ it from the balance due from the insurance company.
    B. If the adjustment is for _____ funds, _____ the check amount and service fee charged by the bank to the patient's balance.

12. Posting Collection Agency Payments

    A. If the patient pays a collection agency and the collection agency forwards the money, _____ that payment to the patient's account and write _____ next to it.
    B. If a credit balance exists and the physician or the office manager approves, issue a _____ check to the patient.

© 2011 Pearson Education, Inc.

13. Balancing the Day Sheet

   A. To ensure that the accounts and entries are correct, the day sheet(s) need to be balanced _____.

   B. Use a calculator to balance the day sheets, and always _____ each total.

   C. When errors in posting are corrected, the corrections should be made in the same _____ as the original posting.

14. Steps for Performing Accounts Receivable

   i. _____

   ii. _____

   iii. _____

   iv. _____

15. Considerations for Selecting Practice Management Software

   i. _____

   ii. _____

   iii. _____

   iv. _____

16. Issues Related to Backing Up Data

   A. Always back up data and information onto a _____ disk, such as a CD-ROM that is then stored _____ in a _____ box.

   B. A paper backup copy of the computer files is not necessary, but a _____ backup file or an off-premises _____ backup file is necessary.

   C. The process by which the backup files can or should be accessed should be written into the office's _____ _____, along with the reasons and circumstances for granting access.

KEY TERMINOLOGY REVIEW

Match the selected key terms with their appropriate definitions.

a. accounting

b. accounts payable (AP)

c. age analysis

d. assignment of benefits

e. bad debt

f. bookkeeping

g. charge slip

h. copayment

i. day sheet

j. encounter form

k. Fair Debt Collection Practices Act

l. ledger card

m. posted

n. professional courtesy (PC)

o. statute of limitations

p. subscriber

q. superbill

r. third-party payer

s. Truth in Lending Form

t. usual, customary, and reasonable (UCR)

1. _____ Physician opts not to charge other physicians, staff, family members, or clergy.

2. _____ Process of determining how long an account has been past due and then instituting the necessary collection procedures.

3. _____ Refers to the fees charged for medical services.

4. _____ The person who holds the insurance.

5. _____ An amount owed and not collected.

6. _____ Federal law that protects debtors from harassment.

7. _____ Contains all of the charges and payments made by both the patient and the insurance company.

8. _____ The system of reporting the financial results of a business.

9. _____ A component of the pegboard system, used to list or post each day's financial transactions—charges, payments, adjustments, and credits.

10. _____ The document generated by the medical office that is a record of services for billing and for insurance processing.

11. _____ A party or person other than the patient, such as an insurance company, who is responsible for paying the patient's bill.

12. _____ Refers to the amount of time a legal collection suit may be brought against a debtor.

13. _____ Ensure that insurance payments are made directly to the physician.

14. _____ If credit is extended and it is determined that the patient will make set payments to the physician over four or more installments, the patient must sign this document.

15. _____ A predetermined amount of money that the patient must pay for medical services at every visit, as determined by the insurance company.

16. _____ Recording an insurance payment.

17. _____ Also known as the encounter form or the charge slip.

18. _____ The amounts that the physician owes to others for supplies, equipment, and services.

19. _____ Also known as the charge slip.

20. _____ The process of managing the accounts for a business.

APPLIED PRACTICE

Complete the activities and answer the questions that follow.

1. Call a local medical office in your area and ask to speak to someone in the billing office. Interview this person about his or her job function. Ask the person the following questions:

   a. What type of system does the person's office use for billing (manual or computerized)?

   _____

   _____

   b. If the office uses a computer system for billing, what is the name of the software used?

   _____

   _____

   c. What functions does the computer system have that helps the billing office staff better perform their jobs?

   _____

   _____

2. Read the scenario below and answer the questions that follow.

> **Scenario**
>
> Kaley McManus, RMA, works for Havensburg Audiology. The payment policy for the audiology practice states that all copayments are expected at the time of service. The patient, Arturo Alamos, is responsible for paying 20% of all services and his insurance company, Healthy Care, will reimburse the physician the remaining 80%.

© 2011 Pearson Education, Inc.

Mr. Alamos was seen today by Dr. Lynst. Two procedures were performed: a comprehensive audio examination and a tympanography. Following is the fee schedule for the office.

AUDIOLOGY SERVICES

Screening audio air only	92551	$ 38.00
Pure tone air	92552	$ 37.00
Pure tone air and bone	92553	$ 50.00
Comprehensive audio	92557	$101.00
Loudness balance test	92562	$ 38.00
Tone decay	92563	$ 41.00
Tympanography	92567	$ 40.00
Acoustic reflex	92568	$ 42.00
Reflex decay	92569	$ 43.00
Visual reinforced audio	92579	$ 78.00
Brain stem audiogram	92585	$327.00

a. How much will Kaley collect from Mr. Alamos today?

_____

_____

b. How much will Healthy Care be billed for the services provided to Mr. Alamos?

_____

_____

c. As Mr. Alamos gets ready to pay for his office visit, he realizes that he has only a $20 bill. What should Kaley do?

_____

_____

_____

_____

_____

LEARNING ACTIVITY: MULTIPLE CHOICE

Circle the correct answer for each of the questions below.

1. _____ are documents that detail the money owed to the medical practice and how long the account has been outstanding.
   a. Accounts payable
   b. Aging reports
   c. Superbills
   d. None of the above

2. The fee is determined by the physician or the practice's partners as a result of taking into consideration the _____.
    a. services involved
    b. economic level of the community
    c. prevailing fees in the community
    d. All of the above

3. The customary fee refers to _____.
    a. what a physician usually charges for a procedure or service
    b. the fee charged for the same procedure by the majority of physicians with the same or similar training
    c. what a physician charges for a modified procedure or service that is more difficult and requires more time and effort than a standard procedure
    d. None of the above

4. When should fees be discussed with patients?
    a. Before care is provided
    b. While care is being provided
    c. After care is provided
    d. Never

5. When using a Truth in Lending form, the original form is given to the patient and a copy is retained by the doctor and must be kept on file for _____.
    a. 1 year
    b. 2 years
    c. 3 years
    d. 5 years

6. Database programs are used to collect and maintain _____.
    a. patient information
    b. procedure and diagnosis codes
    c. insurance company information
    d. All of the above

7. Cycle billing requires that _____.
    a. statements leave the office in time to reach the patient no later than the last day of the month
    b. certain portions of the accounts receivable (AR), or money owed to the practice, are billed at given times during the month
    c. offices have a software medical billing program
    d. All of the above

8. A *skip* is _____.
    a. an individual who has missed his or her appointment.
    b. a bookkeeping procedure
    c. a collection problem that requires immediate action
    d. None of the above

© 2011 Pearson Education, Inc.

9. If a patient has filed for bankruptcy, _____.

    a. the patient is still obligated to address his or her payment issues with the collection agency hired by the medical office

    b. the medical office must file a claim for payment with the courts

    c. no payment will be obtained

    d. All of the above

10. The accounting term "debit" indicates _____.

    a. that a payment has been received on an account.

    b. that a charge has been entered into the account record

    c. the difference between the money owed and the credit

    d. that a charge has been entered and added to the account balance

CRITICAL THINKING

Answer the following questions to the best of your ability. Utilize the textbook and other resources such as the Internet in considering the following questions.

1. Dr. Roger Dominguez operates a single-physician practice. Dr. Dominguez employs one medical assistant, Garrick Sinclair, CMA (AAMA). The clinic has been using a manual accounting system for many years and Dr. Dominguez has asked Garrick to research the pros and cons of moving to a computerized system versus keeping the manual system. What might Garrick list as pros and cons for using a manual system versus a computerized system?

    _____

    _____

    _____

    _____

    _____

2. Margaret Larson, RMA, is working in the billing office of a family practice clinic. The clinic uses a superbill for physicians to indicate the charges assigned to each patient on each patient visit. The superbill used by this clinic was designed nearly 5 years ago and contains several codes that are no longer used by the clinic. Also, there are several codes that the physicians use which are not on the printed superbill, forcing the physicians to write in these codes by hand. What might Margaret suggest that the facility do to solve this problem and make the superbill more accurate for use in this office?

    _____

    _____

    _____

    _____

    _____

RESEARCH ACTIVITY

Utilize Internet search engines to research the following topics and write a brief description of what you find. It is important to utilize reputable websites.

1. Using the Internet as a research source, look up three collection agencies that offer their services in your area. List the pros and cons for using each of these three companies.

_____

_____

_____

_____

_____

_____

_____

_____

_____

_____

_____

_____

_____

_____

_____

_____

_____

_____

_____

_____

_____

_____

_____

© 2011 Pearson Education, Inc.

CHAPTER 16
Financial Management

CHAPTER OUTLINE

General review of the chapter:

Function of Banking
Checks
Paying Bills
Deposits
Accepting Cash
Cash Disbursements
Bank Hold on Accounts
Bank Statement
Saving Documentation
Petty Cash
Payroll

STUDENT STUDY GUIDE

Use the following guide to assist in your learning of the concepts from the chapter.

I. Online Banking and Writing Checks

   1. Basic Banking Functions (List six general functions.)

      i.   _____

      ii. _____

      iii. _____

      iv. _____

      v.   _____

      vi. _____

   2. The MA's Responsibility with Regard to Banking

      A. Ensure _____ when accomplishing accounting and bookkeeping tasks.

      B. Act as an _____ for the physician when dealing with the business's financial matters.

   3. Types of Bank Accounts

      i.   _____

      ii. _____

      iii. _____

   4. Checking Account

      A. Allows the owner of the account to _____ money from the account.

      B. It is not usually an _____ account.

      C. Some accounts earn interest only if there is a _____ balance in the account.

5. Savings Account

    A. This is an _____ account where funds that are not needed for daily expenses are placed.

    B. Interest is earned _____ or _____.

    C. Cash can be withdrawn or transferred in to a _____ account.

6. Money Market Account

    A. Used more as an _____ tool; usually pays a _____ _____ rate.

    B. Typically requires a minimum balance of _____ to _____.

7. Online Banking

    A. The functions that customers can perform include _____ the account, comparing the account with the bank's records, paying bills, and _____ data from the bank.

    B. This is a _____ system that requires notations to be entered into the _____ _____ records.

8. Checks

    A. A check is a document that orders a bank to _____ or _____ money.

    B. It is _____ on demand.

    C. It is a _____ instrument.

9. Preprinted Information on Checks

    i. _____

    ii. _____

    iii. _____

    iv. _____

    v. _____

    vi. _____

    vii. _____

    viii. _____

    ix. _____

    x. _____

10. Advantages of Checks

    i. _____

    ii. _____

    iii. _____

    iv. _____

    v. _____

11. Types of Checks

    i. _____

    ii. _____

    iii. _____

    iv. _____

    v. _____

    vi. _____

    vii. _____

    viii. _____

12. Cashier's Check

    A. Written using the bank's own check or form; issued by the _____.

    B. Funds to pay the check are _____ against the payer's account when the check is issued to the bank.

    C. Can be requested from a bank by _____ _____ holders who do not have a checking account.

© 2011 Pearson Education, Inc.

13. Bank Draft and Limited Check
    A. A bank draft is a check that is drawn up by a bank against funds that are _____ into its account in another bank.
    B. A limited check is issued on a _____ _____ form that indicates a preprinted _____ dollar amount for which the check can be written.
    C. A _____ limit may exist for a limited check.
    D. Limited checks are used for _____ checks and _____ payments.

14. Money Order
    A. Purchased for the _____ value embossed on the check.
    B. Can be purchased from _____, the _____, and other authorized agents.
    C. Frequently used by individuals who do not have _____ accounts and who do not want to send cash by mail.
    D. Considered safe to accept as payment since they are _____ at the value embossed on the check.

15. Traveler's Check
    A. _____ and _____ in certain dollar amounts.
    B. Considered a safe means for carrying money when _____.
    C. Contains _____ spaces for the signature of the _____ one space that is signed upon purchase of the check, the other for when the check is presented in payment.

16. Voucher Check
    A. Contains _____ detachable sections for transaction information.
    B. Frequently used for _____ checks since additional information can be supplied to the payee.
    C. _____ portion of the check contains the actual check.
    D. _____ portion provides details about the transaction.

17. Magnetic Ink Character Recognition
    A. It is a form of identification for the _____ and the _____.
    B. The first series of numbers identifies the _____ and its _____.
    C. The second series of numbers identifies the _____ _____.

18. Guidelines for Writing Checks
    i. _____
    ii. _____
    iii. _____
    iv. _____
    v. _____
    vi. _____
    vii. _____
    viii. _____
    ix. _____

19. The Write-It-Once System
    A. Allows a record to be kept of the _____, _____ _____, _____, and net amount of the check.
    B. The _____ system, the check _____ sheet, and the checks with a _____ writing strip on the back are used for this method.
    C. A check _____ sheet is placed over the pegs of the _____.
    D. Checks must be _____ when using this method.
    E. The check register has space for _____ checks to be recorded on one page.

© 2011 Pearson Education, Inc.

20. Steps for Preparing a Check

    i. _____
    ii. _____
    iii. _____
    iv. _____
    v. _____
    vi. _____
    vii. _____
    viii. _____
    ix. _____
    x. _____
    xi. _____
    xii. _____
    xiii. _____
    xiv. _____

21. Errors in Writing Checks

    A. Do not _____ on checks.
    B. For checks with major errors, _____ a _____ through the check and write _____ in ink across the check.
    C. If the error is minor, _____ the information and _____ the change.

22. Risky Checks

    i. _____
    ii. _____
    iii. _____
    iv. _____

23. Third-Party Check

    A. The first party is the person who _____ the check.
    B. The second party is the _____ who has received a check from another person to pay the _____ own medical bill.
    C. The third party is the MA or other office staff who is _____ the money.

24. Overpayment-of-Account Checks

    A. This can happen accidentally if a patient has not maintained adequate records or if the patient's _____ _____ has also made a payment to the patient's account at the medical office.
    B. If the check has not been deposited, the check can be _____ to the patient and a request for a new check for the _____ amount can be made.

25. "Paid in Full" Checks

    A. Checks written with the statement _____ added are to be avoided.
    B. If the check is deposited, you are _____ that this is correct, making it difficult to collect any further payments.

26. Considerations for Endorsing a Check

    A. Place the endorsement on the _____ of the check within the top _____ inches on the left-hand side of the check as it is turned over.
    B. An endorsement can either be a payee's written signature or a _____.
    C. To prevent theft, checks should be endorsed for _____ as soon as they are received.
    D. Endorsements are regulated by the _____.

27. Types of Check Endorsements (List and explain each.)

    i. _____
    ii. _____
    iii. _____

© 2011 Pearson Education, Inc.

28. Reasons for Returned Checks
   i. _____
   ii. _____
   iii. _____

29. Steps for Posting Non-Sufficient Funds Checks
   i. _____
   ii. _____
   iii. _____

30. Guidelines for Paying Bills
   i. _____
   ii, _____
   iii. _____
   iv. _____
   v. _____

31. Guidelines for Handling Deposits
   i. _____
   ii. _____
   iii. _____
   iv. _____
   v. _____
   vi. _____

32. Steps for Completing a Deposit Slip
   i. _____
   ii. _____
   iii. _____
   iv. _____
   v. _____
   vi. _____
   vii. _____
   viii. _____
   ix. _____
   x. _____
   xi. _____
   xii. _____
   xiii. _____

II. Bank Statements and Payroll

   1. Bank Statement

      A. Provides _____ of the funds in an account.
      B. Assists in _____ errors made by the office or bank bookkeeping system.
      C. Includes all _____ and _____ processed.

   2. Information Included on a Bank Statement

      i. _____
      ii. _____
      iii. _____
      iv. _____
      v. _____
      vi. _____
      vii. _____
      viii. _____

ix. _____

x. _____

3. Instructions for Reconciling a Bank Statement

   A. Compare the _____ balance of the current statement with the _____ balance of the previous statement.

   B. Write the current _____ balance in the appropriate space on the reverse side of the bank statement.

   C. Compare the _____ noted on the statement against your records or _____ by making a check mark next to each correct number.

   D. List _____ all outstanding deposits.

   E. Add these together, and place the total on the _____ side of the statement in the space provided.

   F. Add the _____ balance to the total of the deposits not already included, and write this amount on the _____ line.

   G. Compare the value of the checks listed on the statement with the value listed in the _____ or check subs, and place a check mark next to each correct number.

   H. Note all numbers missing from the _____ list of check numbers.

   I. List all _____ checks.

   J. Add the total for the _____ checks and place that figure on the line indicated on the back of the statement.

   K. Subtract the total for the checks outstanding from the _____ total on the _____ of the statement to determine the current balance.

   L. The current balance should _____ with the amount in your checkbook or stub balance.

4. Documents Used to Verify Banking Procedures

   i. _____

   ii. _____

   iii. _____

   iv. _____

   v. _____

5. Petty Cash

   A. Must be _____ and recorded in a _____ financial log.

   B. A _____ is used to replenish petty cash.

   C. Typically handled by _____ individual in the office.

   D. Kept under _____ and _____ for security purposes.

6. Payroll Periods

   i. _____

   ii. _____

   iii. _____

7. Payroll Information That Employers Must Maintain

   i. _____

   ii. _____

   iii. _____

   iv. _____

   v. _____

   vi. _____

8. Steps for Manually Generating Payroll

   i. _____

   ii. _____

   iii. _____

   iv. _____

© 2011 Pearson Education, Inc.

v. _____

vi. _____

vii. _____

viii. _____

ix. _____

x. _____

xi. _____

xii. _____

xiii. _____

xiv. _____

xv. _____

xvi. _____

xvii. _____

xviii. _____

9. Information to Be Included on the W-4 Form

   A. Employee's name and _____.

   B. Employee's _____ number.

   C. Employee's _____ status.

   D. The number of _____ that the employee is claiming.

KEY TERMINOLOGY REVIEW

Match the vocabulary term to the correct definition below.

a. accounts payable (AP)

b. accounts receivable (AR)

c. American Bankers Association (ABA)

d. audit

e. canceled checks

f. cash disbursement

g. cashier's check

h. certified check

i. credits

j. debits

k. deposits

l. embezzlement

m. gross annual wage

n. magnetic ink character recognition (MICR)

o. negotiable instrument number

p. non-sufficient funds (NSF)

q. payee

r. payer

s. reconciliation

t. stale check

u. stop-payment order

v. tax withholding

w. third-party check

x. warrant

1. _____ Amount of money the employee earns in a year before deductions.

2. _____ Guarantees payment because it is written on a check drafted by a bank.

3. _____ Refers to the comparison of the figures on the bank statements with the records maintained in the medical office and the adjustment of banking records so that both are in agreement.

4. _____ A check that has not been presented for payment within the time suggested on the check.

5. _____ Refers to an official inspection of an individual's or organization's accounts, typically by an independent body.

6. _____ A system of combining characters and numbers located at the bottom left-hand side of checks and deposit slips.

7. _____ Identifies the area where the bank issuing the check is located, as well as identifying the individual bank.

8. _____ The unauthorized taking of funds; involves a breach of trust.

9. _____ If a _____ has been issued by the payer, then the bank will not allow the funds to be disbursed.

10. _____ One that actualizes or permits the transfer of money to another person.

11. _____ Checks that have been processed and paid to the medical practice's creditors by the bank.

12. _____ Refers to money (cash, checks, and money orders) placed in a bank account; can be made to either checking or savings accounts.

13. _____ Additions to an account.

14. _____ Money owed to the physician or medical practice.

15. _____ Charges against an account.

16. _____ Statements issued to indicate that debts should be paid.

17. _____ Similar to cashier's checks because the bank guarantees that the money is available.

18. _____ When the payer's account does not have enough money to cover the amount of the check.

19. _____ When money is withheld from an employee's paycheck.

20. _____ The holder of the check.

21. _____ Refers to a check written by a party unknown to you.

22. _____ One that actualizes or permits the transfer of money to another person.

23. _____ Refers to a payment made to creditors.

24. _____ Money that is owed to vendors, suppliers, utility companies, and others for services rendered.

APPLIED PRACTICE

Read the scenario and answer the questions that follow.

Scenario

Daniel Evans, CMA (AAMA), works as the administrative medical assistant for Happy Valley Medical Center. Handling payroll, accounts payable, and banking procedures are part of his work responsibilities. It is Thursday and he must perform these duties.

1. Daniel must calculate the gross earnings for the two clinical medical assistants who work in the back office. The office pays its employees every week, for the previous week's work. For every hour over 40 hours worked, employees get paid time and a half. Last week, Shelby Coleman worked 43.5 hours. She earns $13.00 per hour. Chantal Jefferson worked 45 hours last week. Chantal earns $13.75 per hour.

   a. What are Shelby's gross earnings?

   _____

   b. What are Chantal's gross earnings?

   _____

2. Daniel Smith has received an invoice from a vendor that supplied the physician with new business cards. The invoice reads as follows:

SELECT STATIONERY UNLIMITED

Bill to: Happy Valley Medical Center
1129 Felicity Road
Springfield, PA 00010
Account #: 288901HVMC

Remit Payment to: Select Stationery Unlimited
PO Box 588
New York, NY 11110

Item Number	Description	Price	Total
0123	250 Business Cards	32.99	32.99
		Tax (5%)	1.65
		Shipping and Handling	4.95
		Total	$ 39.59

a. Complete the check according to how Daniel should pay this bill.

Happy Valley Medical Clinic
1129 Felicity Road
Springfield, PA 00010

13003

Date _____ 20___

Pay to the order of: _____ _____

_____

_____dollars

MEMO: _____ _____

LEARNING ACTIVITY: MULTIPLE CHOICE

Circle the correct answer to each of the questions below.

1. Which of the following would be considered deductions for the purposes of employee payroll?

   a. Federal tax withholding
   b. Vacation pay
   c. Overtime pay
   d. All of the above

2. Petty cash is available for incidentals such as _____.

   a. small purchases
   b. reimbursements
   c. miscellaneous expenses
   d. All of the above

3. In order to have a negotiable instrument, the check must _____.

   a. be written and signed by an authorized payer of the check.
   b. state a sum of money to be paid.

c. be payable on demand or at a fixed date in the future.
d. be payable to the holder (the payee) of the check.
e. All of the above

4. Types of checks include _____.

   a. bank drafts
   b. warrants
   c. money orders
   d. All of the above

5. The American Bankers Association (ABA) number is always located _____.

   a. in the phone book
   b. in the upper right-hand corner of a printed check
   c. in the lower left-hand corner of a printed check
   d. None of the above

6. What are check stubs used for?

   a. As a permanent record of the date, amount, payee, and purpose of the check
   b. As a bookmark
   c. As an example of the correct way to write a check
   d. The quarterly form

7. How much is typically paid to employees as overtime wages?

   a. Twice the employee's normal rate of pay
   b. 1.5 times the employee's normal rate of pay
   c. Three times the employee's normal rate of pay
   d. None of the above

8. The _____ IRS form is used to calculate the correct amount of federal withholding tax for an employee.

   a. quarterly report
   b. W-2
   c. Circular E
   d. None of the above

9. A money market account _____.

   a. is an interest-bearing account
   b. is used more as an investment tool
   c. typically requires a minimum balance of $500
   d. All of the above

10. Banking is one of the critical office procedures because _____.

   a. it requires careful handling of money and records
   b. many offices do not have a bookkeeper or medical assistant assigned to perform this duty
   c. it requires specialized training
   d. All of the above

CRITICAL THINKING

Answer the following questions to the best of your ability. Utilize the textbook and other resources such as the Internet in considering the following questions.

© 2011 Pearson Education, Inc.

1. Ronnie Nguyen, CMA (AAMA), is the office manager for Dr. Hyun Kim. Ronnie has been handling the office payroll, using a manual system for several years. Dr. Kim has asked Ronnie to research the possibility of buying software for the payroll function. Dr. Kim wants Ronnie to provide her with a list of pros and cons for manual and computerized systems for the payroll function. What should Ronnie include?

_____

_____

_____

_____

2. Francie Crook, RMA, has been newly hired to work in a busy family practice clinic. When Francie looks at her first paycheck, she notices that a tax has been taken out for something called FICA. She asks her office manager to explain what this tax is. How might the office manager explain this tax to Francie?

_____

_____

_____

_____

3. Linnea Wagner is responsible for training new employees in the correct way to write checks. In order to do this, she must also explain the parts of the check. What might Linnea include in her instructional sessions?

_____

_____

_____

_____

RESEARCH ACTIVITY

Utilize Internet search engines to research the following topics and write a brief description of what you find. It is important to utilize reputable websites.

1. Using the Internet as a research source, look up three different software programs that can perform the payroll function. Create a list of the pros and cons of these three programs, as well as manual versus computerized payroll systems.

_____

_____

_____

_____

_____

_____

_____

_____

_____

© 2011 Pearson Education, Inc.

CHAPTER 17
Medical Insurance

CHAPTER OUTLINE

General review of the chapter.

The Purpose of Health Insurance
Health Insurance and the Availability of Health Insurance
Managed Care Organizations
Group-Sponsored or Individual Policies
Government Programs
Types of Health Insurance Benefits
Payment of Benefits
Verification of Insurance Benefits
Fee Schedules
Health Care Cost Containment
The *Federal Register*

STUDENT STUDY GUIDE

Use the following guide to assist in your learning of the concepts from the chapter.

I. Health Insurance and Managed Care

   1. Why Learn About Insurance as an MA?

     A. To assist the physician in maintaining a _____ strong business.
     B. To assist the patient in _____ the patient's financial responsibility to the practice.

   2. The Basics of Insurance

     A. Provides protection from _____ and _____ loss.
     B. Money is paid to the _____.
     C. Premiums are paid for by the _____.

   3. The Purposes of Medical Insurance

     A. Assists patients in covering costs incurred for _____.
     B. Expenses that are covered by insurance include the following:
        i. _____
        ii. _____
        iii. _____
        iv. _____

   4. Coverage Offered Through Hospitalization Insurance

        i. _____
        ii. _____
        iii. _____
        iv. _____
        v. _____

5. Insurance Coverage for Surgery

   A. Coverage is typically based on _____ and _____ charges.
   B. Costs vary by _____.
   C. Copays and _____ may apply.

6. Fixed Payment Plan

   A. The payment of a fixed fee provides _____ coverage.
   B. The fixed fee is known as a _____.
   C. Reimbursement is available once the _____ has been paid.

7. Managed Care Organization

   A. The payment of a _____ _____ provides monthly coverage.
   B. Reimbursement is available once the _____ has been paid.
   C. These plans are referred to as _____ plans.

8. Prepaid Plan

   A. Physicians contract to provide services for a _____ fee.
   B. _____ _____ providers may be assigned.

9. The Advantages of Managed Care

   i. _____
   ii. _____
   iii. _____
   iv. _____
   v. _____
   vi. _____
   vii. _____

10. The Disadvantages of Managed Care

   i. _____
   ii. _____
   iii. _____
   iv. _____
   v. _____
   vi. _____
   vii. _____
   viii. _____

11. Health Maintenance Organization (HMO)

   A. An HMO is a type of _____ _____ plan.
   B. The original intent was to _____ health care costs.
   C. Membership is limited to certain _____.
   D. Services are provided for a _____ fee.
   E. Patients must see the plan's _____ physicians.
   F. Emphasizes the _____ of health.

12. Preferred Provider Organization (PPO)

   A. The purpose is to _____ costs.
   B. Patients must use _____ providers.
   C. Members are not restricted to designated _____ or _____.

13. Point-of-Service Plan (POS)

   A. A POS is a type of _____ _____ plan.
   B. Offers more _____ than some HMOs and PPOs.
   C. An out-of-network or _____ provider may be seen.

© 2011 Pearson Education, Inc.

14. Exclusive Provider Organization (EPO)

    A. An EPO is a _____ _____ system.

    B. Patients select physicians from a _____.

    C. _____ are reimbursed on a modified fee-for-service basis.

15. Integrated Delivery System (IDS)

    A. An IDS is an organization of provider sites _____ to offer services to subscribers

    B. Examples include the following:

        i. _____

        ii. _____

        iii. _____

        iv. _____

        v. _____

II. Group-Sponsored or Individual (Commercial) and Government Plans

    1. Commercial Insurance Carriers

        A. These are typically _____ organizations.

        B. Often offer both traditional _____ service plans and _____ _____ plans.

        C. Require subscribers to pay a _____ for membership.

    2. Contents of a Health Insurance Card

        i. _____

        ii. _____

        iii. _____

        iv. _____

        v. _____

        vi. _____

        vii. _____

    3. Blue Cross/Blue Shield

        A. This is the largest _____ medical insurance system in the United States.

        B. Exists in _____ state.

        C. Operates _____ under state laws.

        D. Provides coverage for medical _____ and _____.

        E. Offers various types of health care _____.

    4. Medicare

        A. Medicare is health coverage provided by the _____.

        B. Available to persons who are age _____ and older and those who are _____ _____.

        C. Operated by the _____ _____ Administration.

        D. Medicare is funded through _____ _____.

    5. Medicare Parts A and B

        A. Part A provides coverage for _____ expenses.

        B. No _____ is paid for Part A.

        C. A _____ deductible must be met for Part B.

    6. The Resource-Based Relative Value Scale

        A. This is a formula used to determine Medicare's _____ reimbursement rate.

        B. Developed with the use of values that consider the following:

            i. _____

            ii. _____

            iii. _____

            iv. _____

7. Medicare Coverage

   A. Pays all expenses for the first _____ days of hospitalization.

   B. Pays a portion of hospitalization costs for an additional _____ days.

   C. Coverage does not include _____ nursing home care or costs for _____ or _____ illnesses.

8. Medicare Part D

   A. Implemented in _____.

   B. Offered as a _____ plan for Medicare recipients.

   C. Covers a _____ list of prescription drugs at participating pharmacies.

   D. Includes _____ deductibles, applicable _____ or coinsurance, and _____ benefits.

9. Medicare Supplements

   A. Paid by the _____ individual, not by _____.

   B. May require _____ forms to be submitted prior to paying the insured individual.

10. Medicaid

   A. Medicaid is insurance for individuals who are medically _____.

   B. Paid for by _____ and _____ governments.

   C. Administered by _____ _____.

   D. The rules of eligibility and payment _____ by state.

   E. Typically, individuals must qualify on a _____ basis.

11. Workers' Compensation

   A. Also known as _____ _____.

   B. This is one of the first _____ insurance programs.

   C. Employers pay the _____; employees pay _____.

12. Disability Insurance

   A. Usually begins paying the insured individual after he or she has been disabled for a _____.

   B. The benefit period is the amount of time that the _____ individual will receive a monthly check after the policy begins to pay.

   C. Insurance is not used for the purpose of paying _____ bills, but instead is used to replace the _____ that the patient has lost due to his or her disability.

III. Payment of Benefits

  1. Coverage Provided by Basic Insurance Policies

     i. _____

     ii. _____

     iii. _____

     iv. _____

     v. _____

  2. Major Medical Insurance

   A. Provides coverage for _____ _____ or _____ and _____ _____.

   B. It is typically a _____ policy.

   C. Usually increases the _____ paid by the insured individual.

  3. Dental Insurance

   A. Typically provides coverage for the following:

     i. _____

     ii. _____

     iii. _____

© 2011 Pearson Education, Inc.

iv. _____

v. _____

B. Often requires a _____.

C. Plans generally offer _____ to _____ coverage.

4. Coverage Provided by Vision Insurance

i. _____

ii. _____

iii. _____

iv. _____

v. _____

5. The UCR Method

A. UCR stands for _____, _____, and _____.

B. Used to determine the portion that an _____ _____ is obligated to pay.

C. Takes into consideration the following:

i. _____

ii. _____

iii. _____

6. Indemnity Schedules

A. These are another method used to determine the _____ _____ payment.

B. Based on the _____ amount charged for a specific service.

C. The payment is determined on the basis of the _____ charge submitted by the physician or by the physician's fee schedule.

7. Relative Value Studies (RVS)

A. RVS is a method to determine _____ factors in reimbursement.

B. Areas considered in the accounting include the _____, the _____, and the _____.

8. Filing Requirements

A. Claims must be filed in a _____ manner.

B. If a deadline is not met, then _____ _____ can be retrieved from the insurance carrier.

C. Filing deadlines _____ by insurance carrier.

9. Steps for Filing Primary and Secondary Claims

i. _____

ii. _____

iii. _____

iv. _____

10. Steps for Manually Recording Payments

i. _____

ii. _____

iii. _____

iv. _____

v. _____

vi. _____

vii. _____

11. Preauthorization

A. Preauthorization is also called _____.

B. Must be acquired prior to the patient's appointment, unless it is an _____.

C. Failure to obtain preauthorization may _____ treatment.

D. If service is provided without preauthorization, the insurance carrier may _____ to pay.

12. Calling the Insurance Carrier for Precertification

    A. If possible, obtain precertification at least _____ hours prior to the provision of patient services.

    B. Gather all pertinent _____ information prior to calling the insurance carrier.

13. Pertinent Information for Precertification

    i. _____

    ii. _____

    iii. _____

    iv. _____

    v. _____

14. Steps for Obtaining Approval

    i. _____

    ii. _____

    iii. _____

    iv. _____

    v. _____

15. Steps to Take When Preauthorization Is Denied

    i. _____

    ii. _____

    iii. _____

16. Referrals

    A. Requires paperwork to be sent to the _____ physician.

    B. The referral recommendation must be made _____ _____.

    C. Documentation must be placed in the _____ _____.

17. Materials Needed to Request a Referral

    i. _____

    ii. _____

    iii. _____

    iv. _____

    v. _____

    vi. _____

    vii. _____

18. Why Verify Patient Insurance?

    A. Minimizes _____ and _____ problems.

    B. Ensures that the practice will be paid for _____ rendered.

19. Steps for Verifying Information

    i. _____

    ii. _____

    iii. _____

    iv. _____

    v. _____

KEY TERMINOLOGY REVIEW

Match the selected key terms to their definitions below.

    a. benefit period

    b. capitation rate

    c. claim

    d. closed-panel HMO

© 2011 Pearson Education, Inc.

e. coordination of benefits (COB)

f. crossover claim

g. deductible

h. exclusive provider organization (EPO)

i. fee-for-service

j. fee schedule

k. formulary

l. gatekeeper

m. health maintenance provider organization (HMO)_____(PCP)

n. integrated delivery system (IDS)

o. medical foundation

p. open-panel HMO

q. point-of-service plan (POS)

r. preauthorization

s. preferred provider organization (PPO)

t. premium

u. prepaid plan

v. primary care

w. referral

x. self-referral

1. _____ The type of claim that is submitted if an individual has both Medicare and Medicaid.

2. _____ A nonprofit IDS.

3. _____ Determines the medical necessity of services provided by specialists.

4. _____ Period of time that payments for Medicare hospital benefits are available.

5. _____ Lists the amount to be paid by the insurance company for each procedure or service subject to the managed care contract.

6. _____ Also known as a primary care physician, this is the provider who is responsible for the overall management of the patient's health.

7. _____ The portion the patient must pay before the insurance company will pay any benefits.

8. _____ An HMO enrollee chooses to see an out-of-network provider without authorization.

9. _____ Obtaining permission from the insurance carrier before performing a procedure or providing certain services to subscribers.

10. _____ A predetermined fee.

11. _____ A plan in which patients may choose to use the panel of providers within the HMO network or to utilize the services of non-HMO providers.

12. _____ An approved list of medications specific to each insurance carrier.

13. _____ A managed care system that allows the patient to select only from a defined panel of providers.

14. _____ Involves a group of providers who have a contractual agreement to provide services to subscribers on a negotiated fee-for-service basis.

15. _____ An organization of provider sites (e.g., ambulatory centers, clinics, or hospitals) with a contracted relationship that offer services to subscribers.

16. _____ Used to send a patient for treatment to another facility or physician.

17. _____ A type of HMO where the clinic is owned by the HMO and the providers are employees of the HMO.

18. _____ A fixed monthly fee or semimonthly fee.

19. _____ A separate charge or fee set up by individual physicians for every service.

20. _____ A type of HMO where the health care providers are not employees of the HMO and do not belong to a medical group owned or managed by the HMO.

21. _____ A system that insurance carriers have in place to prevent payment by more than one carrier.

22. _____ Requires the patient to use a provider under contract with the insurance company. The provider is reimbursed at a discounted rate.

23. _____ A type of managed care plan in which a range of health care services performed by a limited group of providers is made available to plan members for a predetermined fee.

24. _____ A written and documented request for reimbursement.

APPLIED PRACTICE

Complete the activity and answer the questions that follow. Select and complete Activity 1 if you currently have health insurance. Select and complete Activity 2 if you currently do not have health insurance.

1. If you have health insurance, do you know everything about your plan? Conduct research either through the Internet or by calling your insurance company to find out the following information:

    a. What conditions does the insurance plan not cover?

    _____

    _____

    b. For conditions not covered, is it possible to receive coverage for an additional fee?

    _____

    _____

    c. When is preauthorization required and who typically should perform this activity?

    _____

    _____

2. If you do not have health insurance, begin to research the types of health insurance plans that may be affordable for you in your area.

    a. Does your school offer health insurance for students? If so, what is the cost and what type of coverage is offered?

    _____

    _____

    b. List two other types of insurance plans you found in your area that may be affordable for you. If your school offers health insurance, what is the difference between these two other plans and the plan offered by the school?

    _____

    _____

    c. When is preauthorization required for the plans you researched and who typically should perform this activity?

    _____

    _____

LEARNING ACTIVITY: TRUE/FALSE

Indicate whether the following statements are true or false by placing a T or an F on the line that precedes each statement.

_____ 1. Children of veterans with total or permanent service-related disabilities are currently not covered under CHAMPVA; only spouses and widows are covered.

© 2011 Pearson Education, Inc.

_____ 2. Most insurance carriers require a deductible.

_____ 3. Insurance is considered a two-party contract between the insured (the patient or the patient's family) and the insurance company.

_____ 4. Most patients are completely aware of what their insurance covers.

_____ 5. The most basic insurance policies cover office visits, hospitalization, emergency room visits, surgical procedures, and wellness examinations.

_____ 6. To reduce unnecessary patient visits to the provider's office, insurance companies typically do not require a copayment.

_____ 7. Managed care organizations (MCOs) offer options that are available through public insurance carriers and through some government programs.

_____ 8. Before HMOs became so widespread, insurance companies reimbursed providers for all of their charges without questioning whether or not the services were medically necessary.

_____ 9. Health care insurance providers determine fees on the basis of three main components.

_____ 10. Most insurance plans have lifetime maximum benefits.

CRITICAL THINKING

Answer the following questions to the best of your ability. Utilize the textbook and other resources such as the Internet in considering the following questions.

1. Monica Swinger is taking an administrative medical assisting course. She has been given the assignment of writing an essay describing how health insurance began in the United States. What information should Monica include?

_____

_____

_____

_____

2. Erica Owsley, CMA (AAMA), is working with Charles Wong, a patient in the clinic where Erica works. Charles tells Erica he has the option of buying into the group insurance plan that his employer offers or he can buy an individual policy on his own. He isn't sure which option to choose and asks Erica if she can tell him the differences between individual and group insurance plans. What should Erica tell Charles?

_____

_____

_____

_____

RESEARCH ACTIVITY

Utilize Internet search engines to research the following topics and write a brief description of what you find. It is important to utilize reputable websites.

1. Using the Internet as a research source, find your state's Medicaid website and research the criteria for being covered under Medicaid in your state. Write an essay describing the persons who may be covered under Medicaid in your state.

_____

_____

_____

_____

_____

_____

_____

_____

_____

_____

_____

_____

_____

_____

_____

_____

_____

_____

_____

_____

_____

_____

_____

_____

© 2011 Pearson Education, Inc.

CHAPTER 18
Medical Insurance Claims

CHAPTER OUTLINE

General review of the chapter:

Types of Health Insurance and Claim Forms
Types of Claims
The Claim Form
Claims Processing
Claims Security
Tracking Claim Forms

STUDENT STUDY GUIDE

Use the following guide to assist in your learning of the concepts from the chapter.

I. Insurance Claim Forms

1. Purpose of the Health Insurance Claim Form

    A. Reports patient _____ and _____ to the insurance carrier.
    B. Helps _____ reporting.
    C. Improves communication between the _____ and the _____.

2. Guidelines for Improving the Communication Process

    i. _____
    ii. _____
    iii. _____

3. Submitting a Medicare Claim

    A. Staying current with their knowledge regarding _____.
    B. The _____ form is used for Medicare claims
    C. Knowing the _____ and _____ is critical to successful claims submission.

4. Submitting a Medicaid Claim

    A. Claims submission _____ from state to state.
    B. Eligibility is not _____.
    C. _____ is required for some services.

5. Submitting a Medicaid Claim

    A. _____ claims are filed for patients with both Medicare and Medicaid.
    B. Claims are submitted on a _____ form.

6. Submitting a Workers' Compensation Claim

    A. The claim form to be used depends on the state and the _____ in that state.
    B. Typically, the _____ form is acceptable.
    C. The patient does not pay for _____ and _____ covered by workers' compensation.

II. Types of Claims

    1. Methods for Submitting Claims

        A. No matter which method is used, the _____ information is provided.

        B. The method used is dependent upon the _____.

    2. Paper Claims

        A. Claims are completed _____.

        B. Problems that occur with this method often include _____, leading to the claim being _____ or time being lost because claims must be _____.

    3. Requirements for Paper Claims

        A. All claims must be on an _____ claim form.

        B. Claims must be _____.

        C. _____ ink must be used.

        D. _____ letters should be used when appropriate.

        E. The use of correction tape is _____.

        F. Documentation must be submitted in the _____ envelope as the paper claim.

    4. Electronic Claims

        A. Electronic claims are sent directly to the _____ or the _____.

        B. All medical offices were required to have the ability to submit electronic claims by _____.

    5. The National Supplier Clearinghouse

        A. Charges for the _____ provided.

        B. Eliminates the need for different carriers to have specific _____.

        C. Checks the claim for _____, thereby reducing the number of claims that are _____.

    6. Steps for Sending Claims Electronically

        i. _____

        ii. _____

        iii. _____

        iv. _____

        v. _____

        vi. _____

    7. Three Ways That Claims Are Transmitted

        i. _____

        ii. _____

        iii. _____

III. The CMS-1500 Form

    1. Information Needed to Complete the CMS-1500 Form

        i. _____

        ii. _____

        iii. _____

        iv. _____

        v. _____

    2. Prior to Submitting a Claim

        A. Check the _____ of the claim form.

        B. If you are submitting a paper claim, make a _____ for the patient's file.

        C. Enter the data on the _____ log.

        D. Send the completed CMS-1500 form and the required documentation to the _____.

© 2011 Pearson Education, Inc.

3. Confidentiality and the CMS-1500 Form

   A. As with all patient data, information must remain _____.

   B. Release of information must be authorized by the _____.

   C. A signed standard _____ form must be used.

   D. The form must be placed in the _____ file.

4. Assignment of Benefits

   A. Assignment of benefits is allowed by _____ and other carriers.

   B. A _____-time form must be signed by the patient.

   C. This form _____ the _____ of patient information.

   D. Once signed, use _____.

   E. The form must be kept _____ in the patient's file.

5. Materials Needed to Complete the CMS-1500 Form

   i. _____

   ii. _____

   iii. _____

   iv. _____

   v. _____

6. The Superbill

   A. Contains the _____, _____, _____, and _____.

   B. Originally created to allow patients to file _____ claims.

   C. Accepted by some insurance companies as a substitute _____.

   D. Provides detailed information on the _____ received.

7. The Birthday Rule

   A. Used only for parents who are _____ married.

   B. The primary plan is the plan held by the parent whose birthday falls _____ in the year.

   C. If both parents' birthdays are on the same day, the parent with the _____ date of inception would hold the primary plan.

   D. The primary plan of divorced parents is determined by the _____.

8. Prior to Submitting a Claim

   i. _____

   ii. _____

   iii. _____

   iv. _____

IV. Claims Security and Tracking Claims

  1. Maintaining the Confidentiality of Patient Information

   A. Maintaining confidentiality is the responsibility of _____ health care workers.

   B. A breach of confidentiality occurs when information is provided to individuals who have not been _____ to _____ the information.

  2. How to Keep Patient Information Secure

   i. _____

   ii. _____

   iii. _____

   iv. _____

  3. Documentation of Permission

   i. _____

   ii. _____

   iii. _____

© 2011 Pearson Education, Inc.

4. The Most Common Reasons for Rejection of Claims
   i. _____
   ii. _____
   iii. _____
   iv. _____
   v. _____
   vi. _____
   vii. _____
   viii. _____
   ix. _____

5. Resubmitting Claims

   A. Information must be _____ and resubmitted.
   B. The use of patient data and other resources is important for ensuring _____.
   C. Refiling must occur within the specified _____ limits.

KEY TERMINOLOGY REVIEW

Match the selected key terms to their definitions below.

a. Assignment of Benefits Form
b. The Birthday Rule
c. breach of confidentiality
d. clean claim
e. The National Supplier Clearinghouse
f. CMS-1500 Form
g. denied claim

h. dirty claim
i. invalid claim
j. nonparticipating provider
k. participating provider
l. primary insurance
m. secondary insurance
n. write-off

1. _____ The failure to keep patient information confidential.

2. _____ The most common health insurance claim form.

3. _____ Has a contractual agreement with an insurance plan to render care to eligible beneficiaries and then bill the insurance carrier directly.

4. _____ A health insurance claim form that has been completed but has some type of incorrect information.

5. _____ Form that allows the insurance carrier to pay the physician directly for billed charges.

6. _____ Applies if the patient has primary insurance and also has coverage available through the spouse's employer.

7. _____ Bills the patient directly. The patient is expected to pay the charges and then submit the claim to the insurance company.

8. _____ A health insurance claim form that has been completed correctly without any errors or omissions.

9. _____ Term used to indicate that the physician has agreed to forfeit the amount that the insurance company does not authorize.

10. _____ Can occur when procedures or services are not covered by the patient's insurance policy or when the patient has not met his or her deductible.

11. _____ When a health insurance claim form is incorrect because it has missing data or errors.

12. _____ The coverage provided by the patient's employer.

© 2011 Pearson Education, Inc.

13. _____ Used by insurance claims administrators to determine which parent's benefit plan will be the primary insurance plan of a dependent child who is covered by the employer-sponsored insurance plans of both parents.

14. _____ An independent entity that reviews claims.

APPLIED PRACTICE

Complete the CMS-1500 form (Figure 18-1) using the patient registration form, the encounter form, and the fee schedule that is provided.

Capital City Medical—123 Unknown Boulevard, Capital City,
NY 12345-2222 (555)555-1234

Phil Wells, MD, Mannie Mends, MD, Bette R. Soone, MD

Patient Information Form

Tax ID: 75-0246810

Group NPI: 1513171216

Patient Information:

Name: (Last, First) Colich, Guy   ☒ Male   ☐ Female   Birth Date: 04/23/1958

Address: 872 Hickory Pl, Capital City, NY 12345   Phone: (555) 555-9069

Social Security Number: 142-86-2078   Full-Time Student: ☐ Yes ☒ No

Marital Status: ☐ Single ☒ Married ☐ Divorced ☐ Other

Employment:

Employer: None   Phone: ( )

Address:

Condition Related to: ☐ Auto Accident ☐ Employment ☐ Other Accident

Date of Accident: _____ State _____

Emergency Contact: _____ **Phone: ( )** _____

Primary Insurance: Aetna   Phone: ( )

Address: 1625 Healthcare Bldg, Capital City, NY 12345

Insurance Policyholder's Name: Same   ☐ M ☐ F DOB: _____

Address: _____

Phone: _____ Relationship to Insured: ☒ Self ☐ Spouse ☐ Child ☐ Other

Employer: _____ Phone: _____

Employer's Address: _____

Policy/ID No: 9567305   Group No: 511669 Percent Covered: ____%, Copay Amt: $ 35.00

Secondary Insurance: _____ Phone: ( )

Address: _____

Insurance Policyholder's Name: _____ ☐ M ☐ F DOB: _____

Address: _____

Phone: _____ Relationship to Insured: ☐ Self ☐ Spouse ☐ Child ☐ Other

Employer: _____ Phone: ( )

Employer's Address: _____

Policy/ID No: _____ Group No: _____ Percent Covered: _____%, Copay Amt: $_____

Reason for Visit: I am here for a recheck on my manic depression

Known Allergies: _____

Were you referred here? If so, by whom?: _____

© 2011 Pearson Education, Inc.

Patient Name <u>Guy Colich</u>

Date of Service
10-07-20XX

New Patient						Laboratory	
Problem Focused	99201	Arthrocentesis/Aspiration/Injection				Amylase	82150
Expanded Problem, Focused	99202	Small Joint		20600		B12	82607
Detailed	99203	Interm Joint		20605		CBC & Diff	85025
Comprehensive	99204	Major Joint		20610		Comp Metabolic Panel	80053
Comprehensive/High Complex	99205	**Other Invasive/Noninvasive**				Chlamydia Screen	87110
Well Exam Infant (up to 12 mos.)	99381	Audiometry		92552		Cholesterol	82465
Well Exam 1–4 yrs.	99382	Cast Application				Digoxin	80162
Well Exam 5–11 yrs.	99383	Location	Long	Short		Electrolytes	80051
Well Exam 12–17 yrs.	99384	Catheterization		51701		Ferritin	82728
Well Exam 18–39 yrs.	99385	Circumcision		54150		Folate	82746
Well Exam 40–64 yrs.	99386	Colposcopy		57452		GC Screen	87070
		Colposcopy w/Biopsy		57454		Glucose	82947
		Cryosurgery Premalignant Lesion				Glucose 1 HR	82950
		Location (s):				Glycosylated HGB A1C	83036
Established Patient		Cryosurgery Warts				HCT	85014
Post-Op Follow Up Visit	99024	Location (s):				HDL	83718
Minimum	99211	Curettement Lesion				Hep BSAG	87340
Problem Focused	99212	Single		11055		Hepatitis panel, acute	80074
Expanded Problem Focused	99213 X	2–4		11056		HGB	85018
Detailed	99214	>4		11057		HIV	86703
Comprehensive/High Complex	99215	Diaphragm Fitting		57170		Iron & TIBC	83550
Well Exam Infant (up to 12 mos.)	99391	Ear Irrigation		69210		Kidney Profile	80069
Well exam 1–4 yrs.	99392	ECG		93000		Lead	83655
Well Exam 5–11 yrs.	99393	Endometrial Biopsy		58100		Liver Profile	80076
Well Exam 12–17 yrs.	99394	Exc. Lesion Malignant				Mono Test	86308
Well Exam 18–39 yrs.	99395	Benign				Pap Smear	88155
Well Exam 40–64 yrs.	99396	Location				Pregnancy Test	84703
Obstetrics		Exc. Skin Tags (1–15)		11200		Obstetric Panel	80055
Total OB Care	59400	Each Additional 10		11201		Pro Time	85610
Injections		Fracture Treatment				PSA	84153
Administration Sub. / IM	90772	Loc				RPR	86592
Drug		w/Reduc		w/o Reduc		Sed. Rate	85651
Dosage		I & D Abscess Single/Simple		10060		Stool Culture	87045
Allergy	95115	Multiple or Comp		10061		Stool O & P	87177
Cocci Skin Test	86490	I & D Pilonidal Cyst Simple		10080		Strep Screen	87880
DPT	90701	Pilonidal Cyst Complex		10081		Theophylline	80198
Hemophilus	90646	IV Therapy—To One Hour		90760		Thyroid Uptake	84479
Influenza	90658	Each Additional Hour		90761		TSH	84443
MMR	90707	Laceration Repair				Urinalysis	81000
OPV	90712	Location	Size	Simp/Comp		Urine Culture	87088
Pneumovax	90732	Laryngoscopy		31505		Drawing Fee	36415
TB Skin Test	86580	Oximetry		94760		Specimen Collection	99000
TD	90718	Punch Biopsy				**Other:**	
Unlisted Immun	90749	Rhythm Strip		93040			
Tetanus Toxoid	90703	Treadmill		93015			
Vaccine/Toxoid Admin <8 Yr Old w/ Counseling	90465	Trigger Point or Tendon Sheath Inj.		20550			
Vaccine/Toxoid Administration for Adult	90471	Tympanometry		92567			

Diagnosis/ICD-9: **296.80**

I acknowledge receipt of medical services and authorize the release of any medical information necessary to process this claim for healthcare payment only. I do authorize payment to the provider.

Patient Signature <u>Guy Colich</u>

Total Estimated Charges: _____

Payment Amount: _____

Next Appointment: _____

New Patient Examinations		
Office Visit, Level 1	99201	$ 55.00
Office Visit, Level 2	99202	$110.00
Office Visit, Level 3	99203	$154.00
Office Visit, Level 4	99204	$226.00
Office Visit, Level 5	99205	$299.00

Established Patient Examinations		
Office Visit, Level 1	99211	$ 45.00
Office Visit, Level 2	99212	$ 60.00
Office Visit, Level 3	99213	$ 80.00
Office Visit, Level 4	99214	$123.00
Office Visit, Level 5	99215	$199.00

Note: This activity has been adapted from Vines/Comprehensive Health Insurance: Billing, Coding, and Reimbursement Student CD. © 2008 Pearson Education, Inc. Upper Saddle River, NJ 07458

LEARNING ACTIVITY: TRUE/FALSE

Indicate whether the following statements are true or false by placing a T or an F on the line that precedes each statement.

_____ 1. Many Blue Cross/Blue Shield plans provide their own type of health insurance claim form.

_____ 2. Depending on the type of service, the CMS-1500 form or the CMS-1450 form may also be used.

_____ 3. The CMS-1500 form was previously known as the UB-04 form.

_____ 4. Most patients are well aware of what their insurance covers.

_____ 5. Medicaid is a state-run insurance program for those individuals who are considered medically indigent.

_____ 6. When working with Medicaid patients, the medical assistant must verify coverage prior to each and every visit.

_____ 7. The most frequently used claim form for workers' compensation is the DD Form 2642.

_____ 8. The electronic filing of claims speeds the processing time for both the provider and the insurance carrier.

_____ 9. It is improper for insurance companies to make special incentives available to physicians who choose to become participating providers.

_____ 10. It is against the law to talk to a patient about his or her condition anywhere but in a professional setting.

© 2011 Pearson Education, Inc.

CRITICAL THINKING

Answer the following questions to the best of your ability. Utilize the textbook and other resources as needed.

1. Josie Svien, CMA (AAMA), is working in the billing office of a family practice clinic. Josie is new to the job and is just beginning the process of filing insurance claims. To what areas should Josie pay particular attention in order to avoid the rejection of claims?

   _____

   _____

   _____

   _____

   _____

2. Erica Miller, CMA (AAMA), has just completed a claim form. Explain the use of the insurance claims log. What information is entered into the log for each step of the reimbursement process? What is the purpose of such documentation?

   _____

   _____

   _____

   _____

RESEARCH ACTIVITY

Utilize Internet search engines to research the following topics and write a brief description of what you find. It is important to utilize reputable websites.

1. Using the Internet as a research source, write an essay on the advantages and disadvantages of electronic medical records and the electronic submission of claims. Cite your sources.

   _____

   _____

   _____

   _____

   _____

   _____

   _____

   _____

   _____

   _____

   _____

Chapter 19
Medical Coding

CHAPTER OUTLINE

General review of the chapter:

Insurance Coding
History of Coding
Understanding the ICD-9-CM
Procedural Coding
Getting to Know the CPT
Insurance Fraud
Compliance Plan

STUDENT STUDY GUIDE

Use the following guide to assist in your learning of the concepts from the chapter.

I. Introduction to Coding and the ICD-9-CM Coding Manual

1. The Purposes of Codes

   A. Provide information to the _____ regarding patient _____ and _____.
   B. Assist in the communications process to ensure _____ and _____ reimbursement.

2. The Superbill

   A. Used as a _____, a statement, and an _____ reporting form.
   B. Must be updated _____ to reflect the most current diagnostic and procedural codes
   C. Can be used as a reference base for traditional _____ insurance forms and _____ insurance forms.

3. The History of Coding

   i. _____
   ii. _____
   iii. _____
   iv. _____
   v. _____

4. Contents of Volume II of the ICD-9-CM Coding Manual

   A. Contains the _____ index.
   B. Lists _____ and _____ found in the _____ list.
   C. Provides information on _____ and the adverse effects of _____ and _____.
   D. Contains an index of injuries resulting from _____ causes.

5. The ICD-9-CM Codes

   A. Each diagnosis is given a _____-digit code.
   B. The _____ and _____ digits are added to the main code to provide more _____.

© 2011 Pearson Education, Inc.

C. If _____ digits are applicable for describing the patient's condition, then the _____ -digit code must be used.

6. The Uses of Tables in the ICD-9-CM Coding Manual
   A. The _____ table is used to code a diagnosis of high blood pressure.
   B. The _____ table is used to code _____, both benign and malignant.
   C. The _____ table is used to code the behavior of the neoplasm.

7. Abbreviations and Symbols Used in the ICD-9-CM Coding Manual (List each that is used.)
   i. _____
   ii. _____
   iii. _____
   iv. _____
   v. _____
   vi. _____
   vii. _____
   viii. _____
   ix. _____
   x. _____

8. Comparing ICD-10 Codes with ICD-9 Codes
   A. ICD-10 has _____ codes, as well as _____ and content modifications.
   B. In the ICD-10, identification is from the _____ versus from the _____.
   C. Conversion to use of the ICD-10 codes has been pushed back to _____.

9. Expectations for the ICD-10 Codes
   A. Support _____ purchasing and Medicare's _____ and _____ activities.
   B. Support _____ reporting of quality data.
   C. Ensure more _____ payments for new procedures and fewer rejected claims.
   D. Improve _____ management, _____ of disease monitoring, and reporting worldwide.
   E. Allow the United States to compare its data with _____ data to track the incidence and spread of _____ and _____ outcomes.

10. HCPCS
    A. Stands for _____.
    B. Used to report services and procedures for _____ and _____ patients.
    C. Consists of _____ coding levels.

11. Contents of HCPCS Level I
    A. Contains codes for _____ and _____.
    B. Provides additional codes not found in the _____.
    C. Contains _____ sections.
    D. Codes are for items covered under Medicare, such as _____, _____, and _____.

12. HCPCS Level II and Modifiers
    A. Level II contains codes that begin with a _____ and then _____.
    B. Modifiers consist of _____ letters.
    C. Modifiers can be used in addition to the modifiers found in the _____ Manual.

II. Getting to Know the CPT Manual
   1. Sections in the CPT Manual
      i. _____
      ii. _____

© 2011 Pearson Education, Inc.

iii. _____

iv. _____

v. _____

vi. _____

2. Evaluation and Management Section

   A. Beginning section in the _____ Manual.

   B. Includes codes for _____ visits and _____.

   C. Codes link the _____ or _____ with the _____ needed for treatment.

3. Factors Affecting Code Selection

     i. _____

    ii. _____

   iii. _____

   iv. _____

4. Four Levels of Decision Making

     i. _____

    ii. _____

   iii. _____

   iv. _____

5. Use of Modifiers

   A. Provides further classification of _____ and _____.

   B. Follows the _____ -digit _____ code.

   C. Contains a _____ -digit code preceded by a _____.

   D. The most common modifier is _____.

   E. Use of multiple modifiers requires the use of the modifier _____ first.

6. Codes Found in the Medicine Section

   A. Codes for _____ procedures and treatment procedures.

   B. Codes for many _____ tests.

7. Items Needed for Proper Coding

     i. _____

    ii. _____

   iii. _____

   iv. _____

    v. _____

8. Steps for Proper Coding

     i. _____

    ii. _____

   iii. _____

   iv. _____

    v. _____

   vi. _____

  vii. _____

III. Insurance Fraud

   1. Tips for the Patient for Preventing Insurance Fraud from the Centers for Medicare & Medicaid Services

     A. Look at your Medicaid bill _____ to ensure that Medicaid has been billed for _____ services and goods that you actually _____. Check that the _____ of service is correct.

© 2011 Pearson Education, Inc.

B. DO NOT give your Medicaid _____ to anyone except your doctor, clinic, hospital, or other health care provider.

C. DO NOT let anyone _____ your Medicaid card.

D. DO NOT _____ your name on a blank form.

E. Ask for a _____ of everything that you sign.

F. If you are offered free tests or screenings in exchange for your Medicaid card number, be _____.

G. Give your Medicaid _____ card only to those individuals who have provided you with _____.

H. NEVER allow a medical services provider to _____ for _____ rendered without _____ you first.

2. The Most Common Forms of Medicare Fraud

   i. _____

  ii. _____

 iii. _____

 iv. _____

   v. _____

 vi. _____

3. Suspicious Office Practices that Should Alert Consumers to Improper Behavior

A. Routinely _____ copayments without checking on the patient's ability to pay.

B. Advertise _____ consultations to Medicare beneficiaries.

C. Claiming that they _____ Medicare.

D. Using _____ or _____ tactics to sell high-priced medical services or diagnostic tests.

E. Bill Medicare for services that the patient _____ recall receiving.

F. Use _____ and _____ selling as marketing tools.

4. Information Requested by the National Fraud Hotline

   i. _____

  ii. _____

 iii. _____

 iv. _____

   v. _____

 vi. _____

5. The Benefits of Having a Compliance Plan

A. The medical office is at a _____ risk for liability.

B. Demonstrates to the physicians, fraud investigators, and insurance carriers that the medical office is making every effort to _____ and _____ errors.

C. Gives the office staff a process for _____, _____, and _____ practices that are illegal.

6. Basic Components of a Compliance Plan

A. Conducting _____ audits of billing and coding practices.

B. _____ written standards and procedures for compliance.

C. Training and educating office staff on _____.

D. Investigating _____ and disclosing _____ to the appropriate government agencies.

KEY TERMINOLOGY REVIEW

Match the selected key terms to their definitions below.

© 2011 Pearson Education, Inc.

a. Current Procedural Terminology (CPT) Manual
b. Established patient
c. Evaluation and Management (E/M)
d. ICD-9-CM
e. ICD-10
f. Kickback
g. Modifier
h. New patient
i. Principal diagnosis
j. Procedural coding
k. Symbols
l. Upcoding
m. World Health Organization (WHO)

1. _____ Based on the following criteria: the history of the patient, the complexity of the examination, and the degree of difficulty in medical decision making.

2. _____ Used in circumstances in which the procedure code does not accurately describe the procedure.

3. _____ Publishes the International Classification of Diseases, 9th Revision, Clinical Modification (ICD-9-CM).

4. _____ Used in the CPT Manual to distinguish changes or give instructions to be used when coding.

5. _____ The process of translating a narrative description of procedures into numbers.

6. _____ Provides a comprehensive list of procedure and service codes.

7. _____ One who has never been seen by anyone in the practice or has not been seen by anyone in the practice for more than 3 years.

8. _____ Contains numeric and alphanumeric diagnostic codes.

9. _____ An incentive provided by another physician, laboratory, hospital, or pharmaceutical representative for using their services.

10. _____ Billing for a service at a higher level than was actually provided.

11. _____ The reason that the patient sought care on a particular date.

12. _____ Contains increased specificity and includes recently discovered or diagnosed diseases.

13. _____ One who has been seen within the past 3 years by any practitioner in the practice.

APPLIED PRACTICE

Follow the directions that apply to each section.

Section A: Provide the correct modifier for each of the following descriptions.

1. Bilateral procedure: _____
2. Discontinued procedure: _____
3. Unusual procedural service: _____
4. Preoperative management only: _____
5. General anesthesia provided by the surgeon: _____

Section B: Code the following using the CPT Manual:

1. Debridement of 10 nails by any method: _____
2. Chemical peel, facial; dermal: _____
3. Mastectomy, subcutaneous: _____
4. Incision and draining (I&D) of hematoma, soft tissue of neck: _____
5. Manipulation, elbow, under anesthesia: _____

© 2011 Pearson Education, Inc.

6. Endoscopy, surgical; operative tissue ablation and reconstruction of atria, without cardiopulmonary bypass: _____

7. Laparoscopy, surgical, appendectomy: _____

8. Vaginal delivery only, including postpartum care: _____

9. Mammography, bilateral: _____

10. Spirometry, including graphic record, total and timed vital capacity, expiratory flow rate measurement with or without maximal voluntary ventilation: _____

Section C: Using Volumes I and II of the ICD-9-CM Coding Manual, identify the diagnostic code for each of the following diagnoses.

1. Diabetes with ketoacidosis: _____

2. Acute idiopathic pericarditis: _____

3. Acute lymphadenitis: _____

4. Pneumococcal meningitis: _____

5. Acute pharyngitis: _____

6. Hirsutism: _____

7. Chest pains, unspecified: _____

8. Special Screening for Diabetes Mellitus: _____

9. Cushing's Syndrome: _____

10. Glycosuria: _____

LEARNING ACTIVITY: MULTIPLE CHOICE

Circle the correct answer for each of the questions below.

1. The CPT Manual has _____ major sections.
   a. three
   b. four
   c. five
   d. six

2. All CPT codes are _____ digits long.
   a. four
   b. five
   c. six
   d. All of the above

3. Within the CPT Manual, _____ indicate(s) that this is a new code.
   a. a black circle
   b. a triangle
   c. two triangles
   d. a circle with an inner dot

4. Within the CPT Manual, _____ indicate(s) that this is a revised code.
   a. a black circle
   b. a triangle
   c. two triangles
   d. a circle with an inner dot

5. Within the CPT Manual, _____ indicate(s) a new or revised description.
   a. a black circle
   b. a triangle
   c. two triangles
   d. a circle with an inner dot

6. When physicians perform procedures that are not listed in the CPT Manual, what must the medical assistant do?
   a. Choose the code for the procedure that most closely approximates the actual procedure.
   b. Not bill for the service.
   c. Ask the physician to choose an appropriate code.
   d. Use an unlisted procedure code and submit copies of the procedure report with the claim.

7. Which volume of the ICD-9-CM Coding Manual contains a tabular list of diseases?
   a. Volume I
   b. Volume II
   c. Volume III
   d. Volume IV

8. Which volume of the ICD-9-CM Coding Manual contains a list of diagnosis codes used for hospital billing?
   a. Volume I
   b. Volume II
   c. Volume III
   d. Volume IV

9. Appendix _____ contains a list of the morphology of neoplasms.
   a. A
   b. B
   c. C
   d. D

10. Volume I of the ICD-9-CM Coding Manual has _____ appendices.
   a. four
   b. five
   c. six
   d. seven

CRITICAL THINKING

Answer the following questions to the best of your ability. Utilize the textbook as a reference.

1. Teresa Clymer is taking a course in medical insurance billing as part of her medical assistant training. She has been asked to write a paper describing how proper diagnostic coding is linked to proper reimbursement from insurance carriers. What information should Teresa include in her paper?

_____

_____

_____

_____

_____

© 2011 Pearson Education, Inc.

2. Mavis Raschenko, RMA, has been asked by her office manager to explain the difference between volumes I and II of the ICD-9-CM Coding Manual. How might Mavis explain the differences?

_____

_____

_____

_____

3. Marc Alaimo, RMA, has been newly hired to work in the billing office in a family practice clinic. Marc has been asked to explain to the physicians how V codes are to be used. What should Marc include in his explanation?

_____

_____

_____

_____

4. Kira Stansfield, CMA (AAMA), is working with Dr. Ramey in an internal medicine clinic. Dr. Ramey is unsure of which evaluation and management code to choose for certain patients whom she has seen. How can Kira advise Dr. Ramey in choosing the appropriate code?

_____

_____

_____

_____

5. Gloria Heritage, RMA, is working in the billing office of a pediatric practice. One of the physicians in the practice frequently chooses a high-level E/M code when billing for his patients. When Gloria consults the patient's charts, she finds that there is not sufficient information to use the higher billing codes and determines that a lower code would be more appropriate. What can Gloria do in this situation?

_____

_____

_____

_____

RESEARCH ACTIVITY

Utilize Internet search engines to research the following topics and write a brief description of what you find. It is important to utilize reputable websites.

1. Using the Internet as a research source, go to your state's website for the Department of Health. Research the laws that apply to billing for medical services in your state. Create a list of the laws that are relevant to the issue of fraudulent practices in billing and coding.

_____

_____

© 2011 Pearson Education, Inc.

CHAPTER 20

Medical Office Management

CHAPTER OUTLINE

General review of the chapter:

Systems Approach to Office Management
The Office Manager
Leadership Styles
Creating a Team Atmosphere
Hiring Procedures: Selecting the Right Staff Members
Orientation and Training
Using Performance Evaluation Effectively
Time Management
Personnel Policy Manual
Office Policies and Procedures Manual
Medical Meetings and Speaking Engagements
Patient Information Booklet
Medical Practice Marketing and Customer Service

STUDENT STUDY GUIDE

Use the following guide to assist in your learning of the concepts from the chapter.

I. Managing the Medical Office

    1. General Skills for Office Management

        i. _____

        ii. _____

        iii. _____

    2. General Duties of the Office Manager

        i. _____

        ii. _____

        iii. _____

    3. Critical Resources Used in Managing a Medical Office

        i. _____

        ii. _____

        iii. _____

    4. Personnel Management Responsibilities

        A. Hiring new employees and establishing _____ training.

        B. Performing _____ reviews.

        C. Disciplinary measures should occur as soon as they are warranted and not be held over until
        an _____.

© 2011 Pearson Education, Inc.

5. Employee Records

    A. Federal law requires records to be maintained for _____ employee.

    B. Payroll records must include the following:

       i. _____

       ii. _____

       iii. _____

       iv. _____

6. Elements of Financial Management

       i. _____

       ii. _____

       iii. _____

       iv. _____

7. Effective Scheduling

    A. Can contribute to the _____ level of the practice.

    B. If the office staff is continuously scheduled inappropriately, it affects _____ and may cause _____ among the physicians and patients.

    C. _____ must be built into the staff schedule to allow for _____ occurrences such as sick days and business appointments.

8. Elements of Facility and Equipment Management

       i. _____

       ii. _____

       iii. _____

       iv. _____

       v. _____

       vi. _____

9. Communications

    A. To be effective, one must be able to communicate at _____ _____.

    B. Contributes significantly to the _____ of the staff.

    C. Includes _____ and _____ materials.

10. The Basic Duties of the Office Manager

    A. Acts as a liaison between the _____ and the _____.

    B. Conducts _____ and _____ reviews.

    C. _____ responsibilities to staff.

    D. Maintains the office procedures _____.

    E. Oversees HIPAA _____.

    F. Plans and _____ staff meetings.

    G. Prepares _____ educational materials.

    H. Supervises employees on a _____ basis.

    I. Supervises the purchase and _____ of equipment and supplies.

11. Qualities of a Good Manager

       i. _____

       ii. _____

       iii. _____

       iv. _____

       v. _____

       vi. _____

       vii. _____

       viii. _____

       ix. _____

© 2011 Pearson Education, Inc.

  x. _____

  xi. _____

  xii. _____

  xiii. _____

12. Managing the Monthly Planning Calendar

 A. Develop a system in which the schedule for the _____ is laid out on a calendar.

 B. List _____ vacations on a calendar because it helps to prevent overlapping of vacations, which can leave an office _____.

 C. Note all physicians' _____, _____, _____, accountant meetings, and vendor visits.

 D. Ensure that all vacations have been _____.

 E. Compare the office's calendar with the _____ calendar on a periodic basis and update the office's _____ calendar as necessary.

13. Staff Meetings

 A. Facilitate communications between _____ and the _____.

 B. Time, date, and agenda are created by the _____ with input from the _____.

 C. Ensure that staff meetings are _____ to help minimize wasted time.

 D. The minutes and the _____ of attendees should be recorded.

14. Equipment Needed for a Staff Meeting

  i. _____

  ii. _____

  iii. _____

  iv. _____

15. Preparing for the Staff Meeting

 A. _____ week before the meeting, request agenda items from the _____.

 B. Before the meeting, create a meeting _____ which includes all topics that need to be discussed.

 C. On the agenda, include the following:

  i. _____

  ii. _____

  iii. _____

16. Ensuring the Success of Staff Meetings

 A. Start the meeting _____.

 B. Begin by _____ reviewing the last meeting.

 C. Address each topic within its _____ amount of _____.

 D. Allow for time at the end of the meeting to have _____ of any new business.

 E. After the meeting, the _____ of the meeting should be distributed to _____.

17. The Staff's Expectations of Management

  i. _____

  ii. _____

  iii. _____

  iv. _____

  v. _____

  vi. _____

  vii. _____

  viii. _____

  ix. _____

  x. _____

  xi. _____

  xii. _____

18. Ways to Show Respect
    A. Greet employees in a _____ manner.
    B. Always _____ employees' hard work.
    C. Never _____ employees in front of their peers.
    D. Be _____ and listen to employees when they need to talk.
    E. Take employees' suggestions into _____.
    F. Work toward having _____ employees.
    G. When possible, provide _____ space for each employee.
    H. Create a sense of _____ with the medical office.
    I. Ensure that employees feel that they have been _____ for the amount of work that they accomplish.
    J. Provide employees with _____ beyond pay.
    K. Maintain a cohesive work environment by ensuring that communication is _____ and _____.

II. Leadership and Team Accountability
    1. Attributes of Good Leaders
        i. _____
        ii. _____
        iii. _____
        iv. _____
        v. _____

    2. Attributes of Authoritarian Leaders
        A. Make most decisions on their own without the _____ of others.
        B. Are not as likely to be team _____ as are solid _____.
        C. Want _____ and _____ from their staff.
        D. Use _____ to achieve obedience from their staff.
        E. Are motivated by _____ and _____ authority.
        F. Work best under great _____ and in _____.

    3. Attributes of Democratic Leaders
        A. Concentrate more on the relationships among _____ and emphasize _____ in the office.
        B. Are motivated from _____ to provide a comfortable work environment for all employees.
        C. Leadership style often results in a _____ staff.

    4. Attributes of Permissive Leaders
        A. Are not strict with regard to _____ and _____.
        B. Leadership style may result in _____ and even _____ conditions in the work environment.
        C. Are self- _____.

    5. Attributes of Bureaucratic Leaders
        A. Very strongly _____ rules.
        B. Are motivated by _____ factors.
        C. Rely on _____ management methods for office matters.
        D. Are _____ because they do not trust themselves when making decisions that affect the office.
        E. Are very _____ and formal.

    6. Types of Power (*List and briefly describe each type.*)
        i. _____
        ii. _____

© 2011 Pearson Education, Inc.

iii. _____

iv. _____

v. _____

vi. _____

7. Task-Oriented Roles That Team Members May Assume

i. _____

ii. _____

iii. _____

iv. _____

v. _____

vi. _____

8. Nurturing Roles That Team Members May Assume

i. _____

ii. _____

iii. _____

iv. _____

9. Holding Team Members Accountable

A. The team must come together to locate and _____ the problem.

B. The team should not _____ or try to _____ a problem on any one member.

C. The team members must decide together how they got off track and how they can _____ a reoccurrence.

10. Methods for Providing the Job Application

A. Send to the applicant by _____ and have him or her bring the application to the interview.

B. Provide a _____ to the online version.

C. Have the applicant fill out the form at the time of the _____.

11. The Benefits of Having the Application Completed at the Interview

A. You will see how the applicant handles filling out forms under _____.

B. You will obtain a visual of the applicant's _____.

C. You will learn how _____ the applicant is at completing a required task.

12. Areas for Consideration During the Interview

i. _____

ii. _____

iii. _____

13. The Contents of Questions Prohibited by the Equal Employment Opportunity Act

i. _____

ii. _____

iii. _____

iv. _____

v. _____

14. Information to Be Obtained About an Applicant

A. Past office _____.

B. Types of _____ with whom the applicant has worked.

C. The applicant's ability to _____ on his or her feet.

15. Possible Office Requirements for an Applicant

i. _____

ii. _____

iii. _____

iv. _____

v. _____

16. The Purpose of the Probationary Period

A. Allows the supervisor to _____ the new employee at work and to _____ if he or she is suited to the position.

B. During the probationary period, an employee can be _____ without cause.

C. After _____ days, the employer must show just cause, or reason, to dismiss an employee.

17. The Contents of an Orientation Checklist

i. _____

ii. _____

iii. _____

iv. _____

v. _____

vi. _____

vii. _____

viii. _____

ix. _____

x. _____

xi. _____

xii. _____

xiii. _____

18. Types of Reviews (*Explain each type.*)

A. Orientation or training: _____

B. Routine performance review: _____

C. Poor performance review: _____

D. Salary review: _____

19. Actions that Require Disciplinary/Probationary Measures

i. _____

ii. _____

iii. _____

iv. _____

v. _____

20. Possible Disciplinary Actions

A. Giving a _____ and/or _____ warning.

B. _____ the employee while the incident is being investigated.

C. Placing the employee on _____ and telling the employee that if the situation occurs again within a set period of time, the employee will be _____.

21. Steps for Creating a Time Management System

A. Define the office _____ in consultation with the _____.

B. Create a _____ list of _____.

C. Incorporate the _____ list into a _____ list.

22. Information Found in an Employee Handbook

i. _____

ii. _____

iii. _____

iv. _____

v. _____

© 2011 Pearson Education, Inc.

23. The Office Procedures Manual
    A. Contains detailed descriptions of _____ and how to perform both _____ and _____ tasks.
    B. The terms "policy" and "procedure" are used _____ in many offices.

24. The Primary Functions of a Procedures Manual
    i. _____
    ii. _____
    iii. _____

25. The Benefits of an Effective Patient Information Booklet
    A. Reduces the number of _____ by telephone from _____.
    B. Enhances the office's _____.
    C. Reduces the number of patients who _____ to remember instructions.
    D. Useful either for _____ with _____ or for teaching methods of _____ prevention.

III. Marketing the Medical Practice

1. Steps to Take After Determining the Services to Be Offered
    A. Look for any _____ or _____ that may arise during the conduct of a marketing plan.
    B. A marketing plan should describe _____ steps that need to be implemented, who is _____ for these steps, and a reasonable _____ for completion.
    C. A marketing plan must be thought through and in place before you begin to _____ and _____ it.

2. Opportunities for Free Marketing
    i. _____
    ii. _____

3. Questions to Be Asked When Establishing a Practice Website
    i. _____
    ii. _____
    iii. _____
    iv. _____
    v. _____

4. Considerations for Operating a Website
    A. Ensure that patient _____ is maintained.
    B. Keep the site _____ to use.
    C. Graphics need to be _____ and colors need to be _____.

5. The Impact of Good Customer Service
    A. Word of mouth can bring you _____ customers.
    B. It can also drive customers _____ if poor services are provided
    C. All patients must be treated with _____ and _____.

KEY TERMINOLOGY REVIEW

Without using information from the textbook, write a sentence using the selected key terms in the correct context.

1. *Colleagues*

    _____

    _____

2. *Discriminatory*

_____

_____

3. *Grievance*

_____

_____

4. *Itinerary*

_____

_____

5. *Probationary period*

_____

_____

6. *Seniority*

_____

_____

7. *Solvent*

_____

_____

APPLIED PRACTICE

Complete the following activity.

1. Develop a patient information booklet as described in Procedure 20-2 in Chapter 20 of your textbook. Your booklet will be graded on accuracy, completeness, and appearance. In addition to other items that may be considered, the following items should be part of the booklet.
    a. Regular office hours
    b. Special services offered by the practice or clinic, such as patient education classes or blood pressure screening
    c. Written procedures for handling prescription refills
    d. Written procedures for how medical insurance forms are processed
    e. General statement about the payment of fees, especially if payment is expected at the time of the delivery of services
    f. Information about the physician and the staff
    g. Written procedures on how emergencies are handled

LEARNING ACTIVITY: TRUE/FALSE

Indicate whether the following statements are true or false by placing a T or an F on the line that precedes each statement.

_____ 1. Personnel management usually requires a performance review every 6 months for each employee.

_____ 2. The clinical aspects of office management are separate from the administrative aspects.

_____ 3. The office manager's time is generally spent on employee and administrative issues.

© 2011 Pearson Education, Inc.

_____ 4. A good office manager strives to become the boss.

_____ 5. Many office managers are promoted based on seniority.

_____ 6. The office manager creates and updates the physician's own calendar.

_____ 7. Staff vacations should be included on the physician's calendar.

_____ 8. If a staff meeting is held outside of normal working hours, staff must be compensated.

_____ 9. Bureaucratic leaders are very open with the staff.

_____ 10. Democratic leaders are typically more receptive to new ideas from staff.

CRITICAL THINKING

Answer the following questions to the best of your ability. Utilize the textbook as a reference.

1. Teresa Clymer, CMA (AAMA), has just been promoted to office manager. In order to create a team atmosphere, what factors should Teresa consider to ensure the building of a successful team?

_____

_____

_____

_____

2. Mavis Raschenko, RMA, must fill an open medical assistant position. What methods might Mavis choose and why?

_____

_____

_____

_____

3. When hiring individuals, what cultural considerations need to be considered?

_____

_____

_____

_____

RESEARCH ACTIVITY

Utilize Internet search engines to research the following topics and write a brief description of what you find. It is important to utilize reputable websites.

1. Using the Internet as a research source, determine the importance of conducting performance evaluations and explore the tools used to perform this task. Write an essay explaining what you have learned through your research. Cite your sources at the end of your essay.

_____

_____

© 2011 Pearson Education, Inc.

CHAPTER 21
Body Structure and Function

CHAPTER OUTLINE

General review of the chapter:

    The Human Body: Levels of Organization
    Chemistry
    Genetics and Heredity

STUDENT STUDY GUIDE

Use the following guide to assist in your learning of the concepts from the chapter.

I. Organization of the Human Body

   1. Organization of the Human Body (Diagram the organization of the body.)

   2. Atom

      A. _____ and _____ constitute the majority of the anatomic mass and reside within the nucleus.

      B. _____, _____, and _____ combine to create elements.

   3. Elements Found in the Human Body

      i. _____
      ii. _____
      iii. _____
      iv. _____
      v. _____
      vi. _____
      vii. _____
      viii. _____
      ix. _____
      x. _____
      xi. _____
      xii. _____
      xiii. _____
      xiv. _____
      xv. _____
      xvi. _____
      xvii. _____
      xviii. _____
      xix. _____

4. Molecules
   A. Can take the form of _____, _____, or _____.
   B. Water contains _____ of molecules.

5. Components of a Cell
   i. _____
   ii. _____
   iii. _____

6. Cell Membrane
   A. Helps maintain the _____ shape.
   B. Allows some substances to pass into and out of the cell while _____ the passage of other substances.

7. Cilia
   A. _____ the overall surface area of a cell.
   B. Propels substances along a cell's surface, which increases the cell's ability to absorb _____ and _____.

8. Cytoplasm
   A. _____ percent water; generally _____ in color, resembling a _____.
   B. Provides _____ and work areas for the cell.

9. Organelles
   A. Each organelle has a specific function and purpose in maintaining the vitality of the _____.
   B. Organelles include _____, _____, _____, _____, _____, and _____.

10. Nucleus
    A. The nucleus is the _____ of the cell.
    B. Within the nucleus are the cell's _____.

11. Nucleic Functions
    i. _____
    ii. _____
    iii. _____
    iv. _____
    v. _____

12. Organs
    A. Composed of several types of _____.
    B. Perform _____ functions.

13. Passive and Active Transport
    A. Passive transport involves a number of processes, including _____, _____, and _____.
    B. Through active transport, _____ are able to obtain what they need through _____ fluid.

14. Electrolytes
    A. An electrolyte is an electrically charged _____ that moves to either a _____ or a _____ electrode.
    B. Used to carry _____ impulses to other cells.
    C. Electrolytes must be _____ to keep their concentrations in the body fluids constant.

15. Electrolytes in the Human Body
    i. _____
    ii. _____

© 2011 Pearson Education, Inc.

iii. _____
iv. _____
v. _____
vi. _____
vii. _____
viii. _____

II. Genetics and Heredity

1. Natural Selection Versus Artificial Breeding

   A. Natural selection occurs when the _____ chooses the _____ that are best suited to the current _____ and allows animals with those _____ to reproductively mature and reproduce.

   B. Artificial breeding is human interaction within the process of _____ selection.

2. Heredity

   A. Heredity is the transmission of genes from _____ to _____.

   B. Individuals carry _____ genes for each _____.

3. Genetic Disorders

   A. Mutations are changes in the _____ sequence of a _____.

   B. Genetic mutations can occur at any time during _____.

4. Albinism

   A. Albinism is a common _____ disorder.

   B. It is a congenital but _____ disorder.

   C. A mutation in a recessive gene causes a hereditary lack of pigment in the _____, _____, and eyes.

   D. The patient may complain of _____ and is prone to _____ because protective melanin is not present.

5. ADHD

   A. ADHD stands for _____.

   B. It is characterized by a person having difficulty _____ and completing a task.

   C. May be caused by _____ factors. It is _____ times more prevalent in _____ than in _____.

6. Cleft Palate

   A. Cleft palate is a _____ defect in the roof of the mouth that occurs when the _____ bones of the skull do not close properly.

   B. The cleft causes a _____ between the mouth and the nasal cavities.

   C. This defect also may be accompanied by a cleft _____.

   D. Affects _____ more often than _____.

7. Color Deficiency

   A. This disorder was previously called _____.

   B. Often entails difficulty in distinguishing between _____ and _____.

   C. This condition is an _____, sex-linked disorder, usually passed from mother to _____.

   D. With total color deficiency, a person is unable to perceive any color at all because of a defect in or absence of _____ in the _____.

8. Cystic Fibrosis

   A. Cystic fibrosis is a chronic and _____ disease, usually diagnosed in _____.

   B. This disease causes mucus to become _____, _____, and sticky.

   C. Mucus builds up and clogs passages, primarily in the lungs and the _____.

© 2011 Pearson Education, Inc.

9. Down Syndrome

    A. Down syndrome occurs when a person has an _____ copy of _____ 21.

    B. A mother who gives birth after age _____ has a higher risk of delivering an infant with Down syndrome.

    C. _____ is generally used as a tool for diagnosing this disorder.

10. Fragile X Syndrome

    A. Fragile X syndrome also is known as _____ syndrome, _____ syndrome, and _____ syndrome.

    B. This condition is the most common form of inherited _____.

    C. Generally, _____ are affected with moderate mental retardation and _____ with mild mental retardation.

11. Hemochromatosis

    A. Hemochromatosis is an inherited disorder in which the body accumulates an excessive amount of _____.

    B. Common among the _____ population, affecting approximately _____ in _____ individuals of _____ ancestry.

    C. _____ deposits in the skin will eventually cause _____ of the skin.

12. Hemophilia

    A. Hemophilia is a _____, _____ disorder in which the time it takes for blood to coagulate is greatly increased.

    B. Caused by a _____ gene mutation in the _____ chromosome.

    C. Females carry the _____ gene and transmit the disorder to their _____ offspring.

13. Klinefelter's Syndrome

    A. Klinefelter's syndrome is a congenital _____ disorder.

    B. Primary _____ failure occurs, which usually is not evident until puberty.

    C. This disorder also can lead to _____ intelligence.

14. Muscular Dystrophy

    A. Muscular dystrophy is a genetic disease that is characterized by a gradual _____ and _____ of the muscles.

    B. Occurs most frequent in _____.

    C. The most common type is _____ muscular dystrophy, which accounts for _____ of all cases.

    D. Death often occurs within _____ to _____ years after the onset of symptoms.

15. PKU

    A. PKU stands for _____.

    B. Caused by a recessive gene _____.

    C. If the condition is not treated early, _____ occurs because of brain damage.

16. Spina Bifida

    A. Spina bifida is a congenital _____ tube defect.

    B. The posterior vertebral arch has a _____ anomaly.

    C. Most often the abnormality occurs in the _____ region.

17. Tay-Sachs Disease

    A. Tay-Sachs disease is an inherited disorder that tends to affect people of _____ and _____ European Jewish or French-Canadian ancestry.

    B. Caused by a faulty gene that targets the _____.

© 2011 Pearson Education, Inc.

  C. Symptoms first appear at around _____ months of age in an otherwise healthy baby.

18. Turner's Syndrome

  A. Turner's syndrome is a congenital disorder caused by the failure of the _____ to respond to the stimulation of _____ hormones.

  B. _____ may be impaired.

  C. The patient is usually _____ in stature.

KEY TERMINOLOGY REVIEW

Match the selected key terms to their definitions below.

a. Active transport
b. Anatomy
c. Atom
d. Cell
e. Cell membrane
f. Chromosomes
g. Cilia
h. Congenital disorder
i. Cytokinesis
j. Cytoplasm
k. Deoxyribonuleic acid (DNA)
l. Diffusion
m. Electrolyte
n. Filtration
o. Flagella
p. Gametes
q. Genetics
r. Heredity
s. Homeostasis
t. Meiosis
u. Mitosis
v. Molecule
w. Negative feedback
x. Neurons
y. Nucleus
z. Organelles
aa. Organs
bb. Osmosis
cc. Passive transport
dd. Pathophysiology
ee. Physiology
ff. Positive feedback
gg. Ribonucleic acid (RNA)
hh. Striated muscle tissue
ii. Systems
jj. Tissue

1. _____ Hairlike projections that cover the surface of some cells.

2. _____ Requires mechanical pressure to diffuse dissolved particles through membranes.

3. _____ Requires cellular energy to carry materials from an area of lesser concentration to an area of greater concentration.

4. _____ The body and its systems work together to maintain a constant balance.

5. _____ A jellylike substance found between the cell membrane and the nuclear membrane.

6. _____ The body's reaction to either internal or external stimuli.

7. _____ A form of diffusion whereby water is pulled through a semipermeable membrane.

8. _____ The outer covering of the cell.

© 2011 Pearson Education, Inc.

9. _____ Tail-like structures that enable a sperm cell to move through the reproductive tract.

10. _____ The study of diseases and disorders within the body.

11. _____ This process forms gametes, such as ova and sperm.

12. _____ Involves moving dissolved particles from an area of greater concentration to an area of lesser concentration until they are evenly distributed.

13. _____ Encourages the stimuli to continue, or even accelerate, which also results in homeostasis.

14. _____ Formed during the process of meiosis in which cells reduce their chromosomal number from 46 to 23.

15. _____ A chemical combination of two or more atoms that forms a specific chemical compound.

16. _____ Does not require the cell to use energy; however, it does involve a number of processes, including diffusion, osmosis, and filtration.

17. _____ During this process, the cytoplasm divides into two identical daughter cells.

18. _____ The study of the structure of an organism.

19. _____ Nerve cells.

20. _____ Voluntary muscle tissue.

21. _____ Microscopic bodies that carry the genes that determine hereditary characteristics.

22. _____ The genetic transmission from parent to child.

23. _____ Formed by similarly functioning tissues.

24. _____ Formed by a group of cells that have similar functions.

25. _____ The most basic unit of life; often considered building blocks of the human body.

26. _____ Responsible for the cell's metabolism, growth, and reproduction.

27. _____ A single chain of chemical bases.

28. _____ The study of the makeup of animals or plants.

29. _____ Formed by organs that make up the human body.

30. _____ Provides the cell's blueprint or genetic makeup.

31. _____ Structures found within cytoplasm.

32. _____ During this process, the nucleus of the cell divides.

33. _____ The study of the function of an organism.

34. _____ A genetic disorder that is present at birth.

35. _____ A molecule that conducts electricity.

36. _____ Consists of at least one proton.

© 2011 Pearson Education, Inc.

APPLIED PRACTICE

1. Label the various cells found in this image.

2. Label the types of tissue found in this image.

EPITHELIAL TISSUE

CONNECTIVE TISSUE

NERVE TISSUE

MUSCLE TISSUE

© 2011 Pearson Education, Inc.

LEARNING ACTIVITY: TRUE/FALSE

Indicate whether the following statements are true or false by placing a T or an F on the line that precedes each statement.

_____ 1. Atoms are found at the most basic level of organization.

_____ 2. Molecules cannot move and thus take the form of solids, liquids, or gases.

_____ 3. DNA is shaped in a single helix.

_____ 4. The golgi apparatus is the location for the production of protein that is essential to the vitality of the cell.

_____ 5. Epithelial tissue is found on the outer layer of skin.

_____ 6. Involuntary or smooth muscle tissues are controlled by the autonomic nervous system.

_____ 7. In the phagocytosis method, the cell "drinks" the fluid required.

_____ 8. The muscular system transmits impulses, responds to change, is responsible for communication, and exercises control over all parts of the body.

_____ 9. Cells utilize electrolytes to maintain voltage or electrical force across their cell membranes.

_____ 10. Genetic disorders are considered medical conditions.

CRITICAL THINKING

Answer the following questions to the best of your ability. Utilize the textbook as a reference.

1. Why is it important for a medical assistant to understand the structures and functions of the human body?

_____

_____

_____

_____

_____

2. When documenting a patient's treatment, why should documentation always take place after the procedure has been performed?

_____

_____

_____

_____

_____

RESEARCH ACTIVITY

Utilize Internet search engines to research the following topics and write a brief description of you find. It is important to utilize reputable websites.

1. Using the Internet as a research source, conduct further research on genetic engineering. Discover more about this fascinating topic and write a brief essay to explain what you learned through your research. Be sure to cite your sources.

© 2011 Pearson Education, Inc.

CHAPTER 22
The Integumentary System

CHAPTER OUTLINE

General review of the chapter:

Functions of the Integumentary System
Structure of the Skin
Accessory Structures of the Skin
Common Disorders of the Integumentary System
Skin Care Treatments

STUDENT STUDY GUIDE

Use the following guide to assist in your learning of the concepts from the chapter.

I. The Integumentary System

  1. The Skin and the Accessory Organs, Known as the Integumentary System

    A. Weighs more than _____ (in adults).
    B. Covers _____ of the body.
    C. Its purpose is as follows:
      i. _____
      ii. _____
      iii. _____
      iv. _____
      v. _____

  2. The Functions of the Integumentary System

      i. _____
      ii. _____
      iii. _____
      iv. _____
      v. _____

  3. Temperature Regulation

    A. Aids in the _____ of body temperature.
    B. To _____ heat, superficial blood vessels in skin _____, bringing more blood to the surface of the skin.
    C. To _____ heat, superficial blood vessels _____, keeping warm blood away from the surface.
    D. A continuous layer of _____ fat acts as insulation.

  4. Sensory Receptors

    A. Detect temperature, pain, _____, and _____.
    B. They are located in the _____.
    C. Nerve endings in the _____ layer of skin convey _____ to the brain and spinal cord.

© 2011 Pearson Education, Inc.

5. The Three Layers of Skin

   A. The epidermis is the _____, _____ membrane layer.
   B. The dermis ("true skin") is the _____, _____ connective tissue layer.
   C. The subcutaneous tissue is the _____ layer.

6. The Layers of the Epidermis: Stratum corneum

   A. The stratum corneum is the _____ layer of skin that consists of dead cells filled with a protein called _____.
   B. Forms a protective _____ for the body.
   C. The _____ of the layer depends on the part of the body.

7. The Layers of the Epidermis: Stratum lucidum

   A. The stratum lucidum is the _____ layer lying directly beneath the _____ _____.
   B. In thinner skin, it is often _____.
   C. Cells in this layer are either _____ or _____.

8. The Layers of the Epidermis: Stratum granulosum

   A. The stratum granulosum consists of several layers of _____ cells that become part of the _____ lucidum and stratum _____.
   B. Cells actively become _____, or hardened, after they lose their _____.

9. The Layers of the Epidermis: Stratum germinativum

   A. Made of several layers of living cells that are still capable of _____, or cell division.
   B. Most responsible for the _____ of the epidermis.

10. The Dermis

    A. The _____ layer of the skin.
    B. Composed of _____ tissue containing nerves and nerve endings, blood vessels, sebaceous and _____ glands, hair follicles, and _____ vessels.
    C. Further divided into two layers: the _____ layer and the _____ layer.

11. The Subcutaneous Layer

    A. Composed of _____ tissue.
    B. Tissue helps support, nourish, insulate, and _____ the skin.

12. Accessory Organs: Hair

    A. Hair fibers are composed of the _____ keratin.
    B. _____ gives hair its color.
    C. Sebaceous glands release _____ into hair follicles.

13. Accessory Organs: Nails

    A. The nails are flat _____ of keratin.
    B. Connected to tissue by the _____ _____.
    C. Grow longer from the _____.
    D. Covered and protected by _____.
    E. The light-colored, half-moon area at the base is the _____.

14. Accessory Organs: Fluid-Producing Glands

    A. Sweat glands assist the body in maintaining its _____ temperature.
    B. Sweat glands create a _____ effect when _____ evaporates.
    C. Sebaceous glands are _____ glands.

© 2011 Pearson Education, Inc.

15. Summary of the Integument: Label the structure of the integument.

II. Pathology of the Integumentary System

1. Facts About Skin Cancer

   A. Skin cancer is the most _____ of all cancers.
   B. Affects more than _____ people each year in the United States.

2. How Skin Cancer Occurs

   A. Occur when normal skin cells undergo a change during which they _____ and _____ without the normal controls.
   B. As the cells multiply, they form a mass called a _____.
   C. Tumors of the skin are often referred to as _____.
   D. Malignant tumors encroach on neighboring tissues, especially _____, because of their uncontrolled growth.

3. Basal Cell Carcinoma

   A. Basal cell carcinoma is the most _____ form of skin cancer.
   B. Most often caused by _____ to the sun.
   C. May often appear as a change in the skin, such as a _____, an irritation or _____ that does not heal, or a change in a _____ or mole.
   D. Although the _____ is the most common site, it may affect the head, neck, back, chest, or shoulders.
   E. Exposure to _____ is the most common cause of this type of cancer.

4. Signs and Symptoms of Basal Cell Carcinoma

   A. Firm, _____ _____, including tiny blood vessels with a spiderlike appearance (telangiectasias).
   B. Red, tender, _____ _____ that bleeds easily.
   C. Small, fleshy bump with a smooth, pearly appearance, often with a _____ center.
   D. Smooth, shiny bump that may look like a _____ or _____.
   E. _____ patch of skin, especially on the face, that is firm to the touch.

© 2011 Pearson Education, Inc.

F. Bump that itches, bleeds, _____ _____, and then repeats the cycle, and has not healed in _____ _____.

G. Change in the _____, _____, or _____ of a wart or mole.

5. Treatment Options for Basal Cell Carcinoma

A. Most common treatment is _____ to destroy or remove the entire skin growth.

B. Microscopically controlled surgery to remove skin cancer is very effective, with cure rates of higher than _____.

6. Squamous Cell Carcinoma: Indicators

A. Changes in an existing wart, mole, or other _____ _____.

B. Development of a _____ _____ that ulcerates and does not heal well.

7. Risks Factors for Squamous Cell Carcinoma

A. _____ predisposition.

B. _____ pollution.

C. _____ to X-rays or other forms of radiation.

D. Exposure to _____.

8. Signs and Symptoms of Squamous Cell Carcinoma

A. A _____ _____, growth, or bump that is small, firm, reddened, nodular, coned, or flat.

B. A _____ or _____ lesion or growth that is located on the face, ears, neck, hands, or arms.

C. Occasionally, the growth may occur on the _____, _____, _____, or _____.

9. Treatment Options for Squamous Cell Carcinoma

A. Surgical removal of the tumor, which may include _____ of the _____ around the tumor.

B. _____ _____ (Mohs' micrographic surgery) may remove small tumors.

C. _____ _____ may be needed if broad areas of skin are removed.

D. _____ treatment.

10. Malignant Melanoma

A. Originates in the _____ of the skin.

B. Develops when the cells do not respond to the normal control mechanisms of _____ growth.

C. The primary tumor begins in the _____.

11. Signs and Symptoms of Malignant Melanoma (List the signs and symptoms.)

i. _____

ii. _____

iii. _____

iv. _____

v. _____

vi. _____

vii. _____

12. Acne Vulgaris

A. Occurs when oil and _____ _____ cells clog the skin's pores.

B. Most often affects _____, with more than 85% of them developing at least a mild form of this condition.

C. While mild acne is merely annoying, severe acne can lead to _____ and _____ scars.

D. Most people outgrow acne by the time they are in their _____ and _____.

© 2011 Pearson Education, Inc.

13. Signs and Symptoms of Acne Vulgaris

   A. Skin blemishes are often _____ and _____.
   B. With a mild case of acne, only _____ and _____ may be present.
   C. Severe acne can mean hundreds of _____ or _____ that can cover the face, neck, chest, and back.
   D. _____ _____ are pimples that are large and deep. These lesions are often painful and can leave scars on the skin.

14. Treatment Options for Acne Vulgaris

   A. The _____ of the acne will determine the most useful and beneficial treatment.
   B. Sometimes treatments will be combined to get the best results and to avoid the development of _____ bacteria.

15. Alopecia

   A. The condition of _____ or _____ of hair.
   B. The most common form is _____ _____, also known as androgenic alopecia.

16. Alopecia Areata

   A. Affects about _____ in _____ people, mostly teenagers and young adults.
   B. Causes patches of baldness that are about the size of a _____ _____, usually appearing on the _____ but can occur anywhere on the body, including the beard, eyebrows, and eyelashes.

17. Male-Pattern Baldness

   A. Tends to follow a _____.
   B. The first stage is usually the _____ of the _____.
   C. The second stage is thinning of the hair on the _____ and _____.
   D. When these two areas meet in the middle, the hair around the back and sides of the head resembles a _____.
   E. Eventually the person may become _____ _____.

18. Treatments for Addressing Baldness

   A. There are drugs that treat both _____ and _____ baldness.
   B. _____ can be rubbed on the scalp.
   C. Shampoos and formulas are available for _____ _____ to the scalp.

19. Contact Dermatitis

   A. An _____ _____ of the skin caused by irritating substances.
   B. Causes include exposure to _____ _____, _____ _____, _____ (especially on jewelry or jeans snaps), lotions, detergents, or other chemicals.

20. Signs and Symptoms of Contact Dermatitis

   A. _____ and _____ skin.
   B. Vesicles (_____) and a rash may appear.
   C. _____ and _____ may be present.
   D. Serious allergic reactions may result in _____.

21. Treatment Options for Contact Dermatitis

   A. _____ (anti-allergy medicines)
   B. _____ _____ creams to reduce inflammation
   C. _____ _____ (oral medications)

22. Calluses and Corns

   A. Excessive growth of the _____ _____ layer of the epidermis that often occurs on the hands and feet.
   B. Can be caused by _____ _____ _____ or by other factors such as ill-fitting shoes and unprotected hands during manual labor.

© 2011 Pearson Education, Inc.

23. Signs and Symptoms of a Callus

   A. An area of _____ _____ that does not have an identifiable border.
   B. May appear _____, _____, or even _____ while being painless, or may feel tender, throb, or burn.

24. Signs and Symptoms of a Corn

   A. A corn has a _____ _____ with various textures; appears most often on the feet.
   B. May be hard or soft; they are _____ _____.

25. Decubitus Ulcer

   A. Also called a _____ _____ or a _____.
   B. Refers to an area of skin and tissue that _____ _____.
   C. Typically occurs when _____ _____ is maintained on a specific area of the skin.
   D. The constant pressure on the area _____ the blood supply, causing the _____ of the affected tissue.
   E. Common locations include the _____, _____, _____, _____, _____, and the back of the head.

26. The Four Stages of the Decubitus Ulcer

   A. Stage I: _____ area on the skin that does not blanch (turn white) when pressed.
   B. Stage II: The skin has a _____ or an _____ _____. The area around the site may be red and irritated.
   C. Stage III: The skin looks like a _____ with damage to the tissue below the skin.
   D. Stage IV: The wound becomes so deep that there is damage to the tissue beneath the _____ _____, including damage to _____ and muscle.

27. Eczema

   A. Called _____ _____.
   B. Chronic skin condition caused by an _____ _____ on the skin.
   C. _____ tends to play a role.
   D. Most common in infants; about half of the cases disappear by _____.
   E. Signs and symptoms include _____, _____, and _____.
   F. Lesions may appear dry or scaly, as well as have a _____ appearance.

28. Treatment Options for Eczema

   A. Weeping lesions are treated with _____ _____ and dressings.
   B. Severe cases and dry, scaly lesions may be treated with mild, _____ _____ or low-potency topical _____.
   C. Very severe cases may require _____ _____ and _____ _____ (TIMs).
   D. Sometimes, short exposures in a _____ _____ are useful to dry up the lesions.

29. Folliculitis

   A. An infection or inflammation of the _____ _____.
   B. Can occur anywhere that there is _____ _____.
   C. Most often appears in areas that become irritated by shaving, the rubbing of clothes, or where follicles and pores are blocked by _____ and _____.
   D. Common sites include the _____, the _____, _____, and on the legs.

30. Signs and Symptoms of Folliculitis

   A. A _____ _____
   B. Raised, red, often _____ lesions around hair follicles
   C. _____ that occur in areas with a high concentration of hair follicles, such as the face, under the arms, on the scalp, and in the groin area, and eventually crust over
   D. _____ at the site of the rash and pimples

© 2011 Pearson Education, Inc.

31. Treatment Options for Folliculitis

   A. Generally involves taking steps to _____ _____ to the hair follicles by avoiding clothes that rub against the skin.
   B. Shaving with an _____ _____ instead of a razor blade.
   C. Keeping the skin clean using soap and water and _____ _____.
   D. Application of _____ _____.

32. Treatment Options for Shingles

   A. Early treatment can help shorten a shingles _____ and reduce the risk of complications.
   B. Oral antiviral medications are generally prescribed within _____ to _____ hours after the first sign of the rash.
   C. _____ are sometimes prescribed in order to reduce swelling and pain.
   D. When pain is severe, _____ _____ or a skin patch that contains a pain-relieving medication may be required.

33. Keloids

   A. Often referred to as _____ _____.
   B. Typically appear following _____ or an _____.
   C. _____ and _____ have been known to cause keloids.

34. Pediculosis

   A. An _____ by eggs, larvae, or adult lice.
   B. Forms of pediculosis include *Pediculus humanus capitis* (_____ _____), *Pediculus humanus corporis* (_____ _____), and *Pthirus pubis* (_____ _____).

35. Signs and Symptoms of Pediculosis

   A. The most common symptom among all types of lice is _____.
   B. Head lice tend to cause itching on the back of the _____ or around the _____.
   C. Itching around the _____ is an indication of pubic lice.
   D. Body lice tend to travel to the body to feed on _____ and then return to _____.

36. Psoriasis

   A. Affects an estimated _____ Americans.
   B. Most commonly affects persons between ages _____ and _____.
   C. The condition has _____ and _____ characteristics.
   D. Thought to be caused by a buildup of _____.

37. Signs and Symptoms of Psoriasis

   A. Episodes of redness, itching, and _____, _____ _____ on the skin.
   B. _____ can be gradual or abrupt.
   C. _____ have been attributed to infection, obesity, and lack of sunlight, as well as sunburn, stress, poor health, and cold climate.
   D. When the case is severe and widespread, large quantities of _____ can be lost, causing _____ and severe secondary infections that can be serious.

38. Treatment Options for Psoriasis

   A. Analgesics, sedation, _____ _____, retinoids, and antibiotics.
   B. Mild cases are treated at home with topical medications such as prescription or nonprescription _____ _____, _____, or other corticosteroids, and antifungal medications.
   C. Severe lesions may require _____ for proper treatment.

39. Rosacea

   A. A disorder primarily of the _____ _____.
   B. Often characterized by _____ and _____.
   C. Affects an estimated _____ Americans.

© 2011 Pearson Education, Inc.

40. Signs and Symptoms of Rosacea

    A. _____ on the cheeks, nose, chin, or forehead.
    B. Small visible _____ _____ on the face, _____ on the face, and watery or irritated eyes.
    C. Over time, the _____ becomes ruddier and more persistent.

41. Scabies

    A. A _____ _____ disorder of the skin.
    B. Caused by the scabies mite or human _____ _____.
    C. Spread by _____ _____, such as shaking hands; sleeping together; or close contact with infected articles such as clothing, bedding, or towels.
    D. Common among schoolchildren, roommates, and sexual partners, scabies is usually found where people are _____ _____.
    E. The sides of the _____, the backs of the _____, wrists, heels, elbows, armpits, inner thighs, and the waistline are common locations for scabies.

42. Signs and Symptoms of Scabies

    A. A very small _____ blister
    B. Intense _____ and a red _____ that occurs around the area

43. Treatment Options for Scabies

    A. Application of a lotion or cream with a 6%–10% concentration of _____.
    B. _____ and _____ are often used to relieve itching.

44. Seborrheic Dermatitis

    A. An _____ condition of the sebaceous or oil glands caused by an increase in sebum.
    B. Most common in infants and children; frequently known as _____.

45. Signs and Symptoms of Seborrheic Dermatitis

    A. Yellow or white scales that attach to the _____ _____.
    B. Thick or patchy crusts on the _____.
    C. Itching or soreness, as well as _____.

46. Treatment Options for Seborrheic Dermatitis

    A. Application of low-strength _____.
    B. Shampooing the scalp daily with _____ _____.

47. *Tinea corporis*

    A. Sometimes called _____.
    B. Not actually a worm, but instead an integumentary disorder caused by a _____.
    C. Can appear _____ on the body.
    D. If the fungus is on the head, it is called _____ _____.
    E. On the feet, it is known as _____ _____, or athlete's foot.
    F. When found in the genital area, it is referred to as _____ _____.
    G. *Tinea cruris* is more commonly known as _____ _____.
    H. Elsewhere on the body, the fungus is called _____ _____.

48. Urticaria

    A. Better known as _____.
    B. Causes severe _____ because of an acute hypersensitivity to medications or environmental stimuli.
    C. A major concern is that it can obstruct the _____ _____.
    D. Because of the possibility of _____ _____, it is important to observe all patients after an injection or allergy test.

49. Signs and Symptoms of Urticaria

    A. _____ areas of pink, itchy, swollen patches of skin.
    B. _____ or _____ sensations are common.

© 2011 Pearson Education, Inc.

C. Hives may vary in size from the diameter of a _____ _____ to the diameter of a cereal bowl.

D. Many times, the hives may _____, forming an even larger area of irritation and swelling.

50. Treatment Options for Urticaria

   A. Removal of _____ _____.
   B. Treatment with _____ and _____.

51. Vitiligo

   A. Also known as _____.
   B. A disorder that causes white patches and large areas of decreased _____ to form on the skin.
   C. Patches form because of the destruction of _____, which are the cells that produce _____.
   D. Often linked to immune system disorders such as _____ _____ or pernicious anemia.
   E. Affects persons with _____ disorders.

52. Treatment Options for Vitiligo

   A. Often aimed at _____ skin tone and color.
   B. Accomplished through _____, _____, or _____ means.
   C. Avoiding tanning and using sunscreen help make the _____ less noticeable.
   D. _____ and _____ lotions may also be used to even out the skin tone.
   E. Medical treatments may include the use of _____, as well as topical ultraviolet therapy.
   F. _____ _____, as well as a form of tattooing called _____, may also be successful.

53. Warts (Verruca)

   A. An infection caused by viruses in the _____ _____ (HPV) family.
   B. There are at least _____ types of HPV viruses that cause warts.
   C. Warts can grow on all parts of the body, including the _____, the inside of the mouth, the genitals, and the _____ _____.
   D. A common wart is the _____ wart, which occurs on the soles of the feet.

54. Signs and Symptoms of Warts

   A. The _____ and _____ of a wart will vary with its location.
   B. Warts may appear _____ or _____, and may vary in color from flesh-toned to red, pink, or white.
   C. Warts may also appear as raised or _____ _____ _____.

55. Treatment Options for Warts

   A. Over-the-counter topical medications that contain _____ _____
   B. _____, which freezes the wart
   C. Various _____ _____
   D. In severe cases, _____ _____ may be an option.

III. Skin Care Treatments

   1. Botox

   A. Popular procedure that is indicated for reducing _____ _____.
   B. A very small, diluted amount of the toxin _____ _____ is injected into the wrinkle lines.
   C. The procedure is usually repeated every _____ to _____ months.
   D. Temporary side effects include headaches, bruising, and _____ _____.

2. Light Chemical Peel

   A. The purpose of this treatment is to reduce the size of _____, make the skin appear _____, and produce more _____ in the skin.
   B. During a light chemical peel, only the _____ layer of the skin is stripped.
   C. The procedure is completed in about an hour and it leaves the skin _____, which disappears over time.

3. Medium Chemical Peel

   A. The purpose of this treatment is to _____ _____, resulting in a much smoother skin than that achieved with the light chemical peel.
   B. This treatment will strip the _____ _____ and some underlying cells, causing collagen and elastin to be stimulated.
   C. Recovery from a medium chemical peel can take up to _____ days because of the peeling, swelling, and redness that occur after treatment.

4. Deep Chemical Peel

   A. An aggressive treatment that can affect the layers of skin down to the _____ layer.
   B. Results are aimed at reducing all _____ in the face, with the exception of certain areas.
   C. This level of treatment can improve conditions such as _____ _____ and remove precancerous lesions.
   D. The healing process includes _____ _____, often felt up to 12 hours after surgery.
   E. _____ medications are required.
   F. It may take _____ for additional peeling, swelling, and redness to subside.

5. Laser Resurfacing

   A. Short, pulsated _____ _____ are used to vaporize damaged or troublesome areas of the skin.
   B. Full-face laser resurfacing takes approximately _____ hours.
   C. Partial-face resurfacing takes _____ minutes.
   D. Resurfacing results in the stimulation and production of new _____ and skin cells.
   E. Immediately following the procedure, _____ _____ and sterile _____ are applied to reduce the incidence of infection.

6. Microdermabrasion

   A. Involves removing the top layer of _____ _____ _____.
   B. _____ _____ are used with abrasion and suction devices to produce healthier-looking skin.
   C. This non-_____ and non-_____ approach is appealing to many patients who do not wish to pursue more aggressive skin-freshening treatments.

KEY TERMINOLOGY REVIEW

Match the vocabulary term to the correct definition below.

a. Acne vulgaris
b. Albinism
c. Alopecia
d. Bacteremia
e. Basal cell carcinoma
f. Callus
g. Carbuncle
h. Cellulitis

i. Contact dermatitis
j. Corn
k. Decubitus ulcer
l. Dermis
m. Dysplastic nevus
n. Eczema
o. Epidermis
p. Erythema

© 2011 Pearson Education, Inc.

q. Folliculitis
r. Furuncle
s. Herpes simplex
t. Herpes zoster
u. Hirsutism
v. Impetigo
w. Keloid
x. Lunula
y. Malignant melanoma
z. Matrix
aa. Melanin
bb. Melanocytes
cc. Pediculosis
dd. Psoriasis
ee. Rosacea
ff. Scabies
gg. Sebaceous glands
hh. Seborrheic dermatitis
ii. Squamous cell carcinoma
jj. Sudoriferous glands
kk. Sweat glands
ll. *Tinea capitis*
mm. *Tinea corporis*
nn. *Tinea cruris*
oo. *Tinea pedis*
pp. Urticaria
qq. Vesicles
rr. Vitiligo
ss. Warts

1. _____ An erosion or ulcer that is eating or gnawing away tissue.
2. _____ An infection or inflammation of the hair follicles.
3. _____ A condition that causes a burning or tingling sensation followed by the development of genital lesions.
4. _____ An abnormal mole.
5. _____ A common skin condition that occurs when oil and dead skin cells clog the skin's pores.
6. _____ Produces sebum, which acts to protect the body from dehydration and the possible absorption of harmful substances.
7. _____ A highly aggressive cancer that tends to spread to other parts of the body.
8. _____ An inherited disorder that causes the absence of melanin in the skin, hair, and eyes.
9. _____ A highly contagious disorder of the skin caused by the scabies mite or human itch mite.
10. _____ Sometimes called ringworm.
11. _____ The most common form of skin cancer; most often caused by overexposure to the sun.
12. _____ Coiled, ball-shaped structures that are located in the dermis or subcutaneous layers.
13. _____ A protective pigmentation that guards the body against the sun's ultraviolet rays.
14. _____ Also known as the nail bed.
15. _____ The middle layer of the skin; often referred to as the "true skin."
16. _____ Excessive growth of the stratum corneum layer of the epidermis.
17. _____ Bacteria arriving from a distant source via the bloodstream.
18. _____ Cells that produce melanin, the pigment that gives the skin its color.
19. _____ The crescent-shaped white area at the base of the nail.
20. _____ A boil that is actually an abscess of a hair follicle and the adjacent subcutaneous tissues.
21. _____ More commonly referred to as jock itch.
22. _____ An inflammatory condition of sebaceous or oil glands caused by an increase in sebum.
23. _____ An allergic reaction of the skin caused by irritating substances.

© 2011 Pearson Education, Inc.

24. _____ A chronic skin condition caused by an allergic reaction on the skin.

25. _____ Also known as athlete's foot.

26. _____ A skin infection caused by bacteria.

27. _____ Small blisters associated with contact dermatitis.

28. _____ The redness associated with cellulitis.

29. _____ A fungus found on the head.

30. _____ Also known as shingles.

31. _____ A collection of furuncles.

32. _____ Divided into four layers or strata.

33. _____ Also known as hives.

34. _____ Thought to be caused by a buildup of dead skin cells.

35. _____ An area of thickened skin that does not have an identifiable border.

36. _____ A malignant tumor that affects the middle layer of the skin.

37. _____ Also known as leukoderma.

38. _____ A type of infection caused by viruses in the human papillomavirus (HPV) family.

39. _____ Often referred to as a hypertrophic scar.

40. _____ A disorder primarily of the facial skin, often characterized by flare-ups and remissions.

41. _____ Baldness or loss of hair.

42. _____ Also known as sweat glands.

43. _____ An infestation of lice in the form of eggs, larvae, or adult lice.

44. _____ A condition of thick abnormal hair growth that affects men and women, although women are more commonly affected by and diagnosed with the disorder.

45. _____ An acute spreading bacterial infection below the surface of the skin.

APPLIED PRACTICE

1. Using information found in the textbook, fill out the table below regarding infectious skin disorders.

Disorder	Symptoms	Diagnosis	Treatment
Furuncles/Carbuncles			

© 2011 Pearson Education, Inc.

Herpes Simplex			
Herpes Zoster (Shingles)			

(*continue*)

© 2011 Pearson Education, Inc.

Disorder	Symptoms	Diagnosis	Treatment
Impetigo			

2. Label the structure of the nail bed.

LEARNING ACTIVITY: FILL IN THE BLANK

Using words from the list below, fill in the blanks to complete the following statements

ABCD rule
appearance
blood and lymphatic
common
connective tissue
curable
cushions
dehydration
dermis
diagnosed early

fat cells
generalized illness
hair growth
heat and cold
inflammation and infection
insulation
irritations or lesions
microorganisms
nails
nerve

polycystic
Staphylococcus
subcutaneous
subcutaneous tissue
support
sweat and sebaceous
toxins
temperature
tumors
vitamin D

© 2011 Pearson Education, Inc.

1. Skin cancers are initially diagnosed according to their _____. Malignant melanoma is identified by the _____.

2. The integumentary system includes the _____, hair, and _____ glands.

3. Skin cancers are the most _____ type of cancer, as well as the most _____ when _____.

4. The skin serves as a barrier to prevent _____ and other foreign bodies from entering; regulates _____; protects against _____; acts as an environmental sensor for pain, temperature, and touch; synthesizes _____ from sunlight; and excretes _____ in perspiration.

5. The dermis contains _____ vessels, _____ cell endings, and skin _____ organs.

6. Hirsutism is a condition of excessive _____, which may be caused by _____ ovaries or _____ of the adrenal glands and ovaries.

7. A break in the defense system of the skin may result in _____, as well as localized _____.

8. Cellulitis is a disease of the skin and subcutaneous tissue that presents as _____. It is commonly caused by _____.

9. Sweat glands are located in the _____ and the _____.

10. The innermost layer of skin, the _____ tissue, is made up of _____ and _____. This layer acts as _____ for the body, provides protection against extreme _____ and against heat loss, and _____ and protects underlying structures.

CRITICAL THINKING

Answer the following questions to the best of your ability. Utilize the textbook as a reference.

1. As you are assisting a geriatric patient get into a gown for an examination, you notice that she has a dime-sized mole with an irregular border on her back. You realize that the patient likely cannot see it and may be unaware of it. Would you mention it to the patient or only to the physician? State the reason for your answer.

   _____

   _____

   _____

   _____

2. Utilize Internet search engines to locate a reputable site that provides pictures of various skin conditions, including lice. Draw a picture of head lice and state how this condition is treated.

   _____

   _____

   _____

   _____

3. What possible advice could you give to a patient who has had a skin cancer removed today and works daily as a lifeguard in the sun?

   _____

   _____

4. A female patient comes in for an examination for excessive dark hair that she has developed in the last 6 months or so. She asks you what it is and what can be done for it, but she has not seen the physician yet. What would you say to this patient at this time? Hint: The answer is not specifically in the book and will require your current knowledge and critical thinking skills regarding the medical assistant's scope of practice.

_____

_____

_____

_____

5. Although not specifically stated in the text, what precautions would you recommend to a patient who has an infectious skin disorder to prevent it from spreading?

_____

_____

_____

_____

RESEARCH ACTIVITY

Utilize Internet search engines to research the following topics and write a brief description of what you find. It is important to utilize reputable websites.

1. Visit the Skin Cancer Foundation at www.skincancer.org. After reviewing the website, answer the following questions:

   a. What "Prevention" information do you find most interesting. Why?
   b. After reading "Skin Cancer Facts," which facts do you find most surprising?
   c. What can you do to further reduce your risk of developing skin cancer?

   _____

   _____

   _____

   _____

   _____

   _____

   _____

   _____

© 2011 Pearson Education, Inc.

CHAPTER 23
The Skeletal System

CHAPTER OUTLINE

General review of the chapter:

Bones and Their Classification
Joints and Movement
The Axial Skeleton
The Appendicular Skeleton
Common Disorders Associated with the Skeletal System

STUDENT STUDY GUIDE

Use the following guide to assist in your learning of the concepts from the chapter.

I. The Skeletal System

1. Bone Classification

   i. _____
   ii. _____
   iii. _____
   iv. _____
   v. _____
   vi. _____
   vii. _____

2. The Six Main Functions of Bones

   A. Provide _____, _____, and the framework of the body.
   B. Provide _____ for the body's internal organs.
   C. Serve as a storage place for _____, _____, and _____.
   D. Play an important role in the formation of blood cells as _____ takes place in the _____.
   E. Provide an area for the attachment of _____ muscle.
   F. Help to make movement possible through _____.

3. Bone Markings

   i. _____
   ii. _____
   iii. _____
   iv. _____
   v. _____
   vi. _____
   vii. _____

© 2011 Pearson Education, Inc.

4. Joints

   A. The positioning of the bones at the joint determines the _____ that the joint performs.

   B. Joints are always classified according to the _____ that they provide.

5. The Rib Cage

   A. Ribs form a protective cage that houses the _____, _____, and other vital components of the human body.

   B. Consists of _____ pairs of ribs.

II. The Pathology of the Skeletal System

1. Scoliosis

   A. Often diagnosed early in _____, _____ and _____.

   B. Persons who have scoliosis may often appear as if either their _____ or _____ are uneven.

2. Lordosis

   A. Lordosis is an _____ curvature of the _____ spine.

   B. When diagnosed in adults, may be commonly found in persons who are _____ and in _____ women.

   C. When diagnosed in children, the most common symptom is a prominently protruding _____ and _____.

3. Kyphosis

   A. Kyphosis is an exaggeration of the _____ curvature.

   B. The normal _____ curvature may become exaggerated because of a _____ defect.

4. Arthritis

   A. Causes include _____ injury, _____ disorders, and normal to _____ wear and tear on the joints.

   B. Can occur at any age; however, it most commonly develops in _____ adults.

5. Treatment for Arthritis

   A. Depends on the _____, _____, and _____ of the patient.

   B. Modification of daily activities and low-impact _____ exercise are helpful.

6. Osteoarthritis

   A. Most frequently occurs in the _____, _____, and finger joints of _____ patients.

   B. Obesity, a history of _____, and various genetic and _____ diseases increase the risk of osteoarthritis.

7. Carpal Tunnel Syndrome

   A. Caused when pressure is placed on the _____ _____.

   B. Certain conditions increase the risk of carpal tunnel syndrome, including _____, _____, and _____ arthritis.

   C. Treatment of carpal tunnel syndrome includes the use of proper _____ when engaging in computer use and other activities.

8. Treatment for Fractures

   A. Generally casted by a _____.

   B. At times, with severe fractures, _____ intervention must be performed.

   C. Pain and _____ medications are often prescribed for patient comfort.

© 2011 Pearson Education, Inc.

9. Treatment for Dislocations
   A. Treat in an _____ department.
   B. Reduction is used to _____ and _____ the joint.
   C. Administer pain relievers and _____ medications.

10. Osteoporosis
    A. Affects more than _____ Americans, mostly women ages _____ to _____ years old.
    B. Persons with osteoporosis are subject to increased _____ potential, especially in the _____, _____, and _____.

11. Individuals at Higher Risk for Osteoporosis
    i. _____
    ii. _____
    iii. _____
    iv. _____
    v. _____
    vi. _____

12. Signs, Symptoms, and Treatment for Osteoporosis
    A. The most common sign is decreased _____ and a _____ posture.
    B. Additional signs and symptoms include _____ pain and frequent _____.
    C. Treatment includes _____ and _____ supplements.

13. Signs, Symptoms, and Treatment for Gout
    A. A _____ joint is often very warm and very sore to the touch.
    B. After joints have been persistently affected by gout, they may become _____.
    C. Treatment includes a diet rich in colorful _____ and _____.

14. Hallux Valgus
    A. The enlargement of the inner portion of the _____ joint at the base of the _____ toe.
    B. Signs and symptoms include _____ skin around the inflamed joint of the _____ toe.
    C. The joint may be filled with _____ and feel _____ to the touch.

15. Treatment for Hallux Valgus
    A. Properly _____ _____ should be worn.
    B. Proper _____ and _____ of the joint should be considered.
    C. _____ surgery and pain medications may be required for severe cases.

16. Hammer Toe
    A. Signs and symptoms include _____ and visible joint _____.
    B. Treatment includes wearing specially designed _____.

17. Rickets
    A. Results in bone _____, especially _____ legs.
    B. Signs and symptoms include _____ and _____ of the bones.
    C. Treatment includes increasing _____ and _____ intake.

18. Osteomalacia
    A. Caused by deficiencies in _____ and _____.
    B. Symptoms include _____ pain, _____ legs, and _____ fractures.
    C. Treatment is similar to the treatment for _____.

© 2011 Pearson Education, Inc.

KEY TERMINOLOGY REVIEW

Match the selected key terms to their definitions below.

a. Abduction
b. Adduction
c. Amphiarthrotic joint
d. Appendicular skeleton
e. Arthritis
f. Articulation
g. Atlas
h. Axial skeleton
i. Axis
j. Bursa
k. Bursitis
l. Cancellous bone
m. Chondrocytes
n. Circumduction
o. Compact bone
p. Diaphysis
q. Diarthrotic joint
r. Dislocation
s. Dorsiflexion
t. Endosteum
u. Epiphysis
v. Etiology
w. Eversion
x. Extension

y. Flexion
z. Gout
aa. Hallux valgus
bb. Hammertoe
cc. Inversion
dd. Kyphosis
ee. Lordosis
ff. Medullary canal
gg. Orthopedic physician
hh. Osteoarthritis
ii. Osteomalacia
jj. Osteoporosis
kk. Periosteum
ll. Pronation
mm. Protraction
nn. Reduction
oo. Retraction
pp. Rheumatoid arthritis
qq. Rickets
rr. Rotation
ss. Scoliosis
tt. Supination
uu. Synarthrotic joint

1. _____ The second cervical vertebra.
2. _____ A disease caused by the formation and accumulation of urate crystals in the joints
3. _____ A joint that permits very slight movement.
4. _____ The process of straightening a flexed limb or the spine.
5. _____ Inflammation of the bursa.
6. _____ The toe bends upward like a claw because of the abnormal flexion of the proximal interphalangeal joint.
7. _____ Occurs when a bone slips out of a joint.
8. _____ The process of moving a body part forward.
9. _____ The first cervical vertebra.
10. _____ The cause or source of the patient's disease or disorder.
11. _____ The most common type of arthritis, resulting from years of wear and tear on joints.
12. _____ The dense, hard layer of bone tissue.

© 2011 Pearson Education, Inc.

13. _____ Often called swayback.

14. _____ The process of bending (or curving) a flexed limb or the spine.

15. _____ The process of moving a body part *away* from the midline.

16. _____ The reticular tissue that makes up most of the volume of bone.

17. _____ The adult onset of rickets.

18. _____ The process of bending a body part backward.

19. _____ The procedure used to align and reposition a joint.

20. _____ Also called a bunion.

21. _____ Inflammation of one or more joints.

22. _____ The process of lying prone, or face down.

23. _____ An early childhood disease caused by a deficiency in calcium, vitamin D, and phosphate.

24. _____ The ends of a developing bone.

25. _____ Characterized by a progressive loss of bone density and the thinning of bone tissue.

26. _____ The process of moving a body part in a circular motion.

27. _____ An abnormal lateral curvature of the spine.

28. _____ The process of turning outward.

29. _____ A joint that produces no movement.

30. _____ A joint located at the place where two bones connect.

31. _____ A physician who treats musculoskeletal conditions.

32. _____ An autoimmune disorder causing joints to become deformed because of inflammation.

33. _____ The shaft of the long bone.

34. _____ Most often known as humpback.

35. _____ The process of lying supine, or face upward.

36. _____ The process of moving a body part around a central axis.

37. _____ A small sac of fluid that cushions and lubricates an area where joint-related tissues rub against one another.

38. _____ The membrane that forms the covering of bones, except at their articular surfaces.

39. _____ The process of moving a body part *toward* the midline.

40. _____ The central portion of the skeleton.

41. _____ The tough, connective tissue membrane lining the medullary canal that contains the bone marrow.

42. _____ The process of turning inward.

43. _____ The process of moving a body part backward.

44. _____ A joint that allows for free movement in a variety of directions.

45. _____ The narrow space or cavity throughout the length of the diaphysis.

46. _____ Consists of 126 bones.

47. _____ Cartilage-forming cells.

APPLIED PRACTICE

1. Label the bones found on the images of the anterior and posterior views of the skeletal system.

A **Anterior view**   **B** **Posterior view**

© 2011 Pearson Education, Inc.

2. Label the types of fractures found in this image.

LEARNING ACTIVITY: TRUE/FALSE

Indicate whether the following statements are true or false by placing a T or an F on the line that precedes each statement.

_____ 1. The bones of the human skeleton have seven main functions.

_____ 2. Women build bone until about age 30 and then begin to lose about 1% of their bone mass annually.

_____ 3. Babies are born with more cartilage and bones than adults.

_____ 4. Older adult bones heal faster than in children.

_____ 5. The axial skeleton consists of both the upper and lower extremities, as well as the clavicles and the scapula, which form the pectoral girdle.

_____ 6. Many times, a scoliatic spine appears to have an S or C shape.

_____ 7. The most telling symptom of kyphosis is the rounded back.

_____ 8. Arthritis can occur at any age; however, it most commonly develops in young adults.

_____ 9. Colles's fractures occur in the ankle and affect both bones of the lower leg (the tibia and the fibula).

_____ 10. In a compound fracture, bone is shattered into a multitude of bony fragments.

CRITICAL THINKING

Answer the following questions to the best of your ability. Utilize the textbook as a reference.

1. If a patient has an injury to the skeletal system, how might the medical assistant be able to assist the patient?

   _____

   _____

   _____

   _____

2. How can the medical assistant stay current with new information that may be occurring in medicine? Why is staying current in one's field so critical?

   _____

   _____

   _____

   _____

3. When obtaining a medical history from a patient, why is it important to check the patient's past medical history?

   _____

   _____

   _____

   _____

   _____

RESEARCH ACTIVITY

Utilize Internet search engines to research the following topics and write a brief description of what you find. It is important to utilize reputable websites.

1. Using the Internet as a research source, conduct further research on two conditions/diseases of the skeletal system. These conditions can be ones that are found in the textbook or others that you may be interested in learning more about. Conduct your research with the idea of learning more about the conditions/diseases than what is found in the textbook. Write an essay on what you learned, including how the disease presents itself, the possible cause of the condition, the treatment, and any new technology that may be available in the future to address the condition/disease. Be sure to cite your resources.

   _____

   _____

   _____

   _____

   _____

© 2011 Pearson Education, Inc.

_____

_____

_____

_____

_____

_____

_____

_____

_____

_____

_____

_____

_____

_____

© 2011 Pearson Education, Inc.

CHAPTER 24

The Muscular System

CHAPTER OUTLINE

General review of the chapter:

Functions of Muscle
Types of Muscle Tissue
Energy Production for Muscle
Structure of Skeletal Muscles
Major Skeletal Muscles
Common Disorders Associated with the Muscular System

STUDENT STUDY GUIDE

Use the following guide to assist in your learning of the concepts from the chapter.

I. The Muscular System

1. Muscle Characteristics

   A. Contains bundles of parallel muscle tissue _____.
   B. Muscles _____ when a message is sent from the _____ via nerves.
   C. The human body has more than _____ muscles.
   D. Muscles make up more than _____ of body weight.

2. The Functions of the Muscular System

   i. _____
   ii. _____
   iii. _____
   iv. _____

3. Skeletal Muscles

   A. Attached to _____ bones.
   B. Wrapped in layers of _____ tissue.
   C. Stimulated by _____ neurons.

4. Smooth Muscles

   A. Found in tissue in the walls of _____ organs.
   B. Responsible for the movement of _____ organs.

5. Adenosine Triphosphate (ATP)

   A. The type of chemical energy needed for _____ or repeated muscular _____.
   B. Can be produced by either _____ or _____ means.

© 2011 Pearson Education, Inc.

6. The Effects of Oxygen Debt
   A. Occurs when skeletal muscles are used for more than _____ or _____ minutes.
   B. Lack of oxygen intake reduces the body's ability to produce energy _____, causing _____ production.
   C. The body can only utilize this energy for about _____ seconds, depending on the individual, before severe fatigue sets in, making it very difficult to recover.
   D. Oxygen "owed" to body is the debt and can only be recovered by _____ respiration, which allows more oxygen into the _____ to reach the _____.

II. The Pathology of the Muscular System

   1. Atrophy
      A. Lipoatrophy is atrophy of the _____ _____.
      B. The signs and symptoms of atrophy include the apparent _____ of a muscle group and extreme _____ and _____ associated with atrophic muscle groups.
      C. Treatment includes _____ exercises of the immobilized muscle.

   2. Fibromyalgia
      A. More common in _____ than _____.
      B. The signs and symptoms include mild to severe _____ pain and _____.
      C. _____ _____ syndrome is a common symptom.

   3. Criteria for Determining Fibromyalgia
      A. The American College of _____ identified specific criteria.
      B. Must show _____ to _____ trigger or tender points to be considered for this diagnosis, as well as a history of widespread pain lasting at least _____ months.

   4. Treatment for Fibromyalgia
      A. Geared toward improving the quality of _____ and reducing _____.
      B. Common medications used in treatment include the following:
         i. _____
         ii. _____
         iii. _____
         iv. _____
         v. _____

   5. Ganglion Cyst
      A. More common in _____ than _____.
      B. The signs and symptoms include masses occurring typically on the _____, _____, and _____.
      C. _____ swelling can occur.

   6. Treatment for a Ganglion Cyst
         i. _____
         ii. _____
         iii. _____

   7. Lyme Disease
      A. Carried by _____ and transmitted through a bite of an infected _____.
      B. The signs and symptoms include the following:
         i. _____
         ii. _____
         iii. _____
         iv. _____

© 2011 Pearson Education, Inc.

8. The Prevention of and Treatment for Lyme Disease

    A. Prevention includes the following:

        i. _____

        ii. _____

        iii. _____

    B. Treatment includes the use of _____, _____, or _____.

9. Muscular Dystrophy

    A. There are _____ major forms of muscular dystrophy.

    B. The signs and symptoms include _____, _____, and _____.

10. Treatment for Muscular Dystrophy

    A. _____ _____ to prevent contraction

    B. _____ for support

    C. Corrective _____ surgery

    D. The Emery-Dreifuss and myotonic forms may necessitate a _____ because of the cardiac problems associated with these forms

11. Rotator Cuff Tears

    A. Common in _____ muscles/tendons.

    B. Caused by many years of _____ of these muscles/tendons.

    C. Also caused by one single _____ injury.

12. Treatment for Rotator Cuff Tears

        i. _____

        ii. _____

        iii. _____

        iv. _____

        v. _____

        vi. _____

13. Shin Splints

    A. Usually caused by _____ or _____ conditioning of the leg muscles.

    B. Found in persons with _____ feet or _____ arches.

    C. The signs and symptoms include the following:

        i. _____

        ii. _____

        iii. _____

14. Treatment for Shin Splints

        i. _____

        ii. _____

        iii. _____

        iv. _____

15. Sprains

    A. Very common in _____.

    B. Often occurs in the _____ of major joints.

    C. The signs and symptoms include the following:

        i. _____

        ii. _____

        iii. _____

        iv. _____

© 2011 Pearson Education, Inc.

16. Strains
    A. A chronic strain occurs from _____ and _____ movement.
    B. An acute strain can occur from _____ lifting of a heavy object.
    C. The signs and symptoms include the following:
        i. _____
        ii. _____
        iii. _____
        iv. _____
        v. _____
        vi. _____
        vii. _____

17. The Signs, Symptoms, and Treatment for Tendonitis
    A. The signs and symptoms include pain and _____ in the affected area.
    B. Treatment involves physical therapy, including _____ to increase range of motion.

18. Tetanus
    A. Tetanus is an often fatal, _____ disease.
    B. Caused by _____ bacterium.
    C. The signs and symptoms include the following:
        i. _____
        ii. _____
        iii. _____
        iv. _____
        v. _____

KEY TERMINOLOGY REVIEW

Match the selected key terms to their definitions below.

a. Antagonist

b. Aponeurosis

c. Aspiration

d. Atrophy

e. Cardiac muscle

f. Contracture

g. Endomysium

h. Epimysium

i. Fascia

j. Fascicles

k. Fibromyalgia

l. Ganglion cyst

m. Insertion

n. Ligament

o. Lyme disease

p. Muscular dystrophy

q. Myasthenia gravis

r. Origin

s. Orthoses

t. Oxygen debt

u. Perimysium

v. Prime mover (agonist)

w. Skeletal muscle

x. Smooth muscle

y. Sprain

z. Strain

aa. Striated

bb. Synergist

cc. Tendon

dd. Tendonitis

ee. Tetanus

ff. Tonicity

© 2011 Pearson Education, Inc.

1. _____ A muscle that counteracts, or opposes, the action of another muscle.

2. _____ A condition in which shortened muscles around joints cause abnormal and sometimes painful positioning of the joints.

3. _____ Connective tissue that connects bones or connects cartilage to a joint.

4. _____ The amount of oxygen "owed" to the body that is needed to recover.

5. _____ A chronic autoimmune neuromuscular disease characterized by varying degrees of weakness of the skeletal or voluntary muscles of the body.

6. _____ A benign saclike swelling or cyst.

7. _____ Inflammation of the tendon.

8. _____ One of a group of genetic diseases characterized by progressive weakness and degeneration of the skeletal or voluntary muscles that control movement.

9. _____ Consists of a group of fibers held together by connective tissue.

10. _____ A fibrous sheath that holds connective tissue together.

11. _____ A wide, thin, sheetlike tendon made up of fibrous connective tissue that typically attaches muscles to other muscles.

12. _____ Orthopedic appliances used for support.

13. _____ An injury to either a muscle or a tendon.

14. _____ The body's ability to maintain posture through a continual partial contraction of skeletal muscles.

15. _____ The band of connective tissue found at each end of a muscle that attaches the muscle to a bone.

16. _____ The sections of a muscle.

17. _____ An injury to a ligament.

18. _____ Responsible for dividing a muscle into sections.

19. _____ The loss of muscle mass and strength that occurs with the disuse of muscles over a long period of time.

20. _____ A disorder in which musculoskeletal pain and fatigue are present.

21. _____ Caused by the *Borrelia burgdorferi* bacterium.

22. _____ The covering of connective tissue that surrounds the individual muscle cell.

23. _____ Composed of elongated, spindle-shaped cells.

24. _____ The attachment to the bone that is more fixed or still.

25. _____ A muscle that acts with another muscle, most often a prime mover, to produce movement.

26. _____ Thin fascia that covers muscles.

27. _____ Removal of fluid by suction.

28. _____ The attachment point on the bone that moves.

29. _____ Striped in appearance.

30. _____ A muscle that is the primary actor in a given movement.

31. _____ Has a single central nucleus and is found in the heart.

32. _____ An often fatal, infectious disease caused by the bacterium *Clostridium tetani*.

© 2011 Pearson Education, Inc.

APPLIED PRACTICE

1. Label the muscles found on the images of the anterior and posterior views of the muscular system.

A

B

2. Label the muscles of the head, neck, and face found in this image.

© 2011 Pearson Education, Inc.

LEARNING ACTIVITY: TRUE/FALSE

Indicate whether the following statements are true or false by placing a T or an F on the line that precedes each statement.

_____ 1. Muscles are responsible for holding bones together so that the joints of the body remain stable.

_____ 2. Muscle tissue has the ability to contract or to shorten.

_____ 3. Smooth muscle cells contain striations.

_____ 4. Skeletal muscle controls involuntary movement.

_____ 5. Muscle fatigue usually develops as a result of an accumulation of lactic acid.

_____ 6. The splenius capitis muscle pulls the head from side to side and to the chest.

_____ 7. The muscle that flexes the thigh is the psoas major.

_____ 8. Genetic predisposition may be a cause of fibromyalgia.

_____ 9. The most common areas for tendonitis include the fingers and toes.

_____ 10. Sprains are generally treated using the RICE method.

CRITICAL THINKING

Answer the following questions to the best of your ability. Utilize the textbook as a reference.

1. When giving children injections, why are injections usually given in the vastus lateralis muscle? When should the gluteus maximus muscle be used when giving an injection to an adult?

   _____

   _____

   _____

   _____

   _____

2. As a medical assistant, what should you do if a patient is upset or concerned about his or her health?

   _____

   _____

   _____

   _____

   _____

3. How does regular exercise help older adults stay healthy?

   _____

   _____

   _____

   _____

   _____

© 2011 Pearson Education, Inc.

RESEARCH ACTIVITY

Utilize Internet search engines to research the following topics and write a brief description of what you find. It is important to utilize reputable websites.

1. Using the Internet as a research source, conduct further research on two conditions/diseases of the muscular system. These conditions can be ones that are found in the textbook or others that you may be interested in learning more about. Conduct your research with the idea of learning more about the conditions/diseases than what is presented in the textbook. Write an essay on what you learned, including how the disease presents itself, the possible cause of the condition, the treatment, and any new technology that may be available in the future to address the condition/disease. Be sure to cite your resources.

CHAPTER 25

The Nervous System

CHAPTER OUTLINE

General review of the chapter:

> Structure and Functions of the Nervous System
> Neurons
> Nerve Fibers, Nerves, and Tracts
> Nerve Impulses and Synapses
> Central Nervous System
> Peripheral Nervous System
> Common Disorders Associated with the Nervous System

STUDENT STUDY GUIDE

Use the following guide to assist in your learning of the concepts from the chapter.

I. An Overview of the Central Nervous System

   1. The Nervous System

      A. Acts to correlate both _____ and _____ factors that affect our bodies by gathering, storing, and deciphering both external and internal information.

      B. Decides how to _____ and _____ in an appropriate manner in order to satisfy certain needs.

      C. Of these needs, the most important is _____.

   2. Types of Neurons: Motor Neurons

      A. Usually have several _____ and only one _____.

      B. Axons may be several feet long and reach from the _____, _____ to the area that is to be activated.

      C. Dendrites resemble _____ _____ and are unsheathed.

© 2011 Pearson Education, Inc.

3. Motor Neurons: On the following image, indicate the location of the axon, dendrite, and myelin sheath.

4. Sensory Neurons

   A. They lack true _____, are sheathed, and more closely resemble _____.
   B. Transmit impulses directly to the _____ _____ _____.

5. Nerve Fibers

   A. Single, elongated process, usually an axon or _____ process from a _____ neuron.
   B. Nerve fibers in the peripheral nervous system (PNS) are wrapped in _____.
   C. Nerve fibers in the central nervous system (CNS) do not contain _____ _____, and thus damage to the CNS is permanent, whereas damage to a _____ nerve can be reversed.

6. Myelinated Sheaths

   A. Myelin is a thick _____ substance.
   B. Myelin sheaths have both an inner sheath of _____ and an outer sheath, or _____, composed of Schwann cells.
   C. _____ _____ are needed for the process of regenerating a damaged nerve fiber.

© 2011 Pearson Education, Inc.

7. Tracts
   A. All nerve fibers that are housed within the nerve tract must have the same _____, _____, and _____.
   B. The spinal cord contains _____ tracts that are _____, which ascend to the brain, and _____ tracts that descend from the brain.

8. Nerve Impulses and Synapses
   A. Each receptor has its own _____ at which it will react to a stimulus, and each will only respond when its _____ has been reached.
   B. The impulse is then transmitted via a _____, which is a knoblike branch ending.
   C. The process is similar to the _____ _____.

9. An Overview of the Brain
      i. _____
     ii. _____
    iii. _____
     iv. The three membranes that encompass the brain are the _____, the _____, and the _____.

10. The Brain
   A. Manages all bodily functions and _____.
   B. Functions and movement are _____ by specific areas of the brain.
   C. Generates _____.
   D. Is the basis for rational thought, _____, and _____.

11. The Cerebrum
   A. The cerebrum is the _____ part of the brain.
   B. Controls higher thought processes such as _____ _____, reasoning, and judgment.
   C. The cerebrum is divided by the _____ _____ into left and right halves called _____ _____.
   D. Each hemisphere has _____ _____.

12. The Cerebral Cortex
   A. Houses _____ of the _____ in the entire nervous system.
   B. Composed of _____ and _____ matter that lies directly below it.
   C. Responsible for interpreting sensory information and initiating _____ _____.
   D. Stores _____ and creates _____.

13. The Diencephalon
   A. Literally means the _____ portion of the brain.
   B. Made up of the _____ and the _____.

14. The Thalamus
   A. The thalamus is two large masses of _____ cell bodies connected by a third mass.
   B. Serves as a relay center for all sensory impulses, with the exception of _____.

15. The Hypothalamus
   A. Lies beneath the _____.
   B. Primarily regulates the _____ nervous activity associated with behavior and emotional expression.
   C. Responsible for a variety of _____ functions that occur throughout the body.

16. The Brainstem
   A. Resembles a _____.
   B. Contains the _____, the _____, and the _____.
   C. These structures relay important information to the cerebrum, including _____, _____, and other sensory data.

   © 2011 Pearson Education, Inc.

17. The Midbrain
    A. Located just below the _____ and above the _____.
    B. Associated with _____ _____ and the tracking movements of the eyes.
    C. The lower two segments are associated with the sense of _____.

18. The Pons
    A. A broad band of white matter anterior to the _____ that is between the midbrain and the _____ _____.
    B. Contains _____ _____ linking the cerebellum and medulla oblongata to higher cortical areas.
    C. Plays a vital role in _____ and _____ motor control.

19. The Medulla Oblongata
    A. Connects the _____ and the rest of the brain to the spinal cord.
    B. The nerve centers in this area are vital to the body's _____ because they exert control of the circulation of blood by regulating both the _____ and arterial blood pressure.
    C. Different areas of the medulla oblongata are also responsible for involuntary bodily functions, including _____, _____, _____, _____, and _____.

20. The Cerebellum
    A. Located in the back of the skull below the cerebrum and behind the pons and the _____ _____.
    B. The cerebellum is the _____ largest portion of the brain.
    C. The surface has a large _____ of gray cell bodies and white matter on its interior.
    D. Coordinates voluntary and involuntary _____ of movement.
    E. Adjusts muscles to automatically maintain _____.

21. A Review of the Brain: Label the parts of the brain as found on the image.

22. The Spinal Cord
    A. Connects the brain with the _____ nerves.
    B. Consists of gray matter (cell bodies) in the _____ _____.
    C. Consists of white matter (_____ _____) in the outer layer.
    D. Like the brain, it is surrounded by _____ fluid.
    E. Impulses are transmitted through the spinal cord along _____.
    F. The spinal cord is encased in the _____ _____.

© 2011 Pearson Education, Inc.

G. The four divisions of the spinal cord are _____, _____, _____, and _____.

H. The levels of the spinal column are numbered (e.g., cervical level 5 is noted as _____).

I. Spinal nerves exit through _____ (openings) in the vertebrae.

23. Cerebrospinal Fluid

   A. Circulates around the brain and spinal cord in the _____ space.
   B. Provides _____ and _____ for the brain and spinal cord.
   C. Contains nourishment and _____.
   D. Produced in the _____ _____ of the ventricles of the brain.

24. Cranial Nerves and Their Functions: Name the nerves that provide each function listed.

   A. _____: Provides the sense of smell.
   B. _____: Provides vision.
   C. _____: Conducts motor impulses to four of the six external muscles of the eye and to the muscle that raises the eyelid.
   D. _____: Conducts motor impulses to control the superior oblique muscle of the eyeball.
   E. _____: Provides sensory input from the face, nose, mouth, forehead, and top of the head; motor fibers to the muscles of the jaw (chewing).
   F. _____: Conducts motor impulses to the lateral rectus muscle of the eyeball.
   G. _____: Controls the muscles of the face and scalp, the lachrymal glands of the eye and the submandibular and sublingual salivary glands, and input from the tongue for the sense of taste.
   H. _____: Provides input for hearing and equilibrium.
   I. _____: Provides a general sense of taste, regulates swallowing, and controls the secretion of saliva.
   J. _____: Controls the muscles of the pharynx, larynx, thoracic, and abdominal organs; swallowing; voice production; the slowing of the heartbeat; and the acceleration of peristalsis.
   K. _____: Controls the trapezius and sternocleidomastoid muscles, permitting movement of the head and shoulders.
   L. _____: Controls tongue movement.

25. Spinal Nerves: Indicate the number of each.

   A. _____ pair(s) of cervical spinal nerves
   B. _____ pair(s) of thoracic spinal nerves
   C. _____ pair(s) of lumbar spinal nerves
   D. _____ pair(s) of sacral spinal nerves
   E. _____ pair(s) of coccygeal spinal nerves

26. The Autonomic Nervous System

   A. The final division of the nervous system occurs in the _____ _____ _____.
   B. The autonomic nervous system is further divided into the _____ and _____ nervous systems.

27. The Sympathetic Division

   A. Branches from the _____ thoracic and the first three _____ spinal nerves form the first part of the sympathetic division of the ANS.
   B. The cell bodies of these nerve fibers are located in the _____ _____ of the spinal cord.
   C. The axons of the nerve cells leave the spinal nerves and enter almost immediately into masses of nerve cell bodies, which are called _____ _____.

© 2011 Pearson Education, Inc.

D. Spinal nerves that synapse with the _____ _____ tend to produce widespread _____ when activated.

E. This occurrence is thought to prepare the body for _____ or _____.

F. During fight or flight, a person experiences increased alertness in conjunction with an increase in _____ _____ and other bodily functions.

G. At this point, the somatic nervous system stimulates the _____ _____ to release _____, the hormone that causes the familiar adrenaline rush.

28. The Parasympathetic Division

A. Long fibers that branch from _____ _____ III, VII, IX, and X in conjunction with the long fibers of _____ _____ II, III, and IV form the first stage of the parasympathetic division.

B. Cranial nerve fibers extend via the _____ nerve to ganglia serving the thoracic, abdominal, and pelvic viscera.

C. The fibers of the sacral spinal nerves form the _____ nerve, which branches to synapse with small ganglia near or within the organs to be innervated.

D. The cell bodies of these ganglia serve the _____ _____, _____, _____, and _____ _____.

E. The parasympathetic division works to conserve energy and innervate the digestive system; thus, its function earned the nickname "_____."

F. Instead of the adrenaline rush that is felt with the somatic nervous system, a _____ in metabolism and bodily function occurs.

II. The Pathology of the Nervous System

1. Alzheimer's Disease

A. _____ history often plays a role in the development of this disease, along with _____ and _____.

B. Onset is most frequent in the later stages of life, generally ages _____ to _____.

2. Signs and Symptoms of Alzheimer's Disease

A. Mild _____ of recent events is the first symptom.

B. The ability to think and rationalize _____.

C. Thought processes are _____.

D. _____ may become difficult to understand.

E. _____ and _____ skills dissipate.

F. _____ patterns change during the later stages.

G. Patients (may) become _____, _____, aggressive, or _____.

H. Eventually, patients are unable to _____, _____, or _____ for themselves.

3. Treatment for Alzheimer's Disease

A. Medications may _____ the progression of the disease in the _____ stages.

B. Patients must continue to take medication throughout their life to avoid _____.

4. Amyotrophic Lateral Sclerosis

A. Breaks down the _____ that are responsible for _____.

B. The disease is also known as motor _____ disease.

5. Signs and Symptoms of Amyotrophic Lateral Sclerosis

A. Loss of control of _____ muscle movement, including that of the arms, legs, and trunk.

B. _____ muscle movement, such as that associated with the _____ of the heart and the smooth muscle of the internal organs, is not generally affected.

C. Depending on the form of ALS, the loss of _____ _____ (dementia) or sensory symptoms may occur.

6. Bell's Palsy

   A. Generally not a serious condition, but does affect the _____ of the face.
   B. Caused by damage to a _____ _____; a facial nerve runs beneath each ear to the muscles on that side of the face.
   C. Also known as _____ palsy.
   D. Named after Dr. Charles Bell, who first documented the disorder in _____.

7. Signs, Symptoms, and Treatment of Bell's Palsy

   Signs and symptoms include the following:

   A. _____ _____ of the face.
   B. Facial _____ and lack of expression on the afflicted side.

   Treatment includes the following:

   A. _____ at the onset ensures good recovery.
   B. Without treatment, it may resolve on its own in a few _____ or _____.

8. Disk Disorders

   A. Disk disorders include painful deterioration of the disks that support the _____ _____.

   B. Signs and symptoms include the following:
      i. _____
      ii. _____
      iii. _____
      iv. _____

9. Treatment for Disk Disorders

      i. _____
      ii. _____
      iii. _____
      iv. _____
      v. _____

10. Encephalitis

    A. Often caused by a _____.
    B. Primarily affects _____ and the _____.

11. Epilepsy and Seizures

    A. The cause of epilepsy is _____.
    B. Epilepsy is often the result of another condition, such as a _____ _____, _____, _____ _____, or _____ _____.
    C. Seizures affect about _____ of the population.

12. Types of Headaches

      i. _____
      ii. _____
      iii. _____
      iv. _____

13. Huntington's Chorea

    A. Huntington's chorea is a hereditary degenerative disorder of the cerebral and _____ _____.

    B. Also referred to as _____ _____.
    C. Generally, onset begins during the mid to late _____; sometimes occurs in juveniles.

© 2011 Pearson Education, Inc.

14. Signs and Symptoms of Huntington's Chorea
    i. _____
    ii. _____
    iii. _____
    iv. _____
    v. _____
    vi. _____

15. Treatment for Huntington's Chorea
    A. _____ and _____ are used to regulate pain, spasms, and seizures.
    B. Death occurs within _____ years of diagnosis.

16. Hydrocephalus
    A. Commonly occurs in _____.
    B. Characterized by an excessive amount of CSF _____ in the brain, causing the brain to _____ against the skull.
    C. Without proper treatment, this condition can result in _____ _____.

17. Signs and Symptoms of Hydrocephalus
    i. _____
    ii. _____
    iii. _____
    iv. _____

18. Signs and Symptoms of Meningitis
    i. _____
    ii. _____
    iii. _____
    iv. _____
    v. _____

19. Treatment for Meningitis
    i. _____
    ii. _____
    iii. _____
    iv. _____
    v. _____
    vi. _____

20. Multiple Sclerosis
    A. MS is a chronic, debilitating autoimmune disease that affects the _____ and the _____ _____.
    B. There is no known _____.
    C. The body directs the _____ and white blood cells to attack the _____ _____ surrounding the nerves in the brain and the spinal cord.
    D. _____ and injury to the sheath and nerves result; _____ is possible.
    E. Transmission of nerve impulses are impeded, making _____, _____, or _____ difficult.

21. Signs and Symptoms of Multiple Sclerosis
    i. _____
    ii. _____
    iii. _____
    iv. _____
    v. _____
    vi. _____

vii. _____

viii. _____

ix. _____

x. _____

22. Neuralgia

    A. _____ _____, _____ (including surgery), _____, and _____ may all lead to neuralgia.

    B. The signs and symptoms of neuralgia include the following:

       i. _____

      ii. _____

23. Treatment for Neuralgia

    A. Rest, stretching, and _____

    B. Aspirin, _____, or ibuprofen

    C. Narcotic pain killers, _____ _____, and anesthetic agents administered via _____ injection

    D. Surgical procedures to decrease _____

24. Parkinson's Disease

    A. Parkinson's disease is a _____ disorder.

    B. Caused by the _____ of nerve cells in the parts of the brain that control _____.

    C. Because of degeneration, there is a shortage of the neurotransmitter _____, causing the _____ impairment that characterizes the disease.

    D. Causes _____, _____ changes, _____, _____ disturbances, _____ impairment, and _____ difficulties.

    E. _____ over time.

25. Signs and Symptoms of Parkinson's Disease

       i. _____

      ii. _____

     iii. _____

     iv. _____

      v. _____

     vi. _____

26. Treatment for Parkinson's Disease

    A. Administration of _____.

    B. _____ must eventually be discontinued because of _____ _____.

    C. _____ intervention helps minimize involuntary movement.

27. Signs and Symptoms of Sciatica

    A. Sharp pain from the _____ _____, down the back of the _____.

    B. Pain may be worse during periods of _____, as well as at _____.

    C. Increased pain when the _____ changes.

28. Treatment for Sciatica

       i. _____

      ii. _____

     iii. _____

     iv. _____

      v. _____

     vi. _____

© 2011 Pearson Education, Inc.

29. Spina Bifida

   A. Spina bifida is the most frequently _____, permanently _____, and devastating of all birth defects.
   B. Affects approximately 1 out of every _____ newborns in the United States.
   C. More children have spina bifida than _____ _____, _____ _____, and _____ _____ combined.
   D. The spine fails to _____ properly during the first month of pregnancy.
   E. All nerve damage is _____.

30. Forms of Spina Bifida

   i. _____
   ii. _____
   iii. _____
   iv. _____

31. Signs and Symptoms of Spina Bifida: Closed Neural Tube

   A. Defects are _____.
   B. Some individuals show no _____.
   C. Others have _____, causing _____ and _____ dysfunction.

32. Signs and Symptoms of Spina Bifida: Meningocele

   A. The _____ protrude from the spinal opening.
   B. There may be no _____.
   C. Symptoms are similar to those of _____ neural tube defects.

33. Signs and Symptoms of Spina Bifida: Myelomeningocele

   A. Myelomeningocele is the most _____ form.
   B. The entire spinal cord is _____.
   C. _____ may be partial or complete below the area of the _____.

34. Treatment for Spina Bifida

   A. Some children may need _____ intervention as they grow and develop.
   B. _____ forms may not require any _____.
   C. Surgery _____ has been tried; however, complications can be great for both the mother and the fetus.

35. Treatment for the Complications of Paralysis

   A. Treatment is aimed at reducing _____.
   B. _____ therapy may be helpful in hemiplegic patients with complications due to stroke.

36. Complications Associated with Paralysis

   i. _____
   ii. _____
   iii. _____
   iv. _____

37. Strokes

   A. Strokes are the _____ leading cause of death in the United States.
   B. The _____ _____ dies when the blood supply to the brain is decreased by _____ or _____.
   C. Brain cells can die when the _____ supply is interrupted for more than a few minutes.
   D. _____ is important in the diagnosis and treatment of strokes.

38. Signs and Symptoms of a Stroke

   i. _____
   ii. _____

© 2011 Pearson Education, Inc.

iii. _____

iv. _____

v. _____

vi. _____

39. Treatment for a Stroke

    A. _____ intervention is vital.

    B. Stabilize condition by either _____ blood clots or stopping the _____.

    C. _____ may be necessary.

    D. Administer medications to control _____ of the brain and _____ _____.

    E. Medications and treatments are given after the incident to _____ the chance of _____.

40. Transient Ischemic Attacks

    A. TIAs are frequently precursors of _____.

    B. _____ can last anywhere from a few seconds to hours.

41. Signs and Symptoms of Transient Ischemic Attacks

    i. _____

    ii. _____

    iii. _____

42. Treatment for Transient Ischemic Attacks

    i. _____

    ii. _____

43. Methods for Reducing the Risk of Future Transient Ischemic Attacks

    i. _____

    ii. _____

    iii. _____

    iv. _____

    v. _____

44. Types of Trauma to the Brain

    A. Subdural _____ cause pressure in the brain that must be relieved by _____.

    B. A _____ is an injury caused by abrupt jarring of, or a blow to, the head.

    C. A _____ is bruising of the brain.

    D. Skull fractures known as _____ can cause brain injury.

45. Signs and Symptoms of Brain Trauma

    i. _____

    ii. _____

    iii. _____

    iv. _____

    v. _____

    vi. _____

    vii. _____

46. Treatment for Brain Trauma

    A. _____ therapy

    B. Medications to suppress seizures, such as _____ and _____.

KEY TERMINOLOGY REVIEW

Match the vocabulary term to the correct definition below.

© 2011 Pearson Education, Inc.

a. Afferent
b. Alzheimer's disease
c. Amyotrophic lateral sclerosis (ALS)
d. Autonomic nervous system (ANS)
e. Bell's palsy
f. Central nervous system (CNS)
g. Cerebrospinal fluid (CSF)
h. Concussion
i. Contusion
j. Corpus callosum
k. Efferent nerves
l. Encephalitis
m. Epilepsy
n. Fissure
o. Hemiplegia
p. Interneurons
q. Meninges
r. Meningitis

s. Motor neurons
t. Multiple sclerosis (MS)
u. Neurons
v. Neuralgia
w. Neurilemma
x. Paraplegia
y. Parkinson's disease
z. Peripheral nervous system (PNS)
aa. Quadriplegia
bb. Sciatica
cc. Seizure
dd. Sensory neurons
ee. Sheaths
ff. Somatic nervous system (SNS)
gg. Spina bifida
hh. Stroke
ii. Sulcus
jj. Tract

1. _____ Inflammation of the brain.

2. _____ Weakness or paralysis of the muscles that control expression on one side of the face.

3. _____ An outer sheath of myelin.

4. _____ Membranes that encompass the brain.

5. _____ Refers to a pain that runs along the sciatic nerve.

6. _____ Often considered to be the "blood" of the nervous system.

7. _____ Made up of nerves that connect the CNS to the other parts of the body.

8. _____ A chronic, potentially debilitating disease that affects the brain and spinal cord; there is no known cure.

9. _____ Also known as Lou Gehrig's disease.

10. _____ Nerves where the impulse is transmitted from the neural cell body to stimulate the target muscle or organ.

11. _____ Transmit sensory information through a peripheral process.

12. _____ Bruising of the brain.

13. _____ Occurs when abnormal and often intense bursts of electrical activity are produced within the brain.

14. _____ Responsible for controlling involuntary bodily functions.

15. _____ A deep groove in the brain.

16. _____ Typically presents as a tremor of a limb, especially when the body is at rest.

17. _____ Often referred to as associative neurons because they are located entirely within the CNS.

18. _____ Nerves that conduct impulses to the CNS.

19. _____ Refers to paralysis from approximately the shoulders down.

© 2011 Pearson Education, Inc.

20. _____ A shallow groove.
21. _____ Term used for general nerve pain.
22. _____ A disorder associated with misfiring or interference.
23. _____ Stimulates the adrenal gland to release epinephrine.
24. _____ A group of nerve fibers within the CNS.
25. _____ Receives impulses from the entire body, requiring it to process information and respond with appropriate actions.
26. _____ Control most of the body's functions as they cause muscles to contract, glands to secrete, and organs to function properly.
27. _____ Formed by accessory cells.
28. _____ An infection of the meninges that surround and protect the brain and spinal cord.
29. _____ Refers to paralysis from approximately the waist down.
30. _____ Known in medicine as a cerebrovascular incident.
31. _____ An injury caused by abrupt jarring of, or a blow to, the head that may result in a loss of consciousness.
32. _____ Nervous system tissue that is made up of specialized nerve cells.
33. _____ Stimulates the adrenal gland to release epinephrine.
34. _____ Occurs when paralysis affects one side of the body.
35. _____ A progressive degenerative disease that attacks the brain and its cognitive functioning.
36. _____ The largest nerve tract that joins the right and left hemispheres of the brain.

APPLIED PRACTICE

Read the scenarios below and answer the questions that follow.

Scenario 1

A 20-year-old female patient presents to your office with the following symptoms: Headache ×3 days, temperature of 103.2°F, dizziness, and blurred vision. She said that since she woke up this morning she has not been able to move her head. In her medical chart, you make a note that "the patient states 'My neck is so stiff, I can't bend it.' Her head appears bent forward toward her chest."

1. What would you suspect the diagnosis might be based on her symptoms? *(Medical assistants never make a diagnosis; this is a question about your knowledge of the signs and symptoms of various conditions.)*

_____

Scenario 2

A 59-year-old male patient presents to your office with observable right-side facial drooping, specifically near the mouth. The patient states that he "woke up this way" and he "can't feel anything on the entire right side of my face."

1. What would you suspect the diagnosis might be on the basis of his symptoms? *(Medical assistants never make a diagnosis; this is a question about your knowledge of the signs and symptoms of various conditions.)*

_____

2. What is the treatment for this condition?

_____

© 2011 Pearson Education, Inc.

Scenario 3

As an administrative medical assistant, one of your duties is transcribing for the neurologists in the office where you work. Dr. Preston dictated notes on a patient whom he saw in the emergency room last night. He dictates "17-year-old male patient presents to the ER with suspected countercoup injury of the head with a 4-inch laceration on the right temporal region of his skull. Due to the extent of the contusion, the patient will remain hospitalized for observation for 48 hours."

1. What is the difference between a concussion and a contusion?

_____

_____

LEARNING ACTIVITY: MULTIPLE CHOICE

Circle the correct answer to each of the questions below.

1. Which of the following applies to a cerebrovascular accident?

    a. It is the third leading cause of death in the United States.
    b. It is caused by a virus.
    c. Brain tissue dies when the blood supply to a part of the brain is decreased.
    d. All of the above

2. Which of the following are signs and symptoms of encephalitis?

    a. Headache
    b. Stiff neck and back
    c. Drowsiness
    d. All of the above

3. Sciatica _____.

    a. usually causes very intense pain
    b. is caused by inflammation due to a pinched root
    c. usually occurs on one side of the body
    d. All of the above

4. Which of the following diseases has a cause that is unknown?

    a. ALS
    b. TIA
    c. Trigeminal neuralgia
    d. Multiple sclerosis

5. The corpus callosum _____.

    a. controls most of the body's functions
    b. joins the right and left hemispheres of the brain
    c. is divided into grey and white matter
    d. All of the above

6. Which of the following make up the central nervous system?

    a. Nerves
    b. Cells
    c. Brain and spinal cord
    d. All of the above

7. Which of the following applies to epidural and subdural hematomas?
    a. They develop when the head receives a blow.
    b. They are typically seen in the elderly.
    c. They are a bruising of the brain.
    d. None of the above

8. Which of the following are associated with epilepsy?
    a. Often occurs after a head or neck injury has healed.
    b. The cause is unknown.
    c. It is a weakness or paralysis of the muscles that control expression on one side of the face.
    d. It is an inflammation of the brain caused by a virus.

9. Which of the following is not associated with meningitis?
    a. It is similar to encephalitis.
    b. It may be caused by a virus or bacteria.
    c. It has a high death rate if untreated.
    d. It is an autoimmune disease.

10. Motor neurons are _____.
    a. greatly affected in ALS
    b. considered afferent nerves
    c. housed within the nerve tract
    d. structurally like a stem

CRITICAL THINKING

Answer the following questions to the best of your ability. Utilize the textbook as a reference.

1. A patient, a 57-year-old female named Katie Gilpatrick, has come into the office and is exhibiting signs of high stress. How can the medical assistant help relieve the patient's stress?

_____

_____

_____

_____

2. A fellow health care worker comes to work and states that she cannot do very much because she has "a migraine." She was out late last night at a party and states that the headache is not because she had some drinks. She hopes that you will help her through the day by taking care of some of her patients. She is incorrect in diagnosing herself with a migraine because it is a specific type of headache, and she has not been diagnosed with migraines by a physician. Explain why it is unlikely that someone with a true migraine would be able to come to work and function even at a slow pace.

_____

_____

_____

_____

© 2011 Pearson Education, Inc.

3. Why is it important to be aware of the laws in your state regarding driving and neurological disorders?

_____

_____

_____

_____

RESEARCH ACTIVITY

Utilize Internet search engines to research the following topics and write a brief description of what you find. It is important to utilize reputable websites.

1. Visit The Parkinson's Disease Foundation at www.pdf.org. Click on the "News and Events" tab on the top of the page, then select "Science News". Choose an article of interest and provide a summary of the information discussed within the article. Discuss what interested you most about the article that you selected.

_____

_____

_____

_____

_____

_____

_____

_____

_____

_____

_____

_____

_____

_____

_____

_____

_____

_____

_____

_____

CHAPTER 26
The Special Senses

CHAPTER OUTLINE

General review of the chapter:

The Eye and the Sense of Vision
Common Refractive Disorders
Disorders Related to Structural Irregularities of the Eye
Infectious Eye Disorders
Age-Related Eye Disorders
Other Eye Disorders
The Ear and the Sense of Hearing
Hearing Loss
Common Disorders Associated with the Outer Ear
Common Disorders Associated with the Middle Ear
Common Disorders Associated with the Inner Ear
The Senses of Taste and Smell
The Sense of Touch

STUDENT STUDY GUIDE

Use the following guide to assist in your learning of the concepts from the chapter.

I. The Eye and the Sense of Vision

   1. An Overview of the Eye and the Sense of Vision

      A. The eye is a _____, _____ organ composed of specialized structures that work together to facilitate vision.

      B. Light rays pass through the _____, _____, _____, and vitreous humor to the retina where they stimulate sensory receptors.

      C. Nerves in the eye control the amount of _____ entering the eye through the _____, the focusing of the light by the lens on the _____, and the transmission of the resulting images to the _____.

      D. The eye is made up of the eyeball and its internal structures, which perform the complex process of translating _____ into _____, and external structures that support and protect the eyeballs.

   2. The Iris

      A. The iris is part of the _____ layer.

      B. Contains the _____, or eye color.

      C. Has a _____ in the center, called the _____, which controls the amount of light entering the eye.

230

© 2011 Pearson Education, Inc.

3. The Innermost Layer of the Eye
   A. Contains the _____ cells in the retina called _____ and _____ that translate light rays into nerve impulses that are transmitted to the brain.
   B. The fovea centralis retinae contains only _____.
   C. The optic nerve enters at the _____ disk and carries this information from the eye to the brain.
   D. A reflexive process called _____ adjusts the eye's optical powers to maintain a clear image at various distances.

4. Eyelids, or Palpebrae
   A. Eyelids close over the eyeballs, protecting them from _____ _____, _____ _____, and _____.
   B. They also keep the eyes moist by preventing _____ from evaporating.
   C. _____ in the margins protect the eye from foreign matter.
   D. The superior and inferior _____ meet at the _____ at each corner of the eye.

5. The Lacrimal Apparatus
   A. The lacrimal gland secretes _____ through ducts on the surface of the _____ of the _____ lid.
   B. _____ cleanse the eyes and keep them moist.
   C. At the inner corner of each eye are two ducts, the _____ _____, which collect and drain the tears in the lacrimal _____.

6. Extrinsic Eye Muscles
   A. Six short extrinsic eye muscles connect the eyeball to the _____ _____.
   B. Muscles provide the eyeball with support and _____ movement.
   C. Four of these muscles, the _____ muscles, are straight; two are oblique, or slanted.

7. The Characteristics of Refractive Disorders of the Eye
   A. Refractive disorders are the most _Common_ disorders of the eye.
   B. Characterized by the _inability_ of the eye to _focus_ correctly.
   C. Caused by factors such as _aging_ and changes in the _shape_ of the eyeball and the various eye muscles.

8. Astigmatism
   A. Caused by irregularities in the _curvature_ of the _cornea_ and _lens_ that cause light to focus on the retina but spread out over an area.
   B. Signs and symptoms include _blurry_ near or distance vision.
   C. Treatment involves the use of _corrective_ lenses or surgery to reshape the _cornea_.

9. Myopia
   A. Also known as _nearsightedness_
   B. The lens focuses the light in front of the _retina_.

10. Hyperopia
    A. Also known as _farsightedness_
    B. The lens focuses light behind the _retina_.
    C. _distant_ objects are seen more clearly than objects that are _closer_.

11. Presbyopia
    A. Characterized by a loss of _elasticity_ in the lens, usually as a result of _aging_.
    B. Signs and symptoms include difficulty in focusing on _close_ objects.

12. Strabismus
    A. Also called _crossed_ eyes or _wall_ eyes.
    B. Signs and symptoms include poor _depth perception_ and diplopia, or _double_ vision.

© 2011 Pearson Education, Inc.

C. Treatment for strabismus
  i. _eyeglasses_
  ii. _eye excercises_
  iii. _Wearing a patch over the stronger eye to_
  iv. _Surgery to realign the eyes_

13. Blepharoptosis
  A. Usually a _congenital_ condition that occurs when the muscles of the eyelid are not strong enough to _raise_ it.
  B. Signs and symptoms include abnormal _drooping_ of one or both _eyelids_.
  C. _Surgery_ is the only treatment option.

14. Exophthalmos
  A. Usually caused by _hyperthyriodism_ or _Graves_ disease.
  B. Unilateral exophthalmos may be caused by an _orbitz tumor_.
  C. Signs and symptoms include _Outward bulging_ of one or both eyeballs.

15. Blepharitis
  A. Inflammation of the _infection_ of the _eyelids_.
  B. Signs and symptoms include redness, _Itching_, and swelling of the eyelids.
  C. Treatment includes warm _Compress_ and _ophtalmic_ antibiotic therapy.

16. Conjunctivitis
  A. Conjunctivitis is an _____ of the conjunctiva.
  B. Commonly known as _pinkeye_
  C. Causes of conjunctivitis
    i. _virus_
    ii. _bacteria_
    iii. _sexually transmitted infections (STI)_
    iv. _allergens_
    v. _irritants_

17. Hordeolums
  A. Caused by _bacteria_, generally *Staphylococcus*.
  B. May accompany blocked or infected eyelid _glands_ or _inflamed_ eyelids.
  C. Contaminated _fingers_ that touch the eye area may cause the infection.
  D. Painful hordeolums can occur _under_ the eyelids.
  E. Signs and symptoms of hordeolums
    i. _redness and tenderness_
    ii. _Itching_
    iii. _swelling_
    iv. _discomfort in the upper or lower eyelid_
  F. Treatment includes a warm, wet _Compress_ applied to the area that may help to relieve the pain.

18. Cataracts
  A. Cataracts are a clouding or _opacity_ of the _lens_ that prevents light from entering.
  B. The cause is unclear, but there may be a correlation between the formation of cataracts and _Smoking_, _diabetes_ and excessive exposure to _Sunlight_
  C. Signs and symptoms of cataracts
    i. _Images look fuzzy_
    ii. _Night vision suffers_
    iii. _double vision or problems with bright lights_
  D. Treatment for cataracts
    i. _Surgery_
    ii. _____

© 2011 Pearson Education, Inc.

19. Dry Macular Degeneration
    A. Dry macular degeneration is the deterioration of the macula, the _____ portion of the _____.
    B. Small yellow deposits called _____ form under the macula, causing it to thin and dry out, leading to a loss of _____ vision.
    C. This form has a _____ progression than does the wet type; however, it sometimes turns into the wet type.

20. Wet Macular Degeneration
    A. _____ new blood vessels grow under the _____ and the macula.
    B. These blood vessels may then _____ and leak fluid, which causes the macula to _____ or lift up, impairing or destroying the central vision.
    C. Vision loss may be _____ and _____.

21. Nyctalopia
    A. The inability to see well in _faint_ light.
    B. Occurs in patients with _retinitispigmentosa_ and _Choroidoretinitis_
    C. May be due to a vitamin _A_ deficiency.
    D. Can be provoked by _Smoking tobacco_

22. Amblyopia
    A. Also called _lazy eye_
    B. This disorder, seen in _Children_, occurs when the muscles are weaker in one eye than in the other.
    C. Patients with more severe amblyopia may suffer from various vision-related disorders, such as _poor depth perception_
    D. For treatment, a _patch_ may be worn over the stronger eye to strengthen the muscles of the weaker eye.

23. Corneal Abrasion
    A. Results from _injury_, _infection_, or both.
    B. Can be very _painful_
    C. The patient will be very sensitive to _light_ and will have difficulty opening the affected eye.
    D. Treatment may include mild _analgesi_ and resting the eye.

24. Diplopia
    A. Also called _double vision_
    B. Frequently follows _trauma_ to the eye or head.
    C. Can be caused by a disease of any of the following structures:
        i. _lens_
        ii. _retina_
        iii. _cranial nerve_
        iv. _Crebellum_
        v. _crebrum_
        vi. _meninges_

25. Glaucoma
    A. Characterized by _increased_ pressure in the eye brought on by an excessive amount of _aqueos_ humor.
    B. If left untreated, the _pressure_ can lead to damage of the _optic nerve_ and, eventually, blindness.
    C. Types of glaucoma include _open angle (acute)_ and _closed angle (chronic)_.
    D. Glaucoma has no symptoms, so it must be diagnosed by _pressure testing_ in a doctor's office.

© 2011 Pearson Education, Inc.

E. Treatment includes eye drops to lower _Intraocular pressure_, as well as possible _laser_ or conventional surgery.

26. Nystagmus or Nystaxis
    A. Characterized by _involuntary_, _repetitive_, _rhylmthmic_ eye movements.
    B. May be _inherited_ or acquired.
    C. Usually results in some _loss_ of vision.
    D. Signs and symptoms include _uncontrolled_ eye movements that may be _lateral_, _horizonator_ or even _circular_.

27. Retinopathy
    A. Patients with _diabetes_ are prone to diabetic retinopathy.
    B. This nerve damage is a result of _hypertensive Retinopathy_ and can lead to permanent blindness.

28. Photophobia
    A. Also known as _sensitivity_ to light.
    B. Sometimes caused by _measles_, _rubella_, _meningitis_, or inflammation of the eyes.

II. The Senses of Hearing, Taste, and Smell
   1. The Three Main Divisions of the Ear
      i. _the external_
      ii. _middle_
      iii. _inner_

   2. The Structure and Function of the External Ear
      A. The pinna, or auricle, funnels sound waves through the _____ _____ to the _____ membrane.
      B. The auditory canal, or auditory meatus, is S-shaped and secretes _____, or _____.
      C. The tympanic membrane, or eardrum, separates the _____ ear from the _____ ear.

   3. The Structure and Function of the Middle Ear
      A. The middle ear is a tiny cavity in the _____ bone of the skull.
      B. Contains three small bones: the _____ (hammer), the _____ (anvil), and the _____ (stirrup).
      C. The function of the middle ear
         i. Transmits _____ _____.
         ii. _____ air pressure on both sides of the tympanic membrane.
         iii. Protects the ear from _____ _____ .
         iv. Sound vibrations are transmitted by _____ from the tympanic membrane to the _____ _____ and into the inner ear.

   4. The Structure and Function of the Inner Ear
      A. The inner ear is a bony labyrinth in the temporal bone that is made up of the _____, the _____, and _____ semicircular canals.
      B. The bony and membranous labyrinths are separated by _____.
      C. Tiny _____ cells function as receptors for hearing and balance.
      D. The cochlea resembles a _____ _____.
      E. The cochlear duct runs between the _____ and _____ chambers.

   5. The Two Most Common Types of Hearing Disorders
      A. Conductive
         i. Temporary hearing loss; sound is not conducted efficiently through the _auditory canal_ to the _eardrum_ and _ossicles_ in the middle ear
         ii. _Conductive hearing loss_ can be corrected.

234   CHAPTER 26

© 2011 Pearson Education, Inc.

B. Sensorineural
   i. Permanent hearing loss is caused by damaged <u>cochlea</u> or <u>nerve pathways</u> from the inner ear to the brain.
   ii. <u>medically or surgically</u> cannot be corrected.

6. Impacted Cerumen
  A. Cerumen is produced by the <u>auditory canal</u> as lubrication.
  B. Impacted cerumen obstructs the <u>auditory canal</u>.
  C. Affects <u>older</u> adults.
  D. Exacerbated by the use of a _____ swab.
  E. Signs and symptoms include blocked or <u>muffled</u> hearing, a <u>plugged</u> feeling in the ear, and <u>even pain</u>.
  F. Treatment includes softening the <u>wax</u>, then flushing with a <u>ear syringe</u>
  G. If left untreated, impacted cerumen leads to <u>hearing loss</u>

7. Ruptured Tympanic Membrane
  A. Caused by <u>objects entering the ear</u> or <u>unequal</u> air pressure on both sides of the membrane.
  B. Signs and symptoms of a ruptured tympanic membrane
    i. <u>drainage of fluid</u>
    ii. <u>tinnitus and hearing loss</u>
  C. Treatment for a ruptured tympanic membrane
    i. <u>antibiotic medication</u>
    ii. <u>flush ears w/ ear wax softners</u>
    iii. <u>room-temperature saline solution</u>

8. Otitis Media
  A. <u>Otitis externa</u> (swimmer's ear) is an inflammation of the outer ear.
  B. <u>Otitis media</u> is an inflammation of the middle ear.
  C. Signs and Symptoms of otitis media
    i. <u>tug at the affected ear</u>
    ii. <u>unusally irritable or fussy</u>
    iii. <u>have a fever and fluid drainage from the ear</u>
    iv. <u>difficulty sleeping</u>
    v. <u>fluid drainage and exhibiting a loss of balance are more serious sympto</u>
  D. Treatment for otitis media
    i. Eliminating the cause of the <u>infection</u>
    ii. Oral <u>antibiot</u> and decongestants
    iii. <u>tubal insufflation</u> every 1 to 2 days

9. Otosclerosis
  A. Otosclerosis is a <u>hereditary</u> condition
  B. The tissue surrounding the staples grows <u>abnormally</u>
  C. Prevents <u>stapes</u> from transmitting sound vibrations.
  D. Signs and symptoms include hearing loss in one or both ears, <u>tinnitus</u>, and <u>dizzines</u>
  E. Treatment includes the use of a <u>otosclerosis</u> or surgery.

10. Tinnitus
  A. Causes of tinnitus
    i. <u>hearing loss</u>
    ii. <u>loud noise</u>
    iii. <u>certain medications</u>
    iv. <u>allergies</u>
    v. <u>tumors</u>
  B. Signs and symptoms include <u>ringing</u> or <u>roaring</u> in one or both ears.
  C. Some relief is provided by the use of <u>hearing aid maskers</u>, _____, and medications such as <u>antiarr</u> and antidepressants.
    <u>ythmics</u>

© 2011 Pearson Education, Inc.

11. Ménière's Disease
    A. Caused by changes in _fluid_ volume in the _inner_ ear.
    B. Signs and symptoms of Ménière's disease
        i. _vertigo_
        ii. _tinnitus_
        iii. _headache_
        iv. _nausea_
        v. _vomiting_
        vi. _diarrhea_
        vii. _hearing loss_
        viii. _pressure-feeling_
        ix. _pain in the affected ear_
    C. Treatment for Ménière's disease
        i. _reducing fluid low-salt diet_
        ii. _avoid caffeine_
        iii. _avoid alchol_
        iv. _Diuretic drugs_
        v. _Other medications_
12. Presbycusis
    A. Caused by loud noises, _infection, injury_, or the side effects of medications.
    B. Occurs in both ears and affects _normal_ and _high-pitched_ tones.
    C. Treatment typically involves the use of a _hearing aid_.
13. How the Senses of Taste and Smell Function Together
    A. _Olfactory_ cells respond to the changes in the chemical concentrations that activate the smell _____.
    B. Receptors send information to the brain via _Olfactory nerves_
    C. _____ move from the nose to the mouth region, stimulating the _taste buds_.
14. The Four Types of Taste Cells
    i. _sweet_
    ii. _sour_
    iii. _salty_
    iv. _bitter_
15. The Sense of Touch
    A. The sense of touch is the oldest, most _primitive_ sense.
    B. It is the first sense that humans experience in the _womb_ and the last one lost before _death_.
    C. Found over the _entire_ body.
    D. Originates in the _dermis_.
    E. Nerve endings in the _dermis_, called receptors, transmit _information_ to the brain via the spinal cord.
    F. More nerve endings equal more _sensitive it is_

KEY TERMINOLOGY REVIEW

Match the vocabulary term to the correct definition below.

a. Accommodation

b. Aqueous humor

c. Canthus

d. Choroid

© 2011 Pearson Education, Inc.

e. Ciliary body
f. Cones
g. Conjunctiva
h. Cornea
i. Diabetic retinopathy
j. Ciplopia
k. Ectropion
l. Entropion
m. Fundus
n. Hearing loss
o. Hordeolums
p. Hypertensive retinopathy
q. Insufflation
r. Labyrinth
s. Lacrimal sac
t. Macula lutea

u. Nasolacrimal duct
v. Orbit
w. Ossicles
x. Palpebral fissure
y. Papilledema
z. Pupil
aa. Refraction problems
bb. Focea centralis retinae
cc. Retina
dd. Retinal detachment
ee. Rods
ff. Sclera
gg. Vertigo
hh. Vitreous chamber
ii. Vitreous humor

1. _____ Provides nutrients to the cornea, lens, and other tissues.

2. _____ Located in the middle of the macula lutea, a yellow spot on the back of the eye.

3. _____ Empties into the nasal cavity.

4. _____ Can be divided into two main conditions: Conductive (temporary) and Sensorineural (permanent).

5. _____ The posterior, or back, section of the eyeball cavity located behind the lens.

6. _____ Also known as sties, which are very common and frequently contagious.

7. _____ Lines the sclera and absorbs extra light entering the eye.

8. _____ The floor of the tympanic cavity.

9. _____ A reflexive process that adjusts the eye's optical powers to maintain a clear image at various distances.

10. _____ Responsible for holding and moving the lens.

11. _____ Causes nerve damage as a result of hypertension and can lead to permanent blindness.

12. _____ A maze of bones inside the inner ear.

13. _____ They are sensitive to bright light and are used to see color.

14. _____ Controls the amount of light entering the eye.

15. _____ A form of severe dizziness.

16. _____ The inability to focus correctly, it occurs because light rays change direction when they pass through the eye.

17. _____ A yellow spot on the back of the eye.

18. _____ A mucous membrane that lines the underside of the eyelids and the anterior part of the eyeball.

19. _____ An inflammation at the optic nerve, usually caused by a tumor, which increases pressure in the eye.

20. _____ Frequently referred to as the "window" of the eye because it allows light to enter.

© 2011 Pearson Education, Inc.

21. _____ Occurs when the retina has separated from the underlying choroid layer.
22. _____ The introduction of gas, vapor, or powder into a cavity every 1 to 2 days.
23. _____ The white part of the eye.
24. _____ A very thick fluid in the vitreous chamber.
25. _____ A disease of the retina and a condition that patients with diabetes tend to have.
26. _____ The photosensitive cells in the retina.
27. _____ It empties into the nasolacrimal duct, which empties into the nasal cavity.
28. _____ Also known as double vision.
29. _____ The innermost layer of the eye.
30. _____ An abnormal condition in which the lower eyelid everts, or turns outward.
31. _____ The outer and inner corners of the eye where the superior and inferior palpebrae meet.
32. _____ The opening between the eyelids that allows light to enter.
33. _____ The cavity in the skull that houses the eyeball.
34. _____ A condition where the eyelid inverts, or folds inward.
35. _____ The name of the three small bones found in the middle ear.

APPLIED PRACTICE

Read the scenario below and answer the questions that follow.

1. On the image provided, label the parts of the eyeball and its anatomical structures.

© 2011 Pearson Education, Inc.

2. On the image provided, label the parts of the ear and its anatomical structures.

auricle(pinna)

Inner ear

middle ear

malleus

Incus

Stapes

lobe

external ear

LEARNING ACTIVITY: MULTIPLE CHOICE

Circle the correct answer for each of the following questions.

1. Which of the following may develop due to maternal infections during the first 5 or 6 weeks of pregnancy?

   a. Strabismus
   b. Sensorineural deafness
   c. Congenital ear problems
   d. All of the above

2. How can intraocular pressure be reduced?

   a. Eyedrops
   b. Oral medications
   c. Surgery
   d. All of the above

3. Labyrinthitis is also known as _____.

   a. Otosclerosis
   b. Otitis media
   c. Nyctalopia
   d. Presbycusis

© 2011 Pearson Education, Inc.

4. The developing infant _____.
   a. has poor visual acuity
   b. is often farsighted
   c. lacks color vision and depth perception at birth
   d. All of the above

5. Refraction problems _____.
   a. involve the inability to focus correctly and occur because light rays change direction when they pass through the eye
   b. are typically seen more in children then in the elderly
   c. include conditions such as blepharoptosis
   d. All of the above

6. The use of an eye patch is recommended for which of the following conditions?
   a. Glaucoma
   b. Nystagmus
   c. Corneal abrasion
   d. Diplopia

7. Hypertensive retinopathy is caused by _____.
   a. a variety of factors
   b. hypertension
   c. hypotension
   d. diabetes

8. Recurrent ear infections may be treated with _____.
   a. myringotomy
   b. keratotomy
   c. osteotomy
   d. None of the above

9. Taste and smells are most acute _____.
   a. at birth
   b. by the toddler stage
   c. in young adults
   d. None of the above

10. The eyes continue to grow and mature _____.
    a. throughout one's life
    b. until adulthood
    c. until the eighth or ninth year of life
    d. None of the above

CRITICAL THINKING

Answer the following questions to the best of your ability. Utilize the textbook as a reference.

1. When dealing with patients who have visual difficulties, why should you understand the rules for driving in your state?

© 2011 Pearson Education, Inc.

_____
_____
_____
_____

2. If the physician is running behind schedule and patients must wait, what should you do?

_____
_____
_____
_____

RESEARCH ACTIVITY

Utilize Internet search engines to research the following topics and write a brief description of what you find. It is important to utilize reputable websites.

1. Visit different websites that deal with speech and hearing loss. What information can you find to help families with speech and hearing deficiencies? What websites did you find most useful? Could these websites be beneficial to staff members of an EENT (eye, ear, nose, and throat) practice? If so, why?

_____
_____
_____
_____
_____
_____
_____
_____
_____
_____
_____
_____
_____
_____
_____
_____
_____
_____
_____
_____
_____
_____
_____
_____

© 2011 Pearson Education, Inc.

CHAPTER 27

The Circulatory System

CHAPTER OUTLINE

General review of the chapter:

Overview of the Circulatory System
The Heart
Blood Vessels
Blood Pressure
Pulmonary and Systemic Circulation
Blood
Blood Types
The Lymphatic System
Common Disorders Associated with the Circulatory System

STUDENT STUDY GUIDE

Use the following guide to assist in your learning of the concepts from the chapter.

I. An Overview of the Circulatory System

1. The Heart

   A. Responsible for _____ the blood thorough the blood _____ throughout the body.
   B. Provides _____ blood to and removes _____ from the cells of the body.
   C. Made up of _____ muscle _____.
   D. Beats an average of _____ to _____ beats per minute or about _____ times a day.
   E. Located in the _____, in the center of the chest cavity.
   F. Located toward the _____ side of the _____.
   G. The tip of the heart at the lower edge is called the _____.
   H. The _____ is located directly in front of the heart.

2. The Blood Vessels

   A. Responsible for carrying the blood through the _____ to get _____ and release _____.
   B. Carries the _____ blood to all the _____ of the body.

3. The Blood

   A. Carries the _____ and waste products through the _____.
   B. A major waste product is _____.

4. The Lymphatic System

   1. Responsible for _____ substances to and from the _____ system.
   2. It is also a part of the _____ system.

© 2011 Pearson Education, Inc.

5. The Chambers of the Heart

    A. Divided into _____ chambers.

    B. The _____ are the receiving chambers of the heart.

    C. The _____ are the pumping chambers.

6. Heart Valves

    A. Act as restraining gates to control the direction of _____.

    B. Situated at the entrances and exits to the _____.

    C. When properly functioning, allow blood to flow only in the _____ direction by blocking it from _____ to the previous _____.

7. The Tricuspid Valve

    A. The tricuspid valve is an _____ valve.

    B. The prefix tri-, meaning _____, indicates that this valve has _____ leaflets or _____.

8. The Pulmonary Valve

    A. The pulmonary valve is also called the _____ valve.

    B. Located between the right _____ and the pulmonary artery.

9. The Mitral Valve

    A. The mitral valve is also called the _____ valve.

    B. Has _____ cusps.

    C. Blood flows through the _____ valve to the left ventricle.

10. The Valves of the Heart (Label the location of each valve of the heart.)

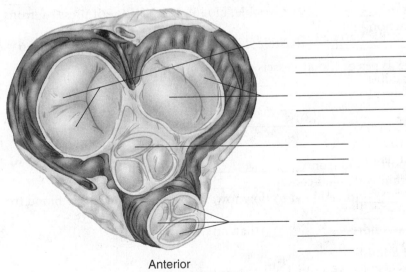

Anterior

11. The Great Vessels of the Heart (Explain what each vessel does.)

    A. The aorta _____.

    B. The pulmonary arteries _____.

    C. The pulmonary veins _____.

    D. The inferior and superior vena cava _____.

© 2011 Pearson Education, Inc.

12. The Normal Flow of Blood Through the Heart
    A. _____ blood from all of the tissues, except the lungs, enters a relaxed right _____ via two large veins called the _____ and the _____.
    B. The right _____ contracts and blood flows through the _____ valve into the relaxed right _____.
    C. The right _____ then contracts and blood is pumped through the pulmonary valve into the _____ artery, which carries the blood to the lungs.
    D. The left _____ receives blood that has been oxygenated by the lungs. This blood enters the relaxed left _____ from the four _____ veins.
    E. The left _____ contracts and blood flows through the _____ valve into the relaxed left _____.
    F. When the left _____ contracts, the blood is pumped through the aortic valve and into the aorta, the _____ artery in the body.
    G. The _____ carries blood to all parts of the body, except the lungs.

13. The Conduction System of the Heart
    A. The _____ _____ system controls the heart rate.
    B. Special tissue conducts _____ impulses that _____ different chambers to _____ in the correct order.

14. The Phases of the Cardiac Cycle
    A. Phase 1: _____
    B. Phase 2: _____
    C. Phase 3: _____

15. Blood Pressure
    A. A measurement of the force exerted by blood against the walls of a _____.
    B. During _____ systole, blood is under a lot of pressure from _____ contraction.
    C. During _____ diastole, blood is not being _____ from the heart.

16. The Three Types of Blood Vessels (List and explain each type.)
    i. _____
    ii. _____
    iii. _____

17. Veins
    A. Transport blood from _____ tissues to the heart.
    B. Have thin walls that contain _____.
    C. _____ force blood to flow toward the heart, preventing blood from _____ in the lower _____.
    D. Veins are more _____ than arteries.

18. Korotkoff Sounds
    A. The sounds heard as the _____ wall _____ when the blood pressure cuff compresses.
    B. Classified according to _____ different phases

19. Average Normal Blood Pressure Readings
    A. Newborn: _____
    B. 6–9 years: _____
    C. 10–15 years: _____
    D. 16 years to adulthood: _____
    E. Adult: _____

© 2011 Pearson Education, Inc.

20. Physiological Factors Affecting Blood Pressure
    i. _____
    ii. _____
    iii. _____
    iv. _____
21. Pulmonary Circulation
    A. The route that blood takes from the _____ to the _____ and then back to the _____.
    B. The function of pulmonary circulation is to _____ the blood.
22. The Physiology of the Lymphatic System
    A. Collects excess _____ fluid throughout the body and returns it to the _____ system, purifying it as it passes through the system.
    B. Assists the _____ system in _____ substances throughout the body.
    C. Defends against the invasion of _____.
23. Lymphatic Vessels
    A. Form a network of _____ throughout the body.
    B. Serve as one-way pipes conducting _____ from the _____ toward the _____ cavity.
    C. These vessels begin as very small _____ _____ in the tissues.
    D. Excessive tissue fluid enters these _____ to begin the trip back to the _____ system.
    E. _____ merge into large lymph vessels that have _____ along their length.
    F. Lymph vessels finally drain into one of two large lymph _____.
24. Lymph Nodes
    A. Lymph nodes are small organs composed of _____ tissue that are located along the route of the _____ vessels.
    B. The functions of the lymph nodes
        i. _____
        ii. _____
        iii. _____
25. Tonsils
    A. Tonsils are lymphatic tissue located on each side of the _____.
    B. There are three sets of tonsils
        i. _____
        ii. _____
        iii. _____
    C. Act as _____ to protect the body.
26. The Spleen
    A. Located in the _____ of the abdomen.
    B. Consists of lymphatic tissue that is highly infiltrated with _____ _____.
27. The Thymus Gland
    A. Located in the upper portion of the _____.
    B. Essential for the proper development of the _____ system.
    C. Assists the body with the _____ function and the development of _____.

II. The Composition and Function of Blood
    1. The Blood
        A. The average adult has about _____ liters of blood.
        B. Circulates through the body in the vessels of the _____ system.
        C. Blood is a mixture of _____ with _____.

© 2011 Pearson Education, Inc.

2. The Functions of Blood
    i. _____
    ii. _____
    iii. _____

3. Erythrocytes
    A. Erythrocytes are _____ blood cells.
    B. There are _____ erythrocytes per cubic millimeter of _____.
    C. The life span of an erythrocytes is _____ days.

4. Leukocytes
    A. Leukocytes are _____ blood cells
    B. Provide protection against _____.
    C. There are _____ leukocytes per cubic millimeter of _____.

5. Neutrophils
    A. Neutrophils are the most common _____.
    B. Categorized as _____.
    C. Develop in the _____ marrow.

6. Eosinophils
    A. Eosinophils are one of the least common _____.
    B. Categorized as _____.
    C. Develop in the _____ marrow.
    D. Engulf and destroy _____ cells.
    E. Release _____ chemicals that kill _____ that invade the body.

7. Basophils
    A. Categorized as _____.
    B. The nucleus of a basophil has _____ lobes.
    C. Release _____ at the site of tissue damage.

8. Lymphocytes
    A. Categorized as _____ because the granules in their cytoplasm are nearly invisible.
    B. Begin their development in the _____ marrow.
    C. Lymphocytes are present in the blood and in the _____ nodes, _____ tissues, and the organs of the _____ system.

9. Monocytes
    A. Monocytes are _____ that engulf and destroy all types of invading microorganisms, cancerous cells, dead leukocytes, and cellular debris.
    B. Found in the _____ and in the _____ nodes of the _____ system.

10. Thrombocytes (Platelets)
    A. Different from other blood cells because they are only _____.
    B. Active in the _____ process.
    C. Begin their development in the red marrow as stem cells, which then become _____.
    D. Thrombocytes are the smallest of all the elements of the _____.
    E. They are not _____ cells.
    F. They are critical in _____, or hemostasis.
    G. Leads to the formation of _____, which converts fibrinogen to fibrin.

11. Blood Types (List the four blood types.)
    i. _____
    ii. _____
    iii. _____
    iv. _____

© 2011 Pearson Education, Inc.

12. Universal Donor
    A. Because type _____ blood has neither marker _____ nor _____, it will not react with _____ or _____ antibodies.
    B. In an emergency, type _____ blood may be given to a person with any of the other blood types.
    C. A person with type _____ blood has no _____ against the other blood types and, therefore, in an emergency, can receive any type of blood.

13. The Rh Factor
    A. A person with the Rh factor in his or her red blood cells is said to be _____.
    B. Since this person has the Rh factor, he or she will not make _____ antibodies.
    C. A person without the Rh factor is Rh _____ and will produce _____ antibodies.

III. The Pathology of the Circulatory System
    1. Anemia
        A. Anemia is a condition characterized by abnormally _____ numbers of healthy _____ blood cells circulating in the body.
        B. Often considered to be the most common dysfunction of the _____ blood cells.
        C. Affects about _____ Americans.

    2. Common Signs and Symptoms of Anemia
        i. _____
        ii. _____
        iii. _____
        iv. _____
        v. _____
        vi. _____
        vii. _____
        viii. _____
        ix. _____
        x. _____

    3. Causes of Anemia
        A. _____ production of healthy red cells by the bone marrow.
        B. _____ erythrocyte destruction.
        C. _____ and _____ deficiencies in the diet that can also slow down the production of _____.

    4. Iron Deficiency Anemia
        A. Occurs when there is not enough _____ in the body.
        B. Iron deficiency anemia is the most _____ type of anemia.
        C. Symptoms include _____, _____, _____, and _____.

    5. Vitamin Deficiency Anemia
        A. Vitamin B12 is essential for normal _____ production. Some people have difficulty absorbing B12, resulting in a vitamin B12 deficiency, a condition known as _____ anemia.

    6. Hemolytic Anemia
        A. Occurs when there are not enough _____ blood cells in the blood.
        B. Caused by a _____ destruction of red blood cells with which the bone marrow cannot keep up.

© 2011 Pearson Education, Inc.

7. Sickle Cell Anemia

    A. The abnormal _____ shape and sharp edges of this sickled _____ are very different from the smooth, rounded contours of a normal erythrocyte.

    B. Repeated sickling causes these fragile _____ to have a shortened life span, resulting in _____.

8. Aplastic Anemia

    A. Occurs when the body stops producing enough _____ blood cells.

    B. Aplastic anemia is a rare and _____ condition.

    C. Treatment includes _____, _____, and a _____.

9. Aneurysm

    A. An aneurysm is an abnormal _____ or _____ of a portion of an _____, related to a weakness in the vessel wall.

    B. Can be congential or _____.

    C. High blood pressure and _____ disease may contribute to the formation of certain types of aneurysms.

10. Treatment for Aneurysms

    A. Surgical intervention may be required to repair the _____ and prevent _____.

    B. Some patients may also be candidates for _____ placement within the affected vessel.

11. Arrhythmias

    A. An arrhythmia is an _____ heartbeat caused by a disturbance of the normal _____ activity of the heart.

    B. Can be _____, especially when they significantly impact the pumping function of the blood.

12. Causes of Arrhythmias

    i. _____

    ii. _____

    iii. _____

    iv. _____

13. Signs and Symptoms of Arrhythmias

    i. _____

    ii. _____

    iii. _____

    iv. _____

    v. _____

    vi. _____

    vii. _____

14. Treatment for Arrhythmias

    i. _____

    ii. _____

    iii. _____

15. Arteriosclerosis

    A. Often referred to as _____.

    B. Arteriosclerosis is the thickening and loss of _____ of the _____.

    C. Causative factors include the following:

        i. _____

        ii. _____

        iii. _____

        iv. _____

© 2011 Pearson Education, Inc.

16. Symptoms of and Treatment for Arteriosclerosis

    A. Symptoms include:

        i. _____

        ii. _____

        iii. _____

    B. Treatment includes relieving the _____ and _____.

17. Atherosclerosis

    A. Narrowing and _____ of the vessel _____ of the _____.

    B. Caused by a buildup of _____ material and _____ within the vessel.

18. Cardiogenic Shock

    A. Cardiogenic shock is the collapse of the _____ system.

    B. Characterized by _____ and fluid shifting away from the heart.

    C. Shock leads to inefficient _____ function.

19. Symptoms of and Treatment for Cardiogenic Shock

    A. Symptoms of cardiogenic shock

        i. _____

        ii. _____

        iii. _____

        iv. _____

    B. Treatment for cardiogenic shock

        i. _____

        ii. _____

        iii. _____

        iv. _____

20. Cardiomyopathy

    A. Cardiomyopathy is a disease of the _____, or heart muscle, resulting in _____ dysfunction.

    B. Thought to be _____ and idiopathic.

21. Symptoms of and Treatment for Cardiomyopathy

    A. Signs and symptoms include an enlarged _____.

    B. Treatment for cardiomyopathy

        i. _____

        ii. _____

        iii. _____

22. Endocarditis

    A. Endocarditis is an inflammation of the _____ of the heart, including the heart _____.

    B. Most commonly caused by a _____ infection.

    C. Frequently affects patients with existing abnormal conditions of the heart _____.

23. Symptoms of and Treatment for Endocarditis

    A. Symptoms of endocarditis

        i. _____

        ii. _____

        iii. _____

        iv. _____

        v. _____

    B. Treatment generally consists of _antibodies_

© 2011 Pearson Education, Inc.

24. Myocarditis
   A. Myocarditis is an inflammation of the _muscular_ layer of the heart.
   B. The most common cause is a _viral_ infection.

25. Symptoms of and Treatment for Myocarditis
   A. Symptoms of myocarditis
      i. _palpitations_
      ii. _heart attack_
      iii. _dyspnea_
      iv. _malaise_
      v. _fainting_
      vi. _decrease of urine output_
   B. The best treatment is the _reduction_ of the inflammation, bed rest, and a _low-sodium_ diet.

26. Pericarditis
   A. Pericarditis is an inflammation of the _pericardium_
   B. Most commonly seen as a complication of a _viral_ or _bacteria_ infection.

27. Symptoms of and Treatment for Pericarditis
   A. Symptoms of pericarditis
      i. _sharp stabbing chest pain_
      ii. _fatigue_
      iii. _fever_
      iv. _dyspnea_
   B. Treatment for pericarditis
      i. _analgesics_
      ii. _diuretic_
      iii. _reduce the amount of fluid around the heart_

28. Cerebrovascular Accident
   A. Occurs when the blood flow to the brain stops, allowing brain cells to _hemorrha_
   B. The two types of stroke are _ischemia_ and _embolish_.

29. Symptoms of a Cerebrovascular Accident
      i. _numbness or weakness on side of the_
      ii. _vision problems_
      iii. _severe dizziness_
      iv. _loss of balance or coordination_
      v. _severe headache_

30. Causes of Congestive Heart Failure
      i. _coronary artery disease_
      ii. _past heart attack_
      iii. _hypertension_
      iv. _heart valve disease_
      v. _rheumatic fever_
      vi. _heart defect_
      vii. _heart musle_

31. Signs and Symptoms of Congestive Heart Failure
      i. _shortness of breath_
      ii. _heart failure_
      iii. _swelling oredema_

© 2011 Pearson Education, Inc.

32. Treatment for Congestive Heart Failure
    i. _____
    ii. _____
    iii. _____
    iv. _____

33. Cor Pulmonale

    A. Also known as _____ heart disease.
    B. Causes the _____ ventricle to _____.
    C. A symptom of cor pulmonale is _____, or an _____ heart.

34. Coronary Heart Disease

    A. Also called _____ disease.
    B. A _____ of the blood vessels that supply blood and oxygen to the heart muscle.

35. Factors that Increase the Risk of Coronary Heart Disease
    i. _____
    ii. _____
    iii. _____
    iv. _____
    v. _____
    vi. _____
    vii. _____
    viii. _____

36. Symptoms of and Treatment for Coronary Heart Disease

    A. Symptoms of coronary heart disease
        i. _____
        ii. _____
        iii. _____
    B. Treatment includes _____ and _____.

37. Myocardial Infarction

    A. Affects more than _____ people each year.
    B. Occurs when the blood supply to a part of the _____ is severely reduced or stopped.

38. Treatment for Myocardial Infarction
    i. _____
    ii. _____
    iii. _____
    iv. _____

39. Leukemia

    A. Malignant cancer of the _____ and _____.
    B. Involves the uncontrolled growth of _____ cells.
    C. Can be acute or _____.

40. Symptoms of Leukemia
    i. _____
    ii. _____
    iii. _____
    iv. _____
    v. _____
    vi. _____
    vii. _____
    viii. _____

© 2011 Pearson Education, Inc.

ix. _adobomid bleeding_
x. _enlargement of the lymph nodes_
xi. _spleen liver_

41. Treatment for Leukemia
    A. _Chemotherapy_ is used to kill leukemia cells with strong anticancer drugs.
    B. _radiation_ therapy is used to kill cancer cells by exposure to high-energy _____.
    C. _bonemarrow_ transplant

42. Mitral Stenosis
    A. Caused by insufficient closing of the _valvular_
    B. Leads to _prolapse_ or a _protruding_ backward.
    C. May cause a _heartattack_
    D. Treatment includes _mediation_ to strengthen heart function.

43. Varicose Veins
    A. Enlarged walls that are _swollen_ and _distended_ above the surface of the skin.
    B. Caused when the _blood pools_ in the veins _engorged_
    C. Affect ___1O___ out of ___2O___ people in the United States.

44. Prevention of Varicose Veins
    i. _exercising_
    ii. _watching your weight_
    iii. _eating high fiber low salt diet_
    iv. _Avoiding high heels and tight hosiery_
    v. _elevating (your legs)_
    vi. _Change sitting or standing position regulat_

45. Symptom Relief of Varicose Veins
    i. _ligation_
    ii. _moderete excerise_
    iii. _Avoid long period of_
    iv. _elevating the leg_
    v. _wearing support stocking_

KEY TERMINOLOGY REVIEW

Without using your textbook, write a sentence using the selected vocabulary terms in the correct context.

1. *Auscultation*

_____

_____

2. *Bruit*

_____

_____

3. *Bradycardia*

_____

_____

4. *Carditis*

_____

_____

© 2011 Pearson Education, Inc.

5. *Carotid artery*

_____

_____

6. *Cyanosis*

_____

_____

7. *Cor pulmonale*

_____

_____

8. *Dyspnea*

_____

_____

9. *Hemophilia*

_____

_____

10. *Hypoxia*

_____

_____

11. *Inferior vena cava*

_____

_____

12. *Ischemia*

_____

_____

13. *Occlusion*

_____

_____

14. *Petechiae*

_____

_____

15. *Purkinje fibers*

_____

_____

16. *Sinoatrial node*

_____

_____

17. *Sphyagomanometer*

_____

_____

18. *Superior vena cava*

_____

_____

19. *Thoracocenesis*

_____

_____

20. *Thrombophlebitis*

_____

_____

APPLIED PRACTICE

1. List the primary pulse points of the body.

Temporal artery

Facial artery

Carotid artery

brachial artery

Radial artery

Femoral artery

popliteal artery

Anterior tibial artery

posterior tibial

Dorsalis pedi artery

© 2011 Pearson Education, Inc.

2. Provide the names of the ducts and nodes of the lymphatic system.

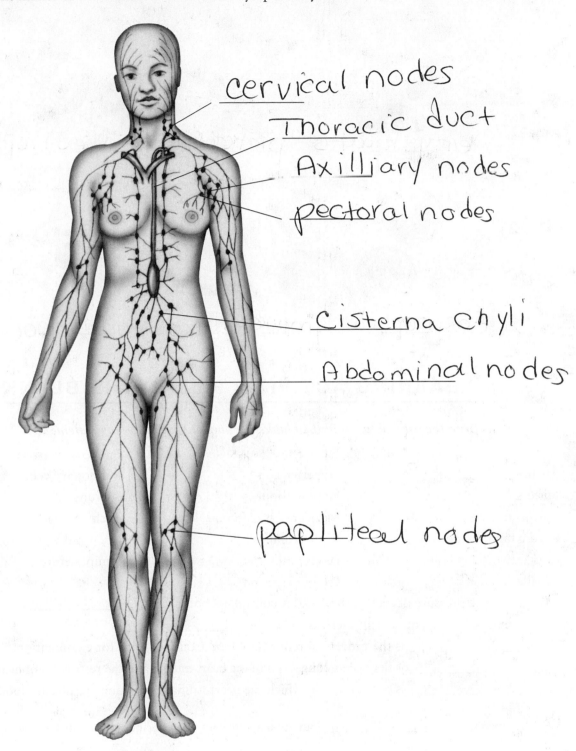

cervical nodes
Thoracic duct
Axilliary nodes
pectoral nodes

Cisterna chyli

Abdominal nodes

papliteal nodes

© 2011 Pearson Education, Inc.

3. Provide the name of each formed element of blood.

erythrocytes   platelets   Neutrophils

Eosinophils   lymphocytes   basophils   monocytes

LEARNING ACTIVITY: FILL IN THE BLANK

Using words from the list below, fill in the blanks to complete the following statements.

Agglutination	Flutter	Pulmonary artery
Aneurysm	Hypertension	Pulmonary vein
Buffers	Hypotension	Septum
Cardic arrest	Myocardial infarction	Tachycardia
Cardic tamponade	Myocardium	Tricuspid valve
Congestive heart failure	Pericardium	Venipuncture
Fibrillation	Prehypertension	

1. A systolic pressure of greater than 120 is considered borderline _____.

2. The middle layer, or heart muscle, is called the _____.

3. _____ is the process of removing blood from the veins for examination.

4. _____ is defined as congestion of the heart muscle and the restriction of heart movement.

5. _____ is a condition in which the heart is unable to pump sufficient blood to the other organs.

6. Symptoms of a _____ include a squeezing pain or heavy pressure in the middle of the chest.

7. When the electrical system has problems, _____ can occur.

8. The AV bundle extends from the AV node into the intraventricular _____.

9. The _____ is the outer lining of the heart.

10. _____ occurs when an antigen on the surface of red blood cells binds to antibodies in the plasma.

© 2011 Pearson Education, Inc.

11. On its return from the lungs, oxygenated blood enters the left atrium via the _____.

12. When an occlusion leads to the heart stopping, it is known as _____.

13. Blood pressure ranging from 120/80 to 139/89 is a symptom of _____.

14. The blood contains _____, which are mechanisms within the blood that balance the pH level.

15. _____ is an abnormally fast heartbeat of more than 100 beats per minute.

16. _____ is an abnormal condition in which a person's blood pressure is much lower than usual.

17. After going through the _____, the blood enters the right ventricle.

18. Common locations for an _____ include the aorta, brain, leg, and intestine.

19. Blood leaves the right ventricle through the pulmonary valve to go to the lungs, via the _____.

20. If the heart trembles, it is known as _____.

CRITICAL THINKING

Answer the following questions to the best of your ability. Utilize the textbook as a reference.

1. You are working at the front desk and looking out at the patients who have been waiting for their appointments. One man appears to be holding his left hand in front of his chest, he seems to be SOB, and his face looks sweaty or clammy. What is your first thought about this patient? Describe what the danger signs are to you even though the patient has not come up to the desk to voice a complaint about how he is feeling. What might you ask the patient and how would you handle this situation?

_____

_____

_____

_____

_____

2. You are performing an EKG. As it is printing, you notice that there is a normal waveform and complex, but the number of beats per minute is more than 100. What do you think the problem could be? Speculate on what the doctor might diagnose.

_____

_____

_____

3. When providing care to a patient, how can you help to ensure that their privacy is protected?

_____

_____

_____

_____

RESEARCH ACTIVITY

Utilize Internet search engines to research the following topics and write a brief description of what you find. It is important to utilize reputable websites.

1. Visit www.americanheart.org and navigate through the website. Pay particular attention to the link entitled "For Healthcare Professionals". Explain what information you think is most useful in this section and why.

_____

_____

_____

_____

_____

_____

_____

_____

_____

_____

_____

_____

_____

_____

© 2011 Pearson Education, Inc.

CHAPTER 28

The Immune System

CHAPTER OUTLINE

General review of the chapter:

Anatomy of the Immune System
The Immune System and the Body's Defenses
Common Disorders Associated with the Immune System

STUDENT STUDY GUIDE

Use the following guide to assist in your learning of the concepts from the chapter.

I. The Immune System

1. The Composition of the Immune System

    i. _____
    ii. _____
    iii. _____
    iv. _____
    v. _____

2. The Structures Central to the Immune System

    A. Central lymphoid tissue is composed of _____ _____.
    B. Peripheral lymphoid tissue consists of the _____ _____, _____, and _____ lymphoid tissue.

3. The Immune System

    A. Operates _____ the body.
    B. The structures are part of the _____ system, which is a subsystem of the _____ system.
    C. The primary function of the lymphatic system is to defend the body against invasion by pathogens such as _____, _____, and _____.
    D. Through the immune response, the _____, _____, and _____ work together to attack organisms and substances that invade body systems and cause disease.
    E. _____, or white blood cells (WBCs), combine to seek out and destroy harmful organisms.
    F. _____ medications and _____ can suppress the immune system.

4. The Bone Marrow

    A. Comprises the _____ _____ tissue.
    B. Contains _____ cells that create all of the cells that make up the tissues and structures of the immune system.

C. Produces _____ _____ cells, _____ _____ cells, and platelets, along with _____ cells and natural killer cells.

5. The Location and Purpose of the Thymus Gland

    A. Comprises the _____ _____ tissue.
    B. Located posterior to the _____, in the anterior _____.
    C. Manufactures infection-fighting _____ cells and helps distinguish normal _____ cells from those that attack the body's own tissues.

6. The Compartments of the Thymus Gland

    A. Consist of an outer _____ and an internal _____.
    B. _____ lymphoid cells enter the cortex, reproduce, and mature; they then move to the medulla where they reenter the _____.

7. The Peripheral Lymphatic System

    A. Consists of the _____ _____, _____, and other lymphoid tissue.
    B. Lymphatic _____, lymphatic _____, and lymphatic _____ are part of the peripheral lymphatic system.

8. Lymph Nodes

    A. Take many different _____ and _____.
    B. Most are _____ _____ and are about 1 inch long.
    C. They are covered with a _____, _____ capsule.
    D. The node is subdivided into different compartments by _____

    _____ .

9. B Lymphocytes

    A. The _____ _____ are the primary locations where B lymphocytes reproduce prolifically.
    B. Responsible for the production of circulating _____.
    C. Each unique type of B cell produces only one type of _____.
    D. When an _____ enters the body, these B lymphocytes rapidly undergo _____ and divide.

10. The Spleen

    A. Located in the _____ of the abdomen.
    B. Consists of lymphatic tissue that is highly _____ by blood vessels.
    C. The spleen's blood vessels are lined with _____, which swallow and digest debris in the blood such as worn-out red blood cells and _____.

11. Tonsils

    A. Located in the depressions of the mucous membranes of the _____ and the

    _____.
    B. The function of the tonsils is to _____ _____ and aid in the _____ of white blood cells.

12. Phagocytes

    A. Phagocytes are a type of white blood cell that attacks the _____ _____.
    B. A number of different cells are considered to be phagocytes, but the most common are _____, which primarily fight bacteria.

13. Lymphocytes

    A. A type of white blood cell that allows the body to _____ and _____ previous invading organisms.
    B. Originates in the _____ _____ and either stays there and matures into B cells or moves to the _____ _____, where they mature into T cells.

© 2011 Pearson Education, Inc.

14. B and T Lymphocytes

    A. B lymphocytes and T lymphocytes have _____ _____ within the immune system.

    B. B lymphocytes seek out invading _____ and send _____ to attach onto them.

    C. T cells _____ the organisms that the B lymphocytes have _____.

15. Antibodies

    A. Immunoglobulins are _____ that function as antibodies.

    B. The terms antibody and _____ are often used interchangeably.

    C. Antibodies are found in _____, _____ _____, and many secretions.

    D. Structurally, antibodies are globulins, which means that they are _____ and _____ by plasma cells derived from the B cells of the immune system.

16. The B Cells of the Immune System

    A. Activated upon _____ to their specific antigen and _____ into plasma cells.

    B. Although antibodies can recognize an antigen and lock onto it, they are not capable of _____ it; that is the job of the _____ cells.

17. T Cells

    A. T cells are a part of the system that destroys antigens which have been tagged by antibodies or cells that have been infected or _____ _____.

    B. Assist other cells, such as _____.

    C. Antibodies can _____ toxins produced by different organisms.

    D. Antibodies can activate a group of proteins called _____, which are also part of the immune system.

18. Innate Immunity

    A. Everyone is born with innate, or _____, immunity.

    B. Provided, in part, by the external barriers of the body, including the _____ and _____ _____ that line the _____, _____, and _____ tract.

    C. If this outer defensive wall is broken, such as by a cut in the skin, _____ _____ _____ on the skin attack any invading microorganisms.

19. Active Immunity

    A. Active immunity is _____.

    B. The individual has lifelong *protection* against the disease.

II. The Pathology of the Immune System

    1. Allergies

        A. An _____ is any substance capable of causing an allergic reaction.

        B. Most allergic reactions are a result of an immune system that responds to a _____ _____.

        C. When a harmless substance such as pollen is encountered by a person who is allergic to that substance, the immune system may react dramatically by producing _____ that attack the allergen.

    2. Anaphylaxis

        A. Sometimes occurs after a _____ or _____ is introduced into the patient.

        B. During anaphylaxis, _____ of the neck can cause breathing to be impeded, which can lead to _____ and death.

    3. Signs and Symptoms of Allergies

        i. _____

        ii. _____

© 2011 Pearson Education, Inc.

iii. _____

iv. _____

v. _____

vi. _____

vii. _____

4. Treatments for Allergies

A. _____ or _____ help combat allergy symptoms.

B. Reactions to certain _____ _____ may be treated by the use of air filters and dehumidifiers.

C. Alternative treatment includes _____ and _____ treatment.

D. In severe cases, optimal treatment may be identified only through _____ _____ _____ and desensitization.

E. If anaphylaxis occurs, it is important for the physician to immediately order medications (such as _____) that will stop the process.

5. Cancer

A. A group of many related diseases that all pertain to _____.

B. Cancer cells are unlike normal cells, which grow and, through _____, divide. Normal cells "know" when to stop growing.

6. Cancer Cells

A. Do not _____ or _____ like normal cells; they grow and spread very rapidly.

B. Cancer cells continue to _____ and _____ erratically and do not die.

C. They are not well _____, nor do they work on behalf of the body.

D. They also make use of the body's resources at the expense of _____ cells.

E. Usually, cancer cells clump together to form _____.

F. A _____ tumor can destroy the _____ cells around it, damaging the body's healthy tissue.

G. Sometimes cancer cells break away from the _____ _____ and travel to other areas of the body, where they keep growing, and form new tumors; this process is called _____.

7. Signs and Symptoms of Cancer

i. _____

ii. _____

iii. _____

iv. _____

v. _____

vi. _____

8. Treatment for Cancer

A. _____, _____, _____, or a combination of all three

B. The choice of treatment generally depends on the _____ of cancer and the _____ to which the cancer has spread within the body.

9. Surgery

A. Surgery is the _____ form of cancer treatment.

B. _____ out of every _____ persons with cancer may require surgery to remove it.

C. During surgery, some _____ cells or tissue may also be removed to ensure that all of the cancer is removed.

10. Chemotherapy

A. Medicines, which are sometimes taken in pill form but are more often given _____

B. Usually given over a number of _____ or _____.

© 2011 Pearson Education, Inc.

C. Often, a permanent IV catheter, called a _____, is placed under the skin into one of the larger blood vessels of the _____ _____.

11. Radiation Therapy

    A. Uses high-energy waves, such as _____, to damage and destroy cancer cells.
    B. Causes tumors to _____ and, in some cases, _____ completely.
    C. Radiation therapy is one of the most _____ treatments for cancer.

12. Immunotherapy

    A. Immunotherapy is the most _____ form of cancer therapy.
    B. It is a technique that involves creating _____ _____ _____ that are "programmed" to specifically target cancer cells.
    C. Empowers the body's own _____ _____ to target only cancer cells, rather than also destroying healthy cells.

13. Possible Causes of Chronic Fatigue Syndrome

    i. _____
    ii. _____
    iii. _____
    iv. _____
    v. _____

14. Signs and Symptoms of Chronic Fatigue Syndrome

    i. _____
    ii. _____
    iii. _____

15. Treatment for Chronic Fatigue Syndrome

    A. Generally begins with a thorough evaluation of the patient's _____ _____ history.
    B. Both the _____ and _____ of sleep are important.
    C. Educating the patient, with emphasis on becoming an _____ _____ in the treatment regimen. is extremely important in the treatment of CFS.

16. Infectious Mononucleosis

    A. Characterized by an increase in white blood cells that are _____, that is, containing a _____ _____.
    B. Often develops in young adults between the ages of _____ and _____.
    C. Commonly referred to as _____.
    D. The _____ period for mononucleosis is generally between 4 and 8 weeks.

17. Signs and Symptoms of Mononucleosis

    i. _____
    ii. _____
    iii. _____
    iv. _____

18. Treatment for Mononucleosis

    A. Getting plenty of _____.
    B. Gargling with _____ or using _____ to soothe the throat.
    C. Taking _____ and _____ medications to reduce fever and relieve sore throat and headache.

19. Types of Lymphedema

    A. Primary lymphedema can be _____ and has several stages.
    B. Secondary lymphedema is generally caused by an _____ of or _____ to the lymph system that interrupts the normal lymphatic flow.

© 2011 Pearson Education, Inc.

20. Causes of Primary Lymphedema

    i. _____

    ii. _____

    iii. _____

21. Causes of Secondary Lymphedema

    i. _____

    ii. _____

    iii. _____

22. Treatment for Lymphedema

    A. _____ (CDT) and _____ (MDT)

    B. CDT is used primarily in the treatment of lymphedema and

    _____.

    C. Other treatments for lymphedema

        i. _____

        ii. _____

        iii. _____

        iv. _____

        v. _____

23. Rheumatoid Arthritis

    A. One out of every _____ persons suffers from chronic rheumatoid arthritis.

    B. Individuals with a family history of rheumatoid arthritis are _____ times more likely to develop the disease.

    C. Occurs when the body's immune defenses attack tissue in the _____, leading to pain and degeneration of the _____.

    D. The disease and its treatment also increase _____; patients often have a shorter life expectancy than their healthy peers.

24. Signs and Symptoms of and Treatment for Rheumatoid Arthritis

    A. Signs and symptoms include pain and _____ in the joints.

    B. Treatment is based on medication regimens and educating the patient on how to

    _____.

    C. Drugs are used to _____ and _____ the symptoms, and help the patient to function at a more productive level.

25. Systemic Lupus Erythematosus

    A. Called a _____ disorder because its effects may appear in many parts of the body.

    B. Ninety percent of patients with SLE are women, who are generally diagnosed before

    _____.

    C. There is a _____ as well; the risk of developing SLE rises if a close family member has it.

    D. It is a chronic, lifelong condition with periods of _____ and _____.

26. Possible Signs and Symptoms of Systemic Lupus Erythematosus

    A. _____ and _____ in the joints.

    B. General _____, _____, _____, and _____.

    C. _____ (discoid) lesions that are raised and scaly.

    D. _____, or inflamed blood vessels, characterized by red marks in any area of the body.

© 2011 Pearson Education, Inc.

E. Sometimes, _____ appear, especially on the leg, where they may develop into _____.

F. In some people, the tips of the fingers and toes may develop _____.

27. Treatment of Systemic Lupus Erythematosus

A. Usually aimed at reducing the immune response using drugs such as _____.

B. The course of the disease for a given individual is difficult to predict, but with immediate treatment, most patients can expect to have a _____.

KEY TERMINOLOGY REVIEW

Match the vocabulary term to the correct definition below.

a. Acquired active immunity
b. Active immunity
c. Adenoids
d. Allergy
e. Anaphylaxis
f. Antibodies
g. Antigen
h. Artificially acquired active immunity
i. Autoimmune diseases
j. B lymphocytes
k. Chemotherapy
l. Chronic fatigue syndrome (CFS)
m. Complement
n. Cortex
o. Germinal centers
p. Immune response

q. immune system
r. Immunosuppressants
s. Infectious mononucleosis
t. Lymphedema
u. Medulla
v. Metastasis
w. Natural immunity
x. Neutrophils
y. Oncogenes
z. Passive immunity
aa. Radiation therapy
bb. Rheumatoid arthritis (RA)
cc. Systemic lupus erythematosus (SLE)
dd. T lymphocytes
ee. Trabeculae
ff. Vaccine

1. _____ Medications that suppress the immune system.

2. _____ Has no single known cause, although some authorities believe that it is a condition shared by many different underlying diseases rather than a separate disorder.

3. _____ Contains fragments of a disease organism or small amounts of a weakened disease organism.

4. _____ Occurs when the person is exposed to a live pathogen, develops the disease, and becomes immune as a result of the primary immune response.

5. _____ The process wherein cancer cells break away from the original tumor and travel to other areas.

6. _____ The cells responsible for the production of circulating antibodies, which are specialized proteins that lock onto specific antigens.

7. _____ An extreme, often life-threatening, response to an antigen.

8. _____ Uses high-energy waves, such as X-rays, to damage and destroy cancer cells.

9. _____ An inherited immunity to certain diseases.

10. _____ Inward-pointing compartments that make up part of the lymph nodes.

11. _____ Induced by a vaccine, which is a substance that contains the antigen and that stimulates a primary response against the antigen without causing symptoms of the disease.

12. _____ One set of three that make up the tonsils.

13. _____ A viral infection caused by the Epstein-Barr virus (EBV).

14. _____ Cells that circulate through the lymph nodes, the bloodstream, and the lymphatic ducts to seek out any infection.

15. _____ A hypersensitivity to a normally harmless substance.

16. _____ Along with the medulla, it is one of two basic parts of the lymph nodes.

17. _____ Consists of tissues, organs, and physiological processes that identify abnormal cells, foreign substances, and foreign tissues, and defends against substances that might be harmful to the body.

18. _____ An autoimmune disorder wherein people produce abnormal antibodies in their blood that target tissues within their own body instead of foreign infectious agents.

19. _____ The most common type of phagocytes, these attack an invading organism.

20. _____ The primary locations where B lymphocytes reproduce prolifically.

21. _____ The production of immunity by infection or with a vaccine.

22. _____ An example of a chronic autoimmune disease.

23. _____ A group of proteins activated by antibodies that assist in destroying bacteria, viruses, or infected cells.

24. _____ "Borrowed" from another source; lasts for only a short time.

25. _____ A foreign substance that invades the body.

26. _____ The response in the body that creates autoimmune diseases, in which the body attacks itself.

27. _____ A treatment where anticancer drugs are used to treat the cancerous growth or tumor.

28. _____ The genes controlling cell growth and multiplication.

29. _____ A condition that results from a damaged or dysfunctional lymphatic system.

30. _____ Along with the cortex, it is one of two basic parts of the lymph node.

31. _____ They are specialized proteins that lock onto specific antigens.

32. _____ Occurs when the cells, tissues, and organs that make up the immune system work together to attack organisms and substances that invade body systems and cause disease.

© 2011 Pearson Education, Inc.

APPLIED PRACTICE

1. Label the components of the lymphatic system.

2. A patient has just been diagnosed with several allergies. It is her first visit and you are providing patient education and various instructions. How would you explain (in layman's terms) antigens and allergens to the patient?

_____

_____

_____

_____

_____

LEARNING ACTIVITY: MULTIPLE CHOICE

Circle the correct answer to each of the questions below.

1. The cells responsible for production of circulating antibodies are _____.
   a. T cells
   b. B cells
   c. A cells
   d. None of the above

2. Which of the following substances may cause an allergic reaction?
   a. Dust
   b. Mold
   c. Pollen
   d. All of the above

3. Which of the following type of immunity occur when a person is exposed to a live pathogen.
   a. Active
   b. Acquired active
   c. Artificially acquired active
   d. Natural

4. Which of the following is a viral infection caused by the Epstein-Barr virus?
   a. Chronic fatigue syndrome
   b. Lymphedema
   c. Infectious mononucleosis
   d. Systemic lupus erythematosus

5. Which of the following risk factors predispose a person to cancer?
   a. Suppressed immune system
   b. Exposure to radiation
   c. Viruses
   d. All of the above

6. Which statement is false with regard to mononucleosis?
   a. It is caused by a herpes virus.
   b. It is much more severe in young children.
   c. It is characterized by an increase in white blood cells.
   d. It is often spread through saliva.

© 2011 Pearson Education, Inc.

7. Which of the following allow the body to remember and recognize previous invading organisms?

    a. Lymphocytes
    b. Neutrophils
    c. Phagocytes
    d. Leukocytes

8. When an antigen is detected, several types of cells work together to recognize and respond to it. These cells trigger the lymphocytes to produce antibodies. This process is known as _____.

    a. active immunity
    b. acquired active immunity
    c. humoral immunity
    d. None of the above

9. The thymus gland enlarges during _____.

    a. birth
    b. childhood
    c. puberty
    d. None of the above

10. Which of the following contains stem cells that create all the cells that make up the tissues and structures of the immune system?

    a. Bone marrow
    b. Liver
    c. Thymus gland
    d. Lymph nodes

CRITICAL THINKING

Answer the following questions to the best of your ability. Utilize the textbook as a reference.

1. Why do the frequency and severity of infections and incidence of autoimmune disease generally increase in elderly persons?

    _____

    _____

    _____

    _____

2. While at work, why should medical assistants not wear strong-smelling perfumes or aftershave lotions?

    _____

    _____

    _____

    _____

RESEARCH ACTIVITY

Utilize Internet search engines to research the following topics and write a brief description of what you find. It is important to utilize reputable websites.

© 2011 Pearson Education, Inc.

1. Research an autoimmune disease that is of interest to you. Identify the signs and symptoms of the disease, how a diagnosis is made, and treatment options. Also, research support groups, societies, or foundations for that disease. Write an essay on your findings and be sure to cite the websites where you found your information.

© 2011 Pearson Education, Inc.

CHAPTER 29

The Respiratory System

CHAPTER OUTLINE

General review of the chapter:

    Overview of the Respiratory System
    Organs of the Respiratory System
    Mechanism of Breathing
    Respiratory Volumes and Capacities
    Common Disorders Associated with the Respiratory System

STUDENT STUDY GUIDE

Use the following guide to assist in your learning of the concepts from the chapter.

I. The Respiratory System

  1. The Process of Breathing

    A. When we breathe, we inhale _Oxgen_ and exhale _carbon dioxide_

    B. Respiration is achieved through the _mouth_, _nose_, _trachea_, _lungs_, and _diaphragm_

    C. Oxygen enters the respiratory system through the _mouth_ and the _nose_.

  2. The Path Taken by Oxygen During Breathing (List the path that oxygen takes during breathing.)

    i. Oxygen passes through the _lelfy x_

    ii. And through the _____, where speech sounds are produced.

    iii. Through the lungs and the bronchioles that connect to tiny sacs, the _____

    iv. After the gas exchange, it then diffuses through the _____ into the _____ _____.

    v. The waste-rich blood from the veins releases _____ _____ into the _____.

    vi. The _____ helps pump air into and carbon dioxide out of the _____.

    vii. Upon _____, carbon dioxide follows the reverse of the path taken by oxygen flowing into the lungs.

  3. The Functions of the Nose

    A. _Warming_ and moistens inhaled air.

    B. Warms the _____.

    C. Assists with _sounds_.

  4. The Internal Structure of the Nose

    A. The septum is a _cavities_ structure.

    B. The septum is lined with _mixeous_ membrane.

    C. The conchae connects the _____ tube, the _pavenas l_, and the _nasotin cut_ duct.

    D. The palatine bone of the skull makes up the _bone_ palate and separates the nose from the _mouth_

© 2011 Pearson Education, Inc.

5. The Pharynx
   A. The pharynx is a _musculomembranous_ tube that is about _5_ inches long.
   B. Contains the _____.
   C. Consists of three parts: the _nasopharynx_, the _oropharynx_, and the
      laryngopharynx

6. The Larynx (The "Voice Box")
   A. The epiglottic cartilage, also called the _epiglottis_, closes over the _trachea_
      during swallowing to keep food out of the _esophagus_
   B. The cricoid cartilage serves as a landmark for performing a _large boluses_ when
      the airway is obstructed.

7. The Trachea
   A. The trachea is a cartilaginous tube about _1_ inch wide and _4.5_ inches long that
      extends between the _larynx_ and the main _bronchi_
   B. The interior of the trachea is lined with _mucus membrane_ and _cilia_ that trap
      foreign matter.
   C. The most important function of the trachea is to serve as an _open passageway_
      through which air reaches the lungs.
   D. The epiglottis is a flap of _tissue_ that covers the trachea when swallowing occurs to
      prevent food from entering the trachea.

8. The Main Branches of the Trachea
   A. The main branches of the trachea that extend into the lungs are called the _bronchi_.
   B. The right bronchus is the _larger_, _than_ branch located along the _left_
      side of the heart.
   C. The left bronchus is _smaller_ and more _gas_.
   D. After entering the lungs at the hilum, the _branches_ subdivide into the _superior_ tree,
      which continues to branch out into smaller and smaller branches called _fiber_.

9. Alveoli
   A. The alveoli are small air _balloons_ at the terminal end of the _pulmonary_
   B. They _bigger_ and _bigger_ with inhalation and exhalation.
   C. They are surrounded by a network of _vessels_ for gas exchange.

10. The Structure of the Lungs
    A. The lungs contain _larger_, _conical_, and _lobed_.
    B. The lungs are spongy, _organs_, and highly _elastic_

11. The Functions of the Lungs
    i. _Help oxgen from the air_
    ii. _carry oxgen around the body_
    iii. _help the body to get Rid of CO2 gas_

12. External Respiration (List and explain the elements of external respiration.)
    i. _____
    ii. _____
    iii. _____

13. The Action of the Diaphragm
    A. _____ and moves downward.
    B. Causes a _____ in pressure, or _____ thoracic pressure, within the chest cavity.
    C. Air enters the lungs to _____ the pressure during _____.

14. Intercostal Muscles
    A. External intercostal muscles assist _____, raise the _____, and enlarge
       the _____ cavity.

© 2011 Pearson Education, Inc.

B. Internal intercostal muscles assist _____, reduce the size of the _____ cavity, and force air from the _____.

15. Respiratory Volume and Capacity

   A. _____ function tests are used to measure lung _____ and _____.

   B. Such tests are used in human _____ testing.

16. Types of Lung Volume (Explain each type.)

   A. Tidal volume: _____
   B. Inspiratory reserve volume: _____
   C. Expiratory reserve volume: _____
   D. Residual volume: _____

17. Types of Lung Capacity (Explain each type.)

   A. Inspiratory capacity: _____
   B. Vital capacity: _____
   C. Functional residual capacity: _____
   D. Total lung capacity: _____

18. Other Respiratory Measurements (Explain each type.)

   A. Respiratory rate: _____
   B. Minute ventilation: _____
   C. Dead space: _____
   D. Alveolar ventilation: _____

II. The Pathology of the Respiratory System

   1. Asthma

      A. Asthma is a chronic _____ disease of the _____.
      B. Causes of asthma
         i. Irritations that cause _____ and
         ii. Affect the _____ and/or _____ _____,
         iii. Resulting in _____, which adds to the irritation.
      C. Treatment includes an _____ for acute episodes and long-term _____ for the prevention of episodes.

   2. Chronic Obstructive Pulmonary Disease (COPD)

      A. COPD is a combination of related diseases—chronic _____ and _____.
      B. _____ is a major cause.
      C. Air and other _____ may increase risk.
      D. A diagnosis is made through _____ and _____.
      E. Signs and symptoms of chronic obstructive pulmonary disease
         i. _____
         ii. _____
         iii. _____
         iv. _____
      F. Treatment for chronic obstructive pulmonary disease
         i. _____
         ii. _____
         iii. _____
         iv. _____

   3. Bronchitis

      A. Bronchitis is a respiratory disease in which the _mucous membrane_ in the _bronchial_ passages become _inflamed_

© 2011 Pearson Education, Inc.

B. As the irritated __membrane__ swells and grows thicker, it narrows or shuts off the tiny airways to the __lungs__.

4. Signs and Symptoms of Acute Bronchitis
   i. __hacking cough__
   ii. __yellow white or green phlegm__
   iii. _____
   iv. _____
   v. _____
   vi. _____

5. Signs and Symptoms of Chronic Bronchitis

   A. A persistent cough that produces _____, white, or _____ phlegm.
   B. Sometimes _____ and breathlessness.
   C. The symptoms of chronic bronchitis are worsened by _____ _____.

6. Treatment for Acute Bronchitis

   A. Conventional treatment for acute bronchitis
      i. _____
      ii. _____
      iii. _____
      iv. _____

7. Emphysema

   A. Emphysema is a long-term, _____ lung disease in which the _____ that support the physical shape and function of the _____ are destroyed.
   B. Deterioration is _____ and may go unnoticed.
   C. _____ smoking is by far the most common cause.

8. Risk Factors for Emphysema
   i. _____
   ii. _____
   iii. _____
   iv. _____
   v. _____
   vi. _____

9. Signs and Symptoms of Emphysema
   i. _____
   ii. _____
   iii. _____

10. Treatment for Emphysema
    i. _____
    ii. _____
    iii. _____
    iv. _____
    v. _____

11. The Common Cold

    A. A common cold is an inflammation of the _____ respiratory tract.
    B. Many cold viruses are highly _____.
    C. The common cold can be spread by _____.

12. Signs and Symptoms of the Common Cold
    i. _____
    ii. _____

© 2011 Pearson Education, Inc.

iii. _____

iv. _____

v. _____

vi. _____

vii. _____

viii. _____

ix. _____

x. _____

xi. _____

13. Treatment for the Common Cold

A. Antibiotics are _____ against cold viruses.

B. Over-the-counter cold preparations do not cure a common cold or _____ its duration.

C. For fever, sore throat, and headache, mild _____ _____ may be helpful.

D. For a runny nose and nasal congestion, _____ or _____ may be useful.

14. Measures for Slowing the Spread of the Common Cold

i. _____

ii. _____

iii. _____

iv. _____

15. Hay Fever

A. Hay fever is also called _____ _____ _____ or pollinosis.

B. It is a seasonal allergy in which the _____ _____ of the nose and eyes become _____.

C. About _____ million Americans experience hay fever symptoms each month.

16. Hay Fever

A. Symptoms of hay fever

i. _____

ii. _____

iii. _____

iv. _____

v. _____

vi. _____

B. Treatment for hay fever

i. _____

ii. _____

iii. _____

17. Influenza

A. Influenza is an illness caused by _____ that infect the respiratory tract.

B. It is often more serious than the _____ _____.

C. Most people who get the flu recover completely in ____ to ____ weeks.

18. Signs and Symptoms of Influenza

i. _____

ii. _____

iii. _____

iv. _____

v. _____

19. The Flu Vaccine

A. The flu vaccine is the best defense against _____.

B. The flu vaccine should be received by _____, the _____, those who are _____, and _____.

20. Lung Cancer

  A. Lung cancer is the leading cause of _____ deaths in both women and men in the United States and throughout the world.
  B. _____ percent of the cases occur in _____ and former _____.
  C. Other causes are _____, _____, and _____ exposure.

21. Treatment for Lung Cancer

  i. _____
  ii. _____
  iii. _____

22. Pleurisy

  A. Pleurisy is an _____ of the _____ that surrounds and protects the lungs.
  B. Causes of pleurisy
    i. _____
    ii. _____
    iii. _____
    iv. _____
  C. Symptoms of pleurisy
    i. _____
    ii. _____
    iii. _____
    iv. _____
    v. _____
  D. Treatment includes _____ drugs and _____ medicine.

23. Pneumonia

  A. Pneumonia is an inflammation of the lung or lungs caused by _____, _____, _____, or _____.
  B. _____ *pneumoniae* is the most common bacteria.
  C. Symptoms of pneumonia
    i. _____
    ii. _____
    iii. _____
  D. Treatment for pneumonia
    i. _____
    ii. _____
    iii. _____

24. Legionnaire's Disease

  A. Legionnaire's disease is a type of _____.
  B. Usually affects _____ or _____ persons.
  C. Caused by the _____ germ, which is spread throughout _____.

25. Pneumothorax

  A. Occurs when air enters the chest _____ of the lungs.
  B. Occurs most frequently when the lung has been _____ through trauma.
  C. Signs and symptoms are _____, _____, _____, and _____.
  D. Treatment must be given quickly to prevent _____ of the heart and lungs.

26. Pulmonary Edema

  A. Pulmonary edema is a condition in which _____ accumulates in the lungs.

© 2011 Pearson Education, Inc.

B. Can be a _____ condition, or it can develop suddenly and quickly become life threatening.

C. Most cases are caused by a failure of the heart's _____ chamber, the left _____, to pump adequately.

D. Symptoms include shortness of breath with _____, respiratory distress after _____, _____ breathing, and coughing.

E. Treatment must be _____ to reduce the amount of fluid.

27. Pulmonary Embolism

A. A pulmonary embolism is a _____ clot that travels to the _____.

B. The result is a _____ infarct.

C. Causes include extended periods of _____, surgery or _____, obesity, and _____ disease.

D. Symptoms of a pulmonary embolism
    i. _____
    ii. _____
    iii. _____
    iv. _____
    v. _____
    vi. _____

E. Treatment includes medications to eliminate the _____ or thin the blood and _____ the blood pressure.

28. Sinusitis

A. Sinusitis is an infection of the _____ of the sinuses.

B. Infection occurs because of lack of _____.

C. Usually caused by a _____ infection, a _____, or a _____ infection.

D. Symptoms include _____ and _____ in the facial area and green or _____ nasal discharge.

E. Treatment includes _____, moist heat for _____, and prevention of sinus _____.

29. Tuberculosis

A. Caused by the _____ tuberculosis complex of bacteria.

B. Individuals become infected by inhaling _____ from an infected person.

C. Symptoms of tuberculosis
    i. _____
    ii. _____
    iii. _____
    iv. _____
    v. _____
    vi. _____
    vii. _____

KEY TERMINOLOGY REVIEW

Use the key terms found at the beginning of the chapter to complete the sentences below.

Apnea	Cyanosis	Nares
Arterial blood gases	Dyspnea	Orthopnea
Asphyxia	Expiration	Pleura
Bronchodilators	Hemoptysis	Sinuses
Carbon dioxide	Hilum	Tonsils
Cilia	Inspiration	Visceral pleura

© 2011 Pearson Education, Inc.

1. _____ is a compound of carbon and oxygen.
2. Three pairs of _____ reside in the pharynx.
3. The external entrances of the nose are called the _____.
4. The absence of breathing for more than 19 seconds is termed _____.
5. Difficulty breathing is known as _____.
6. The bases of the lungs are called _____.
7. _____ are hairlike projections.
8. _____ is another term for suffocation.
9. The _____ covers the outer surface of the lungs and the inside of the thoracic cavity.
10. The symptom of coughing up blood, which can occur with tuberculosis, is known as _____.
11. If a patient has trouble breathing unless a certain position is maintained (such as with the head elevated), it is termed _____.
12. _____ are measured by drawing blood out of the arteries.
13. _____ occurs as a result of lack of oxygen in the tissues.
14. _____ open the bronchial passages.
15. _____, also defined as inhalation, involves a precise sequence of events.
16. _____ are hollow spaces, or cavities, located around the eyes, cheeks, and nose.
17. The pleural space separates two layers of the pleura—the parietal pleura and the _____.
18. Quiet exhalation, or _____, is ordinarily a passive process.

APPLIED PRACTICE

1. Label the sections of the nasal cavity and the pharynx.

Frontal sinus
Superior concha
middle concha
Inferior concha
Nasal cavity
Vestibule
Hard palate
oral cavity
Cranial cavity
Sphenoid sinus
Internal nares
Soft plate
oropharynx
laryngopharyn

© 2011 Pearson Education, Inc.

2. When working with children who have asthma, why should you be aware of the medication require-
ments of the school districts in your area? Every school has rules and might change and that you should kn the requirement in the area that you live in.

LEARNING ACTIVITY: TRUE/FALSE

*Indicate whether the following statements are true or false by placing a T or an F on the line that precedes
each statement.*

_____ 1. The upper respiratory tract includes the larynx, the trachea, the bronchioles, and the lungs.

_____ 2. The nose is part of the apparatus of respiration and voice.

_____ 3. The pharynx consists of two parts: the nasopharynx and the oropharynx.

_____ 4. The tonsils are part of the immune system and help with infection control.

_____ 5. The thyroid cartilage, or Adam's apple, is the smallest of the cartilage structures.

_____ 6. When the vocal cords are long and relaxed, high sounds are produced.

_____ 7. The respiratory rates in older adults may lower as the cumulative effects of pollution, smoking,
and disease wear on the integrity of the tissues.

_____ 8. At birth, the lungs are pinkish in color, but as adulthood approaches they turn a dark slate-gray.

_____ 9. The right lung has three lobes, but the left lung only has two.

_____ 10. Asthma is related to the same process that causes allergic reactions.

CRITICAL THINKING

Answer the following questions to the best of your ability. Utilize the textbook as a reference.

1. You have a patient with obstructive lung disease who wants to know why he has a hard time breathing. This person has a form of COPD that does not allow him to exhale very much. Explain briefly
here, as if explaining to the patient, why he feels so short of breath.

_____

_____

_____

2. SARS (severe acute respiratory syndrome) was spread from China to North America by infected
persons traveling by airplane. How can we control the entry of microbes into a country? What
should China have done to prevent the spread of the disease within and outside of China? Should
the Chinese government have shared information about SARS with the world immediately in case
it spread?

_____

_____

_____

RESEARCH ACTIVITY

*Utilize Internet search engines to research the following topics and write a brief description of what you
find. It is important to utilize reputable websites.*

© 2011 Pearson Education, Inc.

1. Visit www.lungusa.org. What information do you think will be most useful with regard to patient education? What is "hidden" asthma and what age group does it commonly effect? How can this information be useful to patients?

_____

_____

_____

_____

_____

_____

_____

_____

_____

_____

_____

_____

_____

_____

_____

_____

_____

_____

_____

© 2011 Pearson Education, Inc.

CHAPTER 30

The Digestive System

CHAPTER OUTLINE

General review of the chapter:

    Organs of the Digestive System
    Common Disorders Associated with the Digestive System

STUDENT STUDY GUIDE

Use the following guide to assist in your learning of the concepts from the chapter.

I. The Digestive System

  1. The Digestive System

    A. The digestive system _____ food, _____ food, and _____ waste products.
    B. The three main functions are _____, _____, and _____.

  2. The Tongue

    A. The tongue is a _____ muscle covered with a _____ membrane.
    B. The three areas of the tongue
       i. _____
       ii. _____
       iii. _____
    C. Papillae and taste buds are located on the _____ of the tongue.

  3. The Teeth (List the types of teeth.)

       i. _____
       ii. _____
       iii. _____
       iv. _____

  4. The Structure of the Tooth

    A. The _____ is the portion embedded in the top of the gum between the crown and the root.
    B. The _____ is the portion embedded in the gums.
    C. The _____ covers the exposed part of the crown.

  5. The Anatomy of the Tooth—From the Crown to the Root

    A. _____ is the calcified, mostly mineral tissue that forms the bulk of the tooth.
    B. _____ _____ are the fibers that anchor teeth to bony sockets in the maxillary bone and the mandible.
    C. The _____ is the protective layer on the dentin that anchors the periodontal ligament.

  6. The Pharynx

    A. The pharynx is the beginning of the _____.
    B. It also opens to the _____.

© 2011 Pearson Education, Inc.

7. The Esophagus

  A. Carries food to the _____ .
  B. It is about _____ inches long.
  C. Wave-like muscular contractions, called _____, move food to the _____ .

8. The Stomach

  A. Can hold _____ to _____ liters.
  B. Secretes _____ that aid in digestion.
  C. Processes food into a _____ state.
  D. Prepares food for further _____ and _____ in the small intestine.

9. The Sphincters of the Stomach

  A. The sphincters of the stomach are muscular _____ .
  B. Allow the flow of food in a _____ direction.
  C. The stomach has _____ sphincters.
  D. The lower esophageal sphincter is found between the _____ and the top of the stomach.
  E. The pyloric sphincter is between the _____ and the _____ .

10. The Stomach's Role in Digestion

  i. _____
  ii. _____
  iii. _____
  iv. _____

11. The Small Intestine

  A. The small intestine is a tube about _____ feet long, _____ inch in diameter.
  B. Attaches to the _____ at the _____ sphincter.
  C. Ends at the _____ orifice at the beginning of the large intestine.

12. The Sections of the Small Intestine (List the three sections.)

  i. _____
  ii. _____
  iii. _____

13. The Large Intestine

  A. The large intestine begins at the _____ orifice.
  B. The large intestine is about _____ feet long.
  C. The functions of the large intestine
    i. _____
    ii. _____
    iii. _____

14. The Sections of the Large Intestine (List the four sections.)

  i. _____
  ii. _____
  iii. _____
  iv. _____

15. The Salivary Glands (List the three pairs.)

  i. _____
  ii. _____
  iii. _____

16. The Liver

  A. Stores _____ and several vitamins.
  B. The products of the liver include _____, _____, _____, _____, and _____ .

© 2011 Pearson Education, Inc.

17. The Pancreas
    A. The pancreas is about _____ to _____ inches long.
    B. Produces _____ enzymes.
    C. Serves the _____ function.
    D. It is part of two body systems: _____ and _____.
    E. Its function is to secret the hormone _____.

II. The Pathology of the Digestive System
    1. Appendicitis
       A. Appendicitis is an _____ of the appendix.
       B. Symptoms include acute pain on the _____ point of the abdomen.
       C. Treatment is _____ _____ of the appendix.

    2. Cirrhosis
       A. Cirrhosis is damage to the liver caused by _____.
       B. Chronic _____ of the liver prevents normal liver function.
       C. Symptoms of cirrhosis
          i. _____
          ii. _____
          iii. _____
          iv. _____
          v. _____
          vi. _____
          vii. _____
          viii. _____
          ix. _____

    3. Treatment for Cirrhosis
          i. _____
          ii. _____
          iii. _____
          iv. _____
          v. _____

    4. Colitis
       A. Colitis is an inflammation of the _____ intestine.
       B. Symptoms of colitis
          i. _____
          ii. _____
          iii. _____
          iv. _____
          v. _____

    5. Colorectal Cancer
       A. Begins as _____ polyps.
       B. Treatment includes _____, _____, and _____.

    6. Constipation
       A. Causes of constipation
          i. _____
          ii. _____
          iii. _____
          iv. _____

© 2011 Pearson Education, Inc.

B. Treatment for constipation
   i. _____
   ii. _____
   iii. _____
   iv. _____

7. Crohn's Disease

   A. Crohn's disease is a chronic _____ of the _____.
   B. Common symptoms include _____, _____, and _____.

8. Diverticulosis

   A. Diverticulosis is outpouching in the _____ intestinal wall.
   B. There is a higher incidence in the _____.
   C. Can be prevented with a _____ _____ diet.

9. Diverticulitis

   A. Diverticulitis is an inflammation of the diverticulum in the walls of the _____.
   B. Symptoms of diverticulitis
      i. _____
      ii. _____
      iii. _____
      iv. _____
      v. _____
      vi. _____
      vii. _____

10. Gastroesophageal Reflux Disease (GERD)

    A. GERD is a backflow of the _____ juices into the _____.
    B. The lower _____ sphincter does not close.
    C. Symptoms of gastroesophageal reflux disease
       i. _____
       ii. _____
       iii. _____
       iv. _____
       v. _____
       vi. _____
    D. Complications of gastroesophageal reflux disease
       i. _____
       ii. _____
       iii. _____
       iv. _____
       v. _____
       vi. _____

11. Hemorrhoids

    A. Hemorrhoids are dilated veins in the walls of the _____.
    B. Symptoms include _____ with elimination.
    C. Treatment involves _____ changes, topical medication, and _____ (if severe).

12. Hiatal Hernia

    A. The upper stomach protrudes into the chest through the _____ hiatus.
    B. Causes of a hiatal hernia
       i. _____
       ii. _____
       iii. _____
       iv. _____

© 2011 Pearson Education, Inc.

v. _____

vi. _____

vii. _____

viii. _____

C. Symptoms of a hiatal hernia

    i. _____

    ii. _____

    iii. _____

    iv. _____

    v. _____

    vi. _____

13. Inguinal Hernia

    A. The intestine pushes through the _____ wall in _____ area.

    B. Causes include _____ in the abdominal wall; heavy lifting; and _____ as a result of coughing, laughing, or bending.

    C. Symptoms include a bulge in the abdomen when _____, _____, or _____.

    D. The only treatment is _____.

14. Irritable Bowel Syndrome (IBS)

    A. IBS is a common _____ condition.

    B. Causes include _____.

    C. Treatment includes _____ modifications, medications, and _____.

    D. Symptoms of IBS

        i. _____

        ii. _____

        iii. _____

        iv. _____

        v. _____

        vi. _____

        vii. _____

15. Oral Cancer

    A. Risk factors include age, _____, smoking, the use of _____ _____, and _____ exposure.

    B. Symptoms of oral cancer

        i. _____

        ii. _____

        iii. _____

        iv. _____

        v. _____

    C. Treatment for oral cancer includes _____, _____, and _____.

16. Pancreatic Cancer

    A. The most common type is _____ of the pancreas.

    B. Symptoms of pancreatic cancer

        i. _____

        ii. _____

        iii. _____

        iv. _____

        v. _____

        vi. _____

    C. Treatment includes _____, _____, and _____.

17. Peptic Ulcer Disease (PUD)

    A. PUD is characterized by a lesion in the lining of the _____, _____, or _____.

    B. _____ ulcers are common.

© 2011 Pearson Education, Inc.

C. Can be aggravated by _____ infection.

D. Symptoms of PUD

    i. _____

    ii. _____

    iii. _____

    iv. _____

18. Treatment for Peptic Ulcer Disease

    i. _____

    ii. _____

    iii. _____

    iv. _____

    v. _____

19. Pyloric Stenosis

A. Pyloric stenosis is a condition where the _____ sphincter _____ and thickens.

B. Symptoms include _____, _____, and _____.

C. Treatment for pyloric stenosis is _____.

KEY TERMINOLOGY REVIEW

Match the selected key terms to their definitions below.

a. Cholelithiasis

b. Colorectal cancer

c. Diverticulitis

d. Diverticulosis

e. Esophagus

f. Gallbladder

g. Hemorrhoid

h. Hernia

i. Large intestine

j. Liver

k. Mastication

l. Pancreas

m. Pancreatic cancer

n. Peptic ulcer disease (PUD)

o. Pharynx

p. Pyloric stenosis

q. Small intestine

r. Stomach

1. _____ A hollow, sac-like organ.

2. _____ May be secondary to colitis.

3. _____ The formation or presence of stones or calculi in the gallbladder or common bile duct.

4. _____ Lies posterior to the mouth.

5. _____ Caused by an imbalance in stomach acids.

6. _____ Begins at the ileocecal orifice.

7. _____ May be the result of stool in the diverticulum.

8. _____ An abnormal protrusion of an organ or part of an organ through the wall of the body cavity that contains it.

9. _____ The organ that is posterior to the stomach.

10. _____ The tube leading from the pharynx to the stomach.

11. _____ Occurs in infants, usually before 5 months of age.

12. _____ The largest glandular organ.

13. _____ Associated with constipation or chronic diarrhea.

14. _____ Another word for chewing.

© 2011 Pearson Education, Inc.

15. _____ The green membranous sac below the liver.
16. _____ Caused by pressure on and a weakening of the intestinal wall.
17. _____ A condition that typically develops in the exocrine glands.
18. _____ Attaches to the stomach at the pyloric spincter.

APPLIED PRACTICE

1. Label each part of the digestive system.

2. Label each part of the oral cavity.

LEARNING ACTIVITY: TRUE/FALSE

Indicate whether the following statements are true or false by placing a T or an F on the line that precedes each statement.

_____ 1. There are three types of taste buds.

_____ 2. The main part of the digestive system is the digestive or gastrointestinal tract.

_____ 3. Humans have two sets of teeth: 25 deciduous teeth (the baby teeth) and 35 permanent teeth.

_____ 4. The incisor teeth are the largest teeth in the permanent set.

_____ 5. Enamel is the hardest and most compact part of the tooth.

_____ 6. Deciduous teeth erupt from the gums from the age of about 7 months to about 2½ years.

_____ 7. The submandibular glands are located below the tongue.

_____ 8. Anyone can get appendicitis, but it occurs most often between the ages of 10 and 30.

_____ 9. Volvulus is the condition in which the bowel twists on itself and causes an obstruction that is painful and requires immediate surgery.

_____ 10. Crohn's disease is contagious.

_____ 11. A hiatal hernia is thought to contribute to the weakening of this sphincter muscle.

_____ 12. There is no cure for irritable bowel syndrome.

_____ 13. Age increases the risk of oral cancer.

_____ 14. About 50% of pancreatic cancers can be surgically removed at the time of diagnosis.

_____ 15. The accessory organs of digestion are the mouth, pharynx, esophagus, stomach, small intestine, large intestine, and rectum.

© 2011 Pearson Education, Inc.

CRITICAL THINKING

Answer the following questions to the best of your ability. Utilize the textbook as a reference.

1. Mr. McNeill is experiencing constipation and has called in for advice on how to deal with this. Try to recall what you have read in this chapter of your textbook and use your common sense to list a few things that may help. After you have done that, check the book and review the items that you may not have remembered.

   _____

   _____

   _____

   _____

2. Some digestive disorders, such as stomach ulcers, IBS, and GERD, may be associated with a person's lifestyle. As a member of the health care profession, what is your role when assisting in the care of these patients? What should you avoid doing when providing care?

   _____

   _____

   _____

   _____

RESEARCH ACTIVITY

Utilize Internet search engines to research the following topics and write a brief description of what you find. It is important to utilize reputable websites.

1. As a medical assistant, it will be your responsibility to instruct patients on how to prepare for certain types of diagnostic tests, such as a colonoscopy, endoscopy, or sigmoidoscopy. Select a condition from your textoook, research the types of tests performed for diagnosis, select one of the tests, and research the instructions that would be provided to patients. Write a short essay explaining the condition, the procedure, and the preparatory instructions that patients should be given prior to the procedure. Cite your Internet sources.

   _____

   _____

   _____

   _____

   _____

   _____

   _____

   _____

   _____

   _____

CHAPTER 31
The Urinary System

CHAPTER OUTLINE

General review of the chapter:

> Organs of the Urinary System
> Urine
> Common Disorders Associated with the Urinary System

STUDENT STUDY GUIDE

Use the following guide to assist in your learning of the concepts from the chapter.

I. The Urinary System

1. Urine

   A. Urine is the waste product produced by the _____.
   B. Contains mostly water, as well as _____ and _____ compounds.
   C. Drains from the _____, through the _____, to the _____.

2. The Structure of the Kidneys

   A. Located at the _____ region of the abdominal cavity between the _____ thoracic and _____ lumbar vertebrae.
   B. The kidneys are encased in three capsules for protection: the _____, the _____, and the _____.

3. The Nephron

   A. Each kidney contains more than 1 _____ nephrons.
   B. A nephron consists of a _____ capsule and a renal _____.

4. Ureters

   A. Ureters are composed of three layers
      i. _____
      ii. _____
      iii. _____
   B. They are about _____ to _____ inches long and less than _____ inch in diameter.

5. The Urinary Bladder

   A. The urinary bladder consists of four layers
      i. _____
      ii. _____
      iii. _____
      iv. _____
   B. Stretches to hold _____.
   C. The urge to urinate typically occurs when an adult bladder holds _____ to _____ mL of urine.
   D. The bladder empties through the _____ and the _____ meatus.

© 2011 Pearson Education, Inc.

6. The Urethra

   A. In males, the urethra is approximately _____ cm long and transports urine and _____.

   B. The male urethra has three sections: the _____, the _____, and the _____.

   C. In females, the urethra is approximately _____ cm long and transports only urine.

   D. The external opening of the female urethra is situated between the _____ and the opening of the _____.

7. Facts About Urine

   A. Consists of _____, _____, and _____.

   B. An adult passes about _____ to _____ mL of urine daily.

   C. Characteristics of normal urine

      i. _____

      ii. _____

      iii. _____

      iv. _____

II. The Pathology of the Urinary System

   1. Cystitis

      A. Caused by a __Eshericnia coli__ infection of the __Urinary__ tract.

      B. Most prevalent in __sexually__ active women, ages __20__ to __50__, because of anatomical configuration.

      C. Symptoms include __painful__ and __urinationburning__ urination.

      D. Treatment includes __antibotic__ and __antispasmodic medication__

   2. Interstitial Cystitis

      A. Interstitial cystitis is an inflammation of the __bladder woll__

      B. Affects mostly __women__.

      C. Its cause is __unknown__.

      D. It is not responsive to _____.

   3. Glomerulonephritis

      A. Can lead to __Kidney__ failure.

      B. Causes include __Infections__, __Autoimmune disease__ __Inflammation of the__, __Blood vessels__ __Vacutitis__ and __Conditions that scar the glomeruli__

      C. Symptoms glomerulonephritis

         i. __Urine__

         ii. __red blood cells hermaturia__

         iii. __protein in the urine protein__

         iv. __high blood pressure__

         v. __fluid retention__

         vi. __kidney failure__

      D. Treatment includes __diuretis__, __Ace__, __calcium__ and __beta blockers__

   4. Incontinence

      A. Commonly seen in women who have had __children__.

      B. Types of incontinence include __Stress__, __urge__, __overflow__, and __enuresis__.

      C. Treatment includes __medication__, __surgery__, __urge pelvic floor__ and __behavioral modification training__ __excercises__

   5. Kidney Stones, or Renal Calculi

      A. Kidney stones are harmless in the __Kidney__ __ureter__

      B. They become problematic when passed into the _____.

      C. Symptoms include __nausea__, __flank pain__, and __vomitting__

D. Treatment includes _Passing shock_ and _Surgical intervention_
E. Prevention includes controlling the _surgical_ and _disintegrate_

6. Polycystic Kidney Disease (PKD)
   A. Symptoms of PKD
      i. _Kidney disease include HEIGHT blood pressure_
      ii. _baellorside pain related to enlarge kidney_
      iii. _abdomin_
      iv. _abdomen blood in urine_
      v. _Kidney stone, Kidney failure, Kidney infection_
      vi. _headache_
   B. _____ focuses on the symptoms and their complications.

7. Pyelonephritis
   A. Causes of pyelonephritis
      i. _indwelling urinary cather_
      ii. _Cystoscopy visualization of the urinary bladder_
      iii. _Prostate enlargement_
      iv. _Kidney stone_
   B. Symptoms of pyelonephritis
      i. _back and side groin pain_
      ii. _urgency and frequency pain burning terms ur_
      iii. _fever_
      iv. _nausea and vomitting_
      v. _blood and pus_
   C. Treatment is typically the use of _Antibobiotic_
   D. If left untreated, _scaming_ and possible kidney _damage_ may occur.

8. Types of Dialysis (List and briefly explain the two types.)
   i. _acute renal failure occur when something cause a change_
   ii. _____

KEY TERMINOLOGY REVIEW

Without using any material from your textbook, write a sentence using the selected vocabulary terms in the correct context.

1. *ascites*
   _____
   _____

2. *cystitis*
   _____
   _____

3. *dialysis*
   _____
   _____

4. *dysuria*
   _____
   _____

© 2011 Pearson Education, Inc.

5. *enuresis*

_____

_____

6. *hilum*

_____

_____

7. *lithotripsy*

_____

_____

8. *micturition*

_____

_____

9. *nephrons*

_____

_____

10. *renal calculi*

_____

_____

11. *renal pelvis*

_____

_____

12. *urinary meatus*

_____

_____

APPLIED PRACTICE

Using the information found in the chapter, answer the questions following the scenario below.

Scenario

Mr. Bai Feng, born 8-13-66, presents to the office today with a fever of 99.7°F, noticeable beads of sweat on his brow, and complaints of right-sided pain in his lower back. He states, "I am in so much pain I can't stand up straight and I feel like I always have to urinate." A urine specimen is obtained for urinalysis and shows positive for blood in the urine, as well as other abnormalities. His urine specimen is sent to the laboratory for further testing.

1. Based on his urinalysis and symptoms, what would be a likely diagnosis? (Keep in mind that a medical assistant never diagnoses a patient; this is your opinion based on information found in the textbook.)

_____

_____

2. Draw a picture of the urinary system (kidneys, ureters, urinary bladder, and urethra). Circle the area of the urinary system that is likely to be the causative factor for Mr. Feng's pain.

LEARNING ACTIVITY

Match the vocabulary term to the correct definition below.

a. Acute renal failure
b. Chronic renal failure
c. Cortex
d. Frequency
e. Glomerulonephritis
f. Incontinence
g. Interstitial cystitis
h. Kidney stones

i. Kidneys
j. Medulla
k. Polycystic kidney disease (PKD)
l. Pyelonephritis
m. Ureters
n. Urethra
o. Urinary bladder
p. Void

1. _____ Caused by deposits of mineral salts in the kidney.
2. _____ The outer layer of a kidney.
3. _____ A muscular sac in the pelvic cavity that serves as a reservoir for urine.
4. _____ A kidney disease that hampers the kidneys' ability to remove waste and excess fluids.
5. _____ The involuntary and unpredictable flow of urine.
6. _____ The middle portion of the kidney.
7. _____ Two muscular tubes that carries the newly formed urine from each kidney down to the bladder.
8. _____ The need to void often.
9. _____ An infection of the kidney and renal pelvis.
10. _____ A musculomembranous tube extending from the bladder to the urinary meatus.

© 2011 Pearson Education, Inc.

11. _____ Occurs when something causes a change in the filtering function of the kidneys.
12. _____ A pair of bean-shaped organs located at the back of the abdominal cavity.
13. _____ A painful inflammation of the bladder wall.
14. _____ To urinate.
15. _____ A disorder in which clusters of cysts develop primarily within the kidneys.
16. _____ A gradual and progressive loss of kidney function.

CRITICAL THINKING

Answer the following questions to the best of your ability. Utilize the textbook as a reference.

1. Why are the elderly more susceptible to becoming dehydrated?

_____
_____
_____
_____

2. When discussing urinary issues with patients, what cultural considerations should be given?

_____
_____
_____
_____
_____
_____
_____
_____
_____
_____
_____

RESEARCH ACTIVITY

Utilize Internet search engines to research the following topics and write a brief description of what you find. It is important to utilize reputable websites.

1. Visit www.kidney.org. As you navigate through the site, what information do you find that would be helpful for a patient who is in need of a kidney transplant? What information is available for healthcare technicians? How could this website be beneficial for a urology/nephrology office?

_____
_____
_____

© 2011 Pearson Education, Inc.

CHAPTER 32

The Endocrine System

CHAPTER OUTLINE

General review of the chapter:

> Function of the Endocrine System
> Pituitary Gland
> Pineal Gland
> Thyroid Gland
> Parathyroid Glands
> Pancreas
> Adrenal Glands
> Ovaries
> Testes
> Placenta
> Gastrointestinal Mucosa
> Thymus Gland
> Common Disorders Associated with the Endocrine System

STUDENT STUDY GUIDE

Use the following guide to assist in your learning of the concepts from the chapter.

I. The Endocrine System

  1. Types of Glands

    A. Exocrine glands secrete _____ to an _____ surface, but do not circulate into the _____.

    B. Endocrine glands secrete _____ that _____ within the body.

  2. The Functions of the Endocrine System

    i. _____

    ii. _____

    iii. _____

    iv. _____

    v. _____

  3. The Connection Between the Nervous and Endocrine Systems

    A. The nervous system works closely with the _____ system.

    B. The nervous system helps maintain _____.

    C. The _____, located in the brain, is the link between the two systems.

  4. The Pituitary Gland

    A. Regulates all of the other _____ in the _____ system.

    B. Located near the _____ of the _____.

© 2011 Pearson Education, Inc.

C. Attached to the _____ by the _____ stalk.

D. The pituitary gland has two lobes: the _____ and the _____.

5. Anterior Lobe Hormones (List each hormone.)

    i. _____

    ii. _____

    iii. _____

    iv. _____

    v. _____

    vi. _____

    vii. _____

6. The Hormones and the Functions of the Posterior Lobe of the Pituitary Gland (List the functions of each hormone.)

A. Antidiuretic hormone (ADH)

    i. _____

    ii. _____

    iii. _____

    iv. _____

B. Oxytocin

    i. _____

    ii. _____

7. The Pineal Gland

A. Located at the _____ end of the _____.

B. Secretes _____ and _____.

8. The Thyroid Gland

A. Located anterior to the _____, just below the _____ cartilage.

B. The thyroid gland is approximately _____ cm long and _____ cm wide.

C. Weighs _____ grams.

D. Secretes _____ hormones.

9. The Parathyroid Glands

A. Located around the _____ and lower aspect of the thyroid gland.

B. Each gland is _____ mm in diameter.

C. Each gland weighs _____ grams.

D. Secretes parathyroid _____.

10. Parathyroid Hormone (PTH)

A. The functions of PTH

    i. _____

    ii. _____

11. The Pancreas

A. Contains small clusters of cells called the _____ that secrete hormones.

B. _____ types of cells make up the islets of Langerhans.

12. Pancreas Cells (List each cell and briefly explain its function.)

    i. _____

    ii. _____

    iii. _____

13. The Adrenal Gland

A. The adrenal gland is _____ in shape.

B. The adrenal _____ is the outer portion of the gland.

C. The adrenal _____ is the inner portion of the gland.

© 2011 Pearson Education, Inc.

14. The Adrenal Cortex (List the three types of hormones manufactured by the adrenal cortex.)

    i. _____

    ii. _____

    iii. _____

15. The Adrenal Medulla

    A. The adrenal medulla is the _____ portion of the _____ glands.

    B. Synthesizes, _____, and stores _____.

16. Primary Catecholamines (List the functions of each hormone.)

    A. Dopamine

        i. Cause vasoconstriction so the blood pressure is elevate

        ii. Cardiac output and urine production are increased

        iii. Synthetic dopamine can be administed in the treat

        of shock

    B. Epinephrine

        i. Peripheral vasoconstiriction dilation of the

        pupils

    C. Norepinephrine

        i. Sympathetic nervous system

        ii. vasorocontriction

        iii. elevating system and diastolic blood pressure

        iv. Increasing glycoolysis

        v. the breaking down of the glyocem

II. The Pathology of the Endocrine System

  1. Acromegaly

    A. Commonly affects _____ adults.

    B. The most serious health consequences of acromegaly

        i. _____

        ii. _____

        iii. _____

        iv. _____

    C. Commonly characterized by abnormal growth of the _____ and _____.

  2. Signs and Symptoms of Acromegaly

        i. _____

        ii. _____

        iii. _____

        iv. _____

        v. _____

        vi. _____

        vii. _____

        viii. _____

        ix. _____

        x. _____

        xi. _____

        xii. _____

        xiii. _____

        xiv. _____

        xv. _____

        xvi. _____

  3. Treatment for Acromegaly

    A. Reduce GH _____ production to normal levels.

    B. Surgical removal of the tumor.

C. __drug__ therapy.
D. __radiation__ therapy of the pituitary gland.

4. Addison's Disease

   A. Addison's disease is an _____ disease in which the body attacks itself.
   B. May be caused by _____ of the adrenal glands, cancer, or _____ into the glands.
   C. It is a rare condition that occurs in _____ in _____ Americans.
   D. Diagnosed by _____ and _____ tests that measure _____ hormone levels.

5. Signs and Symptoms of Addison's Disease

   i. __Weight loss__
   ii. _____
   iii. _____
   iv. _____
   v. _____
   vi. _____
   vii. _____
   viii. _____
   ix. _____
   x. __diarrhea__
   xi. __abdominal discomfort__
   xii. __mucous membrane__

6. Treatment for Addison's Disease

   A. Replace the _____ hormones and prescribe sodium _____.
   B. Administer intramuscular _____ injections.

7. Cushing's Syndrome

   A. Possibly caused by a _____.
   B. Treatment includes _____ and _____.

8. Signs and Symptoms of Cushing's Disease

   i. __Muscular weakness__
   ii. __thinning of the skin__
   iii. __easy bruising__
   iv. __round of facil feauture mood face__
   v. __weight gain__
   vi. __fatigue__

9. Diabetes Mellitus

   A. Diabetes mellitus is a silent disease that may not be detected until it is at an _____ stage.
   B. Approximately _____ million people have been diagnosed with diabetes, but an estimated _____ million are undiagnosed.

10. Juvenile Diabetes

    A. Typically diagnosed in _____ who cannot produce sufficient quantities, if any, of _____.
    B. Patients are dependent on _____ injections for the rest of their lives.

11. Type 2 Diabetes

    A. Type 2 diabetes is the most _____ form of the disease.
    B. Results from _____ resistance combined with a relative _____ deficiency.
    C. There is a very strong correlation between _____ and type 2 diabetes.

12. Signs and Symptoms of Diabetes

    A. __polyuria__ (frequent urination)
    B. __polydipsia__ (excessive thirst)
    C. __polyphagia__ (excessive hunger)

© 2011 Pearson Education, Inc.

13. Treatment for Diabetes
    A. Type 1 diabetes can usually be treated only by _padancefi the_ tronspkin
    B. Type 2 diabetes is treated with _diet_, _exercise_ and oral _diet_ medications.
    C. May be preventable with modest lifestyle changes, including a healthy _____, _choices_, and _weight_ management.

14. Achondroplasia
    A. Achondroplasia is the most common type of _____, occurring in 1 in 25,000 children.
    B. Abnormal _____ growth is usually diagnosed at birth.
    C. Development of motor skills may be _____, but intellectual development is normal.

15. The Physical Characteristics of Achondroplasia
    i. _trunck of normal length_
    ii. _disproportionatlely short arms and legs_
    iii. _bowed legs_
    iv. _reduced joint mobility in the elbow_
    v. _loose ligaments make other joints jam-_
    vi. _shortened hands / feet_
    vii. _flat midfee_
    viii. _A prominent forehead_

16. Treatment for Achondroplasia
    A. In addition to social and family support, treatment focuses on the _____ and _____ of medical complications.
    B. _____ may be performed to relieve pressure on the _____ system.
    C. Dental and _____ work may be necessary to correct _____ and preserve dental health.

17. Signs and Symptoms of and Treatment for Gigantism
    A. Signs and symptoms of gigantism
        i. _____
        ii. _____
        iii. _____
    B. Treatment includes _____ therapy and _____ removal of the tumor.

18. Signs and Symptoms of Hyperthyroidism
    i. _nervousness_
    ii. _restlesshess_
    iii. _breast palpitation_
    iv. _'menstra'_
    v. _sweating_
    vi. _the tremors_
    vii. _increased activity in the intestinal trait_
    viii. _weight loss_
    ix. _change in fingernails and hair_
    x. _heart failure_
    xi. _endor enlarged heart_

19. Treatment for Hyperthyroidism
    A. _____ medications
    B. Radioactive _____ to destroy the thyroid
    C. _____

© 2011 Pearson Education, Inc.

20. Hypothyroidism
   A. Since it develops slowly, only about half of the _____ million cases in the United States are diagnosed early.
   B. Untreated, it can lead to other conditions. Constant stimulation causes the release of _____ hormones, which can cause the _____ gland to _____.
   C. Untreated hypothyroidism is associated with a higher risk of _____ disease because of the high levels of _____ _____ (LDL).
   D. Other complications include _____, _____, and _____.

21. Other Disorders Related to the Endocrine System (List and briefly explain each.)

   i. _____
   _____

   ii. _____
   _____

   iii. _____
   _____

   iv. _____
   _____

   v. _____
   _____

   vi. _____
   _____

   vii. _____
   _____

   viii. _____
   _____

   ix. _____
   _____

   x. _____
   _____

   xi. _____
   _____

   xii. _____
   _____

   xiii. _____
   _____

   xiv. _____
   _____

   xv. _____
   _____

   xvi. _____
   _____

   xvii. _____
   _____

KEY TERMINOLOGY REVIEW

Match the vocabulary term to the correct definition below.

   a. Acromegaly
   b. Addison's disease
   c. Adrenal glands

   d. Cardiomegaly
   e. Cushing's disease
   f. Diabetes mellitus

© 2011 Pearson Education, Inc.

g. Dwarfism
h. Exophthalmos
i. Gestational diabetes
j. Gigantism
k. Goiter
l. Grave's disease
m. Hashimoto's thyroiditis
n. Hyperthyroidism
o. Hypothyroidism
p. Insulin-dependent diabetes mellitus

q. Islets of Langerhans
r. Lipolysis
s. Myxedema
t. Non–insulin-dependent diabetes mellitus
u. parathyroid glands
v. pineal gland
w. pituitary gland
x. thymus gland
y. thyroid gland

1. _____ Called "The Master Gland".
2. _____ A possible symptom of hypothyroidism, in which the eyeballs protrude beyond their normal protective orbit when the tissues behind them swell.
3. _____ Juvenile diabetes; also known as type 1 diabetes.
4. _____ When the cortex of the adrenal gland is damaged, decreasing the production of adrenocortical hormones.
5. _____ Produce parathormone.
6. _____ The destruction of fats promoted by growth hormone (GH).
7. _____ A rare disorder caused by the hypersecretion of cortisol.
8. _____ Small clusters of cells within the pancreas.
9. _____ Results from excessive secretion of growth hormone (GH) during childhood, before the closure of the bone growth plates.
10. _____ Pregnancy-related diabetes.
11. _____ An enlarged heart.
12. _____ The most common form of hyperthyroidism.
13. _____ This condition, along with cretinism and Hashimoto's disease, can result from hyposecretion of calcitonin and its companion hormones, T3 and T4.
14. _____ Characterized by elevated thyroid hormone levels.
15. _____ A hormonal disorder that results from the overproduction of growth hormone (GH) by the pituitary gland.
16. _____ Also known as Type 2 diabetes, or adult-onset diabetes.
17. _____ Condition where the body is unable to produce enough insulin to properly control blood sugar levels.
18. _____ Releases melatonin.
19. _____ An autoimmune inflammation of the thyroid.
20. _____ When the thyroid produces inadequate amounts of thyroid hormones.
21. _____ Achondroplasia is the most common type of this abnormal skeletal growth condition, which occurs in children.
22. _____ Releases thymosin and thymopoietin.
23. _____ This gland secrets thyroxine, tri-iodothyronine, and calcitonin.
24. _____ The most common cause is Hashimoto's thyroiditis, an autoimmune inflammation of the thyroid.
25. _____ Located on top of each kidney.

© 2011 Pearson Education, Inc.

APPLIED PRACTICE

Follow the directions as instructed with each question below.

1. Using the information from the following patient chart, correctly identify the possible endocrine gland disorder based on the patient's signs and symptoms.

Mikovich, Anya, 10-26-1982
4/02/20XX, 3:45 P.M.
Wt: 134 lbs T: 98.6° F P: 104 bpm, bounding
BP: 118/78
cc: Pt presents to office complaining of restlessness, heart palpitations, tremors, sweating. She states, "I am unable to relax and have been sweating a lot recently. I always feel hot." She is displaying exophthalmos and has lost 6 lbs since her last visit 3 months ago, though she claims she hasn't been trying to lose weight.

Adam Bello, RMA

---

2. Label the primary gland of the endocrine system as seen on the image provided.

© 2011 Pearson Education, Inc.

LEARNING ACTIVITY: TRUE/FALSE

Indicate whether the following statements are true or false by placing a T or an F on the line that precedes each statement.

_____ 1. The nerve cells in the hypothalamus control the pituitary gland by producing chemicals that either suppress or stimulate hormone secretion from the pituitary gland.

_____ 2. Depression is commonly associated with disorders related to the hormone serotonin.

_____ 3. Diabetes mellitus is very rare in children.

_____ 4. A myxedema coma can be triggered by sedatives, infection, or other stress.

_____ 5. Insulin and glucagon are secreted by the pancreas.

_____ 6. Hyposecretion of the adrenal cortex results in dwarfism.

_____ 7. Progesterone is a steroid hormone.

_____ 8. Copulation can occur without testosterone.

_____ 9. The thymus is part of the endocrine gland.

_____ 10. Von Rechlinghausen's disease results in degeneration of the bones due to excessive production of parathyroid hormone.

CRITICAL THINKING

Answer the following questions to the best of your ability. Utilize the textbook as a resource.

1. A pregnant patient who is overdue for going into labor may need a hormone to help stimulate the process of uterine contractions. What hormone may be given? What endocrine gland would produce this hormone naturally? What else does this hormone stimulate?

_____

_____

_____

_____

2. Why is it important to understand your state laws regarding individuals with diabetes who drive school buses and other forms of public transportation?

_____

_____

_____

_____

RESEARCH ACTIVITY

Utilize Internet search engines to research the following topics and write a brief description of what you find. It is important to utilize reputable websites.

1. Visit www.diabetes.org. Research information as to how diabetes plays an ethnic and cross-cultural role. What facts do you find most surprising regarding this topic? How prevalent is diabetes within your ethnic race or culture?

_____

_____

© 2011 Pearson Education, Inc.

© 2011 Pearson Education, Inc.

CHAPTER 33
The Reproductive System

CHAPTER OUTLINE

General review of the chapter:

The Female Reproductive System
The Menstrual Cycle
The Male Reproductive System
Common Disorders Associated with the Female Reproductive System
Common Disorders Associated with the Male Reproductive System

STUDENT STUDY GUIDE

Use the following guide to assist in your learning of the concepts from the chapter.

I. The Female Reproductive System

  1. The Uterus

    A. The uterus is a hollow, _____-shaped organ.
    B. Located in the anterior _____ cavity between the _____ and the symphysis _____,
       above the bladder and in front of the _____.
    C. The functions of the uterus
       i. _____
       ii. _____
       iii. _____

  2. Layers of the Uterine Wall

       i. _____
       ii. _____
       iii. _____

  3. Fallopian Tubes

    A. The fallopian tubes are also called the _____ tubes or the _____.
    B. Functions include moving _____ from the _____ to the uterus.
    C. The three layers of the fallopian tubes
       i. _____
       ii. _____
       iii. _____

  4. Features of the Fallopian Tubes

       i. _____
       ii. _____
       iii. _____
       iv. _____
       v. _____

5. Ovaries

    A. Located on both sides of the _____.
    B. Attached to the _____ by the _____ ligament.
    C. Controlled by the hormones from the _____ gland.
    D. The microscopic structure includes the _____ (the outer layer) and the _____.

6. The Vagina

    A. The vagina is a _____ tube.
    B. Extends from the _____ cervix to the _____.
    C. Located between the _____ and the _____.

7. The Five Organs of the Vulva That Make Up the External Female Genitalia

    i. _____
    ii. _____
    iii. _____
    iv. _____
    v. _____

8. Breasts

    A. Breasts are also called _____ glands.
    B. Composed of compound _____ structures consisting of _____ to _____ glandular tissue lobes separated by the septa of the connecting tissue.
    C. The _____ is the dark, pigmented circular area of skin found on each breast.
    D. The _____ is the elevated area in the center of the _____.

9. Prolactin

    A. Prolactin is the _____ produced by the anterior lobe of the pituitary gland.
    B. Stimulates the _____ glands to produce _____.

10. An Overview of the Menstrual Cycle

    A. The menstrual cycle is normally _____ days.
    B. It has _____ phases.
    C. The occurrence of _____ ends the menstrual cycle.

II. The Pathology of the Female Reproductive System

1. Disorders of the Female Reproductive System (Briefly explain each of the following disorders.)
    A. Abruptio placentae: tears away from uterine wall after 20th week p
    B. Amenorrhea: absence of mentruation
    C. Breech presentation: buttock and feet are presented first for del
    D. Cervical polyps: mucous tumor or growth found in the cervix or
    E. Condyloma: wart like growth on the external genitalia
    F. Cystocele: hernia of the bladder that produces in the vag
    G. Ectopic pregnancy: fetus abnormally implanted outside the ute

2. Cancers of the Female Reproductive System (List the three types and briefly explain each.)
    i. Breast cancer: cancer arising in the breast cancer
    ii. Cervial cancer - rapid, uncontrolled growth of abnorm
    iii. Ovarian caner - in the cells of one or both ovaries

3. Types of Ovarian Cancer (List the three types and briefly explain each.)
    i. Epithelial cell cancer - starts in outer covering of the ovary
    ii. Germ cell tumor - starts in eggs cells, occur in younger women
    iii. Stromel tumor - starts in cells that form the structural frame we

4. Signs and Symptoms of Early Stage Ovarian Cancer
    i. mild abdominal discomfort or pain
    ii. abdominal swelling

© 2011 Pearson Education, Inc.

iii. _____
iv. _____
v. _____
vi. _____
vii. _____
viii. _____
ix. _____
x. _____
xi. _____
xii. _____
xiii. _____
xiv. _____

5. Signs and Symptoms of Advanced Ovarian Cancer
   i. _____
   ii. _____
   iii. _____
   iv. _____
   v. _____
   vi. _____

6. Treatment for Ovarian Cancer

   A. Treatment is based on the type, _____, and _____ of the cancer.
   B. Can include _____, _____ therapy, _____, and _____ therapies.
   C. _____ therapies, such as traditional Chinese medicines or special diets, are sometimes used.

7. Uterine Cancer (Endometrial Cancer)

   A. Generally develops in the _____ tissues of the _____.
   B. If detected and _____ early, treatment is usually very successful.

8. Factors That Can Increase the Risk of Uterine Cancer
   i. Age
   ii. Obesity
   iii. Childlessness
   iv. menopause that begans later than average
   v. prolonged use of medication with the hardmone estrogen
   vi. Tuse of drug tamoxien

9. Signs and Symptoms of Uterine Cancer
   i. Bleeding between menstrual periods
   ii. heavy Bleeding or spotting during periods or after menopause
   iii. bleeding during intercourse
   iv. foul discharge
   v. watery yellow discharge
   vi. cramping pain
   vii. Pressure in the abdomen
   viii. discomfort over the pubic area

10. Uterine Fibroids

    A. Uterine fibroids are bengan growths or tumors.
    B. They are made up of muscle cells and other tissues that grow within the wall of the uterus
    C. Can occur as a single growth or as a cluster of tumors.
    D. Common in women of childbearing age.
    E. AfricanAmerican women are the most susceptible of all racial groups.
    F. There is a higher risk of fibroids among women who are overweight

© 2011 Pearson Education, Inc.

11. Signs and Symptoms of Uterine Fibroids

    i. _____

    ii. _____

    iii. _____

    iv. _____

    v. _____

    vi. _____

    vii. _____

12. Treatment for Uterine Fibroids

    A. _____ medications for mild symptoms

    B. _____ hormone agonists to decrease the size of the fibroids

    C. _____ agents may stop or slow the growth of fibroids.

13. Pelvic Inflammatory Disease (PID)

    A. PID is an infection of the upper _____ area.

    B. Caused by disease-carrying _____.

    C. Can affect the _____, ovaries, and _____ tubes.

    D. If untreated, can cause _____.

14. Signs and Symptoms of and Treatment for Pelvic Inflammatory Disease

    A. Signs and symptoms of PID

        i. lower abnominal pain and abnormal vaginal d

        ii. fever

        iii. pain in the right upper quadrant

        iv. painful intercourse

        v. irregular menstrual bleeding

        vi. _____

    B. Treatment for PID involves treating the underlying _____.

15. Ovarian Cysts

    A. Ovarian cysts are _____ filled with _____ or a semisolid material that develops on or within the ovary.

    B. Functional cysts are relatively common and usually disappear within _____ days without treatment.

16. Signs and Symptoms of Ovarian Cysts

    A. A constant, dull pelvic pain

    B. Abdominal bleeding or distention

17. Treatment for Ovarian Cysts

    A. Oral _____ may be prescribed.

    B. If larger than _____ cm or persisting for longer than _____ weeks, the cyst may require surgical removal.

18. Preeclampsia

    A. Preeclampsia is toxemia during pregnancy.

    B. If untreated, can result in true eclampsiea

    C. Symptoms of preeclampsia

        i. hypertension

        ii. headache

        iii. tender breast

        iv. anxiety

19. Premenstrual Syndrome (PMS)

    A. PMS is also called premenstrual dysphoric disorder.

    B. Estimated to affect 85 % of women who menstruate.

© 2011 Pearson Education, Inc.

C. Only _5_ to _10_ % of menstruating women are severely impaired by PMS.

D. It is believed that PMS is associated with the amount of _horomones_ produced.

20. Signs and Symptoms of Premenstrual Syndrome

    i. _____
    ii. _____
    iii. _____
    iv. _____
    v. _____
    vi. _____
    vii. _____
    viii. _____
    ix. _____
    x. _____
    xi. _____
    xii. _____
    xiii. _____
    xiv. _____
    xv. _____
    xvi. _____

21. Treatment for Premenstrual Syndrome

    i. _____
    ii. _____
    iii. _____
    iv. _____
    v. _____
    vi. _____

22. Disorders of the Female Reproductive System (Briefly explain each.)

A. Prolapsed uterus: _____
B. Rh factor: _____
C. Salpingitis: _____
D. Spontaneous abortion: _____
E. Toxic shock syndrome: _____

23. Breast Cancer

A. Affects women primarily and about __1__ % of men.
B. _80%_ percent of breast cancers develop in the tiny _ducts_ that extend from the _lobules_ of the mammary glands to the nipple.
C. Cancer may also develop in the _lobules_ .
D. The most serious cancers are _metastatic_ cancers, which spread from their origin into other tissues.

24. Risk Factors for Breast Cancer

A. _____ history
B. Women who begin _____ at an early age or experience a late menopause

25. Signs and Symptoms of Breast Cancer

A. A _____ in the breast, under the arm, or above the collarbone
B. _____ discharge
C. Nipple _____

26. Factors to Be Considered When Treating Breast Cancer

    i. _____
    ii. _____

© 2011 Pearson Education, Inc.

iii. _____

iv. _____

v. _____

27. Surgical Treatment for Breast Cancer (List the four types of surgery.)

i. _____

ii. _____

iii. _____

iv. _____

28. Cervicitis

A. Cervicitis is an inflammation of the *Cervix*.

B. Symptoms include *Grayish* or *yellow* vaginal discharge; frequent and *painful* urination; pain during *intercourse*; and *vaginal* bleeding after intercourse, between menstrual periods, or after menopause.

29. Treatment for Cervicitis

A. _____ are used to treat an underlying _____ infection.

B. If the infection is _____, such as genital herpes, an _____ medication is given.

C. The person's sexual partner may also be treated to prevent _____.

30. Dysmenorrhea

A. Signs and symptoms include dull or throbbing pain, usually centered in the *lower* abdomen and radiating toward the *lower* back or *thighs*.

B. Some women may also experience nausea and vomiting, *diarrhea*, irritability, _____, or dizziness.

31. Treatment for Dysmenorrhea

A. Controlled by treating the _____ disorder.

B. _____, such as acetaminophen and ibuprofen, are used to relieve pain.

C. Aromatherapy and _____ are helpful for some women.

32. Endometriosis

A. Occurs when *endometrial* tissue is found *outside* the uterus.

B. One theory as to the cause of endometriosis is that, during menstruation, some of the *endometria* tissue backs up through the *fallopian* tubes into the abdomen.

33. Signs and Symptoms of Endometriosis

i. _____

ii. _____

iii. _____

iv. _____

v. _____

vi. _____

vii. _____

viii. _____

34. Treatment for Endometriosis

A. Early diagnosis and treatment may limit _____ growth and help prevent _____.

B. Pregnancy, _____, and other hormones appear to delay the onset of endometriosis.

C. Treatment with medication focuses on treating the _____.

D. _____ is generally reserved for women with severe endometriosis.

35. Fibrocystic Breast Disease

A. Fibrocystic breast disease involves common, *benign* changes in the tissues of the breast.

B. It is common in *normal* breasts.

© 2011 Pearson Education, Inc.

C. The condition usually subsides with _____.
D. Estimated to affect more than _____% of all women.

36. Signs and Symptoms of Fibrocystic Breast Disease
    i. _dense irreagular cobblestone_
    ii. _persistent or intermittent breast discomfort_
    iii. _at feeling of furness in the breast_
    iv. _premenstrual tenderness_
    v. _swelling and nipples sensation_

37. Treatment for Fibrocystic Breast Disease
    i. _selfcare_
    ii. _eliminating caffeine from the diet_
    iii. _performing a monthly breast selfexam_
    iv. _wearing a well fitted bra_
    v. _oral contraceptives_

38. Sexually Transmitted Infections (STIs)
    A. Transmitted via the exchange of _____, _____, and other bodily fluids, or by direct contact with the affected areas of people with STIs.
    B. STIs are also called _____ diseases.

39. The Most Common Sexually Transmitted Infections in the United States
    i. _Chlampdia_
    ii. _HPV_
    iii. _Genital herpes_
    iv. _gonorrhea_
    v. _syphilis_
    vi. _HIV infection_

40. Reducing the Risk of Contracting a Sexually Transmitted Infection
    i. _____
    ii. _____
    iii. _____

41. Sexually Transmitted Infections (List and briefly explain each.)
    i. Acquired immune deficiency syndrome (AIDS): _Final stage of infection from the HIV virus_
    ii. Candidiasis: _yeast like infection of the skin and mucous membr_
    iii. Chancroid: _____
    iv. Chlamydial infection: _____
    v. Genital herpes: _____
    vi. Genital warts: _____
    vii. Gonorrhea: _____
    viii. Hepatitis: _____
    ix. Syphilis: _____
    x. Trichomoniasis: _____

42. Vaginitis
    A. An inflammation of the vagina that can result in discharge, _____, or _____.
    B. The most common cause is a change in the normal balance of vaginal _____ or an _____.
    C. Reduced _____ levels after menopause are another contributing factor.
    D. The most common types of vaginitis
        i. _____
        ii. _____
        iii. _____
        iv. _____

III. The Male Reproductive System

    1. The Scrotum

        A. The scrotum is a pouch-like structure behind the _____ .
        B. It is suspended from the _____ region.
        C. It is divided into _____ sacs by a septum.

    2. The Penis

        A. Composed of _____ tissue covered by skin.
        B. The size and shape of the penis vary; the average erect penis is about _____ to _____ cm in length.
        C. Covered with a loose fold of skin called the _____ , or _____ .

    3. The Epididymis

        A. The epididymis is a coiled tube lying on the posterior aspect of the _____ .
        B. It is between _____ and _____ feet in length.
        C. It is coiled into a space that is less than _____ cm in length and ends at the _____ _____ .
        D. Its function is to serve as the storage site for maturing _____ .

    4. The Ductus Deferens

        A. The ductus deferens is a slim, muscular tube about _____ cm in length that is continuous with the _____ .
        B. It is the excretory duct of the _____ .
        C. Extends from a point adjacent to the _____ and enters the abdomen at the _____ canal.

    5. The Two Seminal Vesicles

        A. The vesicles are connected by a narrow _____ to the _____ .
        B. Form the _____ duct.
        C. Produce an _____ fluid that becomes part of the seminal fluid, or semen.

    6. The Prostate Gland

        A. Lies behind the _____ bladder.
        B. Wraps around the first _____ cm of the urethra.
        C. It is about _____ cm wide.
        D. Secretes an _____ fluid that aids in maintaining the viability of the _____ .

    7. The Male Urethra

        A. The male urethra is approximately _____ cm long.
        B. It is divided into three sections: _____ , _____ , and _____ .
        C. Extends from the bladder to the _____ orifice at the end of the _____ .

IV. The Pathology of the Male Reproductive System

    1. Disorders of the Male Reproductive System (Briefly explain each.)

        A. Anorchism: _____
        B. Aspermia: _____
        C. Azoospermia: _____
        D. Carcinoma of the testes: _____
        E. Cryptorchidism: _____
        F. Phimosis: _____
        G. Prostatitis: _____
        H. Varicocele: _____

    2. Benign Prostatic Hyperplasia (BPH)

        A. BPH is also known as _____ .
        B. May occur in men _____ years of age and older.
        C. By age _____ , four out of five men have an enlarged _____ .

© 2011 Pearson Education, Inc.

3. Signs and Symptoms of Benign Prostatic Hyperplasia

    i. _weak or difficult to - start urine stream_
    ii. _____
    iii. _____
    iv. _____
    v. _____
    vi. _____
    vii. _____
    viii. _____

4. Treatment for Benign Prostatic Hyperplasia

    i. _____
    ii. _____
    iii. _____
    iv. _____

5. Epididymitis

    A. Epididymitis is an inflammation or _____ of the epididymis.
    B. The most severe pain and swelling are usually associated with the _____ form.
    C. Symptoms may last for more than _____ weeks after treatment begins.
    D. Can occur anytime after the onset of puberty, but is most common between the ages of _____ and _____.

6. Risk Factors for Epididymitis

    A. Infection of the _____, _____, _____, or _____ _____
    B. A narrowing of the _____
    C. Use of a _____ catheter

7. Causes of Epididymitis

    A. Can be caused by the same organisms that cause some ____ or as a result of _____ surgery.
    B. Generally caused by _____-generating _____ associated with infections in other parts of the body.
    C. Can also be caused by an injury to or _____ of the scrotum.

8. Signs and Symptoms of Epididymitis

    A. Sudden redness and swelling of the _____
    B. The affected _____ is hard and sore.
    C. Enlarged _____ nodes in the groin that may cause scrotal pain

9. Treatment for Epididymitis

    A. Because it can cause _____, _____ therapy must be initiated as soon as symptoms appear.
    B. Patients are advised to wear _____ _____ when they resume normal activities.

10. Erectile Dysfunction

    A. Erectile dysfunction is the inability to achieve or _____ an _____.
    B. Is not an _____ part of aging.
    C. Occurs when not enough blood is supplied to the _____.

11. Risk Factors for Erectile Dysfunction

    i. _____
    ii. _____
    iii. _____
    iv. _____
    v. _____
    vi. _____
    vii. _____

viii. _____

ix. _____

x. _____

xi. _____

xii. _____

xiii. _____

xiv. _____

xv. _____

12. Treatment for Erectile Dysfunction

i. _____

ii. _____

iii. _____

iv. _____

v. _____

13. Hydrocele

A. Hydrocele is a painless buildup of _____ fluid around one or both _____ that causes swelling in the _____ or groin area.

B. Can be _____ or acquired.

14. Signs and Symptoms of Hydrocele

A. The scrotum may have a _____ tinge.

B. The swelling is _____, may be soft or firm, and cannot be reduced by changing its position or gently pushing it up.

C. The swelling may change in _____.

15. Prostate Cancer

A. Prostate cancer is a _____ tumor that grows in the _____ gland.

B. It is the second leading cause of cancer _____ in men.

C. By age 50, _____ in _____ American men has some _____ cells in the prostate gland.

D. The average age of diagnosis is _____.

16. Risk Factors for Prostate Cancer

i. _____

ii. _____

iii. _____

iv. _____

v. _____

17. Signs and Symptoms of Prostate Cancer

i. _____

ii. _____

iii. _____

iv. _____

v. _____

vi. _____

vii. _____

viii. _____

ix. _____

18. Treatment for Prostate Cancer

i. _____

ii. _____

iii. _____

iv. _____

v. _____

© 2011 Pearson Education, Inc.

KEY TERMINOLOGY REVIEW

Match the vocabulary term to the correct definition below.

a. Breast cancer
b. Bulbourethral glands
c. Cervicitis
d. Epididymitis
e. Episiotomy
f. Erectile dysfunction
g. Fallopian tubes
h. Fibrocystic breast disease
i. Myomectomy
j. Ovaries

k. Ovulation
l. Ovum
m. Prostate cancer
n. Prostate gland
o. Salpingo-oophorectomy
p. Sexually transmitted infections
q. Spermatozoa
r. Urethra
s. Uterine cancer
t. Uterus

1. ___C___ Most cases are caused by a sexually transmitted infection such as gonorrhea and chlamydia.
2. ___J___ A type of surgery performed for uterine fibroids.
3. ___T___ Contains six sets of ligaments.
4. ___P___ A term for more than 20 different infections.
5. ___G___ Move the egg from the ovary to the uterus.
6. ___K___ The process where a Graafian follicle ruptures on the ovarian cortex and an ovum is released into the pelvic cavity and into one of the fallopian tubes.
7. ___H___ The most common cause of pain in the scrotum.
8. ___R___ Extends from the bladder to the urethral orifice at the end of the penis.
9. ___A___ Composed of glandular, connective, and muscular tissue.
10. ___A___ Second leading cause of death by cancer in women (second only to lung cancer).
11. ___M___ The most common cancer among American men.
12. ___e___ Procedure that is performed to prevent tearing of the perineum during delivery.
13. ___S___ Also called adenocarcinoma.
14. ___b___ Produced by the testes.
15. ___L___ Located inferior to the prostate and on either side of the urethra.
16. ___N___ An egg or reproductive cell.
17. ___Q I___ Also referred to as mammary dysplasia.
18. ___Q___ Removal of the ovaries and the fallopian tubes.
19. ___O___ Their function is to produce estrogen and progesterone.
20. ___P___ A symptom of prostate cancer.

APPLIED PRACTICE

1. Label the uterus, ovaries, and associated structures.

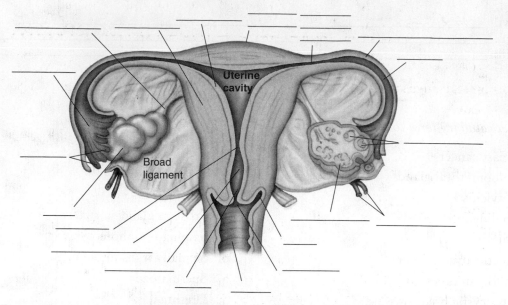

Uterine cavity

Broad ligament

2. Label the structures of the male reproductive system.

© 2011 Pearson Education, Inc.

LEARNING ACTIVITY: FILL IN THE BLANK

Using words from the list below, fill in the blanks to complete the following statements.

Benign prostatic hyperplasia

Cervical cancer

Circumcision

Dysmenorrhea

Endometriosis

Hydrocele

Hysterectomy

Menarche

Ovarian cancer

Ovarian cysts

Pelvic inflammatory disease (PID)

Perineum

Premenstrual syndrome (PMS)

Scrotum

Testes

Urethritis

Uterine fibroids

Vaginitis

1. Phimosis is typically treated by performing a _____.

2. Anorchism is a congenital absence of one or both _____.

3. _____occurs at the age of puberty.

4. The main symptom of a _____ is a swollen scrotum or groin area.

5. The _____ is between the vulva and the anus.

6. _____ is an enlargement of the prostate gland.

7. Symptoms of epididymitis include chills, fever, and acute _____.

8. To test for _____, a pap test is typically performed.

9. A genitourinary infection caused by a parasite that is usually asymptomatic (without symptoms) in both males and females; can produce itching and/or burning and a foul-smelling discharge and result in _____ in women.

10. Typically, by the time _____ is diagnosed, the cancer is usually at an advanced stage.

11. _____ is defined as the symptoms that develop just prior to the onset of a menstrual period.

12. _____ are not disease related and typically disappear on their own.

13. Epididymitis is characterized by sudden redness and swelling of the _____.

14. _____ is described as painful cramping associated with menstruation.

15. A _____ involves the removal of the uterus.

16. _____ is the most common and serious complication of STIs among women.

17. Although the cause of _____ is unknown, one theory suggests that delayed childbearing increases the risk.

18. _____ usually, but not always, shrink or disappear after menopause.

CRITICAL THINKING

Answer the following questions to the best of your ability. Utilize the textbook as a reference.

1. A patient asks you if you think that her infant son should be circumcised. What do you do?

_____

_____

© 2011 Pearson Education, Inc.

2. How can you ensure a patient's privacy when you are calling to talk with them by phone?

_____

_____

_____

_____

_____

_____

_____

RESEARCH ACTIVITY

Utilize Internet search engines to research the following topics and write a brief description of what you find. It is important to utilize reputable websites.

1. Visit www.cdc.gov. As you navigate through the site, what information would be helpful to provide a patient who has a sexually transmitted disease?

_____

_____

_____

_____

_____

_____

_____

_____

_____

_____

_____

_____

_____

_____

_____

_____

_____

_____

_____

© 2011 Pearson Education, Inc.

CHAPTER 34

Infection Control

CHAPTER OUTLINE

General review of the chapter:

History of Asepsis
Microorganisms
The Infection Control System
Universal Precautions
Implementing OSHA Guidelines
Hepatitis
HIV and AIDS
Multidrug-Resistant Organisms
Bioterrorism

STUDENT STUDY GUIDE

Use the following guide to assist in your learning of the concepts from the chapter.

I. Infection Control

1. Microorganisms: A Definition

   A. Microorganisms, also called _____, are living organisms that can be seen only with a _____.

   B. Microorganisms include _____, _____, _____, and _____.

2. The Scientific Fields of the Study of Microorganisms (List and briefly explain each.)

   i. _____

   ii. _____

   iii. _____

   iv. _____

3. The Stages of the Infection Process (Explain each stage.)

   A. Invasion: _____
   B. Multiplication: _____
   C. Incubation period: _____
   D. Prodromal period: _____
   E. Acute period: _____
   F. Recovery period: _____

4. Preventing the Spread of Infection

   A. Prevent the spread of _____ microorganisms.
   B. _____ the microorganisms.

5. The Body's Barriers to Infection (List the four barriers that the body provides against infection.)

   i. _____
   ii. _____

iii. _____

iv. _____

6. Genetic and Acquired Immunity

   A. Genetic immunity does not involve _____.
   B. Acquired immunity may be achieved through active or _____ means.

7. Natural Active and Artificial Active Immunity

   A. Natural active immunity develops as a result of having recovered from a _____.
   B. Artificial active immunity is the result of receiving a _____ containing an inactivated or attenuated organism.

8. Types of Acquired Immunity

   A. Active acquired natural immunity is achieved by having the _____, which results in the production of _____ and "memory cells" that respond if the antigen reappears.
   B. Active acquired artificial immunity is achieved by administering a _____ that stimulates the production of _____ and "memory cells" to prevent that disease from occurring.
   C. Passive acquired natural immunity is achieved by receiving someone else's _____, such as from the mother to the fetus through the placenta or through breast milk.
   D. Temporary protection for passive acquired artificial immunity is achieved from _____.

9. Cardinal Signs of Inflammation

   i. _____

   ii. _____

   iii. _____

   iv. _____

10. The Centers for Disease Control and Prevention's (CDC's) Two-tiered Precautionary System

   A. Universal precautions apply to _____ patients and assume that all _____ fluids and _____ are infected with _____.
   B. Standard precautions apply to _____ patients regardless of medical condition or the risk of spreading _____.
   C. Transmission-based precautions apply to patients who are suspected of carrying _____ diseases or who are known to be _____.

II. Universal Precautions and Aseptic Techniques

   1. The Requirements of Bloodborne Pathogen Standards

   A. Employees must follow _____ precautions to impede contact with _____ material.
   B. Employees must consider all _____ fluids contagious if unable to differentiate among _____ fluids.

   2. Following the Standard Precautions

   A. Medical professionals should change gloves between _____ or if gloves are _____.
   B. Medical professionals should wash their hands _____ or when _____.
   C. Medical professionals should avoid direct _____ resuscitation.
   D. Medical professionals should use _____ waste containers for contaminated material.

   3. Hand Sanitizing and Hygiene

   A. Hand sanitizing is one of the best means of reducing the spread of _____ in a health care facility and at home.

© 2011 Pearson Education, Inc.

B. Hand hygiene recommendations include not wearing _____ fingernails.

C. Natural fingernails should be kept short (less than _____ inch long).

4. The CDC's Guidelines for Respiratory Hygiene/Cough Etiquette

A. Signs are to be posted to remind people to cover their _____ and _____ when coughing and to dispose of tissues properly.

B. Perform _____ hygiene after contact with respiratory secretions.

C. Provide at least _____ feet of space around persons with respiratory infections whenever possible.

5. The CDC's Safe Injection Practices

A. Use _____ technique.

B. No _____ vials should be kept in the immediate treatment area.

C. Do not use bags or bottles of intravenous (IV) solutions among _____ patients.

6. Airborne Precautions

A. Used for patients who are known to be infected with _____ that are transmitted via _____ droplet _____.

B. Often involve patient _____ in a private room if hospitalized, as well as the use of a _____ and _____ by all health care personnel who come in contact with the patient.

C. The transport of the patient should be as _____ as possible, with the patient wearing a _____ during transport.

D. All reusable patient care equipment should be _____ and _____ before use on another patient.

7. Droplet Precautions

A. Used for patients suspected of being infected with _____ spread by _____ during sneezing, coughing, and talking.

B. A _____ should be worn if a caregiver is within _____ feet of an infected patient.

C. _____ and gloves are worn if there is a chance of coming in contact with the blood or bodily fluids of suspected patients.

D. All reusable equipment should be _____ and _____.

8. Contact Precautions

A. Used when infections are difficult to treat and the likelihood of _____ transmission among patients and health care providers is high.

B. Precautions include isolating _____ and wearing _____ and gloves.

C. If there is a chance of coming in contact with bodily fluids, a _____ and eyewear should be worn.

9. Latex Sensitivity

A. Before touching a patient while wearing latex gloves, ask the patient if there is a history of latex _____.

B. High-risk patients, such as those with congenital defects and indwelling _____, must always be assessed for latex _____.

C. Patients with allergies to _____, chestnuts, kiwi, and _____ may have cross sensitivity to latex.

10. The Occupational Safety and Health Administration's Goals and Guidelines

A. Aim to minimize exposure to hepatitis _____ and HIV.

B. Programs include _____ determination, method of compliance, and _____ evaluation.

© 2011 Pearson Education, Inc.

11. Items That Employers Should Have Available to Ensure Worker Safety

    i. _____

    ii. _____

    iii. _____

    iv. _____

    v. _____

    vi. _____

12. Disposing of Infectious Waste (List the guidelines for disposal.)

    i. _____

    ii. _____

    iii. _____

    iv. _____

    v. _____

    vi. _____

    vii. _____

    viii. _____

    ix. _____

13. Physical and Chemical Barriers

    A. Used to maintain _____ control.

    B. Prevent _____ infections and hospital/medical facility-acquired infections.

    C. Barrier is achieved when medical and _____ asepsis are maintained.

14. Medical Asepsis

    A. Medical asepsis is the elimination of _____ that have left the body.

    B. Surgical asepsis is the practice of creating and maintaining a _____ environment in which _____ are destroyed before they enter the body.

15. Practicing Medical Asepsis Hygiene Habits

    i. _____

    ii. _____

    iii. _____

    iv. _____

    v. _____

    vi. _____

16. Medical Asepsis in the Facility

    A. Practices in addition to personal hygiene and equipment cleanliness

        i. Keep examination rooms _____.

        ii. _____ trash cans.

        iii. Replace _____ containers appropriately.

        iv. Look for insect _____.

        v. Separate well patients from _____ patients in seating areas.

17. Steps for Proper Hand Hygiene

    i. _____

    ii. _____

    iii. _____

    iv. _____

    v. _____

    vi. _____

    vii. _____

    viii. _____

    ix. _____

    x. _____

© 2011 Pearson Education, Inc.

18. Alcohol-Based Hand Sanitizers
   A. Hand sanitizers were recently approved by the _____.
   B. Unless the hands are visibly _____ or the professional has used the restroom or _____, the use of hand sanitizers is an alternative to using soap and water.
   C. Approximately _____ to _____ mL of solution should be placed in the palm and vigorously worked into the hands and wrists for _____ to _____ seconds.

19. Personal Protective Equipment
   A. Worn in order to accomplish the following
      i. _____
      ii. _____
      iii. _____

20. Procedures for Applying Gloves
      i. _____
      ii. _____
      iii. _____
      iv. _____
      v. _____

21. Procedures for Removing Gloves
      i. _____
      ii. _____
      iii. _____
      iv. _____
      v. _____

22. Steps for Performing Isolation Techniques
      i. _____
      ii. _____
      iii. _____
      iv. _____
      v. _____
      vi. _____
      vii. _____
      viii. _____
      ix. _____
      x. _____

23. Steps for Removing Barrier Protection
      i. _____
      ii. _____
      iii. _____
      iv. _____
      v. _____
      vi. _____
      vii. _____
      viii. _____

III. Surgical Asepsis
   1. Surgical Asepsis: Sanitizing Instruments
      A. Prevents pathogens from _____ or _____ pathogens.
      B. Should be used for instruments that only touch the _____ surface.

© 2011 Pearson Education, Inc.

2. Sanitizing Equipment and Supplies (List the equipment and the supplies used.)

    i. _____

    ii. _____

    iii. _____

    iv. _____

    v. _____

    vi. _____

    vii. _____

3. Disinfecting Instruments (Explain the use of each of the following methods.)

    A. Alcohol: _____

    B. Chlorine: _____

    C. Formaldehyde: _____

    D. Hydrogen peroxide: _____

    E. Glutaraldehyde: _____

4. Sterilizing Instruments

    A. Any _____ that touch wounds or internal body _____ must be sterilized.

    B. Sterile gloves must be worn when touching _____ equipment.

    C. The process of putting on sterile or nonsterile gloves is called _____.

5. The Autoclave

    A. Autoclaves are used for _____.

    B. Autoclaves cause _____ to explode, thus killing them.

    C. Types of autoclaves

        i. _____

        ii. _____

        iii. _____

        iv. _____

6. Cleaning an Autoclave

    A. An autoclave should be _____ before each use.

    B. If detergent is used, the autoclave should be _____ thoroughly before use.

    C. The air exhaust valve must be _____ and free of lint before use.

7. Wrapping Instruments and Materials

    A. Wrappings must be _____ and strong.

    B. Types of wrappings

        i. _____

        ii. _____

        iii. _____

        iv. _____

    C. The wrapping generally has _____ layers.

    D. The hinges of instruments should be in an _____ position, the tubing should be free of kinks, and _____ should be unassembled.

8. Autoclave Indicator Tapes

    A. Indicator tapes are placed in the _____.

    B. The lines on the tape change color during the process to indicate that the appropriate _____ has been reached.

9. Autoclave Sterilization Pouches and Bags

    A. The instrument must be _____ and _____.

    B. The pouch must not rupture during _____.

    C. The pouch must have _____ indicators inside and outside.

© 2011 Pearson Education, Inc.

10. Autoclave Trays

    A. Used only for those instruments that will be used _____.

    B. Trays are _____.

    C. A _____ is usually placed under instruments to absorb moisture.

    D. The lid should be placed on the tray _____ after sterilization.

11. Handling Individual Packs

    A. Items should be wrapped in _____ packs.

    B. When individual packs are opened, the contents must be removed without introducing _____.

    C. Solutions should be _____ separately.

12. Time and Pressure Requirements

    A. Always follow the _____ requirements.

    B. Items will not be sterilized if the time or _____ is changed.

13. Drying Autoclaved Goods

    A. Improperly dried items can lead to _____ growth.

    B. Procedures for drying goods

        i. Open the autoclave door _____ inch before the drying cycle.

        ii. Run the drying cycle per the _____ instructions.

14. Sterilization Indicators

    A. Used to indicate _____.

    B. The appearance of dots or a change in _____ indicates that proper sterility has been achieved.

15. The Shelf Life of Autoclaved Packages

    A. The oldest items should always be used _____.

    B. Items are considered sterile for _____ to _____ days.

    C. The shelf life is _____ month(s), but depends on how the item was wrapped.

IV. Hepatitis, AIDS, and Bioterrorism

  1. Hepatitis A (HAV)

    A. Transmitted when _____ waste contaminates the food or water supply.

    B. The incubation period is _____ to _____ days.

  2. Symptoms of Hepatitis A

    i. _____

    ii. _____

    iii. _____

    iv. _____

    v. _____

    vi. _____

    vii. _____

  3. Hepatitis B (HBV)

    A. Transmitted through _____ fluids.

    B. HBV is a potentially fatal disease that can be passed from one drug user to another when sharing a _____ needle.

    C. Infection with HBV _____ the risk of contracting HIV and HAV.

    D. The incubation period for this liver infection is _____ to _____ days, with a rapid onset of symptoms.

  4. Symptoms of and Treatment for Hepatitis B

    A. About _____% of infected persons have no signs or symptoms.

    B. Treatment for all forms of hepatitis is a _____ diet and rest for several weeks.

5. Hepatitis B Vaccine

   A. Routine vaccines are recommended from birth to age _____.
   B. Vaccination is recommended for _____ groups.
   C. Any personnel with a high risk of contact with _____ and bodily fluids should be encouraged to receive the vaccine.
   D. If an employee decides not to get vaccinated, a _____ must be signed and placed in the employee's file.

6. Types of Hepatitis B Vaccine

   A. Types include _____ and _____.
   B. Vaccines are administered in _____ doses.

7. Cautions About Receiving the Vaccine

   A. Persons who are sensitive to _____ or any of the other components found in the vaccine should not receive it.
   B. _____ mothers or persons with _____ disease should be cautious about receiving the vaccine.

8. Hepatitis C

   A. Hepatitis C is the most _____ form of new cases each year.
   B. The symptoms are similar to hepatitis _____.
   C. The treatment of choice is _____ and _____.

9. Hepatitis D

   A. Transmitted through the use of _____ drugs and/or _____ contact.
   B. The symptoms are _____ severe than for the other types.
   C. Often seen in conjunction with _____ and _____ cases.

10. The Hepatitis E and G Viruses

    A. Hepatitis E is the result of exposure to food contaminated with human _____.
    B. It is a major infectious disease in developing countries because of poor _____ conditions.
    C. This form of hepatitis is _____ in the United States.
    D. Recently, hepatitis G has been isolated as a _____ infection.

11. HIV and AIDS

    A. There are more than _____ million persons living with HIV in the United States.
    B. The virus was first identified in the United States in _____.
    C. Worldwide, more than _____ million people are infected with HIV.

12. Survival Characteristics of the Human Immunodeficiency Virus

    A. HIV cannot survive on _____ objects.
    B. HIV can survive in bodily _____.

13. AIDS-Related Complex (ARC)

    A. ARC develops before _____ and is milder.
    B. Symptoms of ARC
       i. _____
       ii. _____
       iii. _____
       iv. _____
       v. _____
       vi. _____
       vii. _____
       viii. _____

© 2011 Pearson Education, Inc.

14. Developing AIDS

   A. It can take _____ years or more for HIV infection to advance to AIDS.
   B. A person who becomes infected with HIV develops _____.
   C. A person may experience swollen _____ glands for a number of years.
   D. After the immune system is severely compromised, _____ can occur.
   E. The final stage of HIV infection is _____.

15. Other HIV-related Conditions (List four opportunistic infections that can occur as a result of a suppressed immune system.)

   i. _____
   ii. _____
   iii. _____
   iv. _____

16. Risk Factors for AIDS (List persons who are at highest risk for contracting HIV.)

   i. _____
   ii. _____
   iii. _____
   iv. _____
   v. _____

17. Symptoms of AIDS

   i. _____
   ii. _____
   iii. _____
   iv. _____
   v. _____
   vi. _____
   vii. _____
   viii. _____
   ix. _____
   x. _____
   xi. _____
   xii. _____

18. Caring for a Person with AIDS

   A. Procedures for protecting the caregiver
      i. _____
      ii. _____
      iii. _____
      iv. _____
   B. Procedures for protecting the patient
      i. _____
      ii. _____
      iii. _____

19. Multidrug-Resistant Organisms (MDROs)

   A. MDROs are bacteria and other _____ that have developed a resistance to _____ drugs.
   B. Examples of MDROs
      i. _____
      ii. _____
      iii. _____
      iv. _____

v. _____

vi. _____

20. Risk Factors for Acquiring MDROs

i. _____

ii. _____

iii. _____

iv. _____

v. _____

21. Symptoms of Staph Infection

i. _____

ii. _____

iii. _____

iv. _____

22. Bioterrorism

A. Bioterrorism is the deliberate release of _____, _____, or other agents that can cause illness and death in humans, animals, or plants.

B. Biological agents can be spread through the _____, _____, or _____.

23. Category A Agents or Toxins (List six examples.)

i. _____

ii. _____

iii. _____

iv. _____

v. _____

vi. _____

KEY TERMINOLOGY REVIEW

Use the key terms found at the beginning of the chapter to finish the sentences below. Key terms may be more than one word in length.

1. _____ bacteria require an oxygen supply to live.

2. _____ kills all microorganisms, both pathogenic and nonpathogenic.

3. Microorganisms normally found on the skin may enter the body through a _____ and may cause infections.

4. The body has a natural protective mechanism called _____.

5. Microorganisms that are normally found on the skin and in the urinary, gastrointestinal, and respiratory tracts are known as _____.

6. _____ is the state of being free from germs, infection, and any form of microbial life.

7. During the process of inflammation, phagocytes engulf, digest, and destroy _____.

8. _____ bacteria can survive without oxygen.

9. The principles of asepsis are applied in the hospital setting to prevent the spread of _____.

10. _____ destroys most or all pathogens on inanimate objects with the use of chemicals such as iodine, chlorine, alcohol, and phenol.

11. The pathogen present in the _____ is the beginning of the chain of infection.

12. MRSA is highly resistant to _____.

13. Leukocytes actively fight pathogenic microorganisms with the process of _____.

© 2011 Pearson Education, Inc.

14. _____ such as *Staphylococcus* (staph), *Streptococcus* (strep), and malaria can cause disease.

15. The gastrointestinal tract, containing hydrochloric acid (HCl), causes a _____ action that destroys disease-producing bacteria.

APPLIED PRACTICE

Follow the directions as instructed with each question below.

1. Identify the links of the cycle of infection, as well as the incubation and prodromal periods.

> **Scenario**
>
> Shandra Graham, CMA (AAMA), did not know that she was infected with the flu virus when she went to work at Peachtree Medical Center. She forgot to wash her hands after she had coughed just prior to assisting her patient, Adam Kenney, into the examination room. While she was checking Mr. Kenney's blood pressure, Shandra sneezed and, unfortunately, was unable to cover her mouth.
>
> Two days later, Mr. Kenney developed some muscle aches that he had attributed to his exercise regimen. By day 5 after his office visit, Mr. Kenney had a high fever, chills, and intense muscular aches.

a. Who, in this scenario, represents the reservoir host within the cycle of infection?

_____

b. What is the means of exit of the infectious pathogen?

_____

c. What is the means of transmission of the pathogen?

_____

d. Who is the susceptible host?

_____

e. What is the incubation period for the reservoir host?

_____
_____
_____

f. What is the prodromal period for the person who became infected?

_____
_____
_____

2. Using what you have learned from the chapter, arrange the following steps in order to reflect the process of sanitization, disinfection, and sterilization of instruments. Read through all of the steps carefully. When you find what you think is the first step, write its corresponding letter in the space provided for step one. Continue this process until you have assigned the final step.

a. Completely immerse instruments in a container of disinfectant, cover, and let soak for the recommended length of time.
b. With hinges open, allow instruments to air dry on a cotton towel.
c. Remove instruments from the disinfectant, rinse thoroughly, and dry with paper towels.
d. Place contaminated instruments in an empty basin, cover the basin, and transport to the cleaning area.
e. Load the autoclave.

© 2011 Pearson Education, Inc.

f. Read MSDS for disinfectant and check the expiration date.

g. Place disinfected instruments in the center of dry wrapping paper.

h. Fold wrapping paper as directed and apply sterilization indicator tape.

i. Place instruments in a neutral low-suds detergent.

j. Remove the instruments to a clean container using sterile transfer forceps.

k. Check the distilled water level in the autoclave reservoir, and add distilled water as necessary.

l. Use a soft brush on all serrated and smooth edges, grooves, and open hinges; cleaning one instrument at a time.

m. Turn on the autoclave.

n. Put on disposable gloves and then utility gloves before handling the disinfectant.

Step 1: _____

Step 2: _____

Step 3: _____

Step 4: _____

Step 5: _____

Step 6: _____

Step 7: _____

Step 8: _____

Step 9: _____

Step 10: _____

Step 11: _____

Step 12: _____

Step 13: _____

Step 14: _____

LEARNING ACTIVITY: MULTIPLE CHOICE

Circle the correct answer to each of the questions below.

1. Since _____, the United States has been screening all blood for HIV antibodies.
   a. 1980
   b. 1990
   c. 1978
   d. 1985

2. The initial signs of HIV infection may include _____.
   a. symptoms of an opportunistic infection
   b. flulike symptoms such as fever, sore throat, swollen glands, and muscle aches
   c. symptoms of Kaposi's sarcoma
   d. no symptoms in the primary stage

3. Waterless hand sanitizers kill _____% of common microorganisms in 15 seconds.
   a. 90
   b. 95
   c. 99.9
   d. 100

4. The ordinary hygiene habits of everyday life are a form of _____.
   a. medical asepsis
   b. surgical asepsis
   c. bloodborne asepsis
   d. None of the above

© 2011 Pearson Education, Inc.

5. The CDC Special Pathogens Branch and the CDC National Center for Preparedness, Detection, and Control of Infectious Diseases (NCPDCID) _____.

    a. monitor outbreaks of the category illnesses

    b. have goals that include developing rapid diagnostic tests

    c. offer assistance in control and prevention during outbreaks

    d. All of the above

6. Sodium hypochlorite is actually _____.

    a. alcohol

    b. salt with chloride

    c. household bleach

    d. None of the above

7. The personal protective equipment you will wear for various tasks is determined by _____.

    a. actual or anticipated exposure to microorganisms

    b. actual or anticipated exposure to blood and bodily fluids and OPIM

    c. actual or anticipated exposure to nosocomial infections

    d. actual or anticipated exposure to hepatitis B or HIV/AIDS

8. An exposure control program must be implemented in each facility and must include the following _____.

    a. exposure determination

    b. method of compliance

    c. postexposure evaluation

    d. All of the above

9. The hepatitis B vaccine has been available since _____.

    a. 1965

    b. 1974

    c. 1982

    d. 2000

10. By which of the following means can the AIDS virus enter the body?

    a. Vaginal, anal, or oral intercourse with a person who has the virus

    b. Receiving an organ transplant from a donor who has the virus

    c. Receiving artificial insemination with the sperm of a man who has the virus

    d. All of the above

CRITICAL THINKING

Answer the following questions to the best of your ability. Utilize the textbook as a reference.

1. What is the main premise of Standard and Universal Precautions and the Bloodborne Pathogen Standard? What impact on patient discrimination do you think this has had?

    _____

    _____

    _____

    _____

2. You are working on preparing the sterile field and go to the autoclave for the paper-wrapped packs of instruments that you ran earlier that day. The tape on the outside of the packs has the darkened stripes so you know that the outside of the pack has been sterilized. The physician is behind schedule and irritated about that. There are no extra instruments for this particular procedure, which is why you

planned ahead and autoclaved them earlier. You open all of the packs and transfer the contents to the sterile tray and put the sterile cover over it. As you clean up the empty paper and packages, you notice that the sterilization indicator from the inside of the packs had not changed color. What would you do? Say nothing and assume that the tape on the outside indicated that the entire package had been sterilized? Tell the doctor that it will take another 40 minutes to re-autoclave the items and get them ready for the procedure? Say nothing because you fear the physician's anger or even losing your job?

_____

_____

_____

_____

RESEARCH ACTIVITY

Utilize Internet search engines to research the following topics and write a brief description of what you find. It is important to utilize reputable websites.

1. Research the website for the Occupational Safety and Health Administration, www.osha.gov.
   What information can be found for health care facilities? List some facts found within the website.

_____

_____

_____

_____

_____

_____

_____

_____

_____

_____

_____

_____

_____

_____

_____

_____

_____

© 2011 Pearson Education, Inc.

CHAPTER 35
Vital Signs

CHAPTER OUTLINE

General review of the chapter:

Interviewing the Patient
Correct Documentation
Measuring Weight and Height
Vital Signs
Temperature
Pulse
Respiration
Blood Pressure
Pain
Body Fat Measurement

STUDENT STUDY GUIDE

Use the following guide to assist in your learning of the concepts from the chapter.

I. Documentation of Patient Information

   1. Reasons for Maintaining the Patient's Medical Record

      i. _____

      ii. _____

      iii. _____

      iv. _____

      v. _____

      vi. _____

      vii. _____

   2. Contents of the Patient's Medical Record

      i. _____

      ii. _____

      iii. _____

      iv. _____

      v. _____

      vi. _____

      vii. _____

      viii. _____

      ix. _____

   3. Types of Diagnosis (Explain each of the following types.)

      A. Final or medical diagnosis: _____

      B. Clinical diagnosis or working diagnosis: _____

      C. Differential diagnosis: _____

© 2011 Pearson Education, Inc.

4. Steps for Gathering Information to Ensure Proper Charting
   A. Before a patient has a physical examination or is seen by the physician, a _____ _____ must be obtained.
   B. The initial patient interview is conducted by the medical assistant and the information gathered becomes part of the _____ _____ _____.
   C. After the initial data have been gathered, the patient's _____ _____, _____, and _____ are measured.
   D. The physician then examines the patient and _____ the information obtained.

5. The Initial Patient Interview
   A. Performed to obtain information on the patient's _____ and _____ and treatments.
   B. It is important to ensure the patient's _____ during the interview.

6. Considerations When Interviewing a Patient
   A. Review the _____ _____ before the interview.
   B. Ask the patient's _____ to interview him or her.
   C. Use an "_____" comment to put the patient at ease.
   D. Provide _____ during the interview.
   E. Be aware of _____ and _____ cues.
   F. Avoid making _____ responses.
   G. Avoid providing medical _____.
   H. Treat _____ topics with respect.
   I. Document according to _____ _____.

7. Charting Guidelines
   i. _____
   ii. _____
   iii. _____
   iv. _____
   v. _____
   vi. _____
   vii. _____
   viii. _____
   ix. _____
   x. _____
   xi. _____
   xii. _____
   xiii. _____

8. The Six Cs of Charting
   A. C _____ own words must be used exactly and be in quotes.
   B. C _____ must be used when recording information.
   C. C _____ is essential.
   D. C _____ of entries saves time and chart space.
   E. C _____ order of information is critical.
   F. C _____ of patient information is mandatory.

9. Weighing a Patient
   A. Frequent weight monitoring is particularly important for certain patients (List patients who would benefit from such monitoring.)
      i. _____
      ii. _____
      iii. _____
      iv. _____

© 2011 Pearson Education, Inc.

10. Obtaining a Patient's Weight

    A. Typically done with clothing _____.

    B. Shoes should be _____.

    C. Patients who cannot stand may be weighed on a _____ or a _____.

11. Measuring a Patient's Height

    A. Measured _____ shoes.

    B. Heel, buttocks, and the back of the head should be touching the measuring _____ or bar.

    C. Convert inches and feet to _____ by multiplying by 2.5.

    D. Convert from centimeters to _____ by dividing by 2.5.

II. Temperature

1. Vital Signs (List what is considered to be a vital sign.)

    i. _____

    ii. _____

    iii. _____

    iv. _____

    v. _____

2. Factors That Affect Body Temperature

    i. _____

    ii. _____

    iii. _____

    iv. _____

    v. _____

    vi. _____

    vii. _____

    viii. _____

    ix. _____

    x. _____

3. Fever

    A. A fever is also known as _____.

    B. A fever is a temperature that is above _____ (38°C).

    C. Indicates that the body is producing greater _____ than what is being _____.

    D. Indicates that the body is _____.

    E. _____ or _____ develops if the body temperature exceeds 105.8°F (41°C).

    F. A temperature above _____ (43°C) is typically fatal.

4. Common Types of Fevers

    i. _____

    ii. _____

    iii. _____

    iv. _____

5. Signs of a Fever

    i. _____

    ii. _____

    iii. _____

    iv. _____

    v. _____

6. Hypothermia

    A. Hypothermia is indicated by a temperature that is below _____ (36°C).

    B. A temperature below _____ (34°C) is typically fatal.

C. Clinical signs of hypothermia
   i. _____
   ii. _____
   iii. _____
   iv. _____

7. Sites for Measuring Body Temperature (Explain why each site might be selected.)

   A. Oral: _____
   B. Rectal: _____
   C. Axillary: _____
   D. Tympanic (aural): _____

8. Normal Temperature Values

   A. Oral: _____
   B. Rectal: _____
   C. Axillary: _____
   D. Ear (aural): _____
   E. Temporal artery: _____

9. Considerations When Taking an Oral Temperature

   A. Make sure that the patient closes his or her mouth _____ around the thermometer.
   B. Some facilities do not require the use of the degree symbol (°) when documenting this measurement.
   C. The thermometer is inserted under the tongue on either side of the _____ _____.
   D. For an accurate measurement, the patient must be advised not to _____ during the procedure.
   E. Oral temperature should only be measured if _____ minutes have elapsed since the patient has taken fluids or smoked.

10. Considerations When Taking an Axillary Temperature

   A. Axillary temperatures register _____ (0.6°C) lower than oral temperatures.
   B. The axillary method is the least _____ of the temperature measurements, but it is recommended for small children or patients who have had _____ surgery.
   C. This method is affected by _____; therefore, the underarm area should be _____ in order to obtain an accurate reading.

11. Considerations When Taking an Aural Temperature

   A. This method uses the _____ _____ area at the end of the external auditory canal.
   B. Tympanic thermometers are able to detect _____ waves in the ear canal and calculate body temperature from this data.

12. Considerations When Taking a Temporal Artery Temperature

   A. This method is a new, noninvasive procedure involving a device that measures the temperature over the temporal artery located close to the skin surface on the _____ and the _____ area.
   B. When the probe/scanner is passed over the surface of the forehead toward the temple, it can read the peak _____ temperature.

13. Types of Thermometers

   i. _____
   ii. _____
   iii. _____
   iv. _____

14. Steps for Measuring a Rectal Temperature

   A. If the patient is a child, explain the procedure to both the _____ and the _____.

© 2011 Pearson Education, Inc.

B. Instruct the patient to lie on his or her left side with the top leg bent (this is called the _____ position).

C. Place a small amount of _____ on a tissue and dip the probe into the _____.

D. With one hand, raise the upper _____ to expose the anus, or anal opening.

E. With the other hand, gently insert the lubricated thermometer _____ inch into the anal canal.

F. Hold the thermometer in place until the _____ is signaled, and then withdraw the thermometer.

G. Dispose of the _____ _____ in a biohazard waste container.

H. Wipe the anus from _____ to _____ to remove excess lubricant.

15. Steps for Accurately Using the Tympanic Thermometer

A. Remove the thermometer from its base. The display will read "_____".

B. Attach the _____ _____ cover to the earpiece.

C. With one hand, gently pull _____ on the patient's _____ ear if the patient is an adult or pull back and _____ if the patient is an infant or a child who is 3 years of age or younger.

D. Gently insert the plastic covered tip of the probe into the _____ _____.

E. Press the _____ _____, which activates the thermometer.

F. Observe the temperature reading in the _____ _____.

16. Steps for Accurately Obtaining an Axillary Temperature

A. Ask the patient to expose the _____.

B. Using a tissue, pat the area dry of _____.

C. Place the covered probe into the _____ _____.

D. When the thermometer _____, remove the thermometer and discard the probe cover in a waste container.

17. Steps for Using a Chemical Disposable Thermometer

A. Identify the patient, explain the procedure, and _____ the patient's _____.

B. Place the thermometer strip on the patient's _____.

C. Read the correct temperature by reading the _____ _____.

D. The reading is taken by noting the _____ reading among the dots that changed color.

E. The strip is kept in place for about _____ seconds and is read by the color change on the strip.

18. Steps for Using a Temporal Artery Thermometer

A. Identify the patient, explain the procedure, and _____ the patient's _____ aside.

B. Place the probe _____ on the center of the forehead and depress the _____ _____.

C. Keep the button depressed and slowly slide the probe on the _____ across the _____ to the hairline.

D. Lift the probe from the forehead and place it on the _____ just behind the _____.

E. Release the _____ and read the temperature.

III. Pulse and Respiration

1. The Pulse

A. The pulse is the number of times that the heart _____ per _____ (bpm).

B. A wave of blood is created each time the _____ _____ of the heart contracts.

C. Each pulse beat is one _____ _____, or one heartbeat.

D. A normal heartbeat is about _____ times per minute.

E. Increased _____ results in a faster pulse rate.

2. Factors That Influence the Pulse Rate

    i. _____

    ii. _____

    iii. _____

    iv. _____

    v. _____

    vi. _____

    vii. _____

    viii. _____

    ix. _____

3. Average Pulse Rates by Age

    A. Less than 1 year: _____ bpm

    B. 2–6 years: _____ bpm

    C. 6–10 years: _____ bpm

    D. 11–16 years: _____ bpm

    E. Adult: _____ bpm

    F. Older adult: _____ bpm

4. Characteristics of the Pulse

    i. _____

    ii. _____

    iii. _____

    iv. _____

5. Rate and Volume of the Pulse

    A. The _____ describes the number of pulse beats per minute.

    B. The _____ refers to the strength of the pulse.

    C. The volume is influenced by the _____ of the heartbeat, the _____ of the arterial walls, and _____.

    D. A variance in the _____ of the pulse may indicate heart disease.

6. Rhythm

    A. Refers to the _____, or _____, of the beats.

    B. Normally, the intervals between each heartbeat are of the same _____.

    C. A pulse with an irregular rhythm is known as a _____, or _____.

    D. It is not considered abnormal if the heart occasionally _____ a beat. This is referred to as an _____ pulse.

7. Common Pulse Sites

    i. _____

    ii. _____

    iii. _____

    iv. _____

    v. _____

    vi. _____

    vii. _____

    viii. _____

    ix. _____

8. Steps for Measuring a Radial Pulse Rate

    A. Explain the procedure to the patient and ask the patient about any recent _____ _____ or _____.

    B. Place your fingertips on the _____ _____ on the thumb side of the wrist.

    C. Check the _____ of the pulse.

© 2011 Pearson Education, Inc.

D. Start counting the pulse beats when the second hand on your watch is at ____, ____, ____, or ____.

E. Count the pulse for _____ _____ _____.

F. Immediately write down the number of _____ _____ per _____.

9. Steps for Taking an Apical-Radial Pulse

  A. The first person places the ear pieces of the stethoscope in his or her ears, with the opening in the _____ facing _____.

  B. Locate the _____ of the patient's heart by palpating to the left _____ _____ space at the _____ line.

  C. The second person locates the _____ _____ on the thumb side of the wrist 1 inch below the base of the thumb.

  D. The first person places the _____ _____ of the stethoscope at the _____ of the heart.

  E. When the _____ _____ is heard, a nod is made to the second person and counting begins. Ideally, the count should begin when the _____ _____ of a watch is at the 3, 6, 9, or 12.

  F. Count for _____ _____ minute.

  G. Record the rate and quality of the heartbeat. Include both _____ and _____ rates, using the designation AP.

  H. Calculate the pulse deficit by _____ the radial pulse rate from the _____ pulse rate.

10. Respiration

  A. Respiration is the exchange of _____ and _____ _____.

  B. It consists of one _____ and one _____.

  C. Each _____ and _____ of a patient's chest equals one respiration.

  D. Taken typically at the same time as a _____.

11. The Characteristics of Respiration

  i. _____

  ii. _____

  iii. _____

  iv. _____

12. Respiratory Rate Ranges by Age Group

  A. Newborn: _____

  B. 1 year old: _____

  C. 2–10 years: _____

  D. 11–18 years: _____

  E. Adult: _____

13. Circumstances That Alter Respiration

  i. _____

  ii. _____

  iii. _____

  iv. _____

  v. _____

  vi. _____

  vii. _____

  viii. _____

  ix. _____

  x. _____

14. Terms for Describing Breathing Sounds

  i. _____

  ii. _____

© 2011 Pearson Education, Inc.

    iii. _____
    iv. _____
    v. _____
    vi. _____
    vii. _____

IV. Blood Pressure

   1. Symptoms of Hypertension and Hypotension

    A. Symptoms of Hypertension
      i. _____
      ii. _____
      iii. _____
    B. Symptoms of Hypotension
      i. _____
      ii. _____

   2. Blood Pressure Readings (Briefly explain each.)

    A. Systolic pressure: _____
    B. Diastolic pressure: _____
    C. Pulse pressure: _____

   3. The Five Phases of the Korotkoff Sounds

    A. The first _____ sound is heard.
    B. The sound becomes _____.
    C. The sound becomes less _____ and develops a _____ sound.
    D. The sound begins to _____.
    E. The sound _____.

   4. Blood Pressure Guidelines (List what the readings would be for each of the following.)

    A. Hypertension: _____ or above
    B. Prehypertension: _____ to _____
    C. Normal: _____ or below
    D. Optimal: _____ or below

   5. Average Normal Blood Pressure Readings

    A. Newborn: _____
    B. 6–9 years: _____
    C. 10–15 years: _____
    D. 16 years to adulthood: _____
    E. Adulthood: _____

   6. Physiological Factors Affecting Blood Pressure

      i. _____
      ii. _____
      iii. _____
      iv. _____

   7. Other Factors Affecting Blood Pressure

      i. _____
      ii. _____
      iii. _____
      iv. _____
      v. _____
      vi. _____
      vii. _____
      viii. _____

© 2011 Pearson Education, Inc.

ix. _____

x. _____

8. Other Terms Related to Abnormal Readings

A. Benign: _____-_____ of elevated blood pressure without symptoms.

B. Essential: Primary _____ of unknown cause. May be _____ determined.

C. Secondary: Elevated blood pressure associated with other conditions such as _____ disease, _____, _____, and obesity.

D. Malignant: Rapidly developing elevated blood pressure that may become _____ if not treated immediately.

E. Renal: Elevated blood pressure as a result of _____ disease.

F. Orthostatic: A _____ _____ in blood pressure that occurs when a patient rapidly moves from a lying to a standing position.

G. Postural: A temporary fall in blood pressure from _____ _____ for extended periods of time.

9. Conditions That Require Blood Pressure to Be Monitored Regularly

i. _____

ii. _____

iii. _____

iv. _____

v. _____

vi. _____

vii. _____

viii. _____

ix. _____

x. _____

xi. _____

xii. _____

10. Equipment for Measuring Blood Pressure

i. _____

ii. _____

11. The Components of the Stethoscope

i. _____

ii. _____

iii. _____

iv. _____

v. _____

vi. _____

vii. _____

12. Causes of Errors in Blood Pressure Readings

A. Equipment: The cuff is the _____ _____, or air leaks around the _____ or _____.

B. Procedure: The patient's arm is _____ _____, or the medical assistant is too far from the _____ to accurately read the gauge.

C. Patient: The patient's arm is _____ _____ to obtain an accurate reading.

V. Pain

1. Pain—The Fifth Vital Sign

A. Pain is highly _____ and personal.

B. It is important to document a _____ of the pain.

C. It is important to observe the _____ signs of pain when talking with the patient.

© 2011 Pearson Education, Inc.

D. Use of a _____ pain measurement scale can be useful.

E. Assessment is necessary to establish a _____ plan.

2. Characteristics of Pain (Briefly explain each type.)

   A. Acute pain: _____

   B. Chronic pain: _____

   C. Radiating pain: _____

   D. Referred pain: _____

   E. Intractable pain: _____

   F. Phantom pain: _____

3. Other Terms Used to Describe Pain

   i. _____

   ii. _____

   iii. _____

   iv. _____

   v. _____

VI. Body Fat Measurement

   1. Steps for Using Calipers to Measure Skin-Fold Fat

      A. Grasp the _____ in the _____ _____ with your thumb and index finger.

      B. Place the calipers over the _____ and _____.

      C. Grasp the _____ _____ beneath the shoulder blade and obtain the caliper reading and record it.

      D. Determine the _____ _____ of body fat, using a table provided by the manufacturer.

   2. Steps for Accurately Calculating the Body Mass Index

      A. Insert the patient's _____ and _____ into the formula; use _____ and _____ or kilograms and meters according to facility policy.

      B. Formula BMI = _____

KEY TERMINOLOGY REVIEW

Without using your textbook, write a sentence using the selected key terms in the correct context.

1. *Afebrile:* Absence of a fever

2. *Apical:* heart rate that is counted at the apex of the heart

3. *Asymptomatic:* without symptoms

4. *Basal metabolism:* rate of metabolism when the body is awake a the rest

© 2011 Pearson Education, Inc.

5. *Baseline:* Know value with which follow up values are compared.

6. *Cyanosis:* blush discoloration of the skin and nail beds due to lack of oxgen in the tissue

7. *Dysrhythmia:* Pulse with an irregular rhythm, also known as arrhythmia

8. *Febrile:* Having a fever

9. *Frenulum linguae:* longitudinal fold of mucus membrane under the tongue

10. *Hypertension (HTN):* Condition in which blood pressure is consistently higher than 140/90 mm Hg also known as blood pressure

11. *Hyperthermia:* markedly elevated body temperature

12. *Hyperventilation:* deep, rapid respirations

13. *Hypoventilation:* Shallow ~~resp 5th~~ respirations

14. *Manometer:* part of a sphygomomanometer a scale that reads the actual pressure reading

15. *Metabolism:* Sum of all biochemical and physiological pro that take place in the body

16. *Palpatory method:* feeling the radial pulse while the blood pressure is deflating, used to determine systolic pressure

17. *Phantom pain:* Sensation felt in a missing body part after it has been removed

18. *Pulse deficit:* difference in reading between the apical radical pulses

© 2011 Pearson Education, Inc.

19. *Radiating pain:*

pain that spreads out from ane area

20. *Referred pain:*

Pain that is felt at a site other than the injured or diseased body part

21. *Subjective symptom:*

unmeasurable symptom felt by the patient but not apparent to an observer

22. *Syncope:*

Fainting

23. *Tachycardia:*

abnormally rapid heart rate

24. *Thready pulse:*

Weak or barely perceptible force or blood volume

APPLIED PRACTICE

Follow the directions as instructed with each question below.

1. A patient, who has a normal baseline temperature of 98.6°F has had the following average body temperatures over the past 5 days: **Day 1: 101.2°F, Day 2: 100.1°F, Day 3: 98.6°F, Day 4: 99.0°F, Day 5: 101.3°F.** How would you describe this fever? Explain your answer.

2. Your patient is a 43-year-old female. Her blood pressure is 157/92. What is the patient's pulse pressure? Is the pulse pressure normal? Explain your answer.

3. You are preparing a new patient for a physical examination. Because the patient has recently moved from a European country, he would like the medical assistant to tell him his body temperature in Celsius rather than Fahrenheit. When obtaining his temperature, the thermometer reads 99.0°F. How does this convert to Celsius? What is the conversion formula?

© 2011 Pearson Education, Inc.

LEARNING ACTIVITY: FILL IN THE BLANK

Using words from the list below, fill in the blanks to complete the following statements.

Note: *Some terms are used in more than one statement.*

Anthropometric	Heat waves	Rhythm
Anthropometry	Korotkoff sounds	Sphygmomanometer
Apnea	Movement	Symptom
Arterial	Orthostatic hypotension	Tachypnea
Blood pressure	Pulse	Tympanic membrane thermometer
Bradypnca	Rate	Volume
Core	Rectal	Walls
Eupnea	Respirations	

1. Oral and __Rectal__ temperatures measure the body's __Core__ temperature.

2. __Respirations__ are counted by watching, listening, or feeling the __movement__ of inspiration and expiration on the patient's back, stomach, or chest.

3. The three aspects to note when taking a pulse are __Rhythm__, __Volume__, and __pulse rate__.

4. The __Korotkoff Sounds__ are the sounds actually heard as the __Arterial__ wall distends during the compression of the blood pressure cuff.

5. __Orthosatic hypotension__ refers to the lowered __blood pressure__ that occurs when a patient moves from lying down to an erect position.

6. The __Sphygmomanometer__ is the instrument used for measuring the pressure that the blood exerts against the __walls__ of the artery.

7. The __tympanic membrane thermometer__ or aural thermometer is so named because it is able to detect __heat waves__ within the ear canal and near the eardrum.

8. A respiratory rate of below 12 (called __Bradypnea__) or above 40 (called __Tachypnea__) in an adult should be considered a serious symptom.

9. __Apnea__ means the absence of breathing for longer than 19 seconds, and __Eupnea__ means normal breathing.

10. Weight and height are __Anthropometric__ measurements since they relate to __Anthropometry__, the science of size, proportion, weight, and height.

CRITICAL THINKING

Answer the following questions to the best of your ability. Utilize the textbook as a reference.

1. Why might you take vitals while a patient is receiving a treatment?

_____

_____

_____

2. If a patient walks in without an appointment and presents as extremely short of breath (SOB) and appears weak, do you think that you should spend the time doing weight, height,

and all of the vitals before alerting the doctor of the patient's immediate condition? Explain your answer.

_____

_____

_____

_____

RESEARCH ACTIVITY

Utilize Internet search engines to research the following topics and write a brief description of what you find. It is important to utilize reputable websites.

1. Choose a health condition related to a vital sign (e.g., hypertension, obesity, etc.). Research informational websites related to your chosen condition. What type of information is included in the informational websites? How can this information be useful for patients?

_____

_____

_____

_____

_____

_____

_____

_____

_____

_____

_____

_____

_____

_____

_____

_____

_____

_____

_____

_____

_____

© 2011 Pearson Education, Inc.

CHAPTER 36
Assisting with Physical Examinations

CHAPTER OUTLINE

General review of the chapter:

Preparing the Examination Room
Patient History
Equipment and Supplies Used for Physical Examinations
Examination Methods Used by the Physician
Adult Examination
Assisting the Physician with a Physical Examination
Sequence of Examination Procedures

STUDENT STUDY GUIDE

Use the following guide to assist in your learning of the concepts from the chapter.

I. Preparing the Examination Room and Examination Methods

1. The Medical Assistant's Role in the Patient's Physical Exam

   i. _____
   ii. _____
   iii. _____
   iv. _____
   v. _____
   vi. _____
   vii. _____
   viii. _____
   ix. _____
   x. _____

2. Cleaning the Examination Room

   A. Place the used gown in the _____ receptacle or waste container.
   B. Clean the examination table, allow it to dry, and _____ it with fresh paper.
   C. Clean and _____ used equipment.
   D. Disinfect all surfaces with _____.
   E. Close all biohazard containers, _____, and remove if full.
   F. Ensure that the room is clean and clutter and _____ free.

3. Features of the Examination Room (List the items typically found in an examination room.)

   i. _____
   ii. _____
   iii. _____

© 2011 Pearson Education, Inc.

iv. _____

v. _____

vi. _____

vii. _____

viii. _____

4. Examination Room Safety Issues (List the safety considerations for the examination room.)

i. _____

ii. _____

iii. _____

iv. _____

v. _____

vi. _____

vii. _____

viii. _____

ix. _____

5. Preparing the Examination Room

A. Prepare _____ and _____ for the physician.

B. Ensure that the equipment is not within the _____ of the patient.

C. Position the _____ _____ to provide the correct _____ for the physician.

D. Ensure that the examination light is positioned so that it does not _____ _____.

E. Use proper _____ _____ when assisting with patient care.

6. Ensuring Patient Comfort and Privacy

A. Keep the thermostat around _____ to _____ °F.

B. Provide _____ and _____, as needed, to keep the patient warm.

C. Ensure that the examination room is _____ -_____ to decrease odors.

D. Clearly explain how to put on the _____ _____.

E. Inform the patient where to place his or her _____.

F. Leave the room when the patient is _____, unless assistance is required.

G. Knock and receive _____ when reentering the examination room.

7. Information Provided on the Patient Registration Form

i. _____

ii. _____

iii. _____

iv. _____

v. _____

vi. _____

vii. _____

viii. _____

ix. _____

x. _____

xi. _____

8. The Purpose of the Patient's History

A. Assists the physician in assessing the patient's _____ _____ _____.

B. Helps determine a _____ of the patient's present problem or _____.

9. Contents of the Medical History

i. _____

ii. _____

iii. _____

iv. _____

© 2011 Pearson Education, Inc.

v. _____

vi. _____

10. The Chief Complaint

    A. The chief complaint is referred to as the _____ _____.

    B. Usually consists of one or two _____.

    C. Symptoms are either _____ or _____.

    D. _____ symptoms, such as vertigo or pain, are felt by the patient but are not apparent to an observer and cannot be _____.

    E. _____ symptoms, such as a rash or fever, are felt by the patient, are apparent to an observer, and can be _____.

    F. Symptoms are usually documented using the patient's own _____.

11. Steps for Interviewing a Patient and Preparing for an Examination

    A. _____ the patient, greet the patient warmly, and _____ yourself.

    B. Provide a _____ area in which to conduct the interview.

    C. Ask the patient to fill in the _____ information on the patient data form.

    D. Record the chief complaint in the patient's _____ _____ as appropriate.

    E. Ask the patient other _____-_____ questions to gather more information about the chief complaint to record under present illness.

    F. Use _____ skills during interview.

    G. Ask the patient about _____. Record allergies in _____ ink as required by office policy.

    H. If the patient states that he or she does not have any allergies, record in _____ _____ according to office policy.

    I. Correct any errors by drawing _____ _____ through the error; then date and _____ the correction.

    J. Ask the patient to provide a _____ specimen, if required, or ask the patient to empty his or her bladder.

    K. Explain what _____ the patient should remove, where the opening of the examination gown should be, and where the patient should sit and wait.

12. The Present Illness (PI)

    A. Provides a more complete, expansive description of the _____ _____.

    B. Must contain a detailed description of the symptom(s), including the _____, _____, and _____ of each.

    C. Each _____ should be documented as to its relationship to the _____ _____.

13. Obtaining a Past Medical History

    A. Includes all _____ and _____ _____ that the patient has experienced in the past.

    B. The dates of _____ _____, _____, _____, and _____ _____, including over-the-counter drugs, are noted whenever possible.

14. Information Included on a Complete Medical History

    i. _____

    ii. _____

    iii. _____

    iv. _____

    v. _____

    vi. _____

    vii. _____

    viii. _____

    ix. _____

15. The Family Medical History

   A. A family medical history is a record of the health problems of the patient's _____ relatives.
   B. Information on _____ relatives should include _____ _____, _____ _____ _____, and _____ _____ _____, as well as the age at which the individual died.

16. Information Contained in the Patient's Personal History

   i. _____
   ii. _____
   iii. _____
   iv. _____
   v. _____
   vi. _____
   vii. _____

17. Steps for Documenting a Chief Complaint

   A. Review briefly the patient's _____ _____ before greeting the patient.
   B. Ask _____-_____ questions to gather information about why the patient is being seen today.
   C. Maintain eye _____ and actively _____ to the patient's responses.
   D. Ask the patient to rate pain on a scale of _____ to _____.
   E. Document the _____ _____ and _____ _____ correctly on the correct form in the patient's own words.
   F. Thank the patient and explain that the _____ will be in shortly to examine him or her.
   G. Make sure that the patient is _____ before you leave the room.

18. The Inspection Method of Physical Examination

   A. Accomplished by visually examining the _____ surface of the body.
   B. Notes are made regarding any unusual _____, _____, _____, _____, or symmetry of the areas being inspected.

19. The Palpation Method of Physical Examination

   A. Performed by using the _____ to feel the skin and accessible underlying _____.
   B. Used to determine any unusual _____, _____, _____, or texture.
   C. Oftentimes, abnormalities and _____ and _____ in the abdomen can be discovered through palpation.

20. The Percussion Method of Physical Examination

   A. To use this method, two fingers of one hand are placed on the patient's _____ and then struck with the _____ and _____ _____ of the other hand.
   B. The physician uses his or her fingers to percuss the chest wall and abdomen by gentle _____ or _____, which produces sounds or vibrations.
   C. An alteration in the standard, expected sound or vibration aids in determining the presence of _____ or _____ in a cavity.

21. The Auscultation Method of Physical Examination

   A. Using this method, the physician listens to _____ that are found within the body.
   B. These sounds must be differentiated from _____ body sounds by the physician.
   C. The auscultation method can also be performed by placing the _____ directly over the body surface.

22. The Mensuration Method of Physical Examination

   A. Special tools are used to measure the _____ or specific _____.
   B. To determine a patient's _____, a scale is used.

© 2011 Pearson Education, Inc.

C. A _____ is used to measure the range of motion of a joint.

D. _____ are used to determine the amount of body fat.

23. The Manipulation Method of Physical Examination

A. This method is the passive assessment of the _____ of a joint.

B. When a physician is using this examination method, he or she may _____ the joint for _____ and warmth.

II. Preparing the Examination Room and Examination Methods

1. The Role of the Medical Assistant in Assisting with a Physical Examination

A. Positions and _____ the patient.

B. Hands instruments, _____, and supplies to the physician.

C. Documents and _____ specimens.

D. Acts as a _____ to the behavior of the physician and the patient.

E. Carries out _____ plans.

F. Schedules _____ tests.

2. Draping the Patient

A. Used to protect the patient's _____ and provide some warmth.

B. Drape must not obstruct the _____ view or interfere with the area being examined.

C. Sterile drapes are used during _____ procedures.

3. The Role of the Medical Assistant in Positioning the Patient

A. Provides the patient with clear _____ on what position to assume.

B. Ensures the patient's _____.

4. Nine Standard Positions for Examinations and Procedures

i. _____

ii. _____

iii. _____

iv. _____

v. _____

vi. _____

vii. _____

viii. _____

ix. _____

5. The Supine Position

A. The supine position is also known as the _____ _____ position.

B. The patient lies flat on his or her back, with hands at the _____.

C. Be sure that the patient's feet are supported by _____ the table.

D. This is the position used to examine anything on the anterior or _____ surface of the body.

E. Drape the patient from the _____ down to over the feet.

F. This position may not be comfortable for patients who are short of breath or have _____ _____ problems.

G. Placing a _____ under the patient's head and under the knees may make him or her more comfortable.

6. The Dorsal Recumbent Position

A. The patient is lying flat on his or her back with knees _____ and feet _____ on the table.

B. This position relieves strain on the _____ _____ and relaxes the _____ muscles.

© 2011 Pearson Education, Inc.

C. Used to inspect the _____; _____: _____: and _____, _____, or perineal areas.

D. Can be used for _____ exams of the vagina and rectum.

E. Patients with _____ _____ may find this position uncomfortable.

7. The Lithotomy Position

A. Similar to the _____ _____ position except that the patient's feet are placed in stirrups attached to the side of the table.

B. After the feet are in place in the stirrups, the patient is instructed to _____ _____ until the buttocks are positioned at the edge of the table.

C. Patients with severe _____ or those who are severely _____ or in late-term pregnancy may find this position impossible.

8. The Fowler's Position

A. In this position, the head of the table is raised to a _____-degree angle.

B. This position is useful for examinations of the _____, _____, or _____ body.

C. The drape should be placed over the patient's _____, covering the _____.

9. The Semi-Fowler's Position

A. This position is similar to the Fowler's position, but the head of the table is at a _____-degree angle instead of 90 degrees.

B. Used for _____-_____ examinations, patients with breathing difficulties, or patients suffering from general malaise.

C. The Fowler's or semi-Fowler's positions are more comfortable for patients who have _____ _____ injuries or _____ difficulties.

10. The Prone Position

A. Requires the patient to lie face down, flat on his or her stomach, or the _____ surface of the body, with the head turned to the _____ and arms either _____ the body or _____ under the head.

B. It is the opposite of the _____ position.

C. The drape should cover the patient from the _____ back to over the feet.

D. Used for _____ exams and certain types of surgery.

E. Unsuitable for patients with _____ problems, women in _____-_____ pregnancies, or the _____.

11. The Sims', or Lateral, Position

A. Requires the patient to lie on the _____ side with the right leg sharply bent upward and the left leg slightly bent.

B. The patient's weight is mainly on the _____ area.

C. The right arm is _____ next to the _____ for support.

D. Used for rectal exams, rectal _____, _____, and _____ and pelvic exams.

12. The Knee–Chest Position

A. The patient lies in the _____ position and then pulls the knees up to a _____ position with the thighs at a 90-degree angle to the table and the _____ in the air.

B. The head is turned to one side and the arms may be placed _____ _____ _____ or on either side of the head for comfort and support.

C. Most patients need assistance to assume this position correctly and should never be left _____ in this position at any time.

D. Used for _____ exams, _____, and rectal and vaginal exams.

© 2011 Pearson Education, Inc.

E. The drape should be placed from the _____ _____ at an angle covering the _____ area.

F. A _____ drape, which is a drape with a precut opening in the appropriate area, may be used.

G. Many physicians have _____ tables available for this type of exam.

13. The Trendelenburg Position

A. This position is not normally used in a physician's office except in cases of _____ or low blood pressure.

B. The patient lies in the _____ position and the end of the table is raised to about a _____-degree angle with the patient's legs bent at the knees over the end of the table.

C. Used for _____ surgeries.

14. The Proctological (Jackknife) Position

A. Used for proctological examinations conducted with a _____.

B. This position is similar to the _____-_____ position, but with a greater bend at the hips.

C. The patient will lie face down with the _____ at the _____ of the table.

KEY TERMINOLOGY REVIEW

Write a sentence using the selected key terms in the correct context.

1. *amplify:*

_____

_____

2. *bimanual:*

_____

_____

3. *chief complaint (CC):*

_____

_____

4. *goniometer:*

_____

_____

5. *inspection:*

_____

_____

6. *laryngeal mirror:*

_____

_____

7. *manipulation:*

_____

_____

© 2011 Pearson Education, Inc.

8. *mensuration:*

_____

_____

9. *objective symptom:*

_____

_____

10. *ophthalmoscope:*

_____

_____

11. *palpation:*

_____

_____

12. *present illness (PI):*

_____

_____

13. *reflex hammer:*

_____

_____

14. *review of systems (ROS):*

_____

_____

15. *subjective symptom:*

_____

_____

16. *tongue depressor:*

_____

_____

17. *turgor:*

_____

_____

18. *vaginal speculum:*

_____

_____

APPLIED PRACTICE

Follow the directions as instructed with each question below.

1. Next to each of the supplies shown below, name the supply and state its purpose.

© 2011 Pearson Education, Inc.

Supplies		Purpose
_____ _____		_____ _____
_____ _____		_____ _____
_____ _____		_____ _____
_____		_____ _____
_____		_____ _____ _____
_____ _____		_____ _____
_____		_____ _____
_____		_____ _____
_____		_____
_____		_____
_____		_____
_____		_____
_____		_____

2. Provide the name of the position for each of the pictures provided below.

© 2011 Pearson Education, Inc.

_____   _____

_____

LEARNING ACTIVITY: FILL IN THE BLANK

Using words from the list below, fill in the blanks to complete the following statements. Note: Some terms are used in more than one statement.

Auscultate	Pelvic exams	Tuning fork
Bladder	Percussion	Tympanic membrane
Bowel sounds	Rate	Underlying body parts
Depth	Rhythm	
Fowler's	Sitting erect	
Frequency	Snellen chart	
Lithotomy	Speculum	

1. Using a stethoscope the physician will _____ the patient's breathing sounds, noting the _____, _____, pitch, _____, and location.

2. _____ is the process of using the fingertips to tap the body lightly but sharply in order to assess the position and size of the _____.

© 2011 Pearson Education, Inc. *Assisting with Physical Examinations* **359**

3. The _____ position is used for _____ and Pap smears.

4. Emptying the _____ makes the patient feel more comfortable during the physical examination.

5. When using an otoscope, the light is focused through the disposable _____ to examine the outer ear, then the _____ (eardrum).

6. A _____ is a metal instrument that comes in different sizes and has two prongs extending from the handle that are designed to vibrate at a specific _____.

7. Using a stethoscope, the physician will auscultate the patient's _____ for frequency, pitch, gurgling, and clicking sounds.

8. The _____ position is when the patient is _____ on the table.

9. Prior to the physician seeing the patient, the medical assistant will test the patient's distance vision by using a _____.

10. Using a stethoscope, the physician will _____ the sounds of the heart, noting the _____, rhythm, pitch, and quality.

CRITICAL THINKING

Answer the following questions to the best of your ability. Utilize the textbook as a reference.

1. During a patient's clinical visit, whether for a physical examination or another reason, the medical assistant visually inspects the patient. Think of what may be visible about the patient that the MA may note.

   _____

   _____

   _____

   _____

2. You are assisting a physician with a physical examination. You have prepared all of the supplies and have any equipment ready. The patient is a female and will be having a pelvic exam along with the physical examination. Although the physician does not need you to assist him, you are expected to be present with the doctor anyway. State why the MA would be present in this situation. Would the same be true if the patient were a male? Would the same be true if the doctor was a female and the patient were a male?

   _____

   _____

   _____

   _____

   _____

RESEARCH ACTIVITY

Utilize Internet search engines to research the following topics and write a brief description of what you find. It is important to utilize reputable websites.

1. It is very important to be aware of the cultural norms of the patients seen in the medical office. Cultural norms can affect a patient's approach to having a physical examination. Select a culture.

 © 2011 Pearson Education, Inc.

Research this culture online or by interviewing individuals whom you know from this culture. Discover the cultural differences and/or barriers that may affect the success of performing a physical examination on a patient.

_____

_____

_____

_____

_____

_____

_____

_____

_____

_____

_____

_____

_____

_____

_____

_____

_____

_____

_____

_____

_____

_____

_____

CHAPTER 37

Assisting with Medical Specialties

CHAPTER OUTLINE

General review of the chapter:

  The Role of the Medical Assistant
  Allergy
  Dermatology
  Cardiovascular System
  Endocrinology
  Gastrointestinal System
  Lymphatic System
  Musculoskeletal System
  Nervous System

STUDENT STUDY GUIDE

Use the following guide to assist in your learning of the concepts from the chapter.

I. Diagnosing and Testing Allergies and Skin Disorders

  1. Allergic Reactions

     A. May be localized, such as a mosquito bite, or _____, such as asthma or anaphylactic shock.

     B. Respiratory symptoms include wheezing, _____, coughing, and nasal _____.

  2. Allergic Condition: Asthma

     A. Condition seen most frequently in _____ in which wheezing, coughing, and _____ are the major symptoms.

     B. Asthmatic attacks may be caused by _____ inhaled in the air and ingested in food and drugs.

     C. Treatment is _____ and the control of the _____ factors.

  3. Allergic Condition: Contact Dermatitis

     A. Involves _____ and _____ of the skin.

     B. Treatment consists of topical and _____ medications.

  4. Symptoms of a Severe Allergic Reaction

       i. _____
      ii. _____
     iii. _____
      iv. _____
       v. _____
      vi. _____
     vii. _____
    viii. _____

© 2011 Pearson Education, Inc.

5. Scratch or Skin Testing

   A. Used to determine the specific substances that cause an _____ reaction in the patient.
   B. If a _____ forms within _____ minutes after placing an allergen on the skin, an allergy is indicated.
   C. The patient should be advised to remain in the physician's office for at least _____ minutes after testing has been completed.

6. Intradermal Allergy Test

   A. Performed by injecting _____ to _____ mL of an allergen extract into the anterior surface of the forearm.
   B. Several tests (_____ to _____) can be performed on each arm.
   C. The test is considered to be more accurate than a _____ test.

7. Patch Tests

   A. Consists of placing a small amount of the _____ onto the _____ forearm and then covering it with a plastic wrap.
   B. Several patch tests can be performed at the same time and these are read after the patches have remained in place for _____ to _____ hours.
   C. The test is used to detect the _____ agents in contact dermatitis.

8. Radioallergosorbent Test (RAST)

   A. Measures blood levels of _____ to particular antigens.
   B. The test is expensive, but it is more sensitive and useful for patients who have _____ problems.

9. Skin Lesions

   A. Skin lesions can occur whenever the normal surface of the skin is invaded or _____.
   B. A skin lesion is not always a sign of _____.

10. Cellulitis

    A. Cellulitis is an _____ of the cellular or _____ tissue caused by either _____ or _____ infection of a cut or lesion.
    B. Treatment includes _____ and application of _____ compresses.

11. Psoriasis

    A. Psoriasis is a chronic inflammatory condition consisting of discrete _____ or _____ lesions covered with _____ scaling.
    B. It is not contagious and is thought to be an _____ disease.

12. Acne Vulgaris

    A. Acne vulgaris is an inflammatory disease of the _____ glands and hair follicles that results in _____ and _____.
    B. Treatment includes systemic and _____ antibiotics.

13. Scleroderma

    A. Scleroderma is a chronic, progressive _____ disease that affects the blood _____ and _____ tissue of the skin and other organs.
    B. Integumentary symptoms include hardening of the skin, pallor, edema, and fixating of skin to _____ tissues.

14. Neoplasms

    A. Neoplasms are biopsied by surgically removing a small amount of _____ for testing.
    B. Benign growths may grow in size but are usually _____.
    C. Malignant growths are _____ and tend to take over surrounding tissues.

© 2011 Pearson Education, Inc.   *Assisting with Medical Specialties*   **363**

15. Types of Benign Neoplasms (Briefly explain each type.)
   A. Dermatofibroma: _____
   B. Hemangioma: _____
   C. Keloid: _____
   D. Keratosis: _____
   E. Leukoplakia: _____
   F. Lipoma: _____
   G. Nevus: _____

16. Types of Malignant (Cancerous) Neoplasms (Briefly explain each type.)
   A. Basal cell carcinoma: _____
   B. Kaposi's sarcoma: _____
   C. Malignant melanoma: _____
   D. Squamous cell carcinoma: _____

17. Diagnostic Tests and Procedures to Treat Integumentary System Disorders (Briefly explain each type.)
   A. Adipectomy: _____
   B. Chemobrasion: _____
   C. Cryosurgery: _____
   D. Curettage: _____
   E. Dermabrasion: _____
   F. Dermoplasty: _____
   G. Electrocautery: _____
   H. Exfoliative cytology: _____
   I. Frozen section: _____
   J. Fungal scrapings: _____
   K. Lipectomy: _____
   L. Marsupialization: _____
   M. Plication: _____
   N. Rhytidectomy: _____
   O. Sweat test: _____
   P. Tzanck test: _____

18. Steps for Obtaining a Wound Culture (List each step in this procedure.)
   i. _____
   ii. _____
   iii. _____
   iv. _____
   v. _____
   vi. _____
   vii. _____
   viii. _____
   ix. _____
   x. _____
   xi. _____
   xii. _____
   xiii. _____

II. Examinations and Diagnostic Procedures

   1. Precipitating the Causes of Cardiovascular Disease
      i. _Poor circulation_
      ii. _defective heart valves_

© 2011 Pearson Education, Inc.

iii. _Conduction defect_
iv. _blood clots in the heart layers or bloodvessels_

2. The Most Common Symptoms of Cardiovascular Disease
   i. _Chest pain_
   ii. _Cyanosis_
   iii. _diaphoresis_
   iv. _dyspnea_
   v. _edema, irregular heartbeat_

3. Angiography
   A. X-rays are taken after the injection of an _opaque_ material into a blood _vessel_.
   B. Can be performed on the _aortic_ as an _heart_ angiogram.

4. Arterial Blood Gases
   A. Measurement of the amount of _oxygen_, _carbon dioxide_ _nitrogen_, and _pH_ in the blood.
   B. Provide a valuable evaluation of cardiac failure, hemorrhage, and _kidney_ failure.

5. The Artificial Pacemaker
   A. Controls the beating of the heart through a series of _rhythmic_ electrical impulses.
   B. An external pacemaker has the _electrodes_ on the outside of the body.

6. Cardiac Catheterization
   A. Cardiac catheterization is a diagnostic procedure to detect _abnormalities_
   B. Collects cardiac blood samples and determines the _pressure_ within the cardiac area.

7. Cardiac Enzymes
   A. Cardiac enzymes are complex _proteins_ that are capable of inducing chemical changes within the body.
   B. Taken by blood sample to determine the severity of _heart_ disease or damage.

8. Diagnostic Tests for Cardiovascular Conditions (Briefly explain each type.)
   A. Cardiolysis: _Surgical procedure separate adhesions_ _resectio ribs ste_
   B. Cardiorrhaphy: _Surgical stuturing of the heart_
   C. Cardioversion: _Converting a cardic arrhythmia_
   D. Commissurotomy: _Surgical incision to change the site of the p_
   E. Doppler ultrasonography: _Sound waves bounces off tissue to produce in_
   F. Electrocardiography: _Record of the electrical activity of the heart_
   G. Embolectomy: _Surgical removal of an embolus or blood clot_
   H. Lipoproteins: _measurement of blood to determine serum cho_
   I. Percutaneous balloon valvuloplasty: _Measurement of blood to determine s_
   J. Percutaneous transluminal coronary angioplasty: _Method for treating localized coronary artery narrowing_
   K. Phleborrhaphy: _Suturing of give in_
   L. Prothrombin time: _Measurement of the time it takes for sample of bl_
   M. Stress test: _Method for evaluting cardiovascular fitness_
   N. Venography: _X-ray of the vein in which the venous flow is tro Also called phelbo_

9. Coronary Artery Disease (CAD)
   A. CAD usually results from _atherosclerosis_
   B. If enough of the heart muscle is denied an oxygen-rich blood supply, a _myocardial_ or heart attack, may occur.

© 2011 Pearson Education, Inc.

Assisting with Medical Specialties

10. Congestive Heart Failure (CHF)

   A. CHF may result from _____.
   B. Symptoms occur because the heart muscle becomes _____ and is less able to pump blood to the rest of the body.

11. Factors That Reduce the Risk of Heart Disease

   i. _____
   ii. _____
   iii. _____
   iv. _____
   v. _____
   vi. _____
   vii. _____

12. Dysrhythmia

   A. Dysrhythmia is an abnormality of the _____ or _____ of the heartbeat.
   B. Caused by a disturbance of the _____ system in the heart.

13. The Glands of the Endocrine System (List and explain both types.)

   i. _____
   ii. _____

14. Diabetes Mellitus

   A. Diabetes mellitus is one of the most common _____ imbalances.
   B. Characterized by _____ (too much sugar in the blood).

15. Types of Diabetes Mellitus (Explain both types.)

   A. Type 1: _____
   B. Type 2: _____

16. Procedures and Diagnostic Tests for the Endocrine System (Briefly explain each.)

   A. Blood serum test: _____
   B. Fasting blood sugar: _____
   C. Glucose Tolerance Test (GTT): _____
   D. Parathryroidectomy: _____
   E. 17-hydroxycorticosteroids (17-OHCS): _____
   F. 17-ketosteroids (17-KS): _____
   G. Protein blood iodine test (PBI): _____
   H. Radioactive iodine uptake test (RAIU): _____
   I. Radioimmune assay test (RIA): _____
   J. Serum glucose test: _____
   K. Thymectomy: _____
   L. Thyroid echogram: _____
   M. Thyroparathyroidectomy: _____
   N. Total calcium: _____

17. Procedures and Diagnostic Tests for the Digestive System (Briefly explain each.)

   A. Air contrast barium enema: _____
   B. Anastomosis: _____
   C. Cholecystectomy: _____
   D. Cholecystogram: _____
   E. Choledocholithotomy: _____
   F. Choledocholithotrispy: _____

© 2011 Pearson Education, Inc.

G. Colostomy: _____

H. Endoscopic retrograde cholangiopancreatography (ERCP):
_____
_____

I. Esophagram: _____

J. Esophagogastrostomy: _____

K. Fistulectomy: _____

L. Gastrectomy: _____

M. Gastrointestinal endoscopy: _____

N. Gastric lavage: _____

O. Glossectomy: _____

P. Hepatic lobotomy: _____

Q. Ileostomy: _____

R. Intravenous cholangiogram: _____

S. Jejunostomy: _____

T. Proctoplasty: _____

U. Vagotomy: _____

18. Gastroesophageal Reflux Disease (GERD)

   A. GERD is one of the most common _____ disorders.

   B. It is also known as _____ or _____.

19. Treatment for Gastroesophageal Reflux Disease

   A. Eating small meals _____ times a day.

   B. Eating at least _____ to _____ hours before bedtime.

   C. Moderating coffee and _____ intake.

20. Diverticular Disease

   A. Diverticula are the small _____ found mainly in the _____ part of the colon or _____ intestine.

   B. A diverticulum is a _____ of the inner lining of the _____ wall through the muscular layers of _____.

   C. Diverticulitis is an _____ of one or more _____, causing severe pain, muscle spasms, nausea, and fever.

21. Sigmoidoscopy

   A. A sigmoidoscopy is also called a _____ or _____ examination.

   B. It is an examination of the _____ of the sigmoid colon for diagnostic purposes.

22. Assisting During a Sigmoidoscopy

   A. For this procedure, the patient may be placed in the _____ position or on a _____ examination table.

   B. The patient should be given detailed instructions on how to empty his or her _____ prior to the procedure.

   C. The patient should sign a consent form for both the _____ and any _____ taken.

23. Colonoscopy

   A. Performed in an office or as a hospital outpatient procedure because an _____ sedative is administered prior to the procedure.

   B. Allows the physician to examine more of the _____ intestine than is done in the sigmoidoscopy.

   C. The American Cancer Society recommends that all individuals over the age of _____ have a colonoscopy.

© 2011 Pearson Education, Inc.

24. Steps for Administering a Disposable Enema

    i. _____

    ii. _____

    iii. _____

    iv. _____

    v. _____

    vi. _____

    vii. _____

    viii. _____

    ix. _____

    x. _____

    xi. _____

25. Testing for Occult Blood

    A. Instruct the patient to follow the guidelines for preparation as listed by the _____ of the test kit.

    B. Guidelines should be observed for _____ days prior to collecting specimens and should continue until all _____ samples have been obtained.

26. The Lymphatic System

    A. Contains the _____ glands, ducts, nodes, tonsils, _____ gland, and spleen.

    B. It is the basis of the body's defense, or _____, system.

    C. The system protects the body against the invasion of foreign _____.

    D. Works in conjunction with the _____ system to purify the blood and drain fluids throughout the body.

27. Immunity

    A. Immunity is the body's ability to defend itself against _____ organisms and toxic substances.

    B. It is either natural or _____.

28. Procedures and Diagnostic Tests for the Lymphatic System (Briefly explain each.)

    A. Bone marrow aspiration: _____

    B. ELISA: _____

    C. Lymphadenectomy: _____

    D. Lymphangiogram: _____

    E. Splenopexy: _____

    F. Western blot: _____

29. Musculoskeletal System Specialists

    A. _____ treat the body by realigning the skeletal system to promote healing.

    B. _____ see patients with join inflammations and treat patients with autoimmune disorders.

    C. _____ use manual adjustment of the spine to promote healing and maintain homeostasis.

30. Procedures and Diagnostic Tests for the Musculoskeletal System (Briefly explain each.)

    A. Aldolase: _____

    B. Antinuclear antibody (ANA): _____

    C. Anterior cruciate ligament (ACL) reconstruction:

    _____

    D. Arthrocentesis: _____

    E. Arthrodesis: _____

© 2011 Pearson Education, Inc.

F. Arthrography: _____

G. Arthroplasty: _____

H. Arthrotomy: _____

I. Creatine phosphokinase (CPK): _____

J. C-Reactive Protein (CRP): _____

K. Electromyography: _____

L. Fasciectomy: _____

M. Goniometry: _____

N. Lactic dehydrogenase (LDH): _____

O. Laminectomy: _____

P. Meniscectomy: _____

Q. Myelography: _____

R. Phosphorus (P) blood test: _____

S. Photon absorptiometry: _____

T. Reduction: _____

U. Serum glutamic oxaloacetic transaminase (SGOT): _____

V. Serum glutamic pyruvic transaminase (SGPT): _____

W. Serum rheumatoid factor (RF): _____

X. Thermography: _____

31. Physicians Specializing in the Nervous System

A. A _neurologist_ specializes in treating and diagnosing conditions of the nervous system.

B. A _neurosurgeon_ performs surgical procedures on the nervous system because of disease or trauma.

C. A _psychiatrist_ treats mental and neurological conditions that affect behavior.

32. Neurological Tests and Procedures (Briefly explain each.)

A. Babinski's sign: _to determine lesions and abnormalities in the ner_

B. Carotid endarterectomy: _removing an obstruction within the carotid arteri_

C. Cerebral angiogram: _X-Ray the blood vessels of the brain after injecti_

D. Cordectomy: _Removal of part of the spinal cord_

E. Craniotomy: _Surgical incision into the brain through the cranium_

F. Electromyogram: _written recording ultrasonic echoes_

G. Laminectomy: _Removal of a posterior vertebral arch_

H. Pneumoencephalography: _X-ray examination of the brain follow_

I. Positron emission tomography (PET): _Positive radionucleotides to reconstruct brain sections_

J. Romberg's sign: _Test developed to established neurological funct_

K. Sympathectomy: _excision of a portion of the sympathtic_

L. Trephination: _Process of cutting out a piece of bone in the skull_

M. Vagotomy: _Surgical incision into the vagus nerve._

33. Cerebral Vascular Accident (CVA)

A. A CVA is also known as a _Cerebrovascular_

B. Risk factors for CVA

i. _hypertension_

ii. _Obesity_

iii. _high cholesterol_

iv. _Smoking_
v. _diabetes_
vi. _family history_
vii.

34. Symptoms of a cerebral vascular accident
    i. _loss of speech / diffivlty in speech._
    ii. _confusion_
    iii. _one-sidede numbess_
    iv. _paralysis_
    v. _facial droop_
    vi. _memory loss_
    vii. _blurred vision_

35. Dementia

    A. Dementia is a condition that results in the progressive loss of _memory_ and intellectual ability.
    B. Can occur at any age and is not a normal result of _aging_.
    C. Approximately half of all dementia patients suffer from _Alzheimer_ disease.

KEY TERMINOLOGY REVIEW

Use the key terms found at the beginning of the chapter to finish the sentences below. Key terms may be more than one word in length.

1. Asthmatic attacks may be caused by _____ inhaled from the air or ingested in food or drugs.

2. _____ is defined as excessive thirst.

3. The allergic interaction of an antigen and an antibody causes the release of _____, which is the substance that produces the signs and symptoms of allergies.

4. _____ or hidden blood in feces may be an indication of bleeding in the gastrointestinal tract.

5. _____ are formed in reaction to the scratch testing of allergens.

6. Intracranial pressure may be evaluated by testing for the _____.

7. As the coronary arteries narrow, the blood flow to the heart muscle is lessened and _____ may occur.

8. An _____ is a granular white cell that captures invading microorganisms and antibody–antigen reactions through phagocytosis.

9. _____ is the branch of medicine dealing with malignant neoplasms or tumors.

10. The medical term for excessive sweating is _____.

APPLIED PRACTICE

Follow the directions as instructed with each question below.

© 2011 Pearson Education, Inc.

1. Identify each of the following skin lesions.

_____
_____
_____

_____
_____
_____

_____
_____
_____

_____
_____
_____

_____
_____
_____

_____
_____
_____

_____
_____
_____

_____
_____
_____

_____
_____
_____

_____
_____
_____

2. Using the drawings below, name each of the sites where referred abdominal pain can occur.

LEARNING ACTIVITY: MULTIPLE CHOICE

Circle the correct answer to each of the questions below.

1. Which of the following are methods of diagnostic allergy testing?

    a. RAST Test
    b. Scratch test
    c. Intradermal test
    d. All of the above

2. Which of the following conditions is also called hives?

    a. Allergic rhinitis
    b. Eczema
    c. Urticaria
    d. Contact dermatitis

3. The scratch method of allergy testing is usually performed on the patient's _____.

    a. Back
    b. Leg
    c. Foot
    d. All of the above

4. Bedsores are also known as _____.

    a. erysipelas
    b. decubitus ulcers
    c. psoriasis
    d. acne vulgaris

5. Which of the following is a type of cancer therapy?

    a. Chemotherapy
    b. Cryotherapy
    c. Radiotherapy
    d. All of the above

© 2011 Pearson Education, Inc.

6. Using the results of diagnostic tests such as bone and liver scans and other information gathered from the physical examination to determine the size, depth, and degree of spread of the initial tumor is called _____.

    a. staging a tumor
    b. grading a tumor
    c. biopsying a tumor
    d. All of the above

7. Dermatofibroma is defined as a(n) _____.

    a. benign tumor of dilated vessels
    b. fibrous tumor of the skin
    c. epithelial tumor of the basal cell layer of the epidermis
    d. epidermal cancer

8. Cardiolysis is the surgical procedure _____.

    a. to separate adhesions, which involves a resectioning of the ribs and sternum
    b. that uses a balloon inside a vessel to alter the structure of the vessel by dilating it
    c. to remove an aneurysm
    d. done to change the size of an opening

9. For very high-risk patients, the new goal is to have an LDL _____.

    a. under 130 mg/dL
    b. below 100 mg/dL
    c. below 93 mg/dL
    d. None of the above

10. Hormones are regulated by _____.

    a. the nervous system
    b. endocrine control
    c. a feedback system
    d. All of the above

CRITICAL THINKING

Answer the following questions to the best of your ability. Utilize the textbook as a reference.

1. Read the following case study. How would you respond?

    Benito Salvatore, a 65-year-old business executive, is scheduled to have a sigmoidoscopy with Dr. Bahjat. When David Slate, RMA, escorts him to the procedure room, Mr. Salvatore confides that he is extremely nervous and is concerned that he did not prepare well enough for the sigmoidoscopy.

    _____

    _____

    _____

    _____

2. What would you do if a patient refused to participate in a teaching session regarding their condition and treatment?

    _____

    _____

    _____

    _____

RESEARCH ACTIVITY

Utilize Internet search engines to research the following topics and write a brief description of what you find. It is important to utilize reputable websites.

1. Select one or two of the procedures/diagnostic tests discussed in the chapter. Research the procedure/ diagnostic test on the Internet. Why may the test be performed, how is the test performed, and what are the outcomes that are expected from the test? Write an essay on your findings. Be sure to cite your sources.

_____

_____

_____

_____

_____

_____

_____

_____

_____

_____

_____

_____

_____

_____

_____

_____

_____

_____

_____

_____

_____

_____

_____

_____

_____

© 2011 Pearson Education, Inc

CHAPTER 38
Assisting with Reproductive and Urinary Specialties

CHAPTER OUTLINE

General review of the chapter:

Reproductive System
Female Reproductive System
Male Reproductive System
Sexually Transmitted Infections (STIs)
Urinary System

STUDENT STUDY GUIDE

Use the following guide to assist in your learning of the concepts from the chapter.

I. Assisting with Specialty Examinations of the Female Reproductive System

1. Examination of the Female Reproductive Organs
   i. _____
   ii. _____
   iii. _____
   iv. _____

2. The Importance of the Clinical Breast Examination (CBE)
   A. Over a lifetime, _____ in _____ women will develop breast cancer.
   B. _____, _____ _____ _____ (CBE), _____ _____ _____ (BSE) and MRIs are tools for early detection.
   C. Women who are at a greater risk of developing breast cancer should have an _____ and a _____ every year.

3. Steps for the Breast Examination
   A. The patient lies in the _____ position.
   B. The patient is typically asked to place her hand behind her _____ on the side that is being examined first.
   C. This position allows the physician to examine the _____ nodes under the _____.
   D. The physician _____ the breast using his or her fingertips in a _____ manner around all of the breast tissue to search for lumps, tenderness, or inflammation.
   E. In addition, any _____ or _____ of the skin around the breast and nipple is noted.
   F. The nipples are checked for _____, _____, or discharge.

4. The Health Benefits of Breast Self-Examination (BSE)
   A. The overall goal should be for the patient to be _____ with her own breasts and to report any _____ immediately to her physician.

B. The physician may advise the patient to perform BSE every _____, usually _____ week after the menstrual period ends.

C. Women who have reached _____ should examine their breasts on the same day each month.

5. Correct Application of Fingertips for a Breast Self-Examination in the Shower

A. Raise the right _____.

B. Use the left hand to examine the _____ _____.

C. Then raise the left arm and use the right hand to examine the _____ _____.

D. Using flat _____, check breast tissue and _____ tissue, gently feeling for any lump or thickening.

6. Correct Application of Fingertips for a Breast Self-Examination in Front of a Mirror

A. Inspect the breasts for any _____ in shape while the arms are at the side of the body.

B. Look for _____, _____, or _____ of the skin; lumps; or changes in the _____, such as inversion.

C. Gently squeeze both nipples and look for _____.

D. Raise the arms _____ and look for size, shape, and _____ changes in each breast.

E. With palms resting on _____, flex chest muscles, looking for any obvious differences in the breasts.

7. Correct Application of Fingertips for a Breast Self-Examination Lying Down

A. To examine the right breast, place a _____ or folded towel behind the right shoulder and place the right hand _____ the head.

B. Using the hand with fingers flat, gently press the breast tissue, using small _____ motions starting at the _____ _____ of the breast at the 12 o'clock position and spiraling toward the _____.

C. Gently squeeze the nipple of each breast between the thumb and index finger, noting any _____ or _____.

8. Recommendations from the American Cancer Society for Breast Examinations

A. A baseline mammogram should be done at age _____.

B. Women older than age _____ should have a yearly breast examination by a physician and a mammogram every 1 to 2 years.

C. Women older than age _____ should have a yearly breast examination by a physician and a yearly mammogram.

9. Instructions for a Patient Prior to a Pap Test

A. Avoid sexual intercourse for at least _____ hours before the examination.

B. She should not schedule a Pap test during a time when she may have her _____.

C. Schedule the Pap test for at least _____ days after the last day of menstruation.

10. The Pelvic Examination

A. Begins with an examination of the external genitalia for _____, _____, or _____.

B. Next, the vaginal _____ is inserted into the vagina to inspect the vagina and cervix for _____, _____, _____, or discharge.

C. Vaginal specula may be either _____, and need to be sanitized and sterilized after each use, or disposable, and meant for one use only.

11. The Importance of the Pap Smear

   i. _____

   ii. _____

   iii. _____

© 2011 Pearson Education, Inc

12. Human Papilloma Viruses (HPVs)

    A. Responsible for the majority of _____ cancer cases and for genital warts.

    B. Women who become sexually active at an early age, as well as those who have had _____ _____, are at higher risk of infection from HPV.

    C. A new vaccine, _____, prevents infection.

    D. _____ of cervical cancers and _____ of genital warts will not be prevented by these vaccines.

13. The Older "Dry" Method of Pap Smear Collection

    A. Separate slides are made by the _____.

    B. The medical assistant labels the slides C, V, and E (_____, _____, and _____ canal) based on the source of the cells.

    C. The MA then sprays them with a _____ spray to preserve the cells.

14. The Newer, More Accurate "Liquid" Method of Pap Smear Collection

    A. Requires the _____ to be collected in a manner similar to that used in the dry method.

    B. The plastic vaginal _____ or _____ that is used is swirled in a liquid _____ medium in order to suspend and preserve the sample.

15. Prenatal Care and Postnatal Care

    A. _____ _____ is provided to pregnant women before delivery, including a series of visits and specific tests to promote the health of both the mother and the fetus.

    B. _____ _____ covers the time from the delivery of the infant through the mother's _____-week _____ follow-up appointment.

16. The First Trimester of Pregnancy

    A. Includes the period of time from _____ of the embryo in the uterus through the _____ week.

    B. The period in which the embryo is most _____ to substances that may cause birth defects.

    C. After the _____ week, the embryo is referred to as a _____.

17. The Second Trimester of Pregnancy

    A. Begins at the end of the _____ week and continues to the end of the _____ month.

    B. It is the stage at which the refinement of all the _____ takes place.

    C. Fetal movement, also called _____, may be felt.

18. The Third Trimester of Pregnancy

    A. The period from the end of the _____ month to birth is marked by an increase in the *size* and _____ of the fetus.

    B. During this stage, the fetus usually assumes a _____-_____ position.

    C. It is said to have reached the age of _____ (able to sustain life on its own) at 7 months.

19. Elements of the First Prenatal Visit (List the procedures that are typically performed and ordered during this visit.)

    i. _____

    ii. _____

    iii. _____

    iv. _____

    v. _____

    vi. _____

20. The Contents of the Prenatal History

    i. _____
    ii. _____
    iii. _____
    iv. _____
    v. _____
    vi. _____

21. The Contents of the Past Obstetrical History

    A. _____, or the number of times that the patient has been pregnant (not necessarily delivered)
    B. _____, or births after 20 weeks of gestation, regardless of whether the infant was born alive or dead
    C. The number of _____ or the number of fetuses that did not reach the age of viability

22. Information Requested for the Present Pregnancy History

    i. _____
    ii. _____
    iii. _____
    iv. _____
    v. _____

23. Follow-Up Prenatal Visits

    A. Every _____weeks through the _____ week
    B. Return every _____ weeks up to the _____ week, and then every week until delivery.
    C. During a prenatal visit, the physician will typically do the following
       i. _____
       ii. _____
       iii. _____
       iv. _____
       v. _____

24. The Medical Assistant's Role During Follow-Up Visits

    i. _____
    ii. _____
    iii. _____
    iv. _____
    v. _____
    vi. _____
    vii. _____

25. Amniocentesis

    A. Amniocentesis is the puncturing of the _____ _____ using a needle and syringe for the purpose of withdrawing _____ fluid for testing.
    B. Can assist in determining fetal _____, _____, and _____ disorders.

26. Procedures and Diagnostic Tests for the Female Reproductive System (Briefly explain each type.)

    A. Chorionic villus sampling (CVS): _____
    B. Colposcopy: _____
    C. Conization: _____
    D. Culdoscopy: _____
    E. Human chorionic gonadotropin (HCG): _____
    F. Hysterosalpingography: _____

© 2011 Pearson Education, Inc

G. Hysteroscopy: _____

H. Kegel exercises: _____

I. Laparotomy: _____

J. Laparoscopy: _____

K. Oophorectomy: _____

L. Panhysterectomy: _____

M. Panhysterosalpingo-oophorectomy: _____

N. Pelvimetry: _____

O. Salpingo-oophorectomy: _____

27. Screening Tests Performed During Pregnancy

A. The _____-_____ (AFP) test is a blood test taken between the 15th and 18th week of pregnancy to detect _____ _____ defects.

B. The _____ _____ _____ is a special ultrasound test of the fetus to screen for the risk of Down syndrome and other birth defects.

28. Amniocentesis

A. Performed between the _____ and _____ week of gestation.

B. Involves using a fine needle to take a sample of _____ _____ from the sac around the fetus.

C. Fluid containing _____ _____ is cultured, grown in a laboratory, and screened to detect _____ defects such as Down syndrome.

D. Used to assess fetal _____, _____, and _____.

E. Recommended for women older than _____ and those who have a family history of genetic defects.

29. Glucose Tolerance Test

A. Performed to test for gestational _____.

B. Performed between the _____ and _____ week of pregnancy.

C. After fasting, the patient is given a specific dosage of _____ and blood is taken 1 hour later.

D. An elevated test result requires an additional, more comprehensive 3-hour _____ _____ test.

E. A diet that is low in _____, moderate in carbohydrates, and high in _____, as well as regular exercise, is recommended.

30. Group B *Streptococcus*

A. Commonly found in the _____ and _____ tract; normally does not cause illness.

B. A vaginal culture at _____ to _____ weeks is recommended.

C. One to _____ percent of infants may be infected, and the infection may be life threatening.

D. A patient who tests positive will be treated with _____ during labor to prevent fetal infection.

31. Ultrasound

A. Used to determine the _____, _____-_____, _____ of the fetus, and obvious birth defects.

B. Generally performed at _____ to _____ weeks, and is generally painless.

32. The Process of Birth

A. The first stage of labor varies in length and ends with _____ _____ (widening of the cervix) and _____ (thinning of the cervical walls).

B. Stage two, the pushing stage, occurs from the period of complete _____ and _____ through the birth of the fetus.

C. Stage three is the period from the birth of the fetus to the _____ of the _____.

33. Possible Complications During Birth
    A. _____ _____ is a complication in which the placenta develops in the lower portion of the uterus, blocking the opening of the cervix.
    B. _____ _____ is a complication that occurs when the placenta tears away from the uterine wall, resulting in hemorrhaging and fetal distress.
    C. Hypertension during pregnancy, or _____ _____, occurs in roughly 10% of pregnancies.
    D. _____ is when protein in the urine and edema occur.

34. Postpartum Visit
    A. Should be scheduled approximately _____ weeks after delivery.
    B. Provides time to evaluate the overall _____ _____ of the patient and provide contraceptive information if desired.
    C. The postpartum visit includes the following
        i. _____
        ii. _____
        iii. _____
        iv. _____

35. Methods of Contraception
    A. Barrier contraceptive methods include use of male and female _____, _____, shields, _____, sponges, and _____ caps.
    B. Hormonal methods use hormones to change the levels of female hormones in the body to prevent _____ or _____ of the fertilized ovum.
    C. An intrauterine device (IUD) is a small device with _____ that is placed in the uterus by the physician.
    D. Natural family planning is also known as the _____ _____ or, most recently, fertility-awareness-based birth control, a method in which intercourse is avoided around the time of ovulation.
    E. _____ _____ involves the withdrawal of the male's penis before ejaculation in the vagina.

II. Assisting with Specialty Examinations of the Male Reproductive System
    1. Circumcision
       A. Circumcision is surgical removal of the end of the _peris_, or _foreskin_, of the penis.
       B. The primary reason for this procedure is ease of _infection.s_
       C. Circumcision is also a _customary_ practiced in some religions.

    2. Procedures and Diagnostic Tests for the Male Reproductive System (Briefly explain each type.)
       A. Castration: _____
       B. Epididymectomy: _____
       C. Erickson Sperm Separation: _____
       D. Fluorescent treponemal antibody absorption: _____
       E. Orchidopexy: _____
       F. Orchiectomy: _____
       G. Prostatectomy: _____
       H. Testosterone toxicology: _____
       I. Transurethral resection of the prostate (TURP): _____
       J. Venereal disease research laboratory (VDRL): _____

    3. Steps for Instructing a Male Patient to Perform a Testicular Exam
       A. _Identify_ the patient and introduce yourself.
       B. Explain to the patient that he or she should perform the examination in the _____ or right after a warm shower, which causes the _____ _____ to relax.

© 2011 Pearson Education, Inc

C. Using the testicular model or illustration, explain that he should place his middle and index fingers underneath the _____ and thumb on top and use a gentle motion to roll the _____ between the fingers.

D. Indicate on the model or illustration the location of the _____, a soft tubular cord behind the testis that stores and carries sperm.

4. Vasectomy

   A. Involves cutting the _____ _____ and tying off the ends to prevent sperm from being transported out of the testes.

   B. After a vasectomy, the man still achieves an _____ and ejaculates, but without the presence of _____.

   C. Another birth control method should be used for _____–_____ weeks afterward or until a sample taken after the vasectomy confirms the absence of sperm.

   D. In some cases, the procedure is _____, but a vasectomy should be considered a _____ form of birth control.

5. Sexually Transmitted Infectionss (STIs)

   A. Transmitted by sexual contact from _____ to person or _____ to child.

   B. Caused by _____.

   C. Generally treated successfully with _____.

   D. Viral STDs, such as _____, _____ _____, _____, and _____, are incurable.

6. Symptoms of a Sexually Transmitted Infection

   i. _____

   ii. _____

   iii. _____

   iv. _____

7. Bacterial Vaginosis (BV)

   A. BV is the most common _____ _____ in women of childbearing age.

   B. Certain behaviors increase the risk of infection, such as _____ _____ and douching.

   C. Symptoms include a thin _____ or _____ discharge with an unpleasant fishy odor.

   D. Increases susceptibility to other _____.

   E. Treatment is important for _____ women.

8. Chlamydia Infections

   A. Caused by the bacterium _____ _____.

   B. In males, it is characterized by _____ and _____.

   C. May lead to _____ _____ _____ in women.

   D. Infected females have an increased risk of _____ pregnancy and sterility.

   E. Infants born to infected mothers may develop _____ or _____.

   F. Can be successfully treated with _____ or _____.

9. Genital Human Papilloma Virus Infection

   A. _____ _____, or _____, are found in clusters on the external sexual organs of both males and females, and internally in the female in the vagina and cervix and in the anus and rectum of the male.

   B. Can be discovered in the female by a _____ _____, although the patient may not have visible signs of warts.

   C. Genital warts increase a female's risk of developing _____ _____.

10. Genital Herpes

   A. Genital herpes is caused by _____ _____ _____ _____ (HSV-1) and type 2 (HSV-2).

B. There is no known cure for herpes, but _____ may lessen the duration of symptoms.

C. _____ are usually self-limiting, but may reoccur during stressful situations.

11. Gonorrhea

   A. Gonorrhea is an STD that is caused by the organism _____ _____, a bacterium that grows well under warm, moist conditions.

   B. Can grow in the _____, _____ _____, and uterus in the female.

   C. Can grow in the _____, _____, _____, and _____ of both males and females.

   D. In the male, gonorrhea is characterized by _____ _____, clear at first, and then becoming thick and milky, burning, itching, and producing pain upon urination.

   E. Females are often _____, and then they develop a yellowish-green discharge.

   F. Other symptoms include _____ _____, _____ _____, anal discharge, and fever.

12. Treatment for Gonorrhea

   A. Large doses of _____ or _____ with follow-up examinations.

   B. If left untreated, gonorrhea can cause _____ in males and females.

   C. Gonorrhea can be diagnosed by _____ and _____ _____.

   D. Many people who have gonorrhea also have _____ and must be treated for both.

13. Human Immunodeficiency Virus (HIV)

   A. Causes _____ _____ _____ (AIDS), the final stage of HIV infection.

   B. It is a very delicate virus that cannot survive _____ of the body.

   C. It is not spread by casual contact or day-to-day activities such as _____ _____, _____, or sitting on toilet seats.

14. Methods of Transmission of Human Immunodeficiency Virus

   A. _____, _____, or anal sex with someone who is infected.

   B. Sharing _____ or _____ with someone who is infected.

   C. Being exposed as a _____ or infant to HIV before or during birth or breastfeeding.

   D. Coming in contact with _____ that is infected.

15. Preventing the Transmission of Human Immunodeficiency Virus

   i. _____

   ii. _____

   iii. _____

   iv. _____

   v. _____

   vi. _____

   vii. _____

16. Lymphogranuloma Venereum (LGV)

   A. LGV is an STD that is caused by three strains of the bacterium _____ _____.

   B. It is difficult to diagnose because the symptoms are _____ to that of other conditions.

   C. Can be mistaken for _____ STDs like syphilis and genital herpes.

   D. Untreated, LGV may cause _____ obstruction and _____ (massive swelling of the scrotum).

17. Pelvic Inflammatory Disease (PID)

   A. PID is the term used to describe inflammation of the vagina, cervix, uterus, and _____ _____ in the female.

   B. If left untreated, _____ _____ may develop in the fallopian tube, which then blocks the movement of the ovum in the tubes.

   C. If the tubes are completely blocked, _____ cannot reach the ovum to cause fertilization.

© 2011 Pearson Education, Inc.

D. If partially blocked, a fertilized ovum may begin to grow in the _____ _____ instead of in the uterus.

E. Diagnosed by _____ _____ and an ultrasound of the abdomen.

F. Can result in _____ _____, _____, and even death if untreated.

G. _____ can cure PID.

H. Treatment does not correct any damage already done to the _____ organs.

18. Syphilis

A. Syphilis is an STD that is caused by the bacterium _____ _____.

B. Spread by direct person-to-person contact with a _____ _____, or sore.

C. Sores may occur on the genitals, anus, _____, _____, and _____.

D. May be transmitted to a newborn by an infected mother, resulting in _____ or developmental delays or death after birth.

E. A primary chancre occurs in about _____ weeks or up to _____ months after exposure.

F. Secondary-stage signs are a _____ on the palms of the hands, the soles of the feet, and elsewhere on the body, along with fever, swollen glands, _____ _____, and fatigue.

G. The latent stages occur _____ to _____ years after the first two stages have disappeared.

H. The disease will damage the brain, heart, liver, and other internal organs, causing _____, _____, blindness, and death.

I. Diagnosed by _____-_____ microscopic examination of chancre material or by blood tests for the presence of syphilis antibodies (RPR, VDRL).

J. During the primary stage, a single, large dose of _____ may cure the patient.

19. Trichomoniasis

A. Trichomoniasis is a protozoal infection caused by the organism _____ _____, resulting in an infection of the lower genitourinary tract.

B. Causes a white or yellow, _____ _____ discharge with a foul odor in females.

C. The male is usually _____, except for _____ itching.

D. A diagnosis is made by obtaining a sample of vaginal _____ and preparing a slide with normal saline solution.

E. Treatment for both males and females is a course of the antibiotic _____ or _____ taken orally.

20. Symptoms of Urinary Tract Disorders

A. Increased urine production is seen in _____.

B. Frequent urination is seen in _____ _____ infections.

C. Swelling and weight gain are seen in _____ _____ _____ (CHF) and renal dysfunction.

D. Decreased urinary output is seen in urinary _____.

21. Procedures and Diagnostic Tests for the Urinary System (Briefly describe each.)

A. Creatinine clearance: _____

B. Cystography: _____

C. Cystoscopy: _____

D. Extracorporeal shockwave lithotripsy (ESWL): _____

E. Excretory urography: _____

F. Hemodialysis: _____

G. Intravenous pyelogram (IVP): _____

H. Kidney, ureters, bladder (KUB): _____

I. Meatotomy: _____

J. Peritoneal dialysis: _____

K. Retrograde pyelogram: _____

L. Sound: _____

M. Urography: _____

N. Ultrasonography of the kidneys: _____

22. Benign Prostate Hyperplasia (BPH)

    A. As the _____ enlarges, it presses on the urethra and causes restriction of the flow of urine.

    B. Restricted urinary flow can result in _____ _____ , interruption of the _____ _____ , and difficulty starting to urinate.

23. Prostate Cancer

    A. Prostate cancer is a slow-growing _____ tumor of the prostate gland.

    B. May spread to the adjacent _____ _____ and male reproductive organs, as well as to the lymph nodes and bones.

    C. It is the _____ most common form of cancer in men, with one in eight males affected.

    D. Its cause is unknown, but age, heredity, and a _____-_____ diet increase the risk of developing it.

24. Symptoms of Prostate Cancer

    i. _____

    ii. _____

    iii. _____

    iv. _____

    v. _____

25. Screening for Prostate Cancer

    A. Prostate-specific antigen (PSA) _____ _____ and a _____ rectal examination

    B. The PSA test checks for a _____ released by the prostate.

    C. If levels are elevated, then a _____ of prostate tissue is done, usually in the office.

    D. If the results are positive for cancer cells, then a _____ _____ is done to detect possible spread of the disease.

    E. PSA results of under _____ are considered to be normal.

26. Treatment for Prostate Cancer

    i. _____

    ii. _____

    iii. _____

    iv. _____

    v. _____

27. Acute and Chronic Renal Failure

    A. Kidney failure is the inability of the kidneys to adequately _____ _____ waste products from the blood.

    B. Acute kidney failure has a rapid onset of a few days to a few _____.

    C. Causes of acute kidney failure

        i. _____

        ii. _____

        iii. _____

28. Symptoms of Acute Renal Failure

    i. _____

    ii. _____

    iii. _____

    iv. _____

    v. _____

    vi. _____

© 2011 Pearson Education, Inc

29. Diagnosing Acute Renal Failure (List the types of tests and diagnostic procedures used.)

   i. _____

  ii. _____

 iii. _____

 iv. _____

  v. _____

30. Chronic Renal Failure

   A. Chronic renal failure is a slow _____, decline in kidney function over a period of months to several years.

   B. Acute kidney failure can become chronic if, after treatment, the kidneys do not _____ recover.

   C. Any condition that can cause acute renal failure can cause _____ _____ failure.

31. Common Causes of Chronic Renal Failure

   i. _____

  ii. _____

 iii. _____

 iv. _____

  v. _____

32. Symptoms of Chronic Renal Failure

   A. Patient may experience mild symptoms, including _____ and elevated _____ _____ nitrogen.

   B. As the condition progresses, _____, lack of _____ _____, anemia, loss of appetite, and shortness of breath affect the patient's quality of life.

33. Diagnosing Chronic Renal Failure

   A. Diagnosis is based on patient _____, _____, and blood tests for the levels of _____ and blood urea nitrogen.

   B. Chronic renal failure is _____ if not treated.

   C. Survival for patients with end-stage renal disease is a _____ _____.

34. Treatment for Chronic Renal Failure

   A. Various medications to adjust _____ _____, regulate _____ _____, and counteract anemia.

   B. Restriction of _____ and _____ in the diet.

   C. When these treatments are no longer effective, kidney _____ or _____ are the alternatives.

   D. Most patients with advanced kidney failure die within _____ to _____ years even with dialysis.

KEY TERMINOLOGY REVIEW

Write a sentence using the selected key terms in the correct context.

1. *amenorrhea*

_____

_____

2. *carcinoma in situ*

_____

_____

3. *chancre*

_____

_____

4. *chorionic villus sampling (CVS)*

_____

_____

5. *dysplasia*

_____

_____

6. *eclampsia*

_____

_____

7. *ectopic pregnancy*

_____

_____

8. *endometrium*

_____

_____

9. *fundus*

_____

_____

10. *gonads*

_____

_____

11. *gravida*

_____

_____

12. *human papilloma viruses (HPVs)*

_____

_____

13. *lochia*

_____

_____

14. *menarche*

_____

_____

15. *nocturia*

_____

_____

© 2011 Pearson Education, Inc

16. *oxytocin*

_____

_____

17. *para*

_____

_____

18. *parturition*

_____

_____

19. *placenta abruptio*

_____

_____

20. *placenta previa*

_____

_____

21. *preeclampsia*

_____

_____

22. *puerperium*

_____

_____

23. *quickening*

_____

_____

APPLIED PRACTICE

Follow the directions as instructed with each question below.

1. Sometimes patients are not ready either physically or emotionally to fully understand their medical diagnosis. The medical assistant must be able to clearly explain, in simple language, any terms that are confusing to the patient. The medical assistant must utilize many teaching methods to facilitate the patient's comprehension of his or her diagnosis and treatment plan. List three teaching methods that the medical assistant can utilize to help the patient.

_____

_____

2. Many states mandate that suspicions of abuse be reported. How would you go about reporting any suspicion you may have?

_____

_____

_____

_____

LEARNING ACTIVITY: FILL IN THE BLANK

Using your text as necessary, fill in the blanks to the following questions.

1. ACS suggests that women in their twenties and thirties have a _____ as part of a periodic regular health exam by a health professional every 3 years.

2. Females develop breast cancer 100 times more frequently than males, probably due to the effects of _____.

3. Prior to the patient scheduling a Pap test, the medical assistant should advise her not to douche for _____–_____ hours before the examination.

4. The pelvic examination begins with an examination of the _____.

5. Women who become sexually active at an early age, as well as those who have multiple partners, are at _____ risk of infection from HPV.

6. The Pap smear is _____% accurate in detecting cervical carcinoma.

7. The third trimester is the period from the end of the _____ month to birth.

8. The normal FHT is _____–_____ beats per minute.

9. Condoms have an effectiveness rate of about _____%.

10. Women are fertile for about _____ years of their adult lives.

11. An alternative birth control method should be used for _____–_____ weeks after a vasectomy or until a sample confirms the absence of sperm.

12. The symptoms of gonorrhea do not appear in females until _____ months after exposure.

13. _____ has no known cause and is the most common vaginal infection in women of childbearing age.

14. Untreated, gonorrhea can cause _____ in both males and females and can spread to the blood or joints.

15. Benign prostate hyperplasia (BPH) is an enlargement of the prostate gland that may occur after age _____.

CRITICAL THINKING

Answer the following questions to the best of your ability. Utilize the textbook as a reference.

1. Imagine the following scenario: You are a female. You have completed your externship and have been hired by a urology clinic for your first full-time medical assistant position. You are directed by the physician to instruct a patient in how to perform a testicular self-exam. You are suddenly nervous about doing this with a real patient even though you have practiced this in your medical assisting program with other students. Describe in one or two paragraphs how you would feel and what you would do or tell yourself to bolster your own comfort and confidence.

_____
_____
_____
_____
_____
_____

© 2011 Pearson Education, Inc.

2. A patient, 18-year-old Maria Riojas, has come in with a chief complaint of bleeding between her periods. This will be her third GYN visit since menarche, and she is still quite apprehensive about the examination and getting undressed. She says that she hopes that the doctor won't have to do a pelvic examination today; she just wants a stronger or different birth control pill. Her friend told her that she has breakthrough bleeding because she is on the wrong pill. What would you say to the patient?

_____

_____

_____

_____

3. A patient comes in with her husband, and she asks that he be allowed to come into the examination room with her. When you ask her to disrobe, she looks hesitant, then looks at her husband and doesn't move to take the gown and drape. What do you anticipate is happening? What should you do?

_____

_____

_____

_____

4. A patient who is 6 months pregnant calls in saying that she has been bleeding a little (just spotting) all morning and wanted to let the doctor know. She wants an appointment for Thursday and today is Monday. What would you say?

_____

_____

_____

_____

RESEARCH ACTIVITY

Utilize Internet search engines to research the following topics and write a brief description of what you find. It is important to utilize reputable websites.

1. Select one procedure and diagnostic test for the female reproductive system and one procedure and diagnostic test for the male reproductive system. Conduct research on each using online resources and/or your school or local library. Write a paragraph on what you learned about each procedure/diagnostic test, including why the test is done, how the test is done, and what type of treatment might be available if the test result is positive. Be sure to cite your sources.

_____

_____

_____

© 2011 Pearson Education, Inc.

CHAPTER 39
Assisting with Eye and Ear Care

CHAPTER OUTLINE

General review of the chapter:

The Study of the Eye
Assessing Visual Acuity
Irrigation of the Eye
Instillation of Eye Medication
Patient Safety Guidelines
Changes in the Aging Eye
Assisting the Visually Impaired Patient
The Study of the Ear
Hearing Acuity
Hearing Assessment
Assisting the Hearing-Impaired Patient
Examination of the Nose and Throat

STUDENT STUDY GUIDE

Use the following guide to assist in your learning of the concepts from the chapter.

I. The Study of the Eye

1. The Ophthalmologist

   A. Performs eye _____ and eye _____.
   B. Prescribes medications, _____, and contact lenses.

2. The Doctor of Optometry (OD)

   A. Also referred to as an _____.
   B. Performs eye examinations, prescribes medications, and write prescription for _____ and contact lenses.

3. The Optician

   A. _____ and _____ prescription lenses and contacts.
   B. Completes a _____ to _____-year apprenticeship.

4. The Ophthalmoscope

   A. Used to view the _____ parts of the _____.
   B. The physician positions the ophthalmoscope so that _____ penetrates the _____ of the patient's eye and screens for _____ damage and _____ problems.

5. Evaluating the Status of the Patient's Pupils

   A. PERRLA is an acronym that stands for _____ _____, _____, _____ to _____, and _____ and focus on objects at different _____.
   B. Injuries to the brain may result in the patient having pupils of _____ size.

6. Visual Acuity

A. Normal visual acuity, or clearness of vision, is referred to as _____ vision.

B. Causes of errors in refraction

   i. The eyeball is too _____.

   ii. The eyeball is too _____.

   iii. The lens has _____ its _____.

   iv. The _____ or _____ has an irregular _____.

7. Myopia

A. Myopia is a condition in which the eye sees _____ objects well but _____ objects appear _____.

B. Occurs either because the eyeball is too _____ or because the _____ is too _____, and the light _____ do not reach the _____.

8. Strabismus

A. Children with strabismus appear _____ and may need to wear a _____ over the _____ _____ to _____ the weaker eye.

B. If the _____ and _____ are ineffective, surgery on the eye _____ may be necessary.

9. The Snellen Chart

A. A person with normal vision can read the top line at _____ feet.

B. To the _____ of each line is a _____ indicating that a person with normal vision can read the lines at decreasing distances of _____, _____, _____, _____, _____, and _____ feet.

C. For preschool children or patients who are _____ or have a _____ barrier, the *Snellen E*, the _____ __, or pictorial charts are used.

10. Eye Abbreviations

A. The abbreviation for the right eye is _OD_. ouclus dexter

B. The abbreviation for the left eye is _OS_. oculus sinister

C. The abbreviation for both eyes is _OU_. oculus uterque

11. Steps for Using the Snellen Chart

A. Determine the patient's ability to recognize letter.

B. Place the patient _20_ feet from the chart, either seated or standing, as long as the Snellen chart is at eye level.

C. Following office policies (regarding which eye to test first), have the patient cover the other eye with an _cup or occulder.

D. Instruct the patient to keep both eyes open even though one eye is covered.

E. Use a pointer and point to the letters or appropriate symbols in random order.

F. Starting with the _20/70_ line, ask the patient to identify the letters on each line, and then proceed down the chart to the last line that the patient can read without error.

G. Observe for signs of squinting or tilting the head, which indicate difficulty identifying letters.

H. Record the rati numbers adjacent to the line that the patient can read without error.

I. Following testing of both eyes, clean the occluder with gauze and alchol.

12. Steps for Testing for Near-Vision Acuity Using the Jaeger Card

A. The patient reads the card held at a normal reading distance (_14_ to _16_ inches).

B. The card has a series of paragraphs in decreasing size of print with a number above each.

C. Number one (_J 2_) is next to the paragraph with the smallest text, and as the text becomes larger, the number increases

D. Paragraph _J2_ represents 20/20 vision.

© 2011 Pearson Education, Inc.

20. The Instillation of Eye Medication
   A. Only __Ophthalmic__ or __optic__ medications can be used in the eye and they must be _____.
   B. Encourage patients to discard eye medications when the prescribed treatment time has been __completed__

21. Steps for the Instillation of Eye Medication
   A. Check the __name__ of the medication, the __expiration__ date, and the __concentration__ three times.
   B. Ask the patient if he or she has any known __allergies__ to the medication.
   C. Position the patient with his or her headed tilted __back__, with eyes looking __up__.
   D. Pull down the ~~head~~ __lower eyelid__, exposing the __conjunctiva__
   E. Place the dropper about __1/2__ inch above the __eyeball__ with your dominant hand.
   F. Insert the proper number of drops into the __center__ of the conjunctiva. If ointment is used, apply as a thin strip from __inner__ to __outer__ canthus.
   G. Ask the patient to gently __close__ the eye and __rotate__ the eyeball.
   H. Dry the excess medication from the __inner__ canthus to the __outer__ canthus using __sterile__ gauze.
   I. Explain to the patient that his or her vision may be __blurry__.

II. The Study of the Ear

   1. Steps for Irrigating the Ear
      A. Check the name, _____, and _____ date of the irrigating solution _____ times.
      B. Have the patient sit with the affected ear tilted slightly _____.
      C. Place a towel over the patient's _____ and ask the patient to hold the _____ basin.
      D. Clean the _____ ear with a _____ cotton ball.
      E. Pour the warmed solution into a _____ basin and fill the syringe with _____ cc of solution.
      F. Aim the stream of flow toward the _____ of the _____

   2. Steps for Instilling Ear Medication _Perform hand hygiene_
      check doctor's orders
      434
      i. Check the name of the medication, expiration date &
      ii. Ask patient if he or she has any known allergies to medica
      iii. Give the patient a tissue to blot cheeks
      iv. Put on gloves
      v. Position the patient w/ head tilted back and looking up
      vi. Pull down the lower eyelid exposing the conjunctiva
      vii. Place the dropper about 1/2 inch above the eyeball w/ domi
      viii. Do not touch dropper or ointment is used to apply
      ix. Ask patient to gently close the eye and rotate the ey
      x. Use sterlie guaze, dry excess medication from the inner
      xi. Explain to the patient that vision may be blurry
      xii. Clean the area and dispose of unused medication

   3. Steps for Performing Audiometric Testing _Remove gloves and perform hand hygiene_
      Document the procedure.
      i. Test the equipment and make sure the power is on
      ii. Identify the patient and explain the procedure
      iii. Establish signal response that patient will give if no auto
      iv. Have the patient assume a comfortable position
      v. Place headphones over the patients ears
      vi. Begin w/ low frequency and wait patient for indication
      vii. Gradually increase the frequency until test is completed
      viii. Proceed to the other ear and repeat the entire proce
      ix. Remove headphones
      x. Perform hand hygiene
      Document procedure appropriately

© 2011 Pearson Education, Inc.

13. Color Vision Impairment

A. Defects in color vision are _Congenital inherited_, or acquired through disease or injury.

B. Changes in color vision may indicate diseases of the _retina optic nerve_, or _thyroid_

14. The Ishihara Test

A. Screens for color vision _acuity_

B. The patient is shown ___14___ color plates or pages and must correctly identify ___10___ to be considered to have color vision within a normal range.

15. Contrast Sensitivity

A. Used to measure the patient's ability to distinguish faint _differences_ in shades of _gray_

B. Several new testing procedures have been used to test for contrast sensitivity, including the _Vistech Consultrant System_ and the _Pelli Robson chart_.

16. Procedures and Diagnostic Tests Related to the Eye

A. _Corneal transplant -_
B. _electroretinogram -_
C. _Fluorescein angiography -_
D. _Gonioscopy -_
E. _Keratomy -_
F. _Keratoplasty -_
G. _laser surgery -_
H. _Optomyometer -_
I. _Phacoemulsification -_
J. _Radial keratotomy -_
K. _Slit-lamp microscopy -_
L. _tonometry -_
M. _Visual acuity -_
N. _Vitrectomy -_

836

17. Fluorescein Angiography

A. This is the process of injecting _____, followed by a series of _____ of the _____ through dilated pupils.

B. Provides diagnostic information about the blood flow in the _____.

C. Detects _____ changes in diabetics and _____ _____.

D. Identifies _____ in the macular area of the _____, determining whether there is _____ of the _____.

18. Radial Keratotomy

A. Radial keratotomy is a surgical procedure that may be performed to correct _nearsightedness myopia_

B. Incisions are made in the _cornea_ to flatten it, thereby shortening the _eyeball_ so that _light_ reaches the _retina_.

C. Complications of surgery can lead to _blindness_

19. Steps for Irrigating the Eye

A. The label of the irrigating solution must be checked ___3___ times to ensure that it is the correct _solution_ and _concentration_ as ordered by the physician.

B. The solution is brought to room temperature by _wrapping_ the bottle in a _dry heating pad_ or by standing the bottle in a _warm_ water _bath_.

C. If both eyes are to be irrigated, then ___two___ separate sets of equipment must be used to prevent _cross infection_

D. Hold the syringe ___1/2___ inch from the eye.

E. Gently irrigate from the inner to the outer _canthus_, or _corner_ of the eye, aiming at the _lower conjunctiva_

© 2011 Pearson Education, Inc.   *Assisting with Eye and Ear Care*   **393**

Testing ordered for Check-offs

27gauge

PPD~0.1mL *Intradermal (27gauge)*

<10 gauge
21gauge **MMR~0.3mL** *-Subcu*

llegay
a5 **HepB~0.5mL** *- Intramusular*

Blood work order

Light Blue **PT/PTT**

grey ~~**CBC**~~ *Glucose*

Perform a blood sugar fingerstick.

Competencies

Course Competency Summary

Student's Name ___Harrison, Stevei___

The purpose of this form is to ensure that all required competencies have been performed and scored.

Directions:

a. Insert the student's "Total Competency Criteria Score" from the appropriate competency form into the "Criteria Score" column.

b. Circle Y if the student achieved a minimum score of 75% for that competency. Circle N if the student scored less than 75%.

c. Enter initials and date for each competency.

d. To determine final grade on competencies:

    1) Total "Criteria Score"

    2) Multiply total "Criteria Score" by 0.61919

    3) Enter resulting value in KIT classroom gradebook under "Competencies"

	Competency	Criteria Score	Passed with 75%? (circle one)		Date	Instructor's Initials
C1.	Administering an Intradermal Injection	(out of 30)	Y	N		
C2.	Administering Parenteral, Subcutaneous, or Intramuscular Injections	(out of 31)	Y	N		
C3.	Applying a Holter Monitor	(out of 21)	Y	N	12/7/15	
C4.	Assigning a CPT Code	(out of 19)	Y	N	12/7/15	
C5.	Cleaning the Examination Room	(out of 16)	Y	N	12/7	
C6.	ICD-9-CM Coding	(out of 16)	Y	N	12/7	
C7.	Interviewing a New Patient to Obtain Medical History Information and Preparing for a Physical Examination	(out of 24)	Y	N	12/7	
C8.	Measuring Blood Pressure	(out of 28)	Y	N	12/7	
C9.	Measuring Oral Temperature Using an Electronic or Digital Thermometer	(out of 19)	Y	N	12/7	
C10.	Measuring Radial Pulse	(out of 15)	Y	N	12/7	
C11.	Measuring Respirations	(out of 11)	Y	N	12/7	

Competency	Criteria Score	Passed with 75%? (circle one)		Date	Instructor's Initials
(C12) Measuring Temperature Using an Aural (Tympanic Membrane) Thermometer	(out of 16)	Y	N	12/7/15	
C13. Performing a Capillary Puncture (Manual)	(out of 19)	Y	N		
C14. Performing a Venipuncture Using the Vacutainer Method	(out of 22)	Y	N		
C15. Preparing Injections	(out of 9)	Y	N		
C16. Recording a 12-Lead Electrocardiograph	(out of 27)	Y	N		

Total [   ] × 0.61919= [   ] pts

(323 max)   (200/323)   (200 max)

ALL COMPETENCIES MUST BE PASSED WITH A MINIMUM OF 75%.

xi. _____
xii. _____
xiii. _____
xiv. _____

(4.) Tests and Procedures for the Ear (Briefly explain each of the following.)

546

A. Audiometric test: Test of hearing ability by determining the lowest and highest intensol and frequencie

B. Electrochochleography: Recording of the electrical activity

C. Falling test: Test used to observe balance and equilibrium

D. Mastoid antrotomy: Surgical opening made in the cavity within the mastoid pracc

E. Myringoplasty: Surgical reconstruction of the ear drum

F. Otoplasty: Corrective surgery to change the size of the external ear

G. Stapedectomy: Removal of the stapes bone to treat otosclerosis

H. Tympanoplasty: Another term for the surgical reconstruction of the ear

I. Rinne test: The base of the vibrating fork against the patients mastoid bone

J. Weber test: The turning fork placed on the center of the forehead

5. Examination of the Nose and Throat

A. The physician uses a nasal _____ to inspect the _____ lining of the nose for signs of _____ and _____.

B. Includes the use of a tongue _____ to examine the _____ for signs of _____, enlarged _____, and abnormalities of the tongue or _____ _____.

(6.) Signs and Symptoms of Nasal Problems

i. nose bleeds or epistaxis

ii. reduced sense of smell

iii. congestion

iv. allergic rhinitis

(7.) Steps for Instilling Nasal Medication

i. Check physicans order

ii. Perform hand hygiene

iii. Assemble the equipment

iv. Apply gloves

v. Identify the patient and explain the prodeure

vi. Position the patient w/ head lower than the shoulder to inst

vii. Place patient in supine postition w/pillow

viii. Check the medication 3 times for correct name dosage, expiration date

ix. Draw the medication into a dropper and hold over the center

x. Administer the medication

xi. Repeat in the other nostril if ordered

xii. Tell the patient to stay in that position for 5 mins

xiii. to prevent medication from running out of the nostril

xiv. Provide tissues for the patient to wipe excess

xv. from the skin.

xvi. Discard the dropper in the biohazard waste container recap the meds

xvii. Clean the area and remove gloves

xviii. Provide home Instruction if needed. Verify

xix. Perform hand hygiene

xx. Document the procedure in patients record

© 2011 Pearson Education, Inc.

KEY TERMINOLOGY REVIEW

Match the vocabulary term to the correct definition below.

a. acuity
b. astigmatism
c. audiogram
d. cerumen
e. cornea
f. decibel
g. frequencies
h. hyperopia

i. myopia
j. myringa
k. organ of Corti
l. otorhinolaryngologists
m. presbycusis
n. speculum
o. strabismus

1. _____ Impacted earwax or foreign matter in the ear.

2. _____ The medical term for the eardrum.

3. _____ Used by the physician to evaluate the patient's hearing.

4. _____ Any instrument that holds open an opening in the body to permit inspection.

5. _____ Visual and auditory sharpness.

6. _____ Also known as farsightedness.

7. _____ The clear, transparent covering of the eye.

8. _____ An eye disorder caused by weakness in the external eye muscles, resulting in the eyes looking in different directions.

9. _____ A refractive disorder in which irregularities in the curvature of the cornea cause light not to focus on the retina but instead to spread out over an area, causing overall blurring of vision.

10. _____ Also known as nearsightedness.

11. _____ Individual who specializes in treating conditions related to the ear, nose, and throat.

12. _____ The auditory nerve.

13. _____ The intensity of the sound.

14. _____ A decline in hearing acuity, a normal part of aging.

15. _____ Number of fluctuations per second of energy in the form of sound waves.

APPLIED PRACTICE

Follow the directions as instructed with each question below.

Activity 1: Read the following scenario and then answer the questions.

Shawn Collins, RMA, is working as a medical assistant at a local family practice. Rajan Avuri, a 17-year-old patient, is being seen for a driver's license eye examination. As part of the exam, Shawn tests Rajan's vision with a Snellen eye chart similar to the Snellen eye chart below. Shawn asks Rajan to cover his right eye and read line 8. Rajan reads the following letters from left to right: "D, E, F, P, O, T, E, C." Shawn asks Rajan to continue on and read line 9. Rajan reads the following letters from left to right: "L, E, P, O, D, R, O, T."

Shawn then asks Rajan to uncover his right eye and cover his left eye for assessment. Beginning with line 8, Rajan reads the following letters from left to right: "D, E, F, R, O, T, E, C." Rajan is not able to distinguish any letters on the lines below line 8.

© 2011 Pearson Education, Inc.

1. How should Shawn record Rajan's vision in his left eye? Explain your answer.

   _____

   _____

   _____

   _____

2. How should Shawn record Rajan's vision in his right eye? Explain your answer.

   _____

   _____

   _____

   _____

Activity 2

1. A 2-year-old child must have a myringotomy performed because the child has had reoccurring ear infections. Explain to the parents what this procedure entails.

   _____

   _____

   _____

   _____

   _____

   _____

LEARNING ACTIVITY: MULTIPLE CHOICE

Circle the correct answer to each of the questions below.

1. Which of the following specialists is not a medical doctor?

   A. Ophthalmologist

   B. Otorhinolaryngologist

C. Optometrist

D. None of the above

2. Which instrument measures intraocular pressure?

   A. Ophthalmoscope
   B. Tonometer
   C. Slit lamp
   D. Otoscope

3. The ability to distinguish colors depends on the cones of the _____, which react to light and permit us to see shades of red, green, and blue.

   A. choroid
   B. cornea
   C. retina
   D. iris

4. Which of the following surgical procedures may be performed to correct myopia?

   A. Keratoplasty
   B. Radial keratotomy
   C. Phacoemulsification
   D. None of the above

5. To be declared legally blind, a person must only be able to see at _____ feet what a normal person would see at 200 feet.

   A. 20
   B. 40
   C. 50
   D. 100

6. The most common type of color vision defect, which is inherited, is the inability to distinguish _____.

   A. blue and yellow
   B. blue and black
   C. red and green
   D. All of the above

7. The abbreviation AD (aurus dextra) is for _____.

   A. both ears
   B. the left ear
   C. the right ear
   D. None of the above

8. Which of the following instrument(s) is used in the office for ear examinations?

   A. Otoscope
   B. Tuning fork
   C. Audiometer
   D. All of the above

9. Sensorineural hearing loss is due to _____.

   A. nerve damage
   B. obstruction of sound waves
   C. old age
   D. None of the above

© 2011 Pearson Education, Inc.

10. When instilling ear medication into a child's ear, the ear should be pulled
_____.

    A. up and back
    B. down and back
    C. up
    D. Any of the above

CRITICAL THINKING

Answer the following questions to the best of your ability. Utilize the textbook as a reference.

1. You need to perform a Snellen visual acuity test and an Ishihara color vision test per the physician's orders. You do not have an occluder or the Ishihara plates. Which of the tests, if any, could you still perform using a different item and what replacement item(s) can you use?

_____
_____
_____
_____
_____

2. As a medical assistant, how can you help patients with diminished visual or hearing capacities?

_____
_____
_____

RESEARCH ACTIVITY

Utilize Internet search engines to research the following topics and write a brief description of what you find. It is important to utilize reputable websites.

1. Visit different websites that deal with vision and hearing loss. What information did you find that could be used to help families dealing with vision and hearing deficiencies? What websites did you find to be most useful? Could these websites be beneficial for staff members of an EENT practice. If so, why?

_____
_____
_____
_____
_____
_____
_____
_____
_____
_____
_____

CHAPTER 40
Assisting with Life Span Specialties: Pediatrics

CHAPTER OUTLINE

General review of the chapter:

Assisting in Pediatrics
The Pediatric Office
The Pediatric Patient
Pediatric Office Visits and Procedures
Pediatric Diseases and Disorders
Child Safety Recommendations
Adolescence and Puberty
Eating Disorders

STUDENT STUDY GUIDE

Fill in the study guide below using both your textbook and notes from your instructor's lecture.

I. Assisting in Pediatrics

   1. Specialists Who Treat Children

      A. Most pediatricians recommend that, at age _____, patients find a primary care physician.
      B. Primary care physicians and _____ also care for pediatric patients.

   2. The Pediatric Office Reception Room

      A. Needs to be bright, _____, and interesting.
      B. Easy-to-clean _____ toys without tiny pieces are most practical.
      C. During office hours, toys should be _____, as necessary, and put away to prevent falls.
      D. _____ toys should be done on a regular basis.
      E. Sick children should be brought _____ into an examination room.

   3. Patient Safety in the Pediatric Office

      A. No child should be _____ _____ on an examination table.
      B. Three positions are used for carrying an infant
         i. _____
         ii. _____
         iii. _____

   4. Steps for Wrapping a Child for Restraint

      A. Speak to the child in _____, _____ tones.
      B. Place a_____ blanket or small sheet on the table and fold _____ the top corner.
      C. Place the child _____ on the blanket, keeping one hand on the _____ to ensure safety.
      D. Wrap the _____ corner across the _____, covering the _____ arm, and tuck snugly under the _____ arm.

© 2011 Pearson Education, Inc.

E. Wrap the _____ corner across the torso, covering the _____ arm, and tuck snugly under the _____.

F. To restrain the head, place yourself at the end of the table where the infant's head is located and place one hand on _____ side of the head.

G. Avoid sealing the _____ or touching the _____.

5. Developmental Checklist for 1 to 2 Month Olds

A. Able to _____ head when lying on the stomach.

B. Moves _____ and _____ in an energetic manner.

C. Likes to be held and _____.

6. Developmental Checklist for 2 to 3 Month Olds

A. Rolls _____ to the side when lying on the back.

B. Startled by _____ sounds.

7. Developmental Checklist for 3 to 4 Month Olds

A. Eyes follow _____ objects.

B. Able to hold head _____.

C. _____ objects in hands.

D. _____ out loud.

E. Rolls from _____ to _____.

8. Developmental Checklist for 4 to 5 Month Olds

A. Reaches for and _____ objects.

B. Stands _____ when held.

C. Turns toward the _____ of a voice.

9. Developmental Checklist for 5 to 6 Month Olds

A. Turns over from _____ to _____.

B. Sits with a _____ support.

C. Listens to _____ voice.

10. Developmental Checklist for 6 to 7 Month Olds

A. Can _____ an object from one hand to the other.

B. Can sit for a _____ minutes alone.

C. Is _____ at first with strangers.

11. Developmental Checklist for 7 to 8 Month Olds

A. Can sit steadily for _____ minutes.

B. Crawls on _____ and _____.

C. Grasps things with the _____ and the first _____ fingers.

D. Likes to be near the _____.

12. Developmental Checklist for 8 to 9 Month Olds

A. Responds to _____ _____.

B. Can stand for a _____ time holding onto support.

C. _____ with fingers.

D. Responds to _____.

13. Developmental Checklist for 10 to 12 Month Olds

A. Able to pull self up at side of crib or _____.

B. Can drink from a _____ when it is held.

C. Walks around holding onto _____.

D. Repeats a few _____.

14. Developmental Checklist for 12 to 15 Month Olds

A. Pulls _____ while walking.

B. Shows what he or she wants by _____ and _____.

C. Cooperates with _____.

15. Developmental Checklist for 15 to 18 Month Olds

    A. Can build a tower with _____.
    B. Can say _____ words.
    C. Drinks from a cup held in _____ hands.

16. Developmental Checklist for 18 Months to 2-Year-Olds

    A. Walks up and down _____, alternating feet.
    B. Says at least _____ to _____ words.
    C. Sometimes uses _____-word sentences.

17. Developmental Checklist for 2- to 3-Year-Olds

    A. Can repeat _____ numbers in a row.
    B. Dresses self except for _____.
    C. Can build tower of _____ blocks.

18. Developmental Checklist for 4- to 5-Year-Olds

    A. Can repeat a simple _____-word sentence.
    B. Can wash hands and face _____ help.
    C. Can follow _____ commands.

19. Growth from Infancy to Adulthood

    A. The average infant weights about _____ lbs. at birth.
    B. By 6 months, that weight has _____, and at a year, the child's length has _____ and the weight has _____.
    C. From ages 5 to 10, the child grows _____ to _____ inches and gains _____ to _____ pounds yearly.
    D. Adult proportions will not be reached until about age _____.

20. Failure to Thrive (FTT)

    A. Children have _____ growth patterns.
    B. A baby whose weight is under the _____ percentile on the growth chart is in the failure-to-thrive syndrome category.
    C. The most frequent cause of FTT is _____ nutrition.

21. Obtaining a Blood Pressure Reading on a Child

    A. Most pediatricians do not require a blood pressure measurement unless there are _____ or _____ disorders.
    B. Some physicians require blood pressure readings on every patient regardless of age and others monitor blood pressure once a year after age _____.
    C. A blood pressure cuff measuring no wider than _____-_____ of the child's upper arm must be used.

22. Steps for Measuring an Infant's Blood Pressure

    i. _____
    ii. _____
    iii. _____
    iv. _____
    v. _____
    vi. _____

23. Steps for Obtaining a Temperature with a Tympanic Thermometer

    i. _____
    ii. _____
    iii. _____

© 2011 Pearson Education, Inc.

iv. _____

v. _____

vi. _____

vii. _____

24. Steps for Obtaining a Temperature Reading Using the Axillary Method

i. _____

ii. _____

iii. _____

iv. _____

v. _____

25. Steps for Obtaining a Temperature Rectally by Using a Digital Thermometer

i. _____

ii. _____

iii. _____

iv. _____

v. _____

vi. _____

vii. _____

viii. _____

ix. _____

26. Steps for Measuring Heart Rate/Pulse by Apical Measurement

i. _____

ii. _____

iii. _____

iv. _____

v. _____

vi. _____

27. Normal Body Temperature

A. Oral: _____°F (_____°C)

B. Aural: _____°F (_____°C)

C. Axillary: _____°F (_____°C)

D. Rectal: _____°F (_____°C)

28. Normal Values for Respiration

A. Infants: _____

B. Toddlers: _____

C. Preschool age: _____

D. School age: _____

E. Adolescents: _____

29. Normal Values for Pulse

A. Infants: _____

B. Toddlers: _____

C. Preschool age: _____

D. School age: _____

E. Adolescents: _____

30. Normal Systolic and Diastolic Valves

A. Infants: _____ systolic, _____ diastolic

B. Toddlers: _____ systolic, _____ diastolic

C. Preschool age: _____ systolic, _____ diastolic

D. School age: _____ systolic, _____ diastolic

31. Height, Weight, and Head and Chest Circumference
   A. Infants should be weighted without a _____ to ensure that the most accurate weight is obtained.
   B. Height and weight are measured without _____.
   C. The measurement of the circumference of the _____ is part of each well-baby office visit until age _____.
   D. Rapid growth of the head may indicate _____.
   E. Head growth that falls below the normal percentile may indicate _____.
   F. Normal head circumference at birth should be between _____ and _____ inches (_____ to _____ cm).
   G. Generally, the head and chest circumferences are equal at about _____ to _____ years of age.

32. Growth Charts
   A. Every patient should have a copy of the _____ growth chart as part of his or her permanent medical record.
   B. Individual growth graphs are available for boys and girls from birth to _____ months and _____ to _____ years.
   C. Once the measurements are obtained, the values are plotted according to the child's age and _____ and the _____ is obtained.

33. Evaluating a Child's Hearing and Vision
   A. Hearing tests are done in many hospitals at _____ as part of special federal and state programs to detect hearing difficulties at an early age.
   B. Early detection is important because _____ development depends on a child's ability to mimic sounds, word selection, and use of words.
   C. If the child tests below normal during the first test, it is repeated at about _____ weeks.
   D. At the yearly examination, visual acuity is measured for children _____ years and older using the _____ _____ chart.

34. Steps for Performing a Snellen Test on a Child
   i. _____
   ii. _____
   iii. _____
   iv. _____
   v. _____
   vi. _____
   vii. _____
   viii. _____
   ix. _____

35. Steps for Applying a Urine Collection Device on a Child
   i. _____
   ii. _____
   iii. _____
   iv. _____
   v. _____
   vi. _____
   vii. _____
   viii. _____
   ix. _____
   x. _____
   xi. _____

© 2011 Pearson Education, Inc.

II. Pediatric Conditions and Disorders

1. The Common Cold
   A. Caused by more than _____ varieties of rhinovirus.
   B. In infants and children, there may be a _____ fever, nasal congestion, and _____.
   C. Children from age _____ to _____ may have _____ to _____ colds a year.
   D. Treatment usually includes use of _____ medications to reduce fever.
   E. Due to recent studies, the use of _____ and cough _____ is not recommended by many physicians.

2. Strep Throat
   A. Strep throat is caused by group __A__ beta hemolytic *hemolytic* C *pyogenes.*
   B. The physician may order a throat *culture* to confirm that strep is the causative agent.
   C. Many pediatrician's offices perform these tests onsite with the use of a *rapid strep* test.
   D. A child who has recurring strep throat infections may be a candidate for a *tonsillectomy*
   E. Strep throat is treated with *antibotics*
   F. _____ is the best defense for warding off upper respiratory infections.

3. Otitis Media
   A. Otitis media is an infection of the *middle* ear.
   B. It is due to colds, *allergies*, or other respiratory infections.
   C. Fluid builds up and applies pressure to the *eardrum*
   D. Treatment includes *decongestants, analgesics*, and sometimes *antibiotics*
   E. Children with chronic ear infections may require a *myringotomy*

4. Croup
   A. Leads to a distinctive barking cough and *hoarsens*.
   B. There are two types of croup
      i. *Spasmodic*
      ii. *Stridor*

5. Bronchitis
   A. Bronchitis is an inflammation of the *bronchioles*
   B. It is more common in children under *2* years old.
   C. Children with asthma and those exposed to *second hand* smoke are at higher risk.
   D. Symptoms of bronchitis
      i. *Coldlike symptoms*
      ii. _____
   E. Treatment for bronchitis
      i. _____
      ii. _____

6. The Respiratory Syncytial Virus (RSV)
   A. Can be spread by contact with upper respiratory *Secertions*
   B. Confirmation of RSV is the presence of *viral* antibodies obtained from a *throat* swab or *sputum* culture.

7. Asthma
   A. Asthma is the most common *chronic* disease in children.
   B. Affects _____ out of _____ children, usually before age _____.
   C. Symptoms of asthma
      i. _____
      ii. _____
      iii. _____
      iv. _____
      v. _____

8. Diarrhea

   A. Defined as _____ or more watery stools within _____ hours.
   B. May be caused by bacterial, _____, or parasitic infections; food _____; and medications.
   C. If it persists for more than _____ days, the child may need to be seen by the physician.

9. Colic

   A. Colic is severe _____ pain in infants that occurs in both breast-fed and formula-fed babies.
   B. Cause is unknown, although some suspect _____ of the digestive system.
   C. Symptoms of colic
      i. _____
      ii. _____
      iii. _____
      iv. _____
      v. _____
   D. Treatment for colic
      i. _____
      ii. _____

10. Obesity

   A. Defined as being _____ over the patient's ideal weight with a body mass index greater than _____.
   B. Causes of obesity
      i. _____
      ii. _____
      iii. _____
      iv. _____
      v. _____

11. Autism

   A. Autism is a _____ system disorder or group of disorders that begin in childhood.
   B. It is four times more frequent in _____.
   C. It is noticeable by age _____.
   D. Affects 1 in _____ children.

12. Possible Causes of Autism
      i. _____
      ii. _____
      iii. _____
      iv. _____
      v. _____
      vi. _____

13. Symptoms of Autism
      i. _____
      ii. _____
      iii. _____
      iv. _____
      v. _____
      vi. _____

14. Sudden Infant Death Syndrome (SIDS)

   A. Usually occurs during _____.
   B. It is the leading cause of death in children during the _____ year of life.
   C. The highest number of deaths occur between _____ and _____ months.
   D. More prevalent in _____.

© 2011 Pearson Education, Inc.

15. Probable Causes of Sudden Infant Death Syndrome
    i. _____
    ii. _____
    iii. _____

16. Risk Factors and Prevention Techniques for Sudden Infant Death Syndrome
    A. Risk factors
       i. _____
       ii. _____
       iii. _____
       iv. _____
       v. _____
       vi. _____
    B. Possible prevention techniques
       i. _____
       ii. _____
       iii. _____

17. Febrile Seizures
    A. Seizures can involve jerking arms and legs, loss of consciousness, and _____ of the child's body.
    B. After a seizure, the child may be _____ and have a _____.
    C. Not associated with _____.

18. Meningitis
    A. Meningitis is an inflammation of the _____ surrounding the brain and the _____.
    B. Usually results from an _____ originating elsewhere in the body.
    C. Can be caused by viral or _____ infection.
    D. _____ meningitis is more common and is not life threatening.

19. Recommendations for the Meningitis Vaccination
    A. The _____ (ACIP) has made a recommendation regarding meningitis vaccinations.
    B. ACIP recommends that children _____ to _____ years of age, teens entering high school, and college freshmen receive the newly licensed _____ vaccine.

20. Fifth Disease
    A. Fifth disease is also called _____ _____.
    B. It is a mildly contagious viral disease that occurs during springtime in children older than _____ years.
    C. Caused by _____ B19.
    D. Symptoms of fifth disease (which last about a week)
       i. _____
       ii. _____
       iii. _____

21. Roseola
    A. Roseola is a common early childhood _____ infection characterized by the following
       i. _____
       ii. _____
    B. Treatment for roseola
       i. _____
       ii. _____

22. Hand, Foot, and Mouth Disease (HFM)
    A. HFM is a mild _____ infection.

© 2011 Pearson Education, Inc. *Assisting with Life Span Specialties: Pediatrics*

B. Affects young children in daycare or nursery schools up to _____ years of age.

C. Usually caused by the _____ virus.

D. Spread by the _____ route, saliva, or direct contact with _____.

23. Symptoms of and Treatment for Hand, Foot, and Mouth Disease

A. Symptoms of HFM

    i. _____

    ii. _____

    iii. _____

B. Treatment for HFM

    i. _____

    ii. _____

    iii. _____

24. Recommendations for General Child Safety

A. Place smoke and _____ detectors on every floor of the house.

B. Use _____ covers over electrical outlets.

C. Keep _____ rails up on cribs.

D. Place chemicals, cleaning products, and medications in a _____ cabinet.

E. Teach all children how to dial _____.

25. Early Adolescence

A. Early adolescence is considered ages _____ to _____.

B. The leading cause of death is _____.

26. Middle Adolescence

A. Middle adolescence is considered ages _____ to _____.

B. Conflicts with parents may _____.

27. Eating Disorders

A. Females suffer from eating disorders _____ frequently than males.

B. _____ eating affects males and females equally.

C. Some medical and _____ treatments, including family counseling, are effective for some eating disorders.

28. Anorexia Nervosa

A. Some anorexic patients lose weight by _____ dieting, _____, taking _____ or diuretics, or administering enemas.

B. Patients with this condition are _____ times more likely to die than those without the illness.

29. Signs of Anorexia Nervosa

    i. _____

    ii. _____

    iii. _____

    iv. _____

    v. _____

    vi. _____

    vii. _____

30. Treatment for Anorexia Nervosa

    i. _____

    ii. _____

    iii. _____

31. Bulimia Nervosa

A. Bulimic patients are _____ about their condition and deny that they have any problem with food.

© 2011 Pearson Education, Inc.

B. Binging and _____ may occur _____ times a week.

C. Patients have coexisting conditions, such as _____, _____, and substance abuse problems.

32. Symptoms of Bulimia Nervosa

    i. _____

    ii. _____

    iii. _____

    iv. _____

    v. _____

    vi. _____

33. Eating Disorders Not Otherwise Specified (EDNOS)

A. An EDNOS is an eating disorder that does not fit into the category of _____ or _____.

B. Characterized by _____ eating episodes, which are reoccurring, leading to _____.

C. This disorder is often associated with feelings of _____, guilt, depression, and other coexisting psychological disorders.

D. Treatment is much the same as for bulimia, including the possible use of _____ suppressants.

KEY TERMINOLOGY REVIEW

Match the selected key terms to their definitions below.

a. adolescence

b. amenorrhea

c. anorexia nervosa

d. BRAT diet

e. bronchiolitis

f. bulimia nervosa

g. croup

h. excoriation

i. failure to thrive (FTT)

j. febrile seizures

k. genitalia

l. hydrocephalous

m. meatus

n. microencephaly

o. myringotomy

p. pediatrician

q. purging

r. respiratory syncytial virus (RSV)

s. rhinovirus

t. sleep apnea

u. stridor

v. sudden infant death syndrome (SIDS)

w. tonsillectomy

1. _____ The death with no known cause of an apparently healthy infant, usually before age 1.

2. _____ A condition wherein patients binge eat and then either use self-induced vomiting, laxatives, diuretics, or all three to rid themselves of the large amounts of calories consumed.

3. _____ A medical doctor who specializes in the treatment of newborns, infants, children, and adolescents.

4. _____ Absence of menses.

5. _____ A highly contagious virus that is the most common cause of bronchiolitis.

6. _____ Excessive fluid around the brain.

7. _____ The transition period between puberty and adulthood.

8. _____ A method of losing weight by vomiting, taking laxatives or diuretics, or administering enemas.

9. _____ "Noisy breathing," which is a possible symptom of viral croup.

10. _____ Painful chafing or rawness of the skin.

11. _____ The urinary tract opening.

12. _____ Surgical removal of the tonsils.

13. _____ The reproductive organs.

14. _____ A syndrome identified when an infant gains insufficient weight according to the standardized baby growth charts.

15. _____ A condition associated with a distorted sense of body image and the persistent quest for thinness.

16. _____ An inflammation of the larynx and trachea.

17. _____ Periods of absence of breathing during sleep.

18. _____ A highly contagious condition with more than 200 varieties.

19. _____ Often recommended by pediatricians for infants with diarrhea.

20. _____ Present in some children with high fevers following a rapid spike in body temperature.

21. _____ A procedure in which an incision is made into the eardrum and a tube is inserted through the eardrum to permit the drainage of fluid.

22. _____ Symptoms include cold-like symptoms such as nasal and chest congestion and low-grade fever.

23. _____ Head growth that falls below the normal percentile.

APPLIED PRACTICE

Read the scenario below and answer the questions that follow.

Scenario

Sandra Norwood has brought her daughter, Maya, into the office for her 6 month well-baby visit. Austin Shwartz is the medical assistant working with Ms. Norwood and Maya. From reading Maya's chart, Austin knows that Maya has had two doses of the following vaccines: HepB, Rota, DTaP, Hib, and PCV. *(Maya's chart entry for today's visit appears below.)*

Norwood, Maya
04-23-20XX

10/30/20XX, 9:30 A.M.
weight: 21 lbs., length: 27¼"
Head Circumference: 17½", Chest Circumference: 18"

CC: Mother states, "Maya is here for her 6 month checkup and immunizations."

A. Shwartz, RMA

Activity 1

1. Using the growth chart found in the textbook and the information noted above in the chart, determine the percentile for Maya's length-for-age and weight-for-age:

    a. Length-for-age percentile: _____

    b. Weight-for-age percentile: _____

© 2011 Pearson Education, Inc

Activity 2

Kayla Jefferson, age 18 months, is being seen by Dr. Penningworth for a well-child check. The pediatrician is concerned about Kayla's size and developmental delays. He diagnoses her with failure to thrive.

1. Describe three possible signs and/or symptoms that might indicate developmental delays in the 18-months-old Kayla.

   _____

   _____

   _____

   _____

2. If the physician suspects and/or sees signs which might indicate that neglect or abuse caused the FTT, what steps might he or she take?

   _____

   _____

   _____

   _____

3. What federal law requires the physician to report abuse? Is a medical assistant responsible for reporting abuse? If so, how and to whom?

   _____

   _____

   _____

   _____

LEARNING ACTIVITY: TRUE/FALSE

Indicate whether the following statements are true or false by placing a T or an F on the line that precedes each statement.

_____ 1. Injuries are the number-one cause of death in children.

_____ 2. In California, carrying and undressing a pediatric patient is the responsibility of the parent.

_____ 3. In some states, triaging can only be done by nurses and is considered to be beyond the scope of the medical assisting practice.

_____ 4. Children mature at consistent rates; however, the stages that they pass through are variable, as are the age ranges.

_____ 5. By 5 years old, the child reaches half his or her adult height.

_____ 6. Abused children are at increased risk of suffering from low self-esteem and depression, and, as adults, they often are substance abusers and have eating disorders.

_____ 7. Exposing the child to warm, moist night air is also frequently effective to combat the effects of croup.

_____ 8. Most upper respiratory infections are spread easily by droplets from the nose or throat, or contaminated items handled by the infected person.

_____ 9. A CDC survey found that 28% of high school students had suicidal thoughts and 8.3% had attempted suicide.

_____ 10. EDNOS is characterized by binge eating episodes that are recurring and lead to obesity.

CRITICAL THINKING

Answer the following questions to the best of your ability. Utilize the textbook as a reference.

1. You have an order to obtain blood from a patient for a test. The patient is a 4½-year-old girl who is at the office with her father. She starts to get tears in her eyes when you approach, and the father tells her to quit that crying or he will tell the medical assistant to stick her a second time. What would you do?

   _____

   _____

   _____

2. You have a parent of a 3-month-old baby who calls in two to three times per day, extremely anxious and worried over every little thing and leaving messages with questions for the doctor. When you get the advice from the physician and return her calls, she keeps talking in detail for long periods of time. This is her first child, and she has no family in town to help her through this time of learning how to care for an infant. Everyone in the office is aware of her neediness, and many feel some annoyance at the amount of time and attention that this one patient requires. How would you handle the continuing phone calls? What would you do and/or say?

   _____

   _____

   _____

RESEARCH ACTIVITY

Utilize Internet search engines to research the following topics and write a brief description of what you find. It is important to utilize reputable websites.

1. To learn more about eating disorders and how they are treated, go online or use resources from your school or local library. Conduct research and then write a one-page essay on your findings and what you learned. Be sure to cite your resources.

   _____

   _____

   _____

   _____

   _____

   _____

   _____

   _____

   _____

   _____

© 2011 Pearson Education, Inc.

Assisting with Life Span Specialties: Geriatrics

CHAPTER OUTLINE

General review of the chapter:

The Aging Population
The Aging Process
Legal and Medical Decisions
Elder Abuse
Safety Guidelines for the Elderly Population

STUDENT STUDY GUIDE

Use the following guide to assist in your learning of the concepts from the chapter.

I. The Aging Process

1. A History of Gerontology

   A. The word "geriatric" is derived from the Greek word "_____," meaning "old age," and from "_____." meaning "physician."

   B. _____ illness is a major problem for the elderly.

2. Legislation to Benefit the Elderly

   A. 1935: _____ was created under the Social Security Act.

   B. 1965: The Administration on Aging, the _____ _____ Act, Medicaid, and Medicare were created.

3. Groups of Elderly (Indicate the age range of the individuals in each of these categories.)

   i. Young-old: _____
   ii. Old: _____
   iii. Old-old: _____
   iv. Elite old: _____

4. Baby Boomers

   A. Baby boomers are persons born between _____ and _____.
   B. The oldest members of this group reach senior citizen status in _____.
   C. As of 2007, _____ of the U.S. population is between 44 and 62 years old.

5. Characteristics of Baby Boomers That Affect Health Care

   A. Have fewer _____ or have waited later than previous generations to start a _____.

   B. Economic hardship, combined with advancing age and the deterioration of health, means that there will be an increased strain on _____ _____ for health care and prescription drug assistance.

© 2011 Pearson Education, Inc.

6. Physical Changes That Accompany Aging: The Integumentary System

   A. Hair loses its color and becomes _____.
   B. Skin dries, becomes less _____, and _____ develop.
   C. Skin tears and bruises easily (called _____ _____).
   D. Fingernails and toenails _____.
   E. Reduced amount of _____.
   F. Increased sensitivity to _____.
   G. Age _____ become more common.

7. Physical Changes That Accompany Aging: The Nervous System

   A. Problems with _____
   B. Temperature _____ is off.
   C. Sensation of pain _____
   D. _____ sleep is shortened; there is more awakening during the night.
   E. Brain cells are lost, but intelligence is intact unless a _____ condition is present.
   F. Decreased sensitivity of _____ _____ for heat, cold, pain, and pressure

8. Physical Changes That Accompany Aging: The Sensory System

   A. It is more difficult to see _____ objects.
   B. Night vision may _____.
   C. _____ (clouding of the lens) are more common.
   D. Peripheral vision and depth perception _____.
   E. Smell and taste receptors are less _____.

9. Physical Changes That Accompany Aging: The Musculoskeletal System

   A. There is less muscle _____ and _____.
   B. Arthritis and _____ are more common.
   C. The body is more _____.

10. Physical Changes That Accompany Aging: The Urinary System

   A. The kidneys _____ in size.
   B. Urine production is less _____.
   C. _____ incontinence may develop.

11. Physical Changes That Accompany Aging: The Digestive System

   A. The primary _____ sensations of salty, sweet, and sour decrease.
   B. _____ increases; flatulence increases.
   C. Movement of food through the digestive tract _____ _____.

12. Physical Changes That Accompany Aging: The Cardiovascular System

   A. Blood vessels are less _____ and more _____.
   B. The heart may not pump as _____.
   C. Decreased _____ output and circulation.

13. Physical Changes That Accompany Aging: The Endocrine System

   A. Decrease in _____ and progesterone.
   B. Hot _____, _____ feelings
   C. Higher levels of _____ and thyroid-stimulating hormone
   D. _____ gain
   E. _____ production is less efficient.
   F. Diabetes _____ is more likely.

14. Physical Changes That Accompany Aging: The Reproductive System

   A. Females: Ovulation and menstruation cease; the vaginal walls are _____ and _____.
   B. Males: The scrotum is less _____; the prostate gland may _____.

© 2011 Pearson Education, Inc.

15. Diseases and Condition That Affect the Elderly (Briefly explain each disease and condition.)
    A. Alzheimer's disease and other dementias: _____
    B. Aortic aneurysm: _____
    C. Atrophic urethritis and vaginitis: _____
    D. Decubitus ulcers (bedsores): _____
    E. Benign prostatic hyperplasia: _____
    F. Cataracts: _____
    G. Chronic lymphocytic leukemia: _____
    H. Diabetes mellitus type 2: _____
    I. Glaucoma: _____
    J. Hypothyroidism: _____
    K. Osteoarthritis: _____
    L. Osteoporosis: _____
    M. Parkinson's disease: _____
    N. Prostate cancer: _____
    O. Shingles (herpes zoster): _____
    P. Stroke: _____
    Q. Urinary incontinence: _____

16. Considerations When Treating Elderly Patients

    A. Allow extra time for older patients to _____ _____ and _____ to questions.
    B. Do not _____ sentences for older patients or _____ a patient while talking about the patient to his or her family members or caregivers.
    C. Offer your _____ to patients when walking, and _____ them on and off the examination table as needed.
    D. Make sure that the _____ _____ is secure as patients get on and off the examination table.
    E. If you use a _____ scale in your office, assist patients onto and off of the platform and provide wall-mounted _____ for additional support.

17. Sensory Changes in the Elderly (Provide the word for the given definition.)

    A. _____ is an impairment of hearing that is associated with aging.
    B. _____ is the inability to focus on objects at close range, which reduces the ability of the elderly to interact with the environment around them.

18. Inquiring About Sensory Abilities

    i. _____
    ii. _____
    iii. _____
    iv. _____

19. Addressing Issues Associated with Aging

    A. Provide information on exercises that the elderly can perform at home while seated to increase _____ strength.
    B. Encourage eating proper amounts of _____ products to supply needed _____.
    C. Discuss _____ issues at home that can put the elderly patient at risk.

20. Mental Changes Observed in the Elderly

    i. _____
    ii. _____
    iii. _____

21. Mental Deterioration

    A. Mental deterioration is not a _____ part of aging.
    B. As people age, the risk of mental _____ increases.

C. Mental health is the capacity to cope _____ with life changes, manage life's _____, and achieve a state of _____ balance.

D. Brain _____ slows with aging.

E. For optimal mental health, the elderly should have a sense of _____ and feel that they are of _____ to society.

22. Cognitive Ability

A. Cognitive ability is the ability to think _____.

B. The _____ status of the mind is altered by health status, genetics, social factors, educational accomplishments, and physical activity.

C. Normally, an individual's personality does not change with age unless there is a _____ problem.

23. Three Types of Memory (Briefly describe each type of memory.)

A. Short-term memory: _____

B. Long-term memory: _____

C. Sensory memory: _____

24. Memory

A. Aging does not necessarily mean a loss of _____ or _____ ability in the elderly.

B. With age, the ability to retrieve information from _____-_____ memory may be slower.

C. Physical exercise increases _____ flow and helps maintain blood supply to the brain, improving memory _____.

25. Learning

A. The ability to learn is not _____ by aging.

B. _____ memory (the ability to retain information while using other information) slows with age.

C. Keeping the brain active with games, puzzles, and other types of stimulation helps maintain _____ _____.

26. Sleep

A. Studies have shown that memories and information are _____ during sleep.

B. _____ physical rest delays the brain's response time.

27. The Four Areas of Memory Loss

    i. _____

    ii. _____

    iii. _____

    iv. _____

28. Suggestions for Dealing with Memory Loss

A. Encourage recalling distant memories.

    i. Caregivers can review with patients _____, _____, and _____.

B. Retaining new information

    i. Keep new information _____ and _____ it frequently.

    ii. If the information has more than _____ steps, break these steps down into smaller _____ so that they can be learned individually.

C. Remembering names

    i. Consistently _____-_____ yourself and what your intentions are.

D. Separating fact from fiction

    i. It is important to correct the patient in a _____ manner.

© 2011 Pearson Education, Inc.

29. Addressing the Effects of Medications on Mental Abilities

   A. Provide the patient or caregiver with a _____ organizer and a printed list of the _____ that he or she is taking and why he or she is taking them.

   B. Warn the patient about possible food or drug _____ with written and _____ information.

   C. When taking a patient history, specifically ask about _____-_____-_____ preparations, vitamins, and _____ supplements because the patient may not view these products as "medications."

30. Confusion in the Elderly

   A. "Confusion" is the term used by physicians and health care providers to indicate that the person cannot:

      i. _____

      ii. _____

      iii. _____

      iv. _____

   B. Acute confusion is characterized by symptoms that last for less than _____ months.

   C. Chronic confusion is characterized by symptoms that persist for longer than _____ months.

31. The Three Categories of Confusion (Briefly explain each category.)

   A. Systemic confusion: _____

   B. Mechanical confusion: _____

   C. Psychosocial/environmental confusion: _____

32. Common Causes of Confusion

   A. The most common cause of acute confusion is a _____ _____ _____ (UTI).

   B. The confusion will be resolved with no _____ damage as soon as the infection has cleared.

33. Sundowners Syndrome

   A. This is a type of confusion that occurs after sundown or at night in patients with _____ or other forms of _____.

   B. Tends to be more common in persons with _____ impairments.

   C. Factors that may increase the incidence of Sundowners syndrome

      i. _____

      ii. _____

      iii. _____

      iv. _____

      v. _____

34. Characteristics of Depression

      i. _____

      ii. _____

      iii. _____

      iv. _____

35. Facts About Depression

   A. Depression in the elderly may be caused by _____ _____ that seem overwhelming.

   B. Depression can be worsened by some _____ interactions.

36. Dementia

   A. Dementia is marked by a _____ loss of memory and other _____ functions.

   B. Can occur at any _____, but is more frequently found in the elderly.

C. Currently, there are more than _____ different types of dementia.

D. Affects about _____ of people who are over age 65.

E. Onset is usually _____.

F. It is not a normal _____ of aging.

G. It is irreversible unless caused by a treatable condition such as an _____ _____ or a thyroid dysfunction.

H. Half of all persons over _____ years of age have no signs of dementia.

I. Approximately half of all dementia patients suffer from _____ _____.

37. Causes of Dementia

i. _____

ii. _____

iii. _____

iv. _____

38. Symptoms of Dementia

A. Dementia gradually worsens at different rates over _____ to _____ years.

B. The first sign is usually _____.

C. The person has difficulty learning new _____.

D. The person may forget what he or she is _____.

E. He or she may forget the correct _____ for _____ objects, have difficulty with time _____, and misplace items or put them in an inappropriate place.

F. The person may show a lack of _____, have mood swings, and demonstrate lack of initiative or disinterest in something that he or she previously _____ to do.

39. Alzheimer's Disease

A. Alzheimer's disease is a progressive disorder of the _____ _____ system that eventually destroys mental capacities.

B. Occurs more frequently in the _____.

C. Scientists have pinpointed several _____ abnormalities that are linked to the type of Alzheimer's disease that tends to run in families.

D. While there is a normal loss of some memory as people age, the memory loss associated with Alzheimer's disease is _____.

40. Diagnosing Alzheimer's Disease

A. Diagnoses of dementia and Alzheimer's disease are obtained by _____ other possibilities.

B. After ruling out possible causes, the patient should be given the _____ _____ _____ _____ to evaluate recall, writing, and math skills.

C. A significant portion of the Alzheimer's disease/dementia diagnosis depends on _____ revealed by the patient and family members or caregivers.

41. Symptoms of Alzheimer's Disease

i. _____

ii. _____

iii. _____

iv. _____

v. _____

vi. _____

42. Treatment of Alzheimer's Disease

A. During the early stages, medications, such as _____, are purported to slow the progression of the disease.

B. Patients should not drink _____, which can worsen the symptoms of Alzheimer's Disease.

C. Some depressed Alzheimer's patients may benefit from taking _____ in the early stages.

© 2011 Pearson Education, Inc.

D. Creating a soothing home environment, avoiding _____, and avoiding constantly correcting _____ all help to reduce the stress on Alzheimer's patients.

43. Caring for the Dementia Patient in the Medical Office

A. Always tell the patient what you are going to _____ and what to _____ next.
B. Speak to the patient _____ and in _____ terms, and be ready to repeat instructions.
C. Make _____ _____ with the patient and use appropriate body language.
D. Provide a warm smile and a _____ _____ on the arm to be encouraging.
E. Use the tactics of _____ and _____ when necessary.
F. Allow the patient to "_____ _____" and maintain his or her _____.
G. Take a _____ stand with the patient when necessary.

44. Steps for Communicating Effectively with the Elderly

A. Welcome the patient warmly and with a _____.
B. Face the patient, and speak _____ and _____ to him or her.
C. Treat the patient with _____.
D. If it appears that the patient does not comprehend, _____ using other words and simple gestures.
E. Allow sufficient time for the patient to _____ the information.
F. _____ the patient to the examination room and provide _____ if needed.

45. Obtaining Informed Consent

A. You may provide the family with information about how to proceed with obtaining it and identify a _____ _____ that is able to assist them.
B. _____ invalidates a power of attorney because a power of attorney implies the competency of the patient.

46. Advanced Medical Directives

A. Provide _____ or _____ formulated by the patient that express his or her desires with regard to terminal care.
B. May state whether or not _____ is desired.
C. Other directives should spell out the wishes of the patient if he or she degrades into a persistent _____ state.
D. These directives may indicate whether he or she wants medicine to be _____, except for pain relief, and whether he or she wants nutrition and _____ withheld.
E. In most states, unless the physician writes a specific order restating what the patient has expressed, a directive is not _____ on the staff and facility.

47. Forms of Elder Abuse

i. _____
ii. _____
iii. _____
iv. _____
v. _____
vi. _____

KEY TERMINOLOGY REVIEW

Match the vocabulary term to the correct definition below.

a. Ageism
b. Assisted-living facilities
c. Cognitive ability

d. Extended-care facilities
e. Geriatrician
f. Geriatrics

g. Gerontology
h. Medicare

i. Medigap insurance
j. Respite care

1. _____ A physician who diagnoses and treats diseases and conditions that mainly affect older patients.

2. _____ Offered by the American Association of Retired Persons (AARP) as a supplement to Medicare.

3. _____ Prejudice against and incorrect assumptions about an individual or individuals because of their age.

4. _____ The ability to think clearly, reason, and perceive is affected by many factors.

5. _____ The study of the process of aging and the effects of aging on people.

6. _____ Short-term care for the chronically ill.

7. _____ Facilities designed for residents who cannot live independently but do not require 24-hour care.

8. _____ The field of medicine that specializes in treating elderly patients.

9. _____ U.S. government insurance program for persons aged 65 and older and others with special conditions.

10. _____ Facilities that provide specialized care for the elderly.

APPLIED PRACTICE

Follow the directions as instructed with each question below.

1. Read the following scenario and answer the questions that follow.

> **Scenario**
>
> Fredrick Alamar, age 73, presents to your office today for a physical and a flu vaccination. Upon obtaining his weight, it is apparent that Mr. Alamar has lost 18 pounds since his last visit 2 months ago, which was shortly after his wife died. You make a note of this in his chart. Prior visits to the office have shown Mr. Alamar to be in fairly good health for his age. He only takes metoprolol succinate for hypertension. As you obtain his blood pressure, Mr. Alamar removes his sweater. You notice scratches and bruising on his lower back. He states "I fell after stepping out of the bathtub. I have been falling down a lot more lately and I don't seem to have any strength." After noting this in his chart, you excuse yourself from the examination room and inform the doctor of Mr. Alamar's changes since his last visit.

a. What are the likely causes of Mr. Alamar's significant weight loss?

_____

_____

b. What could be the cause of his recent lack of strength?

_____

_____

c. What things could be done to help Mr. Alamar at home?

_____

_____

© 2011 Pearson Education, Inc.

d. The doctor may recommend a form of permanent care for Mr. Alamar. What options may be available for Mr. Alamar?

_____

_____

LEARNING ACTIVITY: MULTIPLE CHOICE

Circle the correct answers to each of the questions below.

1. Which of the following characteristics do baby boomers have that will affect health care and your role as a provider of health care?
    a. They are considered to be the best-educated generational group.
    b. They will be receiving less family assistance as they age because of fewer children.
    c. They may be caring for an ailing parent and a young child at the same time.
    d. All of the above

2. Which of the following is not an assistive device to aid older individuals?
    a. Handrails and grab bars
    b. Throw rugs
    c. Cane
    d. Bedside commode

3. Life expectancy is increasing due to _____.
    a. better living conditions
    b. new medications
    c. better nutrition
    d. All of the above

4. Factors that affect how we age include _____.
    a. genetics
    b. sports cars
    c. occupational hazards
    d. All of the above

5. Musculoskeletal system aging is characterized by _____.
    a. decrease in muscle strength
    b. inability to see far distances
    c. increased risk of falling
    d. All of the above

6. Which of the following are true statements?
    a. Changes in sensorimotor abilities improve how the elderly interact with their environment.
    b. The loss of hearing, taste, smell, and mobility can lead to depression.
    c. The nervous system begins to speed up.
    d. All of the above

7. Urinary system changes that can occur with aging include _____.
    a. thyroid hypofunction
    b. reduced ability to concentrate urine

© 2011 Pearson Education, Inc.   *Assisting with Life Span Specialties: Geriatrics*   **421**

    c. faster waste removal by the kidneys

    d. orthostatic hypotension

8. According to your textbook, which of the following does not accelerate the aging process?

    a. Disease

    b. Stress

    c. Depression

    d. Lack of social interaction

9. What factors are related to the mental health of aging populations?

    a. Capacity to cope effectively with life changes

    b. Sleep 8–10 hours per night

    c. Achieve a state of emotional balance

    d. All of the above

10. What might you do to find out if an elderly patient is receiving proper nutrition?

    a. Engage elderly patients in a discussion of favorite foods.

    b. Ask which restaurant is their favorite.

    c. Observe their teeth and oral hygiene.

    d. Ask when their last meal was.

CRITICAL THINKING

Answer the following questions to the best of your ability. Utilize the textbook as a reference.

1. Your patient is an 82-year-old woman who is in fairly good health, but she is worried about money. She states that Medicare doesn't pay for enough things, and she wonders if you know of any other resources for her. What can you suggest to this patient regarding medical costs?

_____

_____

_____

_____

2. Because your patient, Mr. Bjorklund, has diminished short-term memory, what can you do to ensure that any patient education you deliver will not be ignored because the patient forgot?

_____

_____

_____

_____

3. A 68-year-old patient named Mrs. Royer has come in today because she is depressed. She says she used to have lots of friends and family but now she is alone. Make a list of possible reasons that this patient feels so isolated.

_____

_____

_____

_____

© 2011 Pearson Education, Inc.

RESEARCH ACTIVITY

Utilize Internet search engines to research the following topics and write a brief description of what you find. It is important to utilize reputable websites.

1. In addition to what is mentioned in your textbook, research additional "assistive aids" that can help elderly patients with their daily activities. What aids do you think might be the most helpful? Which would you be most likely to recommend to future patients? Why?

_____

_____

_____

_____

_____

_____

_____

_____

_____

_____

_____

_____

_____

_____

_____

_____

CHAPTER 42
Assisting with Minor Surgery

CHAPTER OUTLINE

General review of the chapter:

Ambulatory Surgery
Principles of Surgical Asepsis
Surgical Instruments
Surgical Assisting
Preparing the Patient for Minor Surgery
Postoperative Patient Care
Surgical Procedures Performed in the Medical Office

STUDENT STUDY GUIDE

Use the following guide to assist in your learning of the concepts from the chapter.

I. Surgical Asepsis

1. Ambulatory Surgery

   A. The patient is able to _____ into and out of the surgical facility on the same _____.
   B. Includes outpatient surgery, _____ surgery, and office surgery.
   C. Hospitalization is not required unless _____ are expected.

2. Categories of Surgery (List and briefly explain each type.)

   i. _____
   ii. _____
   iii. _____
   iv. _____
   v. _____

3. Medical Versus Surgical Asepsis

   A. Medical asepsis is the elimination of _____ that have left the body.
   B. Surgical asepsis is the practice of creating and _____ a sterile environment.

4. Principles of Surgical Asepsis

   A. Surgical asepsis is necessary for any _____ procedure.
   B. Items required for surgical asepsis include sterile scrubs and sterile _____, as well as sterile technique when handling materials.

5. Guidelines for Surgical Asepsis

   i. _____
   ii. _____
   iii. _____
   iv. _____
   v. _____

© 2011 Pearson Education, Inc.

      vi. _____

     vii. _____

6. Steps for Surgical Hand Hygiene/Sterile Scrub

  A. Remove _____ and dirt from behind the nails.

  B. Stand at the sink without allowing your body to _____ it.

  C. Regulate running water to _____, not _____.

  D. Place hands under running water with hands pointed _____.

  E. Vigorously scrub hands and wrists with a scrub brush for about _____ minutes per hand.

  F. If performing a second lather, use _____ minutes per hand.

7. Steps for Surgical Gloving

       i. _____

      ii. _____

     iii. _____

     iv. _____

      v. _____

     vi. _____

     vii. _____

    viii. _____

     ix. _____

8. Steps for Removing Gloves

       i. _____

      ii. _____

     iii. _____

     iv. _____

9. Sterile Packaging

  A. Packs are set up on a _____ stand.

  B. The inside of the packet's wrapper is the _____ field.

10. Steps for Opening a Sterile Pack

       i. _____

      ii. _____

     iii. _____

     iv. _____

      v. _____

     vi. _____

     vii. _____

    viii. _____

     ix. _____

      x. _____

     xi. _____

    xii. _____

11. Steps for Dropping a Sterile Packet onto a Sterile Field

  A. Assemble the equipment; check the _____ date and the condition of the sealed packet.

  B. Locate the edge on the prepackaged item, and pull it apart by using the _____ and _____ of each hand.

  C. Do not let your fingers touch the _____ of the packet.

  D. Pull the packet apart by securely placing the remaining _____ fingers of each hand against the outside of the packet, one on each side.

  E. Holding the item securely about _____ to _____ inches away from the sterile field, gently drop the packet contents inside the sterile field.

© 2011 Pearson Education, Inc.   *Assisting with Minor Surgery*   **425**

12. Sterile Transfer

    A. Used to move items around the _____ field or to place instruments onto a _____ field.

    B. Must put on _____ gloves or use _____ forceps.

II. Sterile Instruments

  1. Instruments Used in Minor Surgery

      i. _____

     ii. _____

    iii. _____

    iv. _____

     v. _____

  2. Cutting Instruments

    A. _____ or _____ are the terms used to name the instrument used to make an incision.

    B. The scalpel _____ must be inserted into the scalpel handle.

    C. Blades come in various sizes; the choice of blade depends on the type of _____ and _____.

  3. Scissors

    A. The two primary uses of scissors are for _____ and to cut _____.

    B. The _____ of the scissors vary; the choice of scissors depends on how they are to be used.

  4. Types of Scissors (List each type of scissors and their use.)

      i. _____

     ii. _____

    iii. _____

    iv. _____

  5. Forceps

    A. Forceps are used to grasp _____ or objects.

    B. Two-pronged forceps are used to clamp together tightly to prevent _____.

    C. A ratchet clasp allows the forceps to close with different degrees of _____.

  6. Types of Forceps (List the different types of forceps and briefly describe their use.)

       i. _____

      ii. _____

     iii. _____

     iv. _____

      v. _____

     vi. _____

    vii. _____

  7. The Speculum, Scope, Probe, Trocar, and Punch

    A. A speculum is an unlighted instrument inserted into a body _____.

    B. An _____ is placed inside the scope to _____ it into a canal, and then it is removed during visualization of the _____ site.

    C. The probe is used to explore _____ and cavities; it usually has a curved, _____ point to facilitate insertion.

    D. A trocar is used to _____ fluids from cavities.

    E. The two parts of a trocar are a _____ and a _____.

    F. A punch is used to _____ tissue for _____ or microscopic examination of the tissue in order to detect cancerous cells.

© 2011 Pearson Education, Inc.

8. Disciplines That Use Specialized Instruments

    i. _____

    ii. _____

    iii. _____

9. Absorbable Sutures

    A. Absorbable sutures are digested by tissue _____ and are absorbed by the body.

    B. Absorption usually occurs _____ to _____ days after insertion.

10. Types of Absorbable Sutures (List and briefly explain each type.)

    i. _____

    ii. _____

    iii. _____

11. Nonabsorbable Sutures (List and briefly describe the characteristics of each type.)

    i. _____

    ii. _____

    iii. _____

    iv. _____

    v. _____

    vi. _____

12. The Size of Suture Material

    A. Measured by the _____ or _____.

    B. Stated in terms of _____.

    C. _____ in size with the number of zeros.

13. Suture Needles

    A. Available in various shapes, depending on where they are _____.

    B. Have either a _____ cutting point used for tissues that provide some resistance or a _____ noncutting point used for more _____ tissue.

14. The Straight Needle

    A. Used when the needle is pushed and pulled through the tissue without the use of a needle _____.

    B. Has an _____ that is threaded with the suture material.

15. The Curved Needle

    A. Allows the surgeon to go in and out of _____ where there is not enough room to maneuver a _____ needle.

    B. Requires a needle _____.

16. The Swaged Needle

    A. A swaged needle and suture materials are combined in _____ length.

    B. Because the suture material is attached to the needle, the material will not _____ off.

17. Steri-Strips™

    A. Steri-Strips are non_____ and are available in a variety of widths.

    B. Used instead of _____ when not much _____ is to be applied to a wound, such as on a small facial cut.

18. Staples

    A. Made of _____.

    B. Applied with a surgical _____.

© 2011 Pearson Education, Inc.

19. Skin Adhesives

    A. Composed of _____ adhesives that react with _____ to create an instant, strong, flexible bond.

    B. Used to close _____ or small surgical incisions.

20. Guidelines for Handling Instruments (List specific guidelines for instrument care.)

    i. _____

    ii. _____

    iii. _____

    iv. _____

    v. _____

    vi. _____

III. Preparing the Patient for Surgery

  1. The Role of the Nonsterile Assistant

    A. _____ the patient.

    B. Holds the vial of local _____ while the surgeon draws up the correct dosage into a syringe; _____ dressings.

  2. Factors the That Make a Medical Assistant Valuable

    i. _____

    ii. _____

    iii. _____

    iv. _____

  3. The Responsibilities of the Scrub Assistant

    A. Arranges the surgical _____ to meet the operating physician's preferences.

    B. _____ bodily fluids away from the operative site.

    C. _____ the incision area.

    D. _____ suture materials.

  4. Guidelines for Sterile Techniques

    A. Immediately _____ if sterility is broken.

    B. _____ all instruments before passing them.

    C. Protect the surgeon from injury by _____ needles away from the surgeon.

    D. _____ the surgeon's needs by _____ the types of instruments used in a procedure.

    E. Place the _____ of the instrument into the surgeon's hand with a firm _____.

    F. When required to cut a suture, cut both ends at the same time, _____ to _____ inches above the knot.

  5. Steps for Transferring Sterile Fluid into a Sterile Basin

    A. Check the _____ on the solution and the sterile basin pack.

    B. Set up the sterile basin on the Mayo tray using the inside of the wrapper to create a _____.

    C. Remove the cap of the solution and place it on a clean surface with the outer edge _____ (inside facing up).

    D. Check the _____ on the solution bottle before pouring the solution.

    E. Pour a small amount of the liquid into a _____ _____ for discarding.

    F. Pour from the bottle with the label held against the _____ to protect the label from _____.

    G. Hold the bottle about _____ inches above the basin and pour slowly.

  6. Steps for Assisting with Minor Surgery

    A. Open a set of _____ gloves for the physician.

    B. Cleanse the vial of anesthetic with a _____ alcohol swab and hold it _____ in the palm of your hand with the label facing toward the _____.

© 2011 Pearson Education, Inc.

C. Collect and place all soiled instruments in a _____ out of the patient's view.

D. Place all soiled gauze sponges and dressings in a _____.

E. Do not allow _____ items to remain on a sterile field.

F. Immediately _____ all specimens as they are obtained.

G. Periodically, check the patient's _____ during the procedure.

H. Provide clear _____ and _____ postoperative instructions for the patient.

I. Send the _____ to the laboratory with a _____.

7. Steps for Disposing of Soiled Dressings

    i. _____

    ii. _____

    iii. _____

    iv. _____

    v. _____

    vi. _____

8. The Role of the Floating Assistant

    i. _____

    ii. _____

    iii. _____

    iv. _____

    v. _____

    vi. _____

    vii. _____

    viii. _____

    ix. _____

    x. _____

    xi. _____

    xii. _____

9. Proper Floating Technique During Surgery

A. Immediately report any _____ observations about the patient to the operating _____.

B. Use care not to touch the _____ while assisting.

C. Provide additional medications, such as local _____, that are needed during the procedure.

10. Guidelines for Providing Medication During a Procedure

A. Follow the correct procedure for _____ the medication.

B. Clean the top of the vial/bottle with _____.

C. Hold the vial/bottle upside down so that the physician can insert a sterile needle into the vial without touching the contaminated _____ surface.

D. Do not hold the vial in front of your _____.

11. Surgical Setup for a Typical Minor Surgical Procedure

    i. _____

    ii. _____

    iii. _____

    iv. _____

    v. _____

    vi. _____

    vii. _____

    viii. _____

    ix. _____

    x. _____

    xi. _____

xii. _____
xiii. _____
xiv. _____

12. Methods for Preoperative and Postoperative Instructions

    i. _____
    ii. _____
    iii. _____
    iv. _____
    v. _____

13. Informed Consent

    A. Any invasive procedure with a scalpel, scissors, or other device requires _____ permission.
    B. Every attempt must be made to determine whether the patient actually _____ the explanation given.
    C. A medical assistant _____ witness the patient's signing of the consent form.

14. Anesthesia

    A. Anesthesia is the medication that causes the _____ or _____ loss of sensation.
    B. Used to block the _____ of surgery.
    C. Can relax _____, produce _____, calm _____, and cause sleep.

15. General Anesthesia

    A. Depresses the _____ to cause unconsciousness.
    B. Usually administered by _____ or _____.
    C. Sedatives and narcotics are usually administered _____ before surgery.

16. Local Anesthesia

    A. Provides a loss of _____ in a particular area of the body without an overall loss of _____.
    B. Also referred to as a _____ anesthetic.
    C. Takes about _____ to _____ minutes to become effective and lasts from _____ to _____ hours.

17. Local Infiltration Anesthetic

    A. Injected directly into the _____ that will be operated on.
    B. Used for such procedures as removal of skin _____, skin suturing, and dental _____.

18. Epinephrine

    A. Epinephrine is a vasoconstrictor that causes the _____ blood vessels to _____.
    B. Often added to the local anesthetic when the physician is operating on the _____ and _____.

19. Nerve Blocks

    A. Administered by _____ into a nerve adjacent to the operative site.
    B. Used for surgery on _____, _____, and toes.

20. Topical Anesthetics

    A. Local pain control medications that are applied to the _____ to produce a _____ effect.
    B. Can be applied by drop, _____, or swab.
    C. Commonly used in _____ procedures.

21. Instructions for a Dry Shave

    A. To remove hair, _____ shavers are preferred to razor blades because they lessen the likelihood of accidental nicks in the skin.

© 2011 Pearson Education, Inc.

B. Hair should be manually clipped as short as possible with _____.

C. The medical assistant should apply firm _____ to the skin with his or her _____ hand.

D. Hair should be removed in the _____ of hair growth.

22. Instructions for a Wet Shave (List the steps for performing a wet shave.)

i. _____

ii. _____

iii. _____

iv. _____

v. _____

vi. _____

vii. _____

viii. _____

KEY TERMINOLOGY REVIEW

Match the vocabulary term to the correct definition below.

a. Ambulatory surgery

b. anesthesia

c. Biopsy

d. Cryosurgery

e. Debridement

f. Dehiscence

g. Eschar

h. Evisceration

i. Hyfrecator

j. Incisions

k. Invasive procedure

l. Mayo stand

m. Outpatient surgery

n. Scrub assistant

o. Sterile field

p. Surgical scrub

1. _____ A scab.

2. _____ Removal of dead tissue around wound edges using sterile technique.

3. _____ Hand instruments to the surgeon.

4. _____ Microscopic examination of tissue to detect cancerous cells.

5. _____ A procedure in which the body is entered.

6. _____ Separation of wound edges and protrusion of abdominal organs.

7. _____ The process of removing microorganisms.

8. _____ Surgery performed on a person who is admitted and discharged from a surgical facility on the same day.

9. _____ A small portable table with enough room to hold an instrument tray.

10. _____ The use of subfreezing temperatures to destroy tissue.

11. _____ A specific area free of all microorganisms that will be the work area for a surgical procedure.

12. _____ A miniature electrocautery unit.

13. _____ Generally limited to procedures requiring less than 60 minutes to perform.

14. _____ Medication that causes the partial or complete loss of sensation.

15. _____ Separation of wound edges.

© 2011 Pearson Education, Inc.

APPLIED PRACTICE

1. Identify each of the gynecological instruments as seen in the picture below.

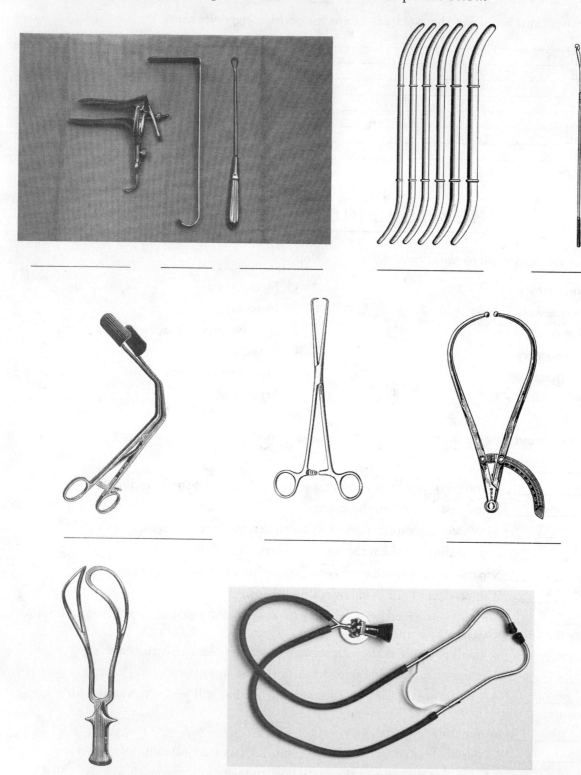

© 2011 Pearson Education, Inc.

2. Using the information from the following patient chart, correctly identify the instruments that you would prepare for an I&D (incision and drainage).

> Horsley, Will
> 10-26-1963
>
> 04/02/20XX_, 12:45 P.M.
> Wt: 175 lbs., T: 98.6°F, P: 104, BP: 118/78
> cc: Pt presents to office complaining of a cut that appears to be inflamed. Upon examination, the area sounding the cut is red and painful. The physician has requested that the patient be prepped for an I&D. I&D is successfully performed and the patient is discharged on antibiotics.
>
> Adam Bello, RMA

LEARNING ACTIVITY: MULTIPLE CHOICE

1. Which of the following types of drainage exhibit clear, watery drainage, such as the fluid in a blister?

   a. Serous drainage
   b. Sanguineous drainage
   c. Serosanguineous drainage
   d. Purulent drainage

2. Which of the following is an absorbable type of suture?

   a. Plain catgut
   b. Surgical catgut
   c. Chromic catgut
   d. All of the above

3. A wound that has torn edges in an irregular shape would be called a _____.

   a. puncture
   b. laceration
   c. abrasion
   d. incision

4. Which of the following forceps are used to grasp foreign bodies?

   a. Tissue
   b. Thumb
   c. Splinter
   d. Needle

5. The general classification of instruments is based on which of the following?

   a. Cutting
   b. Dissecting
   c. Grasping
   d. All the above

6. The three basic steps of skin preparation include all of the following except _____.

   a. apply antiseptic solution to the surgical area
   b. scrub with an antiseptic soap and rinse
   c. air dry the skin prior to cleansing
   d. shave as necessary

7. Which of the following is not a sign of inflammation?
    a. Swelling
    b. Warmth
    c. Decreased drainage
    d. Pain

8. Sutures on the face are usually removed in _____.
    a. 24–48 hours
    b. 3–5 days
    c. 5–7 days
    d. 7–10 days

9. Which of the following electrosurgery destroys tissue by creating a spark gap when the probe is inserted into unwanted tissue.
    a. Electrocoagulation
    b. Electrodessication
    c. Electrofulguration
    d. All of the above

10. Colposcopy is performed in which of the following cases?
    a. When an abnormal tissue development is observed by the physician during a routine pelvic examination
    b. When a Papanicolaou (Pap) smear result is in the abnormal range
    c. For magnified visualization
    d. All of the above

CRITICAL THINKING

Answer the following questions to the best of your ability. Utilize the textbook as a reference.

1. Patient instructions should be given both orally and in writing. Many errors can be made by the patient if instructions are not clear. Come up with a scenario of something harmful that could happen if a patient did not have any written instructions and did not remember the oral instructions provided by the physician or medical assistant.

   _____

   _____

   _____

2. During a sterile cyst removal procedure, the physician reaches up to scratch her head briefly. She is wearing a surgical cap and no visible bodily fluids are on her gloves. Take some time and think through this scenario. Has the sterile procedure been compromised? If so, indicate your thoughts in a paragraph.

   _____

   _____

   _____

   _____

© 2011 Pearson Education, Inc.

RESEARCH ACTIVITY

Utilizing your textbook and Internet search engines research the following topics and write a brief description of what you find. It is important to utilize reputable websites.

1. Research one surgical procedure discussed in your textbook. Why is the procedure preformed? How is the procedure preformed? What instruments would be required to perform this procedure?

_____

_____

_____

_____

_____

_____

_____

_____

_____

_____

_____

_____

_____

_____

_____

_____

_____

_____

_____

_____

CHAPTER 43
Assisting with Medical Emergencies and Emergency Preparedness

CHAPTER OUTLINE

General review of the chapter:

Emergency Resources
Guidelines for Providing Emergency Care
Office Emergency Crash Kit
Medical Emergencies
Emergency Preparedness

STUDENT STUDY GUIDE

Use the following guide to assist in your learning of the concepts from the chapter.

I. Responding to a Medical Office Emergency

1. The Emergency Medical Services (EMS) System

   A. Established to provide _____ care.
   B. Provides safe and prompt _____ to an emergency facility.

2. Good Samaritan Laws

   A. These state laws protect a health care professional from _____ while giving emergency care to an accident victim.
   B. The laws are in place to encourage _____ to offer aid in emergency situations without fear of being prosecuted for _____ injury or death.

3. The Chain of Survival

   i. _____
   ii. _____
   iii. _____
   iv. _____

4. The Medical Assistant's Emergency Response Primary Assessment

   A. Determine the patient's name, _____ _____, and gender.
   B. Determine whether the patient is ill or _____.
   C. Determine the patient's need for _____.
   D. Obtain a history of the _____.
   E. Gather the patient's _____ information.
   F. Determine the patient's _____.
   G. Do a _____ examination.
   H. Take the patient's _____ _____.

© 2011 Pearson Education, Inc.

5. Items in an Emergency Crash Kit
      i. _____
     ii. _____
    iii. _____
     iv. _____
      v. _____
     vi. _____
    vii. _____
   viii. _____
     ix. _____

6. The Medical Assistant and the Crash Kit

   A. The MA should do _____ checks of emergency supplies in the crash kit.
   B. Tasks involved in checking the crash kit include the following
        i. _____
       ii. _____
      iii. _____
       iv. _____

II. Medical Emergencies

    1. General Guidelines for Emergency Care

       A. Access for the adult patient is initiated by calling 911 as soon as it has been determined that
          the patient is _____ and _____ _____.
       B. In general, _____ _____ for an unresponsive adult.
       C. With children and infants, EMS access is made after _____ minutes of CPR.

    2. The Heimlich Maneuver

       A. Stand _____ the patient with your feet slightly apart, placing _____
          _____between the patient's feet and _____ to the outside.
       B. Place the _____ finger of one hand at the person's _____or belt buckle.
       C. Make a _____ with your other hand and place it, _____ side to the patient,
          above your other hand.
       D. Place your marking hand over your _____ fist and begin to give quick _____ and
          _____ thrusts.
       E. Continue to give thrusts until the object has been expelled or the patient becomes
          _____.
       F. Before administering the _____ breaths, open the airway with the _____-
          _____ chin lift and look for a foreign body in the patient's mouth and remove it if one
          is visible.
       G. _____ finger sweeps are no longer recommended and should not be performed.
       H. Continue with cycles of _____ compressions and ____ _____ breaths until the
          foreign body is expelled or advanced medical personal arrive to relieve you.

    3. Steps for Adult Rescue Breathing and One-Rescuer CPR

       A. _____ the patient and determine whether help is needed.
       B. Shout, "_____ _____ _____?" while gently shaking the patient's
          shoulders.
       C. If the adult patient is determined to be _____, activate EMS immediately by calling
          911 and get an _____ if one is available.

    4. Assessing the ABCs

       A. Airway: Perform a head-_____ chin _____, or, if a neck injury is suspected,
          a jaw _____.
       B. Look and feel for _____and _____movements.

C. If you are alone, begin the rescue sequence for ___ _____ and then attempt to call 911 yourself.

D. If you have a _____ mask, place it on the patient.

5. Performing Breaths

A. If breathing is absent, put on a _____ _____ and administer _____ _____ breaths.

B. If your breaths do not cause the chest to _____, look in the patient's mouth and remove the object if one is seen.

C. If no object is seen, make a second attempt to administer a _____ breath.

D. If the breaths cause the chest to _____, assess the patient's _____ by feeling for a pulse at the _____ _____.

6. Feeling a Pulse

A. If you feel a pulse, begin _____ _____.

B. Administer one breath every _____ seconds, or _____ every minute.

C. After _____ minute, reassess the patient for _____ and _____.

7. Performing Chest Compressions

A. If you do not feel a pulse, begin _____ _____.

B. Kneel at the patient's side and place your hand in the center of the _____ between the _____.

C. Place your other hand on _____ of the first hand, making sure to lift your _____ off the chest, using only the heels of your hands to administer compressions.

D. Keep your shoulders directly over your _____.

E. Compress the chest _____ to _____ inches; then allow the sternum to relax.

F. Do not lift your hands off the _____.

G. Continue to compress the chest a total of _____ times; then administer _____ breaths.

H. Repeat this sequence for _____ total cycles. Reassess the patient and continue CPR if necessary.

8. Steps for Infant or Young Child Rescue Breathing and One-Rescuer CPR

A. If the infant is determined to be _____, perform CPR for _____ minutes prior to activating _____ by calling 911; get an _____ if one is available.

B. Gently, with _____ fingers, tilt the patient's _____ and open the _____.

C. If breathing is absent, secure a _____ _____ over the patient's mouth and nose.

9. Administering Chest Compressions on a Child

A. Place _____ _____ in the center of the chest just below the nipple line.

B. Compressions should be made _____ to _____ the depth of the chest. Perform 30 quick compressions.

C. Give two more rescue breaths followed by _____ more compressions. Continue the _____ compressions and breaths.

D. After 2 minutes, leave the _____ and call 911 if you are still alone.

E. Continue compressions and breaths until the infant _____ or _____ arrives.

10. Automated External Defibrillation (AED)

A. Highly effective when used immediately after or within minutes of an adult _____ _____.

B. AED is not used on _____.

11. Symptoms of Respiratory Distress

    i. _____

    ii. _____

    iii. _____

    iv. _____

© 2011 Pearson Education, Inc.

v. _____
vi. _____
vii. _____
viii. _____

12. Steps for Administering Oxygen

 A. Check the _____ _____ on the oxygen tank to make sure that it has enough oxygen in it.
 B. Start the flow of oxygen by opening the _____.
 C. Attach the _____ tubing to the flow meter.
 D. Adjust the oxygen _____ according to the physician's order.
 E. Hold the cannula tips over the _____ of your _____, without touching the skin, to determine whether oxygen is flowing.
 F. Place the tips of the _____ _____ into the patient's nostrils.
 G. Wrap the tubing behind the patient's _____.
 H. Instruct the patient to breathe normally through the _____ and _____.
 I. Check the patient's oxygen level with an _____.
 J. Place the probe over the _____ finger and record the reading.
 K. If necessary, have the patient take a short _____ to verify that the oxygen flow rate is sufficient for activity.

13. Symptoms of Hyperventilation

 i. _____
 ii. _____
 iii. _____
 iv. _____
 v. _____
 vi. _____

14. Treatment for Hyperventilation

 A. Inform the physician and encourage the patient to _____ _____.
 B. Have the patient breathe into an _____ _____ (not connected to any oxygen), block one nostril, or breathe into a _____ _____.

15. Chest Pain

 A. The primary complaint will be pain in the _____ or _____ side of the chest, described as _____, _____, _____, _____, or aching.
 B. The pain may radiate to the _____ arm, to the _____, or up the neck.
 C. Sometimes the pain is brought on by _____.

16. Care of Chest Pain

 A. Have the individual stop what he or she is doing and _____, feet _____ if possible.
 B. Ask a coworker to stay with the patient while you inform the _____ of the situation.
 C. Sometimes the pain is brought on by _____.
 D. If oxygen is available, administer it according to office protocol by _____ cannula at _____ to _____ liters per minute until the physician or emergency personnel arrive.
 E. If the patient has previously been diagnosed with angia and has nitroglycerin tablets, insert _____ tablet under the _____.
 F. Tablets may be administered every _____ minutes up to _____ doses.
 G. If the _____ is not relieved, inform the _____ or EMS on the scene.

17. Shock

 A. Shock is the collapse of the _____ system caused by insufficient cardiac output.
 B. _____, shock can progress very rapidly to death.

18. Causes of Shock

    i. _____

    ii. _____

    iii. _____

    iv. _____

    v. _____

    vi. _____

    vii. _____

    viii. _____

19. General Signs of Shock

    i. _____

    ii. _____

    iii. _____

    iv. _____

    v. _____

    vi. _____

    vii. _____

    viii. _____

    ix. _____

    x. _____

    xi. _____

    xii. _____

    xiii. _____

    xiv. _____

20. Anaphylactic Shock

    A. Anaphylactic shock is a severe _____ _____ to a foreign substance, such as medications, bug bites, and latex gloves.

    B. Inform the physician immediately and call _____.

    C. The physician may order _____ and/or an _____.

    D. _____ is the most important factor in anaphylactic shock.

21. Signs of Insulin Shock or Diabetic Coma

    i. _____

    ii. _____

    iii. _____

    iv. _____

    v. _____

    vi. _____

    vii. _____

    viii. _____

22. Arterial Bleeding

    A. Arterial bleeding is usually copious, rapid, and _____ _____.

    B. Blood often spurts, echoing the _____

    C. Must be brought _____ _____ as soon as possible.

    D. Pressure applied directly over the _____ _____ may halt the flow of blood.

    E. If not successful, _____ _____ on the pressure points may be necessary.

    F. Elevating the injured part higher than the _____ may also slow the blood flow.

23. Bleeding from Veins and Capillaries

    A. Venous blood can usually be controlled with _____.

    B. Blood from the capillaries _____ rather than flows and can be halted with direct pressure.

© 2011 Pearson Education, Inc.

24. Pressure Points

    A. Use pressure points if external bleeding cannot be stopped by _____ _____.

    B. Most often you will use the _____ and _____ pressure points.

25. Abrasions

    A. Occurs when the _____ _____ of skin is scraped away, leaving the underlying tissue exposed.

    B. Common terms for abrasions

       i. _____

       ii. _____

       iii. _____

       iv. _____

26. Avulsions

    A. An avulsion is a _____ _____ of skin or tissue.

    B. Usually occurs on _____ and _____.

    C. Cleanse minor avulsion wounds with _____ and _____ and return any skin flap to its normal position.

    D. Apply direct pressure, and then apply a dressing after _____ is controlled.

27. Amputation

    A. If body part has been _____, cleanse the _____ _____ with sterile saline.

    B. Wrap it with moist, sterile gauze. Seal it in a _____ _____; place the _____ _____ in a container on ice.

    C. Prompt medical attention and preservation of the _____ _____ enhance the chances for successful reattachment.

28. Lacerations

    A. A laceration is an _____ _____ in which the skin and underlying tissue are torn.

    B. Usually has _____ edges that may interfere with the healing process.

    C. If bleeding is _____, a physician should direct the cleansing process.

    D. Lacerations over a joint may require joint _____ for a few days while healing progresses.

29. Incisions

    A. An incision is a cut with smooth edges that is made with a knife or other _____ object.

    B. It is treated in the same manner as any _____.

    C. If there is damage to underlying _____, such as a tendon or ligament, surgical intervention is required.

30. Puncture Wounds

    A. A puncture wound is the result of a pointed _____ _____ penetrating the skin and tissue.

    B. Often the wound edges close, trapping _____ and _____ in the tissue.

    C. Depending on the nature of the pointed object, cleansing may consist of simply soaking the area, or may require invasive _____.

    D. After cleansing, a _____ is applied.

31. Impaled Objects

    A. The general rule is to leave the _____ in place until it can be safely removed by trained personnel.

    B. Control _____ and _____ the impaled object with a bulky dressing held in place with tape or bandages.

    C. _____ the area to prevent movement.

© 2011 Pearson Education, Inc.

32. Soft Tissue Injuries

   A. Involves both the skin and _____ tissue.
   B. Avulsions, amputations, and _____ insults are considered soft-tissue injuries because tissue, as well as skin, is involved.
   C. Damage to the underlying tissue may involve _____ _____, _____, muscles, and _____ tissue.

33. Crush Injuries

   A. Result when force is applied to the _____.
   B. Depending on the area involved, the crush may be similar to the _____ of tissue or it may be so severe as to involve _____ and _____.
   C. Elevating the body part above the _____ and applying _____ are often the only intervention needed.
   D. With a more severe injury, the body part should be _____.
   E. Monitoring vital signs and observing _____ _____, _____, and _____ are essential to deciding whether more extensive intervention is needed.

34. Open Wounds (Define each type.)

   A. Superficial: _____
   B. Deep: _____

35. Open Wound Care

   A. Apply _____ _____ to the wound.
   B. If necessary, use a _____ dressing.
   C. Cleanse the wound from the _____ _____, beginning with vigorous irrigation using a disinfecting solution prescribed by the physician.
   D. Wipe the edges of the wound with sterile gauze in all directions, _____ from the wound.
   E. Cover with a _____ dressing and fasten the dressing in place.
   F. Make sure that you do not apply the bandage _____ _____, because it can restrict the blood flow out of the extremity, which may increase the bleeding instead of stopping it.

36. Applying a Triangular Bandage

   A. Keep the injured arm as _____ as possible.
   B. Carefully slide the triangular bandage under the _____ to be held.
   C. The two shorter sides should be pointing toward the _____, and the remaining longer edge should be parallel to the _____ _____ _____.
   D. Bring the _____ side up and over the arm.
   E. Tie the ends of the bandage behind and slightly to the _____ of the neck.
   F. Tuck the peak of the bandage in toward the _____ _____ of the bandage.

37. Applying a Figure 8 Bandage

   A. Place the _____ of one hand on one end of the bandage
   B. Anchor the bandage with your _____ _____, then complete one _____ around the extremity or body part.
   C. Continue to alternate wrapping above and below the _____ _____ or dressing, circling behind the _____ or dressing area until the injured area is covered adequately.
   D. If applying a bandage to a _____, ensure that the _____ are exposed to evaluate circulation.

38. Applying a Tubular Bandage (List the steps for applying this type of bandage.)

   i. _____
   ii. _____
   iii. _____

© 2011 Pearson Education, Inc.

iv. _____

v. _____

vi. _____

vii. _____

viii. _____

ix. _____

x. _____

39. Epistaxis (Nosebleeds)

A. Epistaxis is usually _____-_____ threatening.

B. Tends to occur more commonly in _____ weather or under dusty conditions.

40. Caring for a Patient with a Nosebleed

A. The physician will twist a _____ _____ and pack the patient's nose.

B. A _____ _____ pack should be held against the bridge of the patient's nose.

C. A patient may need an _____ procedure if the bleeding does not stop.

41. When to Worry About Persistent Nosebleeds

i. _____

ii. _____

iii. _____

iv. _____

42. Classification of Burns (Briefly explain each type.)

A. First degree burns: _____

B. Second degree burns: _____

C. Third degree burns: _____

43. Caring for a Patient with First Degree Burns

A. _____ water.

B. Use _____ and _____, if ordered by the physician.

44. Caring for a Patient with Second Degree Burns

A. Cool the burn with water as long as there are no _____ _____.

B. _____ _____ use analgesic creams and ointments.

C. Cover with a _____ _____ _____.

D. Treat for _____, if necessary.

45. Caring for a Patient with Third Degree Burns

A. Transport the patient to a _____ _____.

B. Cover burns with _____, _____ _____.

C. _____ the dead skin or damaged tissue (should be done only by a physician).

D. Manage the pain with _____ as ordered by a physician.

E. Separate the _____ or _____ with dry, sterile gauze on hand or foot burns.

F. Do not remove _____ from the burned area.

46. Caring for a Patient with Upper Airway Burns

A. Prompt _____ by the physician or EMS.

B. Transport to a _____ center.

C. Listen for _____ (noisy breathing).

D. Administer _____ as ordered by the physician.

47. Caring for a Patient with Large Surface Area Burns

i. _____

ii. _____

iii. _____

48. Hyperthermia: Heat Exhaustion

A. Extreme _____ due to heat.
B. Occurs as the result of _____ and _____ depletion from the body.
C. Strenuous _____ often preceded heat exhaustion.

49. Hyperthermia: Heat Stroke

A. Advanced heat exhaustion; body temperature _____
B. Many patients will not _____.
C. No _____ takes place, so the body stores heat in increasing amounts.
D. Eventually, the _____ cells begin to die and permanent damage or death may result.

50. Signs and Symptoms of Heat Exhaustion

i. _____
ii. _____
iii. _____
iv. _____
v. _____
vi. _____
vii. _____
viii. _____

51. Treating Heat Exhaustion

A. Move to a _____ environment.
B. Encourage patient to _____.
C. Apply _____, _____ compresses and give sips of water.

52. Signs and Symptoms of Heat Stroke

i. _____
ii. _____
iii. _____
iv. _____
v. _____
vi. _____
vii. _____
viii. _____
ix. _____
x. _____
xi. _____
xii. _____
xiii. _____

53. Treating Heat Stroke

A. Remove the patient from _____ of heat.
B. _____ the victim's clothing.
C. _____ the body as quickly as possible by pouring _____ water over the patient.
D. Contact _____ if physician is not available.

54. Hypothermia

A. Hypothermia is an _____ drop in body temperature.
B. Results from prolonged exposure to _____ or _____ water.

55. Signs and Symptoms of Hypothermia

i. _____
ii. _____
iii. _____

© 2011 Pearson Education, Inc.

iv. _____

v. _____

56. Treating Hypothermia

A. Remove _____ and _____ clothes.
B. Wrap the patient in _____ blankets.
C. _____ packs may be used, but not directly on the _____.
D. Sips of _____ liquid.
E. _____ to treatment facility for assessment by a physician.

57. Convulsions (Seizures)

A. Produced by _____ _____ activity in the brain.
B. Characterized by _____ _____ _____ that alternate between the contraction and relaxation of muscles.

58. Caring for a Patient with Convulsions (Seizures)

A. _____ spasms of the full body can restrict breathing.
B. Patient may bite his or her _____, causing bleeding and swelling, which may obstruct the airway.
C. Prevent _____.
D. Pay close attention to what the patient is _____ so that you can _____ it later.

59. Fainting (Syncope)

A. Fainting is a _____ loss of consciousness.
B. Patient usually _____ and becomes _____, but should awaken and return to normal functioning within a minute.
C. Patients seldom become _____ or have _____ as a result of simple fainting, but may be injured in the course of a fall.

60. Caring for a Patient Who Has Fainted

A. If the patient fainted and there is no response, provide _____ if the physician orders this.
B. Check the _____ and call for help.
C. If the patient is breathing well but will not wake up, place him or her on the _____ side and notify the physician.
D. If the physician is unavailable, contact _____.
E. Obtain a full set of _____ and obtain a _____ reading if possible.

61. Fractures (Briefly explain both types.)

A. Closed (simple): _____
B. Open (compound): _____

62. Splinting Injuries

A. Fractures of long bones require _____ by splinting to prevent joint movement _____ and _____ the fracture.
B. _____ the fracture.
C. Never try to _____ or _____ a bone in a compound fracture.

63. Sprains

A. Occurs when _____, _____, or ligaments are torn.
B. May be the result of trauma or cumulative _____ of the joint.

64. Strains

A. A strain is often called a _____ _____.
B. Occurs when a muscle or tendon is overextended by _____.
C. The patient may be unable to use the _____.
D. In the lower extremities, _____ _____ is painful and sometimes impossible.

© 2011 Pearson Education, Inc.

65. Dislocation
   A. The bone is actually pulled away from the _____, stretching or tearing the _____ and tendons.
   B. A _____ is generally noted.
   C. Must be reduced and the bone _____ into the joint.
   D. Injured body parts should be _____ to prevent additional damage and to reduce pain.
   E. The application of _____ also helps with the pain and slows edema.

III. Emergency Preparedness
   1. The Role of the Medical Assistant During an Emergency
      A. Be knowledgeable in the area of emergency _____.
      B. Know how to respond in the event of a _____ disaster, such as a terrorist event, and to a _____ disaster, such as a hurricane.
      C. Remaining _____ in the event of an emergency is paramount to the success of handling the emergency.

   2. Preparing for an Earthquake
      A. Check for _____ around the facility.
      B. Identify safe places both _____ and _____.
      C. Educate yourself and your _____.
      D. Have _____ supplies on hand.
      E. Develop an emergency _____ plan.

   3. Checking for Facility Hazards
      A. Make sure that _____ are fastened securely to walls.
      B. Do not place large or heavy objects on the _____ _____.
      C. Store any breakable items in low, closed _____ equipped with locks.
      D. Avoid hanging _____ _____ on walls above where patients will sit or lie.
      E. Secure overhead _____ _____.
      F. Repair any defective _____ _____ or leaky gas connections.
      G. _____ water heaters to wall studs bolted to the floor.
      H. Repair _____ _____ in the ceilings or foundations.
      I. All _____ products should be stored in closed cabinets with locks, on the bottom shelf.

   4. Safe Places to Go During an Earthquake
      A. Under sturdy _____
      B. Against an _____ wall
      C. Away from _____ that could shatter
      D. Away from _____ or furniture that could fall over
      E. If outside, stay away from _____, trees, telephone or _____ lines, overpasses, or elevated expressways.

   5. Disaster Supplies
      i. _____
      ii. _____
      iii. _____
      iv. _____
      v. _____

   6. Warning Signs of a Tornado
      i. _____
      ii. _____
      iii. _____

© 2011 Pearson Education, Inc.

7. Safety During a Tornado

A. Move to the basement of a building or the _____ _____ of a structure.
B. If a basement is not available, it is advisable to seek shelter in a _____ or _____ hallway.
C. Above all else, stay away from _____, _____, and outside walls.
D. Avoid _____ and use the stairs to reach the lowest level of the facility.

8. Fire Preparedness

A. Equip the office with properly working _____ _____ placed on every level of the building on the ceiling or high on the walls.
B. Equip every room with a _____ detector and test and clean once per month.
C. Know the _____ routes to use in the event of a fire.
D. Ensure that _____ _____ are available if the office is located above the first level.
E. Store _____ items in well-ventilated areas.
F. Repair any _____ wiring to avoid a fire hazard.
G. Locate _____ _____ throughout the office and train staff on their use.

9. Escaping a Fire

A. If a person's clothes are on fire, that person should _____, _____, and _____ until the fire is extinguished.
B. Check closed doors for _____ before opening.
C. If the door is hot, it should not be _____, and another route of escape should be sought. If the door is cool, it should be _____ _____.
D. When escaping a fire, _____ _____ under any smoke on the way to the exit and close doors as they are passed through to delay the spread of fire.
E. Once out of the building, do not attempt to _____ until or unless the fire department declares that it is safe to do so.

10. In the Event of a Flood

A. Listen to the radio for _____.
B. Move to _____ ground.
C. If there is time before evacuating, disconnect any _____ _____ and shut off utilities at their main valves.
D. When evacuating, be careful not to walk through _____ water.

11. Preparing for a Hurricane

A. Secure the windows using _____.
B. Trees and shrubs around the office should be well _____.
C. If the medical office is to be evacuated before a hurricane, listen to the radio or television for information provided by local _____ _____ _____.
D. During the hurricane, listen to the _____ or _____ for information and prepare for high winds and possible flooding.

12. Types of Terrorist Attacks

i. _____
ii. _____
iii. _____

13. Questions to Ask If a Bomb Threat Is Made

i. _____
ii. _____
iii. _____
iv. _____
v. _____

© 2011 Pearson Education, Inc.

14. Biological Threats (List and briefly explain each type.)

    i. _____

   ii. _____

  iii. _____

  iv. _____

15. In the Event of a Biological Attack

    A. Be prepared to evacuate the area _____.

    B. Wash with _____ and _____.

    C. Contact the _____.

    D. Listen to the radio for _____.

    E. Remove and bag clothing if _____.

16. In the Event of a Nuclear Blast

    A. Take cover as quickly as possible, _____ _____ if the building has a basement.

    B. Remain in a safe location, listening to the radio for _____.

    C. Do not look at the _____ or _____.

    D. Lie flat on the ground with your head _____.

    E. Seek _____ as quickly as possible.

17. The Role of the Medical Assistant in a Mock Environmental Exposure Event

    A. Aid in _____ planning.

    B. _____ patients to determine which patients require immediate attention.

    C. Assist in _____-_____ response for wounded individuals.

    D. Administer _____ and other vaccines under the direction of a physician.

    E. Facilitate order and organization in the midst of _____.

    F. Implement and follow through on an _____ safety plan.

✮ KEY TERMINOLOGY REVIEW ✮

Match words to their definitions.

  a. Anaphylactic shock

  b. Bandage

  c. Crash cart

  d. First responders

  e. Heat exhaustion

  f. Hyperglycemia

  g. Hyperthermia

  h. Hypoglycemia

  i. Hypothermia

  j. Intubate

  k. Patent

  l. Primary assessment

  m. Rule of nines

  n. Stat

  o. Triage

1. __Hypothermia__ A prolonged exposure to extremely hot temperatures that results in an elevated body temperature.

2. __First responders__ EMS providers trained to recognize medical conditions, initiate basic life support, and access other parts of the system.

3. __Intubate__ Inserting a tube into the trachea as an emergency airway.

4. __Hyperglycemia__ High blood sugar level.

5. __Anaphylactic shock__ A severe allergic reaction that causes respiratory distress because of swelling of the upper airways.

6. __Patent__ An unobstructed airway.

© 2011 Pearson Education, Inc.

7. _____ _Rule of nines_ A useful tool for estimating body surface area.
8. _Hypothermic_ A core temperature of below 95°F.
9. _Crash cart_ Resembles a large roll-around toolbox with drawers that can be used to store emergency equipment and medications. Sometimes called an emergency kit.
10. _Triage_ Assessing the emergency care needed by patients.
11. _Stat_ Immediate.
12. _Heat exhaustion_ Extreme fatigue caused by heat, which occurs as the result of sodium and water depletion from the body.
13. _Primary assessment_ Initial patient contact by a medical professional beginning with a few simple questions and a basic patient examination.
14. _Hypoglycemia_ Low blood sugar level.
15. _Bandage_ A strip of binding material used to hold a dressing in place.

APPLIED PRACTICE

Follow the directions as instructed with each question below.

Scenario A

Tasha Lopez, RMA, has recently been hired as a clinical medical assistant for a brand new family practice. She has been asked to stock the emergency medical box with drugs and make sure that it is ready in case of an emergency.

This is what she found:

- Atropine
- Diphenhydramine
- Furosemide
- Instant glucose
- Lidocaine
- Local anesthetics
- Normal saline
- Phenobarbital and diazepam
- Solu-Cortef
- Syrup of ipecac
- Verapamil

---

1. Based on the inventory list, what are some items that Tasha should add?

_____
_____
_____

Scenario B

Sasha Daniels, CMA (AAMA), is employed at Community Urgent Care. A 47-year-old male patient has been brought to your facility. His right index finger was partially torn from his hand while he was working on a piece of farming machinery. His coworker has driven him to the medical facility.

---

1. What type of injury has this man sustained?

   _____

2. How should he be treated?

   _____

   _____

   _____

   _____

Scenario C

Later in the day at Community Urgent Care, Sasha encounters a 36-year-old female patient who is presenting with a liquid chemical burn covering the entire front and back of her right arm. Residue from the liquid chemical still remains on the patient's arm.

---

1. What will the first step likely be for treating this patient? Explain your answer.

   _____

   _____

   _____

2. Because the patient's skin was extremely sensitive to the chemical agent, the physician has diagnosed a second degree burn on the front and back of the patient's arm. According to the rule of nines, what percentage of her body has been affected?

   _____

✰

LEARNING ACTIVITY: TRUE/FALSE

Indicate whether the following statements are true or false by placing a T or an F on the line that precedes each statement.

__T__ 1. An AED can be used on children ages 1 to 8 years old.

__F__ 2. Lock jaw is also known as an avulsion.

__T__ 3. A nosebleed that occurs after a head injury and does not stop should be considered a serious emergency until proven otherwise.

__T__ 4. In general, perform "CPR first" for unresponsive children and infants.

__T__ 5. Shock, the collapse of the cardiovascular system, is caused by insufficient cardiac output.

__F__ 6. Arterial bleeding is usually slow and pale red.

__T__ 7. Simple direct pressure with a dressing will usually stop bleeding from a soft tissue injury.

__F__ 8. Nosebleeds may be messy and embarrassing and are usually life threatening occurrences.

__T__ 9. The severity of a burn depends on the amount and depth of tissue injury.

__F__ 10. Once a seizure stops, especially a full-body seizure, it is normal for a patient to remain unconscious for as long as 2 hours.

© 2011 Pearson Education, Inc.

FILL IN THE BLANK

Using words from the list below, fill in the blanks to complete the following statements.

105°F
Chemical
Contamination
Darker in color
Dislocations
Distal
Dressing

EMS
Immobilized
Intact skin
Irrigated
Life threatening
Occluded airway
Perspire

Poisoning
Prehospital
Tendons
Tissue damage
Venous
Water

1. ___distal___ blood flows more slowly, is ___darker in color___, and can usually be controlled by direct pressure.

2. An individual experiencing heat stroke usually fails to ___perspire___ and has a body temperature of ___105 °F___ or higher.

3. Internal bleeding occurs with ___tissue damage___ and ___intact skin___

4. Open wounds are seldom ___life threatening___ unless they penetrate the head, chest, throat, or abdomen.

5. A ___dressing___ is a sterile covering placed directly over a wound to absorb blood and other body fluids, prevent ___contamination___ and protect the wound from further trauma.

6. The ___EMS___ was established to provide ___prehospital___ care and safe and prompt transportation from any location, including the medical office, to an emergency facility.

7. Musculoskeletal injuries involve bones, muscles, ___tendons___ and ligaments and include fractures, ___dislocations___, sprains, and strains.

8. Respiratory and cardiac arrest may be caused by an ___occluded airway___, electrocution, shock, drowning, heart attack, trauma, anaphylaxis, drugs, ___poisoning___, or traumatic head or chest injury.

9. Bone breaks can be complete, twisted, or splintered. The affected part is ___immobilized___ and examined for impaired circulation to the ___venous___ aspect.

10. Patients with ___chemical___ burns should have the area ___irrigated___ immediately with large amounts of ___water___.

CRITICAL THINKING

Answer the following questions to the best of your ability. Utilize the textbook as a reference.

1. A patient has presented to the front desk without an appointment and is obviously SOB, her lips and fingertips appear a bit cyanotic. How would you assess her treatment?

_____

_____

_____

2. Your first job out of school is in an emergency care facility that has had an unfortunate number of lawsuits brought against it and its staff. What are your legal responsibilities as a medical assistant?

_____

_____

3. An 85-year-old man is choking on a hot dog. How will his advanced age affect your treatment of him?

_____

_____

_____

_____

RESEARCH ACTIVITY

Utilize Internet search engines to research the following topics and write a brief description of what you find. It is important to utilize reputable websites.

1. There is much to learn about how to face various types of emergencies. Select some emergencies that you know you may face on the job as a medical assistant. Then conduct research on these emergencies, utilizing the Internet or your school or local library. Write an essay on what you learned through your research. Be sure to cite your resources.

_____

_____

_____

_____

_____

_____

_____

_____

_____

_____

_____

_____

_____

_____

_____

_____

_____

_____

_____

© 2011 Pearson Education, Inc.

CHAPTER 44

The Clinical Laboratory

CHAPTER OUTLINE

General review of the chapter:

The Role of the Clinical Laboratory in Patient Care
Types of Clinical Laboratories
Clinical Laboratory Departments
Clinical Laboratory Personnel
Laboratory Safety Regulations
Laboratory Hazards
Quality Assurance
Laboratory Equipment
Laboratory Measurements and Equipment
The Clinical Laboratory and Patient Communication

STUDENT STUDY GUIDE

Use the following guide to assist in your learning of the concepts from the chapter.

I. The Clinical Laboratory

    1. The Role of the Clinical Laboratory in Patient Care

        i. _____

        ii. _____

        iii. _____

        iv. _____

        v. _____

    2. The Outside Laboratory

        A. Handles specimens collected from many types of _____.

        B. Performs tests ranging from the _____ to the very _____.

    3. The Reference Laboratory

        A. Handles more _____ tests than an outside laboratory and those tests that are _____ requested.

        B. Tests performed on a regular basis at a reference laboratory may provide more _____ results than tests performed a few times a year in an _____ laboratory.

    4. The Physician's Office Laboratory

        A. In the office laboratory, the doctor has the advantage of receiving the results more _____ than if the tests were done outside of the office.

        B. Disadvantages

            i. _____

            ii. _____

© 2011 Pearson Education, Inc.

5. Departments Within a Clinical Laboratory

    i. _____

    ii. _____

    iii. _____

    iv. _____

    v. _____

    vi. _____

    vii. _____

    viii. _____

    ix. _____

    x. _____

    xi. _____

    xii. _____

6. Personnel Within a Clinical Laboratory (Briefly describe the required training for each of the following persons.)

    A. Director of a Clinical Laboratory: _____

    B. Clinical Laboratory Scientist (CLS) or Medical Technologist (MT): _____

    C. Medical Laboratory Technician (MLT): _____

    D. Medical Laboratory Assistant (MLA), Clinical Laboratory Assistant (CLA), Certified Medical Assistant (CMA), and Registered Medical Assistant (RMA): _____

    E. Medical Assistant: _____

7. Laboratory Safety Regulations

    A. Patients are entitled to _____ medical care and health care personnel deserve to work in a _____ environment.

    B. The accuracy and _____ of the test results are crucial to the health of the patient.

8. The Agencies and Committees That Set and Review Laboratory Safety Guidelines

    i. _____

    ii. _____

    iii. _____

    iv. _____

    v. _____

9. The Occupational Safety and Health Administration (OSHA)

    A. Creates safeguards covering nearly every _____ in the United States.

    B. If no specific guidelines exist, then the "_____ _____ _____" must be followed.

10. Standard Precautions

    A. Developed by the _____.

    B. Combine the major features of _____ precautions and _____ _____ isolation precautions into one set of recommendations.

    C. The CDC's precautions are enforced by _____.

11. The Clinical Laboratory Improvement Amendments (CLIA)

    A. Enacted by Congress in _____.

    B. States may have their own _____ _____ _____, but they must be at least as stringent as the federal government's regulations.

    C. Information regarding state _____ may be obtained from state health departments.

© 2011 Pearson Education, Inc.

12. The Clinical Laboratory Improvement Amendments' Classification of Tests

    i. _____

    ii. _____

    iii. _____

13. Requirements for a Physician's Office Laboratory to Perform Waiver Tests

    A. Must _____ to perform these tests.

    B. Restricted to performing _____ of the more complex tests from Level I or Level II.

    C. Exempt from complying with CLIA _____ standards.

    D. May be subject to _____ _____ and investigations if test results are questioned or there are complaints against the laboratory.

14. Level I Tests

    A. Level I tests are moderately _____ and include _____ of specimens.

    B. Any laboratory that wishes to perform Level I tests must be headed by a _____/_____ or _____.

    C. All personnel must have training past _____ _____.

    D. The laboratory must perform _____ testing and is subject to unannounced inspections.

15. Types of Level I Tests

    i. _____

    ii. _____

    iii. _____

    iv. _____

    v. _____

    vi. _____

    vii. _____

16. Level II Tests

    A. Level II tests include those which are highly _____.

    B. Laboratories that perform tests in this category are subject to unannounced _____, perform _____ testing, and are headed by an _____ or _____ scientist.

    C. Tests may only be performed by _____ personnel as specified in the CLIA 1988 standards.

17. Laboratory Safety Regulations

    i. _____

    ii. _____

    iii. _____

    iv. _____

18. Contents of the Material Safety Data Sheet (MSDS)

    i. _____

    ii. _____

    iii. _____

    iv. _____

    v. _____

19. Biohazards

    A. Biohazards have the potential to _____ others.

    B. Since 1992, all laboratories must have OSHA's _____ _____ _____ _____ _____ _____ in place.

    C. The CDC's _____ _____ must be employed when dealing with any infectious materials.

20. The Bloodborne Standards Requirements for Health Care Employers

  A. Review all new safety devices that lessen the risk of _____ to employees.
  B. Ask for safety input from employees on an _____ basis.
  C. Keep a detailed report of all _____ _____ incidents.

21. Addressing Fire and Safety Hazards in the Medical Office

  A. Have an awareness of the _____ plan and _____.
  B. Know the location of safety devices such as _____ _____, _____, and safety blankets.
  C. Remove _____ _____ properly.

22. Goals of a Quality Assurance Program

  A. Provide mechanisms for evaluating _____ _____ and policies.
  B. Identify and _____ problems.
  C. Ensure _____ and prompt reporting of results.
  D. Ensure that testing is performed by _____ persons.

23. CLIA Requirements for the Laboratory

  A. Evaluate the _____ of laboratory policies and procedures.
  B. Identify and _____ problems.
  C. Ensure reliable and _____ test results.
  D. Ensure the competence and _____ of staff.
  E. Take _____ _____ if errors are found.
  F. Integrate _____ _____ into future policies and procedures.
  G. Document employee _____ and assess _____ yearly after the first year.
  H. Maintain the _____ and _____ of patient samples during the entire testing process.
  I. Be subject to inspection every _____ years if performing moderate- or high-complexity tests.

24. Quality Control (QC) Programs in Clinical Laboratories

  A. Monitor the testing of patient _____ to ensure reliable and consistent results.
  B. Requirements (List the requirements of a QC program.)
      i. _____
      ii. _____
      iii. _____

25. Proficiency Testing

  A. May be performed on _____ _____, _____, _____, or urine.
  B. The samples will have a _____ of results similar to any group of patients.

26. Equipment Generally Found in a Physician's Office Laboratory

  A. An _____ is used to sterilize equipment or instruments that are used on patients or in certain test procedures.
  B. A _____ is used to separate urine so that sediment can be examined under the microscope.
  C. A _____ is used to separate whole blood samples into layers to measure a patient's hematocrit.
  D. A _____ is a type of handheld photometer that is used to test glucose levels in patients.

27. Microscope

  A. Frequently used in the medical office to examine _____ _____ and various types of smears.
  B. It is an optical instrument that magnifies structures which are unseen by the _____ eye for the purpose of counting, naming, or _____.
  C. Better microscopes have better _____.

© 2011 Pearson Education, Inc.

28. The Process of Using and Cleaning a Microscope
    A. Always carry the microscope with one hand on the _____ and one hand under the _____.
    B. Make sure that the stage is in the _____ position before starting.
    C. Clean objectives with _____ _____ starting with 10X and ending with oil immersion.
    D. Turn on the light and rotate the nosepiece until the _____ _____ is directly over the slide.
    E. Place the prepared slide on the _____.
    F. Use the _____ _____ knob to raise the stage until the objective is close to the slide on the stage.
    G. Look through the _____ and adjust the _____ _____ knob until the microscope field is seen (it is a round circle of bright light).
    H. Use the _____ _____ knob to obtain a clearer image.
    I. Open the _____ and adjust the _____ to focus if necessary.
    J. Raise or lower the _____ to alter light refraction.
    K. Change the objective to _____ and readjust as needed.
    L. Move the objective and place a _____ of _____ on the slide before completing the turn to the oil immersion lens.
    M. When focusing and examination is complete, lower the _____ before removing the slide.
    N. Turn off the _____.
    O. Clean the _____ and objectives with _____ paper.
    P. Clean the oil immersion lens with _____ cleaner.
    Q. Unplug the _____ _____ and wrap it around the base.
    R. Cover the microscope with a _____ _____.
    S. Clean the _____ and store it.
    T. Document _____ and _____ in the logbook.
29. Thermometers in the Medical Laboratory
    A. Used to measure the temperature of various pieces of equipment, such as _____, _____, incubators, and _____ _____.
    B. Must be maintained within _____ ranges.
30. Temperatures Routinely Associated with the Laboratory Environment (List both the Fahrenheit and Celsius temperature for each piece of equipment.)
    A. Freezer: _____
    B. Autoclave: _____
    C. Refrigerator: _____
    D. Incubator: _____
    E. Room: _____
31. The Timing of Laboratory Tests
    A. Tests must be timed _____ in order to provide accurate, meaningful test results.
    B. Laboratory time is based on the _____-_____ clock, or military time, to avoid the confusion that may result from using the A.M. and P.M. designations of _____ Mean Time.
    C. The 24-hour clock uses _____ _____, with noon expressed as 1200 (twelve hundred hours) and midnight as 2400 (twenty-four hundred hours).
    D. _____ _____ for 4:15 P.M. would be 1615 (sixteen-fifteen hundred hours), which is calculated by adding 4 hours and 15 minutes to 1200.
32. Laboratory Units of Measurement
    A. A laboratory result must never be reported without a unit of _____ after it
    B. _____ _____ units are used most frequently in the laboratory.
    C. The metric system is based on a decimal system combined with various designations.

© 2011 Pearson Education, Inc.

      i. _____
     ii. _____
    iii. _____

33. Units Used to Express Laboratory Results

      i. _____
     ii. _____
    iii. _____

34. Abbreviations Commonly Used to Report Patients' Test Results

    A. Gram: _____
    B. Milligram: _____
    C. Liter: _____
    D. Milliliter: _____
    E. Microliter: _____
    F. Microgram: _____
    G. Millimoles per liter: _____
    H. Cubic centimeter: _____
    I. Milligrams per deciliter: _____
    J. Pint: _____
    K. Quart: _____
    L. Ounce: _____
    M. Quantity not sufficient: _____

35. Measuring and Mixing Devices Used in the Laboratory

    A. Beakers and flasks can be used to mix liquids but are not _____ measuring devices.
    B. The _____ cylinder and the _____ flask are accurate measuring devices.

36. Pipettes

    A. A _____ pipette is used for measuring and is marked with _____, which means "to deliver"; it will deliver that specific amount.
    B. If a graduated pipette is marked with _____, "to contain", it must be emptied _____ to deliver the exact amount.
    C. A _____ pipette is used for transferring liquid from one vessel to another.
    D. A _____ pipette has graduations down to the tip and is used to make _____ _____ in the laboratory.
    E. _____ are used to deliver very small amounts (microliters) of liquid; the _____ directions must be carefully followed.

37. The Phases of the Laboratory Testing Cycle (Briefly describe each phase.)

    A. Preanalytical phase: _____
    B. Analytical phase: _____

38. Tests Requiring Special Instructions

    A. For most fasting tests, the fasting period is at least _____ hours.
    B. Two-hour Postprandial (PP) or post cibum (pc) glucose means that the patient eats a _____ _____ of food for a meal and a blood glucose level is drawn exactly _____ hours after the completion of the meal.

39. Information Required on a Specimen Label

      i. _____
     ii. _____
    iii. _____

40. Steps for Correctly Completing a Laboratory Requisition

    A. Check the patient's record for _____ or specific laboratory tests.
    B. Verify which laboratory will be doing the testing and locate its _____ _____ form.

© 2011 Pearson Education, Inc.

C. Complete the patient _____ section.
D. Complete the section that requires the physician's _____, _____, telephone number, and _____ number.
E. Complete the patient's _____ and _____ information.
F. Mark the appropriate boxes to indicate each _____ that is being ordered by the physician.
G. If a test is ordered that is not _____ on the requisition, write in the name of the test on the lines provided.
H. Indicate what _____ and _____ of specimen is to be tested.
I. Enter the patient's _____ on the requisition as needed.
J. If no diagnosis has been made, then _____ the patient's symptoms.
K. Complete the patient authorization to _____ and assign the benefits portion as needed.

41. Steps for Preparing a Specimen for Transport

A. Assemble the equipment and supplies needed to obtain the _____.
B. Perform _____ _____ and don gloves.
C. Obtain the required specimen after explaining the _____ to the patient.
D. Label the specimen with the patient's _____, the _____, the physician's _____, the _____ of collection, and other information required by the facility.
E. _____ the laboratory requisition, and complete the date and time that the specimen was obtained.
F. Process the specimens and, if they are not to be sent out until later in the day, store them according to laboratory _____ _____ requirements.
G. Attach the laboratory _____ securely to the specimen before sending.
H. Remove gloves and dispose of them in the _____ _____ container.
I. Record the specimen in the laboratory _____, indicating the date, the time of collection, the type and source of the specimen, the _____ ordered, where the _____ were sent, and the date that they were sent.

42. Steps for Monitoring and Following Up on Laboratory Test Results

A. Review incoming laboratory _____, and compare them with the _____ values provided by the analyzing laboratory.
B. Many laboratories highlight or indicate _____ results on the laboratory results sheet with an H or an L, for high and low, respectively.
C. Highlight any _____ results per facility policy.
D. Obtain the patient's _____ _____ and attach the new laboratory results and submit it to the _____ for review.

KEY TERMINOLOGY REVIEW

Match the vocabulary term to the correct definition below.

a. Aliquot
b. Analyte
c. Calibrate
d. Centrifuge
e. Certificate of Waiver Tests (WTs)
f. Clinical Laboratory Improvement Amendments (CLIA)
g. Compound microscope

h. Control samples
i. Diluent
j. Fasting
k. Hemolyzed
l. Icteric
m. Incubator
n. Outside laboratory

o. Photometer
p. Physician's office laboratory
q. Pipettes
r. Post cibum (pc)
s. Postprandial (PP)
t. Proficiency testing

u. Qualitative testing
v. Quantitative testing
w. Reagents
x. Reference library
y. Resolution
z. Turnaround time

1. _____ Instrument used to separate specimens into component layers.
2. _____ A microscope with two sets of lenses, oculars, and objectives.
3. _____ The patient must not consume any food for a prescribed number of hours prior to the collection of a specimen.
4. _____ After a meal.
5. _____ Analyzes for the presence or absence of a substance.
6. _____ Refers to the microscope's ability to distinguish clearly between two adjacent, but distinct, objects.
7. _____ The least complex and present the least risk if performed incorrectly.
8. _____ Bilious yellow-green color.
9. _____ Substances required for a chemical reaction or used to detect the presence of another substance.
10. _____ A laboratory in which some of the tests that the physician orders are performed right in the office.
11. _____ When red cells burst, causing serum to be a cherry-red color.
12. _____ Mandates that all laboratories that test human specimens must be regulated to ensure accurate patient test results.
13. _____ Some laboratory tests require the medical assistant do this to the machine or instrument prior to testing a specimen.
14. _____ Samples similar to the required testing specimen that have been previously tested and have a known value.
15. _____ It is either hospital-based or independent and handles specimens collected from many types of facilities.
16. _____ After a meal.
17. _____ An agent that dilutes a substance or solution to which it is added.
18. _____ Analyzes a specimen for the presence of a substance and the amount of the substance present.
19. _____ One of the various measuring and mixing devices that are employed in the laboratory.
20. _____ How long it takes for the test to be performed and the results generated, sent back to the physician for review, and added to the patient's chart.
21. _____ External quality control program that monitors the accuracy of test systems by comparing your results to results provided by a survey program of the College of American Pathologists or the American Association of Bioanalysts.
22. _____ The presence or absence of a substance.
23. _____ May be associated with a specific teaching hospital or medical school, or be independently owned.

© 2011 Pearson Education, Inc.

24. _____ An instrument that measures light intensity.

25. _____ Used to maintain a specific temperature to achieve a specific result.

26. _____ A small portion of the whole.

APPLIED PRACTICE

Follow the directions as instructed with each question below.

1. Label the parts of the binocular microscope.

2. **Scenario**

On your first day of work at a clinical laboratory, you are ordered to clean up any hazardous waste after each procedure and at the end of each day. How does your training prepare you for this task? What is the definition of hazardous waste? Briefly explain what you would do.

_____

_____

_____

_____

_____

_____

LEARNING ACTIVITY: TRUE/FALSE

Indicate whether the following statements are true or false by placing a T or an F on the line that precedes each statement.

_____ 1. A binocular microscope has one ocular lens.

_____ 2. The condenser is located on the substage of a microscope.

© 2011 Pearson Education, Inc.

_____ 3. Oil immersion is used with the 10X lens to increase the power to 100X.

_____ 4. The United States uses the English system of measurement in everyday life.

_____ 5. Measuring devices may be made of glass or plastic and be reusable or disposable.

_____ 6. The laboratory testing cycle is divided into two phases: preanalytical and postanalytical.

_____ 7. There are two focus knobs—one for low power and the other for high power.

_____ 8. In tests such as the glucose tolerance test (GTT), specimen collection must be timed precisely in order to provide accurate, meaningful test results.

_____ 9. When you are finished working with a microscope, you must clean the lenses with any soft cloth or paper.

_____ 10. Under no circumstances will the physician allow patient results to be given to the patient by telephone.

CRITICAL THINKING

Answer the following questions to the best of your ability. Utilize the textbook as a reference.

1. The office is unusually busy, patients are crabby, and the doctor has repeatedly berated you for working too slowly. You have thought about cutting corners. Is this ever a good idea? Why or why not?

   _____

   _____

   _____

2. Michelle Oswald's blood test has returned and it is found to be abnormal. You were the medical assistant who took the test and felt especially close to Mrs. Oswald because she reminded you of your mother. Should you call the patient yourself? What is your responsibility in this case?

   _____

   _____

   _____

RESEARCH ACTIVITY

Utilize Internet search engines to research the following topics and write a brief description of what you find. It is important to utilize reputable websites.

1. To learn more about the agencies and committees that set and review safety guidelines affecting clinical laboratories, go online or utilize your school or local library to conduct further research. Write an essay on your findings and what more you learned beyond what is presented in the textbook about these agencies and committees and the guidelines established for laboratories. Be sure to cite your resources.

   _____

   _____

   _____

   _____

© 2011 Pearson Education, Inc.

© 2011 Pearson Education, Inc.

CHAPTER 45
Microbiology

CHAPTER OUTLINE

General review of the chapter:

Role of the Medical Assistant in Microbiology
Classifications of Microorganisms
Types of Microorganisms
Specimen Collection and Transportation
Diagnosing Infection
Microbiology Equipment and Procedures
Types of Specimens
Serology Testing

STUDENT STUDY GUIDE

Use the following guide to assist in your learning of the concepts from the chapter.

I. Introduction to Microbiology
  1. Microorganisms: A Definition
     A. Microorganisms are also called _living organism_
     B. They are living organisms that can be seen only with a _microscope_
     C. Harmless microorganisms can be found on your _skin_, in your digestive tract, and in your _respirat_ tract.
     D. Microorganisms include _protozoa_, viruses, _fungi_, and bacteria.
  2. Pathogens
     A. Pathogens are _Harmfull_ microorganisms.
     B. Basic types of pathogens
        i. _Rickettsia_
        ii. _virus_
        iii. _protozoa_
        iv. _PBacteria_
        v. _fungi_
        vi. _prarsitic worms_
  3. What Microorganisms Need in Order to Grow
     i. _food_
     ii. _moisture_
     iii. _darkness_
     iv. _temperature_
  4. Microbiology and Microorganisms
     A. Microbiology is the study of _living organisms_ that cannot be seen with the naked eye.
     B. Microorganisms are the _____ _____ that microbiology studies.

464

© 2011 Pearson Education, Inc.

5. The Role of the Medical Assistant in Microbiology
   i. *proper use of personal protective equipment*
   ii. *monitoring equipment for repairs needed*
   iii. *performing quality control checks needed*
   iv. *patient teaching*
   v. *confidentiality concerning the patient and test results*
   vi. *proper collection and the patient of certain specimen*

6. Classifications of Microorganisms (List the two classifications.)
   i. *pathogens*
   ii. *non pathogens*

7. Retention of Dyes
   A. Bacteria are *characterized* by how they react to stain or dye.
   B. *A* stain is used for most gram-positive and gram-negative bacteria.
   C. Others use *violet - color* stain.

8. Hemolytic Properties
   A. One way in which to classify bacteria is by the bacteria's ability to *hemolyze* red blood cells in blood *sugar*.
   B. A microbiologist observes the characteristics of a _____ of cells.
   C. The organism that causes *alpha hemolysis* is beta hemolytic.

9. Diseases Caused by Pathogenic Microorganisms
   i. *Streptococcus pyogenes*
   ii. *Corynebacterium dyphtheriae*
   iii. *Mycobacterium tuberculosis*
   iv. *Haemophilus influenza type B*
   v. *Streptococcus pneumoniae*
   vi. *Neysseria meningitidis*
   vii. *polioviruses*
   viii. *Rabies virus*
   ix. *Herpes simplex viruses 1 and 2*
   x. *Candida albicans (fungus)*
   xi. *Chlamydia albicans trachomatis*
   xii. *Escherichia coli*
   xiii. *Straphylococcus aureus*
   xiv. *Varicella zoster virus*
   xv. *Hepatitis A, B and C virus*
   xvi. *escherichia coli*
   xvii. *Streptococcus pyogenes*
   xviii. *Staphylococcus aureus*
   xix. *Plasmodium flaciparum, P. vivax*
   xx. *P. malariare · P. ovale*
   xxi. *Human immunodeficiency virus*
   xxii. *epstein - Barr virus*
   xxiii. *Borrelia burgdorferi*
   xxiv. *streptococcus pyogenes*
   xxv.
   xxvi. *Whooping cough*

10. Bacterium/Bacteria
    A. Bacteria are small, *unicellular* microorganisms that are capable of rapid *reproduction*.
    B. Their reproductive ability explains how some infections become *over whelming* in a short time and can be dangerous.

© 2011 Pearson Education, Inc.

C. Bacteria may be named for their _____ (shape). (List the shapes.)
   i. _____
   ii. _____
   iii. _____

11. Cocci
   A. Cocci are _____ bacteria that are arranged in various configurations.
   B. Staphylococci are _____-_____, grape-like clusters of _____, some of which are pathogenic.
   C. Nonpathogenic staphylococci are found on our _____ and in many of our body _____, or openings.

12. *Staphylococcus aureus* (S. aureus), or Staph
   A. *S. aureus* is the major pathogen of this genus and may be found as _____ _____ in the nose and on the skin.
   B. Causes _____, especially when _____ is lowered by a break in the skin or in the mucous membranes.
   C. It is a common cause of _____ infections and may also cause _____, meningitis, and _____ in persons who have reduced resistance.

13. Methicillin-Resistant *Staphylococcus aureus* (MRSA)
   A. MRSA is a form of _____.
   B. Tests are available to indicate the _____ or _____ of this enzyme and to help determine the most favorable treatment.

14. Streptococci
   A. Streptococci are round, _____-_____ bacteria that are arranged in chains.
   B. Some are _____ and others are dangerous to humans.
   C. They are part of the normal flora of the _____ tract and skin.

15. Group A Beta-hemolytic Streptococcus Pyogenes
   A. Cause a variety of diseases, varying from mild to life threatening
   B. Diseases caused by group A beta-hemolytic streptococcus pyogenes
   i. _____
   ii. _____
   iii. _____
   iv. _____
   v. _____
   vi. _____
   vii. _____
   viii. _____

16. Diplococci
   A. Diplococci occur in pairs
   B. Some diplococci are gram positive and others are gram N gonorrhoeas.
   C. Diseases caused by diplococci
   i. pneumonia
   ii. gonorrhoeae
   iii. Neisseria meningitidis
   iv. septicemia

17. Bacillus/Bacilli
   A. Rod-shaped bacilli may be pathogenic or nonpathogenic.
   B. Some bacilli are gram positive and others are gram negative.

© 2011 Pearson Education, Inc.

C. Bacilli are responsible for a wide variety of illnesses. (List some of these illnesses.)

    i. _____

    ii. _____

    iii. _____

    iv. _____

    v. _____

    vi. _____

18. Gram-Negative Bacilli

A. _____ are a large family of gram-negative bacilli that are found mainly in the intestinal tract.

B. Many of them will cause infections in other _____ in the body.

C. One type, _____ _____, is most frequently associated with urinary tract infections.

D. The group of _____ organisms is a major cause of foodborne illnesses worldwide.

19. *Helicobacter pylori* (*H. pylori*)

A. *H. pylori* is a _____-_____ bacillus.

B. It was discovered in the early _____.

C. The organism is found in about _____ of the population and causes _____ symptoms in most individuals.

D. It was discovered that *H. pylori* is the causative agent of _____ ulcers and a risk factor in _____ malignancy in some infected persons.

E. The organism is responsive to a number of antibiotics, including _____.

F. The discovery of *H. pylori* led to major breakthroughs in treatment for _____.

20. Gram-Positive Bacilli

A. May be found in _____ or singly and are _____ forming or _____ forming.

B. Notable gram-positive bacilli

    i. _____, which causes botulism

    ii. _____, which causes tetanus

21. Vibrios

A. Vibrios are _____-_____ bacilli.

B. The main pathogen is *Vibrio cholerae*, whose _____ causes cholera.

C. Cholera

    i. Characterized by profuse _____ stools, vomiting, leg cramps, _____, and shock.

    ii. Caused by ingesting drinking water or eating _____ from water contaminated with infected urine, feces, or _____.

22. Spirilla and Spirochetes

A. Spirilla and spirochetes are _____-shaped or _____-shaped organisms.

B. They are _____ that are twisted in various shapes.

C. They are classified as a separate category of _____.

D. Some are nonpathogenic and are found in certain areas of the body and others, such as _____ _____, cause the sexually transmitted infection syphilis.

E. *Borrelia burgdorferi*, a spirillum, was discovered in the mid-1970s to be the causative agent of _____ _____.

23. Mycobacteria

A. Mycobacteria have a different type of material in the _____ _____ and can be stained only with an _____-_____ stain.

B. _____ _____ is the causative agent of tuberculosis, and *Mycobacterium leprae* is the cause of _____.

© 2011 Pearson Education, Inc.

C. These organisms do not stain well with a _____ stain.

D. In a positive slide for _____-_____ _____ (AFB), the slender bacilli will appear pink when exposed to an acid-fast stain.

24. Rickettsia and Chlamydia

    A. Rickettsia is a bacterial parasite that lives in _____ and _____, which transmit the disease when they bite.

    B. Chlamydia

        i. Chlamydia is an _____ parasite, but it does not live in arthropod hosts.

        ii. It must invade _____ cells to reproduce.

25. Viruses

    A. Viruses are the smallest known _____ organisms.

    B. They depend on the _____ _____ of other organisms for growth.

26. Diseases Caused by Viruses

    i. _____

    ii. _____

    iii. _____

    iv. _____

    v. _____

    vi. _____

    vii. _____

    viii. _____

    ix. _____

27. Types of Microorganisms: Protozoa

    A. Protozoa are _____-_____ organisms.

    B. Some are _____ and others are nonparasitic.

    C. They move with _____, or _____ feet.

    D. Diseases caused by protozoa

        i. _____

        ii. _____

28. Types of Microorganisms: Fungus/Fungi

    A. Fungi include parasitic and nonparasitic _____ and _____.

    B. They depend on other _____ _____ for nutrition.

    C. Reproduction occurs through _____.

    D. They feed on _____.

II. Specimen Collection and Testing Procedures

    1. Steps for Specimen Collection and Transportation

        A. _____ the patient properly.

        B. Follow the _____ carefully.

        C. Complete the label and _____ carefully.

        D. Maintain the appropriate environment and _____ to preserve the specimen.

    2. Information Required on a Specimen Label

        i. _____

        ii. _____

        iii. _____

        iv. _____

        v. _____

© 2011 Pearson Education, Inc.

3. Information for the Laboratory Requisition
    i. _____
    ii. _____
    iii. _____
    iv. _____
    v. _____
    vi. _____
    vii. _____
    viii. _____
    ix. _____
    x. _____
    xi. _____

4. Collection Devices
    A. The culturette system (List the items included.)
        i. _____
        ii. _____

5. Microbiology Equipment and Procedures
    A. Inoculating Equipment
        i. _____
        ii. _____
        iii. _____
    B. Culture Media
        i. _____
        ii. _____
        iii. _____

6. Common Culture Media
    i. _____
    ii. _____
    iii. _____
    iv. _____
    v. _____
    vi. _____

7. Microbiology Equipment and Procedures: Inoculating Media

    A. An inoculating _____ is used to create a _____ culture.
    B. After inoculation, a _____ dish is placed in an _____ to allow the organism to grow.

8. Microbiology Equipment and Procedures: Sensitivity Testing

    A. Determines which _____ will kill the _____.
    B. Tools include a _____ dish and _____ agar.

9. Steps for Performing a Direct Smear

    A. Perform hand _____ and don gloves.
    B. _____ the equipment.
    C. _____ a clean slide.
    D. _____ the slide.
    E. Allow the slide to air dry for _____ to _____ minutes.
    F. Hold the slide with _____ forceps and pass over the _____ _____ flame.
    G. Slide is ready to be _____.

© 2011 Pearson Education, Inc.

10. Steps for Preparing a Wet Mount Slide

    A. Perform _____ _____ and don gloves.

    B. _____ a dry slide.

    C. _____ the dry slide.

    D. Place a drop of _____ solution on top of the specimen.

    E. Place a _____ onto the smeared slide.

11. Gram Stain

    A. Used to differentiate, or separate, bacteria into two groups: gram _____ and gram _____.

    B. Different bacteria stain differently, depending on the _____ in their walls.

    C. Gram-positive bacteria retain the crystal _____-_____ color and gram-negative bacteria retain only the _____ _____ color.

    D. Gram stains must always be accompanied by a culture for _____ identification.

12. Throat Specimens

    A. One of the most _____ requested specimens in an office laboratory.

    B. Based on the _____ and _____ with which the patient presents, the physician will order a test to identify the pathogen involved and will begin treatment.

    C. Confirmation of _____ _____ is important because of its virulence and possible complications.

    D. When performing a throat culture, it is important not to touch the _____ of the mouth or the tongue with the _____ to avoid contaminating it.

13. The Sputum Sample

    A. Sputum is the _____ _____ that is expelled by coughing or clearing the bronchi.

    B. To obtain a sample, the patient must be carefully instructed to _____ _____, spitting the coughed up material into a sterile container.

    C. Explain to the patient that this should not be _____ from the mouth.

    D. The purpose of obtaining a sputum specimen is to isolate and diagnose diseases such as _____ _____, influenza, and _____.

14. The Urine Specimen

    A. For a culture it must be either a _____ specimen or a _____-_____ midstream sample (CCMS).

    B. Both methods provide _____ samples.

    C. Any other type of urine specimen would be contaminated by organisms in the container or on the _____ or _____ of the patient.

    D. In doctor's offices and smaller facilities, _____-_____ culture units are used.

    E. Often, urine cultures require a means to provide a _____ result of the number of microorganisms in the sample.

15. The Stool Specimen

    A. May be tested for _____, _____, or _____ infections; for the presence of occult blood; and for excessive amounts of fat _____.

    B. The method of collection varies with the _____ of _____ ordered.

    C. Fecal specimens must be free of _____ or _____ from the toilet and toilet tissue.

16. Occult Blood

    A. Patients are instructed to write their _____, _____, and _____ _____ on the label of the unit.

    B. Patients should close the unit and take it or _____ it to the doctor's office or the laboratory as requested.

    C. It is important to check the _____ _____ of any test kit before giving it to the patient.

© 2011 Pearson Education, Inc.

17. The Stool Specimen for Ova and Parasites
    A. The presence of *microbial* organisms, such as ova and parasites, may be determined by testing feces or stool.
    B. The presence of ova, or *eggs*, or other forms of a parasite indicates parasitic *infestion*.
    C. Identification of the parasite aids in the selection of the *correct* treatment.
    D. Commercial kits are available that provide containers for fresh stool specimen and two additional vials for preserved specimens, one containing *formalin* and the other containing *polyvinyl* alcohol.

18. Wound Specimens
    A. Sterile swabs are used to obtain a specimen from a wound, *abscess*, or *incision* to test for pathogenic microorganisms.
    B. The procedure is similar to obtaining a *throat* culture.
    C. Several specimens may be necessary from different *locations*.
    D. Be sure to *label* each specimen appropriately as to the source.

19. The Collection of Cerebrospinal Fluid (CSF)
    A. CSF is always treated as a *stat* procedure.
    B. The procedure is *uncomfortable* for the patient, and the specimen must be handled with care.
    C. Usually *3* tubes are collected under sterile conditions and are sent for testing.
    D. The *culture* and *sensitivity* test should be performed before chemical and other tests using the second of the three tubes.
    E. Tubes one and three are more likely to be *contaminated* because of the entry and removal processes of collection.

20. The Group A Strep Screen
    A. The group A strep screen is performed frequently in *pediatric office*.
    B. It is especially efficient in the *pediatric* office because it is *self-contained* and can be done while the patient waits.
    C. The screen is an *antigen detection* test for group A beta-hemolytic streptococci.
    D. There are many *clia-waved group* *streptococcus antigen* available that test for the extracted group A beta-hemolytic streptococcus antigen.

KEY TERMINOLOGY REVIEW

Without using any material from your textbook, write a sentence using the selected key terms in the correct context as related to the topics presented in Chapter 45.

1. **acid-fast stain**

_____

_____

2. **candidiasis**

_____

_____

3. **culturette**

_____

_____

4. *enteritis*

_____

_____

5. *exudates*

_____

_____

6. *facultative anaerobes*

_____

_____

7. *fixed*

_____

_____

8. *inoculated*

_____

_____

9. *microbiology*

_____

_____

10. *moniliasi*

_____

_____

11. *morphology*

_____

_____

12. *necrotizing fasciitis*

_____

_____

13. *normal flora*

_____

_____

14. *sequela*

_____

_____

15. *serology*

_____

_____

16. *spore*

_____

_____

© 2011 Pearson Education, Inc.

17. *sputum*

_____

_____

18. *steatorrhea*

_____

_____

19. *subcellular*

_____

_____

20. *swabs*

_____

_____

APPLIED PRACTICE

Follow the directions as instructed with each question below.

1. Obtaining a stool specimen for ova and parasites versus for pinworms

    a. List the equipment and supplies needed for obtaining a stool specimen for ova and parasites.

    _____

    _____

    _____

    _____

    _____

    _____

    _____

    b. List the equipment and supplies needed for obtaining a stool specimen for examination for pinworms.

    _____

    _____

    _____

    _____

    _____

    c. Discuss the differences and similarities between the two procedures.

    _____

    _____

    _____

    _____

    _____

_____

_____

_____

_____

2. List the diseases that can occur from the following pathogens.

Body Location	Pathogen	Disease
Respiratory system	Streptococcus pyogenes Corynebacterium diphtheriae Mycobacterium tuberculosis Haemophilus influenzae type B Streptococcus pneumoniae	_____ _____ _____ _____ _____
Central nervous system	Neisseria meningitidis Polioviruses Rabies virus	_____ _____ _____
Genitourinary system	Herpes simplex viruses 1 and 2 Candida albicans (fungus) Chlamydia trachomatis Escherichia coli	_____ _____ _____ _____
Integumentary system	Staphylococcus aureus Varicella zoster virus	_____ _____ _____ _____
Gastrointestinal system	Hepatitis A, B, and C viruses Salmonella enteritidis Escherichia coli	_____ _____ _____
Circulatory system and blood, immune system	Streptococcus pyogenes Staphylococcus aureus Plasmodium falciparum, P. vivax, P. malariae, P. ovale Human immunodeficiency virus Epstein-Barr virus Borrelia burgdorferi	_____ _____ _____ _____ _____ _____
Tissue	Streptococcus pyogenes	_____

LEARNING ACTIVITY: FILL IN THE BLANK

Using words from the list below, fill in the blanks to complete the following statements.

Note: Some terms are used in more than one statement.

agar	laboratory	prokaryotic
agglutination	lawn technique	seaweed
cephalosporins	methicillin-resistant	smear
colony	microorganisms	_Streptococci_
culture medium	motility	viable
eukaryotic	organelles	wet mount
feces	ova	

© 2011 Pearson Education, Inc.

1. The Group A Strep Screen is an antigen detection test for group A beta-hemolytic _____ and follows the general procedure for antigen–antibody _____ tests, which produce a clumping of cells.

2. Differences such as cell structure and the presence or absence of _____ are used to classify organisms.

3. The "super bug" _____-_____ *Staphylococcus aureus* (MRSA) produces an enzyme that makes the organism resistant to penicillin and _____, which are normally used for treatment, and renders these antibiotics ineffective.

4. A _____ is a thin layer of _____ spread on a glass slide for identification purposes.

5. _____ is a gelatinous substance made from seaweed that is added to a _____ to provide nutrition and a semisolid surface on which microbes can grow.

6. _____ cells have a nucleus and _____ in the cytoplasm, while _____ cells are simpler in structure, without a nucleus or organelles, such as bacteria.

7. A _____ is a preparation in a liquid that will preserve the _____ of the microbe.

8. The Mueller–Hinton agar is inoculated with the pure culture specimen in overlapping strokes in a technique called the _____ or _____ count.

9. Microorganisms must remain _____ (capable of living) when they reach the _____.

10. The stool or _____ of the patient can be inspected for the presence of _____ and mature forms of the worm.

CRITICAL THINKING

Answer the following questions to the best of your ability. Utilize the textbook as a reference.

1. A patient has been instructed to collect stool specimens to be tested for occult blood. You ask him to refrain from eating red meat or taking vitamin C for 3 days prior to testing for occult blood. Why? What other instructions does this patient need to follow in order to obtain an accurate test result?

   _____

   _____

   _____

   _____

2. Mrs. Chen is a 70-year-old woman from mainland China who has come to the clinic because of recent, sudden constipation. Mrs. Chen is shy and very hesitant to speak with a male medical assistant about her condition. How can the clinic help Mrs. Chen?

   _____

   _____

   _____

3. You are preparing a specimen smear for a microbiological examination by the doctor. You heat-fix the slide, but you realize that you have heated it too much because it has become hard to hold. What does this do to the specimen and what would you do?

   _____

   _____

_____
_____
_____

RESEARCH ACTIVITY

Utilize Internet search engines to research the following topics and write a brief description of what you find. It is important to utilize reputable websites.

1. Methicillin-resistant *Staphylococcus aureus* (MRSA) has become a very real threat, not only to health care workers, but also to the general population. Visit www.cdc.gov and research the following topics:

    a. Provide a brief description of MRSA.
    b. What are some other multidrug-resistant organisms (MDROs)?
    c. In your opinion, what can be done to prevent the transmission of these organisms?

_____
_____
_____
_____
_____
_____
_____
_____
_____
_____
_____
_____
_____
_____
_____
_____
_____
_____
_____

© 2011 Pearson Education, Inc.

CHAPTER 46
Urinalysis

CHAPTER OUTLINE

General review of the chapter:

> Asepsis
> Collecting the Specimen
> Routine Urinalysis
> Urine Pregnancy Testing
> Quality Control

STUDENT STUDY GUIDE

Use the following guide to assist in your learning of the concepts from the chapter.

I. Urinalysis

1. An Overview of Urinalysis

    A. The purpose of performing a urinalysis
       i. Checks for the presence of _____ or _____.
       ii. Provides information about bodily _____.
    B. Properties of urine that are examined
       i. _____
       ii. _____
       iii. _____

2. Types of Urinalyses: Routine Sample

    A. Collected in a _____ container.
    B. Collected in the office or brought from _____.
    C. Used only for _____ screenings.

3. Types of Urinalyses: Morning Sample

    A. A morning sample is the most _____ urine.
    B. Collected _____ upon on arising in the morning.
    C. Used for _____ testing, urine _____, and _____ examination.
    D. The specimen should be brought in within _____ minutes to an hour after collection.
    E. Refrigerate the sample if an examination cannot be done within _____ hours, or add a preservative.

4. Types of Urinalyses: Timed Specimen

    A. Necessary for _____ analysis of substances
    B. Used to analyze _____, _____, and _____.

5. Types of Urinalyses: Twenty-Four Hour Specimen

    A. Collection begins after the patient _____ for the first time in the morning.
    B. Every drop of urine is collected in a container for _____ hours.

C. Used to determine _____ rate, check specific _____ levels, and check for _____ abnormalities.

6. Types of Urinalyses: Two-Hour Postprandial

   A. Collected _____ hours after a meal has been eaten.
   B. Used to screen for _____ that may be spilled into the urine once the blood levels exceed the _____ threshold.

7. Types of Urinalyses: Catheterized Specimen

   A. Used to collect a _____ urine specimen.
   B. Collecting urine with the use of a catheter ensures that the specimen is free of

   _____.
   C. The _____ and its surrounding tissues are cleaned to create a _____ field.
   D. A small, _____ tube is inserted through the _____ to the _____.

8. Types of Urinalyses: Suprapubic Specimen

   A. A suprapubic puncture is performed using a _____ needle and syringe.
   B. Used for _____ examinations.

9. A Review of Urine Chemistry

   A. Testing for chemical characteristics (List the substances for which urine is tested.)
      i. _____
      ii. _____
      iii. _____
      iv. _____
      v. _____
      vi. _____
      vii. _____
      viii. _____
      ix. _____

10. Reagent Strips

    B. The strip is dipped into the _____ sample.
    C. Color changes indicate the presence and _____ of substances in the urine.

11. Clinitests®

    A. Clinitests® are chemically treated tablets that are added to urine to determine the amount of _____ in the urine.
    B. The tablets change color according to the _____ in the urine.
    C. Checks for _____, _____, _____, and
       _____.

12. Steps for Preparing a Urine Sample for Microscopic Analysis

    A. Perform the required _____ and chemical tests.
    B. Place the urine in a _____ tube and the tube into a _____.
    C. Pour off the _____.
    D. Microscopically analyze the _____ material.

13. Microscopic Analysis (List the formed elements in urine that are evaluated.)
    i. _____
    ii. _____
    iii. _____
    iv. _____
    v. _____

© 2011 Pearson Education, Inc.

vi. _____

vii. _____

viii. _____

14. Calculating Formed Elements

    A. Examine under the _____ power field.

    B. Locate _____.

    C. Scan _____ to _____ fields.

    D. Note the number of cells, or _____, in each field.

    E. Report the _____ range of the observations.

KEY TERMINOLOGY REVIEW

Match the vocabulary term to the correct definition below.

a. Amorphous

b. Anuria

c. Bacturia

d. Crystals

e. Glomerulonephritis

f. Glycosuria

g. Hematuria

h. Ketones

i. Micturate

j. Occult

k. Oliguria

l. Parasites

m. Polyuria

n. Proteinuria

o. Renal threshold

p. Sediment

q. Specific gravity

r. Spermatozoa

s. Turbid

t. Urinalysis

1. _____ To urinate.

2. _____ The absence of urine.

3. _____ Excessive amounts of urine production.

4. _____ Blood in the urine.

5. _____ The male reproductive cell.

6. _____ Bacteria in the urine.

7. _____ It means that the urine is opaque and does not allow light to pass through.

8. _____ The term for the presence of abnormal sugar in the urine.

9. _____ The solid material that settles at the bottom of a test tube after centrifugation.

10. _____ Provides valuable information about many functions in the body, including kidney function.

11. _____ Formed by the precipitation of urinary salts when the pH, temperature, or concentration changes.

12. _____ The concentration at which a substance excreted by the kidneys, such as glucose, begins to appear in urine.

13. _____ The byproducts of fat metabolism.

14. _____ The weight of a substance in relation to the weight of the same amount of distilled water.

15. _____ Chemical material without shape.

© 2011 Pearson Education, Inc.

16. _____ The presence of hidden blood in the urine.

17. _____ Organisms that live within other organisms.

18. _____ The presence of protein.

19. _____ Decreased amounts of urine production.

20. _____ A kidney disease that involves inflammation and lesions in the glomeruli.

APPLIED PRACTICE

Follow the directions as instructed with each question below.

1. Label the parts of the refractometer.

© 2011 Pearson Education, Inc.

2. By each of the following microscopic images, note what is being seen in each urine sample.

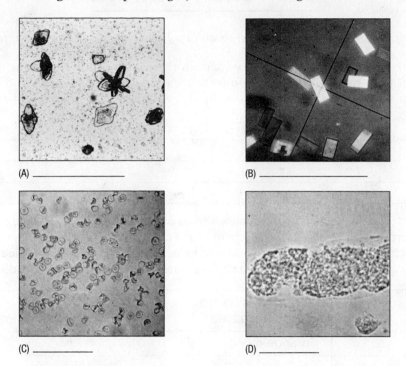

(A) _____

(B) _____

(C) _____

(D) _____

LEARNING ACTIVITY: FILL IN THE BLANK

Using words from the list below, fill in the blanks to complete the following statements.

acidity	organisms
alkalinity	overall
bile duct	physical
foreskin	positive
fruity	random
labia	slows

1. Urine samples provide valuable indicators of the _____ health of the patient.

2. A _____ sample of urine is the most commonly collected type of urine specimen.

3. When collecting clean-catch specimens, be sure that the female patient understands how to clean the _____ and the male knows how to clean the _____.

4. Refrigeration of a specimen _____ the growth of bacteria and specimen deterioration, but does not stop it.

5. The _____ characteristics of urine may be important diagnostic tools for the physician.

6. Individuals testing positive for ketones may have a _____ odor to their urine.

7. The pH of a solution indicates _____ and _____.

8. If urobilinogen is not present, a _____ _____ obstruction may be present.

9. If a leukocyte test is positive, then a protein test should be _____.

10. Microscopic examination identifies the type and approximate number of _____ present in a urine specimen.

© 2011 Pearson Education, Inc.

CRITICAL THINKING

Answer the following questions to the best of your ability. Utilize the textbook as a reference.

1. You are to instruct a 68-year-old female patient in the collection of a 24-hour urine specimen. Explain this, in your own words, as if you were speaking to the patient. Avoid medical terms that the patient may not understand very well; also avoid treating the patient as if she were a child.

   _____

   _____

   _____

2. You have collected a clean-catch urine specimen from Mrs. Gonzalez, a long-time patient, and you have already performed the physical assessment of the color, odor, and clarity. The following are the results of your chemical testing. Fill in the normal value for each, circle those which are abnormal as if you were flagging them for the physician, and then state the possible reasons for the abnormal results.

Tests	Your Results on Mrs. Gonzalez	Normal Value	Possible Causes
Color	orange-red		
Clarity	cloudy		
pH	7.8		
Specific gravity	1.026		
Protein	++ or positive		
Glucose	0		
Ketones	0		
Bilirubin	0		
Urobilinogen	4		
Blood	+		
Leukocytes	++++		
Nitrite	0		

RESEARCH ACTIVITY

Utilize Internet search engines to research the following topics and write a brief description of what you find. It is important to utilize reputable websites.

1. To learn more about the Clinical Laboratory Improvement Amendments (CLIA) waived test, consult the Internet and/or use school or local library resources. Write an essay on what you learned from your research regarding CLIA and waived tests.

   _____

   _____

   _____

© 2011 Pearson Education, Inc.

© 2011 Pearson Education, Inc.

CHAPTER 47
Hematology

CHAPTER OUTLINE

General review of the chapter:

    The Medical Assistant's Role
    Blood Formation and Components
    The Function of Blood
    Blood Specimen Collection
    Routine Blood Tests
    Erythrocyte Sedimentation Rate
    Phenylketonuria
    Mono Testing
    Blood Chemistry Panels

STUDENT STUDY GUIDE

Use the following guide to assist in your learning of the concepts from the chapter.

I. The Formation and Components of Blood

  1. Blood Formation and Blood Components

    A. Blood cells originate from the _____ _____ cell.
    B. Blood cells mature into one of _____ individual types of cells.

  2. Red Blood Cells (RBCs)

    A. RBCs are formed in _____ _____.
    B. Contain _____.
    C. Formation is controlled somewhat by _____.
    D. They last for about _____ months and are continuously being reproduced in the body.
    E. The normal RBC range for a male adult is _____ to _____ million/mm^3.
    F. The normal RBC range for a female is _____ to _____ million/mm^3.

  3. The Function of Hemoglobin

    A. Carries oxygen from the lungs to the _____ of the body.
    B. Carries _____ _____ from the body back to the lungs, where it can be expelled with exhalation.

  4. White Blood Cells (WBCs)

    A. WBCs are also known as _____.
    B. Produced in the bone marrow from _____ _____.
    C. They are larger than _____ blood cells.
    D. Their principal function is to _____ against infection.
    E. The range of WBCs in an adult is _____ to _____ thousand/mm^3.

© 2011 Pearson Education, Inc.

5. Leukocyte Classification
    A. Granulocytes (Briefly explain each.)
        i. Basophils: _____
        ii. Eosinophils: _____
        iii. Neutrophils: _____
    B. Agranulocytes
        i. Monocytes: _____
        ii. Lymphocytes: _____

6. Basophils
    A. Thought to be produced by the _____ _____.
    B. Produce _____.
    C. Patients who have had excessive exposure to radiation may have _____ basophils.
    D. Appear in tissues where an _____ _____ is occurring.

7. Eosinophils
    A. Assumed to be produced by the _____ _____.
    B. Detection of a large number of eosinophils can indicate a _____ condition or the presence of certain _____ conditions.
    C. Have granules that produce a _____ color on the laboratory-stained slide.

8. Neutrophils
    A. Divided into two categories: _____ neutrophils and _____ neurophils.
    B. The body reproduces neutrophils on an ongoing basis, and they only survive for _____ days.
    C. Reproduction is increased when _____ _____ is occurring.
    D. Neutrophils combat infection by _____.
    E. Phagocytosis is the process in which the _____ surrounds, swallows, and digests the _____.

9. Monocytes
    A. Formed in the _____ _____ from stem cells.
    B. Assist in _____.
    C. Ingest foreign particles or _____ that the neutrophils are unable to digest.
    D. Assist in cleaning up _____ debris that may have been left from the infection.
    E. An increase in monocytes is seen in patients who have certain diseases such as tuberculosis, typhoid, and _____ _____ _____ fever.

10. Lymphocytes
    A. Produced in the _____ _____ and in _____ _____ such as the spleen and lymph nodes.
    B. Produce _____ against foreign substances such as bacteria, viruses, and pollens.
    C. Are small and large and can proliferate into _____ and _____ cells.
    D. Lymphocytes do not have _____ and are nonsegmented.

11. Platelets (Thrombocytes)
    A. Formed in the _____ _____.
    B. Main function is to assist in the _____ of blood.
    C. Leads to formation of thrombin, which converts _____ to _____.
    D. Typically between _____ and _____ platelets/mm^3.

12. Solutes in the Plasma
        i. _____
        ii. _____
        iii. _____
        iv. _____

© 2011 Pearson Education, Inc.

  v. _____

  vi. _____

  vii. _____

  viii. _____

  ix. _____

  x. _____

13. The Function of Blood

  i. _____

  ii. _____

  iii. _____

  iv. _____

  v. _____

II. Blood Specimen Collection

1) Steps for Quality Control When Collecting a Blood Specimen

 A. *Review* the request and *verify* the test ordered.

 B. Prepare the necessary _____ and work area.

 C. Perform _____ _____ and don gloves.

 D. Confirm that the patient has followed any _____ _____ requirements.

 E. _____ the specimen properly, using the appropriate equipment and technique.

 F. Use the appropriate _____ container and the correct preservatives.

 G. Immediately label the specimen with the patient's _____, the date and _____ of collection, the test's name, and the _____ of the _____ who collected the specimen.

 H. Follow the correct procedures for disposing of _____ _____ _____ and decontaminating the work area and equipment according to OSHA guidelines.

 I. If the specimen is to be transported to an _____ _____, prepare it for transport in the proper container, with all of the appropriate information according to _____ guidelines.

 J. The type and amount of the _____ required are determined by the _____ that will be performed.

2) Venipuncture

 A. Used to collect _____ volumes of blood.

 B. Three methods are used

  i. A vacuum tube is used for a _____ _____.

  ii. A syringe and needle are used if there is no _____ _____.

  iii. A butterfly is used for a _____ _____.

3.) Vacuum Blood Tube Order for Filling

  i. _____

  ii. _____

  iii. _____

  iv. _____

  v. _____

  vi. _____

  vii. _____

4. Vacutainer® Color, Additive, and Function (Briefly explain each additive and function.)

 A. Yellow

  i. The additive is _____.

  ii. Prevents _____.

  iii. Used for _____.

© 2011 Pearson Education, Inc.

B. Light blue
    i. The additive is _____.
    ii. Removes _____.
    iii. Used for _____.
C. Red
    i. Contains _____.
    ii. Used for _____.
D. Red marbled
    i. The additive is _____.
    ii. Enhances _____.
    iii. Used for _____.
E. Green
    i. The additive is _____.
    ii. Prevents _____.
    iii. Used for _____.
F. Light green
    i. The additive is _____.
    ii. Aids in _____.
    iii. Used for _____.
G. Lavender
    i. The additive is _____.
    ii. Removes _____.
    iii. Used for _____.
H. Pink, white, or royal blue
    i. The additive is _____.
    ii. Prevents _____.
    iii. Used for _____.
I. Gray
    i. The additive is _____.
    ii. Removes _____.
    iii. Used for _____.
J. Dark blue
    i. The additive is _____.
    ii. Detects _____.

5. Sites for Venipuncture
    i. _____
    ii. _____
    iii. _____

6. Patient Preparation
    A. Educate the patient properly _____ and _____ the procedure.
    B. Assemble the equipment ahead of time to show _____.
    C. Deal with _____ events professionally.
    D. Wear _____ for safety.

7. Steps for Obtaining Venous Blood with a Sterile Syringe and Needle
    A. Apply a tourniquet _____ to _____ inches above the antecubital space.
    B. _____ the vein, clean the venipuncture site with an _____ sponge, and then dry with clean gauze.
    C. Have the patient make a _____ and hold it shut until he or she is told to release it.
    D. Make sure that there is no _____ in the syringe and that the _____ moves freely.
    E. Remove the _____ _____ and insert the needle into the vein.
    F. Slowly pull back the syringe _____ until the proper amount of blood has been obtained.
    G. Instruct the patient to _____ his or her fist.

© 2011 Pearson Education, Inc.

H. Release the _____ and withdraw the needle quickly.

I. Place a piece of cotton or gauze on the puncture site, and instruct the patient to maintain _____ on the site and to bend his or her arm.

J. Fill the appropriate _____ tubes to the proper level.

8. The Butterfly Method of Venipuncture

A. Uses a needle that is attached to _____- to _____-inch tubing.

B. The end of the tubing can be attached to the _____ or the _____ _____ tube holder.

C. The butterfly method is used for _____ veins that are difficult to draw from with the standard vacuum container method or syringe and needle method.

D. It is called the butterfly method because the needle on the end has a _____ portion that keeps the needle from turning and _____ the needle into the small vein.

E. The needle used for the butterfly method is a small _____-, _____-, or _____-gauge needle.

F. The drawback to performing the butterfly method is the _____.

9. Capillary Puncture

A. Capillaries are the blood vessels between the _____ and the _____.

B. _____ _____ and oxygen are exchanged at this level.

C. Use this method to collect _____ amounts of blood.

10. Equipment and Supplies for Capillary Puncture

i. _____
ii. _____
iii. _____
iv. _____
v. _____
vi. _____
vii. _____
viii. _____
ix. _____
x. _____

11. Steps for Performing a Capillary Puncture

A. Select the _____ or _____ finger on the nondominant hand; wipe with alcohol.

B. Remove the plastic protective tip of the _____.

C. Grasp the patient's hand and squeeze the finger gently 1 inch _____ the puncture site.

D. Puncture with a quick, jabbing motion across the _____ to get a full blood drop.

E. Wipe away the _____ _____ with gauze.

F. Obtain the sample using a _____ capillary tube.

G. Apply clean gauze over the site and ask the patient to apply _____.

12. Routine Blood Tests

i. _____
ii. _____
iii. _____
iv. _____
v. _____
vi. _____
vii. _____
viii. _____

13. Recording Laboratory Test Results

A. Methods by which results are received

i. Phone calls

ii. copies being faxed or sent by courier

Unit 6
11/25/16

© 2011 Pearson Education, Inc.

B. Contents of most lab reports include:
   i. __Patient's name__
   ii. __Written results Of the test__
   iii. __range values__

14. Equipment Used for Determining Blood Glucose
   i. __Sterile lancet__
   ii. __testing strips__
   iii. __glucometer__
   iv. __examination Gloves__
   v. __cotton balls__
   vi. __alchol Sponges__
   vii. __gauze Squares__
   viii. __Pen__
   ix. __lab coat__
   x. __patient record__

15. Steps for Screening for Blood Glucose Level

A. Identify the patient and make sure that the patient has __fasting__, if required.
B. Make sure that the __glucometer__ has been turned on for the required amount of time and has been __calibrated__ for accuracy according to the manufacturer's instructions.
C. Perform a __capillary__ blood puncture with a sterile lancet.
D. Remove a plastic __test strips__ from the bottle without touching the chemically treated portion.
E. After wiping away the first drop of blood with a __cotton ball__ gently touch the test strip to the second drop of blood that has formed on the patient's finger.
F. Immediately _____ _____ for the duration specified by the manufacturer.
G. Provide the patient with a _____ _____ ____ to hold over the puncture site after wiping the site with an alcohol sponge.
H. Record in the patient's chart the number of __milligrams__ of glucose per __deciliter__ as displayed on the glucometer screen. __(mg)__ __(mg/dL)__

16. Normal Values for Common Laboratory Tests

A. Total cholesterol: __130 - 200 mg/dL__
B. Glucose: __70-120 mg/dL__
C. Triglycerides: __40-150 mg/dL__
D. Creatinine: __0.7 - 1.4 mg/dL__
E. Uric acid: __3.5 - 7.5 mg/dL__
F. BUN: __8 - 20 mg/dL__
G. Sodium: __132 - 142__
H. Potassium: __3.5 - 5.5__
I. Chloride: __98 - 106 mEq/L__
J. CO_2: __25 - 32 mEq/L__
K. White blood cells: __5,000 - 10,800/mm^3__
L. Red blood cells: __3.5 - 5.5 x 10^6 mm^3__
M. Hemoglobin: __12 - 16 g/dL__
N. Hematocrit: __35.5 - 49 percent__
O. Sedimentation rate: __0 - 10 mm/hr__
P. Platelets: __150,000 and 400,000 per ul^3__

17. Microhematocrit

A. Provides the physician with information about the patient's __Red Blood count__ cell volume.
B. A __low__ hematocrit indicates anemia or hemorrhaging.
C. An __elevated__ hematocrit indicates dehydration or polycythemia.
D. A __normal__ hematocrit is 40–50% in males and 35–45% in females.

18. Performing a Microhematocrit
    A. Fill __two__ capillary tubes three-quarters full.
    B. Seal one end with the __sealing clay__.
    C. Place the capillary tubes in the __centrifuge__ with the sealed ends against the __rubber gasket__
    D. If more than one patient's blood is being tested, write down the __number__ of the __slot__ that the patient's tube is in.
    E. Spin for 3 to 5 minutes at __10,000__ rpms.
    F. After centrifuging, the sample will be separated into three layers.
        i. The top layer is __plasma__.
        ii. The middle layer, or the buffy coat, is made up of __WBC's__ and __platelets__
        iii. The bottom layer is __RBC's (Red Blood Cells)__
    G. Remove the tubes immediately after the centrifuge __stops__. If the tubes are not removed immediately, the blood may begin to __mix together__
    H. Use the __Hct card__ by placing the sealing clay just below the zero line on both tubes. Then, on both tubes, match the __top__ of the __plasma__ with the 100 line.
    I. Read the results on both tubes directly below the __buffy coat__. Then add those results together and divide by __2__.
    J. Discard the tubes into the __sharps__ container.
    K. Record the value as a __percentage__ on the patient's medical record.

19. Hemoglobin
    A. Low hemoglobin may indicate __iron__-__deficiency anemia__
    B. Elevated readings are present in patients with __polycythemia__ and in extreme situations, such as burns.
    C. Normal values for adult females are __12__ to __16__ g/dL, and for males, __14__ to __18__ g/dL.
    D. Can either be measured by an automated blood analyzer or manually by using a __hemoglobinometer__
    E. Typically, the __manual method__ is less accurate and not as reliable as the automated blood analyzer.

20. Equipment Used to Measure Hemoglobin
    i. _____
    ii. _____

21. Methods for Determining Hemoglobin Values
    i. __Specific gravity method__
    ii. __Cyanmethemoglobin method__

22. White Blood Cells (WBCs)
    A. There are __5__ types of WBCs, each with distinct characteristics.
    B. Count __100__ WBCs, then express each cell type as a __%__.
    C. Values may differ between __manual__ and __automated__ analyses.

23. Normal White Blood Cell Values for Adults
    A. Neutrophils: __50-70 %__
    B. Eosinophils: __1-4 %__
    C. Basophils: __0-1 %__
    D. Lymphocytes: __20-35 %__
    E. Monocytes: __3-8 %__

24. Red Blood Cells (RBCs)
    A. RBCs are __salmon__ colored.
    B. They appear __oval__ with slightly __pale__ centers.
    C. They have no __nucleus__ or __granules__

© 2011 Pearson Education, Inc.

D. RBCs with nuclei are called _reticulocytes_.

E. Normal-looking RBCs are recorded as _normal RBC morphology_.

25. Performing a Manual Red Blood Cell Count

    A. Requires a small specimen sample to be _diluted_ in a special solution.

    B. Place the sample in a _hemacytometer_.

    C. Place the _slide_ on a _microscope_ used to count RBCs and WBCs.

    D. The automated test for _RBC_ is more common than _manual_ testing.

26. Differential White Blood Cell Count

    A. Determines the _percentages_ of each type of WBC, RBC morphology, and platelet estimation.

    B. Performing this test _ing manually_ is a skill that requires practice to achieve proficiency.

    C. Testing is done using a microscope with a bright light and _100X_ magnification with an _oil immersion_ slide.

    D. Focus near the edge of the stained slide where the cells are _feathered_ and where the cells are _one_ layer thick.

    E. The test can also be performed by the _automated_ analyzer.

27. Preparing Slides for a Differential White Blood Cell Count

    A. Obtain a whole-blood sample using _EDTA_ as the anticoagulant of choice. Blood must be _mixed_ thoroughly before testing.

    B. Using a dropper, place one drop of _room temperature_ blood on the end of a clean, glass slide.

    C. Using the short side of another _clean_, _glass_ slide, back the slide to the drop of blood.

    D. Allow the blood to spread across the _short_ side of the slide.

    E. Holding the spreader slide at a _30-degree_ angle, spread the blood across the length of the slide.

    F. Use gentle, continuous pressure and a smooth gliding motion to create a _smear_.

    G. Notice that the smear has a _thick_ side that gradually changes to a _thin_ side.

    H. The thin side has a _feathered_ edge, and the blood covers _one-half_ to _three-quarters_ the length of the slide.

    I. Allow the slide to air dry on a _rack_.

    J. Label the _frosted_ edge of the slide with the patient's name and the date.

    K. Stain the slide using _Wri_ staining method.

    L. Flood the slide with stain for exactly _45_ seconds or the amount of time indicated by the manufacturer.

    M. Rinse with _distilled_ water until the water runs clear.

    N. Allow the slide to _air dry_ before examining it under the microscope.

    O. _Abnormal_ findings may need to be referred to a laboratory technician for analysis.

28. Platelets

    A. Platelets are about _half_ the size of RBCs.

    B. They stain _purple_ and tend to appear in a clump.

    C. They appear to have a _rough outer_ edge and contain small granules.

    D. There are typically between _5_ and _20_ platelets in one field of view.

29. The Erythrocyte Sedimentation Rate (ESR)

    A. The ESR is also called the _sed_ rate.

    B. Drawing a patient's ESR can be done using either the _Wintrobe_ or _Westergren_ method.

    C. When performing the _Wintrobe_ method, the _Wintrobe_ tube is calibrated in millimeters per hour.

    D. Depending on the type of method used, the _normal_ values may vary.

    E. The Wintrobe method indicates that the normal ESR in an adult female is _0_ to _20_ mm/hr; in an adult male, it is 0 to 9 mm/hr.

© 2011 Pearson Education, Inc.

F. Increased values may indicate an _inflammation_

G. A person's ESR may also be elevated because of a variety of reasons, including _menstru_ _pregnan_c and malignant tumors.

H. The sed rate is related to the condition of the red blood cells and the amount of _fibrin_ in the plasma.

I. When a sed rate test is conducted on a patient, the rate at which the RBCs _fall_ indicates the existence of possible conditions.

30. Phenylketonuria (PKU)

   A. PKU is a _congenital_ disease.

   B. The unmetabolized portion of the _amino acid_ phenylalanine accumulates in the bloodstream.

   C. If undetected, it results in _____ _____.

   D. The PKU test is always performed on _____ to determine the presence of the _____ protein phenylalanine.

31. Equipment for Performing a Phenylketonuria Test

   i. _Sterile lancet_

   ii. _alcohol sponge_

   iii. _Gloves_

   iv. _sterile dry guaze_

   v. _Special filter paper card_

32. Testing for Mononucleosis (Mono)

   A. The test is called the mononucleosis _spot_ test.

   B. Used to help determine whether a patient has _____ _____.

   C. Ordered with a _____ and a strep test.

   D. Common in _____ patients who show symptoms of fever, headache, swollen glands, and fatigue.

   E. If a patient has a positive mono test, an increased number of white blood cells, _____ _____, and symptoms, then the patient is diagnosed with infectious mononucleosis.

   F. If the mono test is _____, but other symptoms exist, it may be too early to detect mono.

33. Equipment for Performing a Mononucleosis Spot Test

   i. _antiseptic cleaner_

   ii. _biohazard waste container_

   iii. _disposable lancet_

   iv. _capillary tube_

   v. _test tube_

   vi. _mono test diluent_

   vii. _Gloves_

   viii. _mono test stick_

   ix. _blood specimen_

34. Performing a Mononucleosis Spot Test

   A. Perform a _puncture_ stick on the patient.

   B. Fill a _capillary_ tube end to end, dispensing all of the blood into the test tube.

   C. Slowly add _one_ drop of _diluent_ to the bottom of the test tube and mix.

   D. Remove the _test_ stick(s) from the container and recap the container immediately.

   E. Place the _absorbent_ end of the test stick into the treated sample. Leave the test stick in the test tube.

   F. Read the results at _5_ minutes.

   G. Positive results may be read as soon as the _red_ _control_ _line_ appears.

   H. Document the findings in the patient's record.

      i. Positive: A blue _test_ line and a red _control_ line is a positive result.

      ii. Negative: A red _control_ line but no blue _test_ line is a negative result.

© 2011 Pearson Education, Inc.

KEY TERMINOLOGY REVIEW

Match the vocabulary term to the correct definition below.

a. Anemia
b. Antecubital space
c. Basophils
d. Capillaries
e. Carboxyhemoglobin
f. Electrolytes
g. Erythrocyte sedimentation rate (ESR)
h. Erythropoietin
i. Hematology
j. Hematopoiesis

k. Hemoglobin
l. Heparin
m. Lymphocytes
n. Microhematocrit
o. Monocytes
p. Mononucleosis
q. Oxyhemoglobin
r. Phenylketonuria
s. Platelets
t. Serum

1. __E__ Blood carrying carbon dioxide.
2. __J__ The formation of blood cells.
3. __G__ The rate at which RBCs settle at the bottom of a tube.
4. __A__ Deficiency of hemoglobin caused by a lack of RBCs.
5. __N__ A crit performed on an extremely small quantity of blood.
6. __T__ Plasma without the fibrinogen.
7. __I__ The study of blood and the tissues that produce it.
8. __P__ A contagious viral infection that frequently is spread through oral contact.
9. __F__ Ionic solutions containing free ions.
10. __B__ A depression in the front of the elbow, it is the most commonly used site for venipuncture.
11. __M__ The WBCs produced in the lymphoid tissue, such as the spleen and the lymph nodes.
12. __D__ The smallest of the body's blood vessels.
13. __m__ The largest of WBCs, they have a nucleus that is shaped like a kidney bean.
14. __R__ A congenital disease caused by a defect in the metabolism of the amino acid phenylalanine.
15. __K__ A metalloprotein that aids in oxygen transportation in the RBCs.
16. __Q__ Hemoglobin-carrying oxygen.
17. __C__ Like other white cells, these are thought to be produced by the bone marrow; they produce heparin.
18. __L__ A substance that prevents clotting.
19. __H__ A glycoprotein hormone that controls RBC production.
20. __J__ The smallest cells found in the blood, they are formed in the bone marrow.

APPLIED PRACTICE

Unit 5
11/25/15

Follow the directions as instructed with each question below.

© 2011 Pearson Education, Inc.

1.

handwritten in left margin: units 11/25/15

Scenario

Julie Turner is working as a clinical medical assistant. A patient, Hector Olanski, comes in for a blood draw. The physician's order reads as follows:

COOK FAMILY MEDICINE
(188) 555-1111

Patient: Hector Olanski

DOB: 7-3-1938
Date: 3-22-20XX

Rx PTT and CBC
light Blue   lavender
Dx: (1) Heparin monitoring (E934.2)
   (2) Phlebitis of lower extremities (451.2)

Dr. Liam Cook

While gathering supplies, Julie grabs a lavender-topped tube, a red-topped tube, and a light-blue-topped tube.

a. Did Julie collect the correct tubes for Mr. Olanski's blood draw? Why or why not? Explain your answer based on each of the tubes of blood that Julie collected.

Yes b/c you have to check the order of draw the ptt use the light blue and the CBC the Lavender

b. What would be the correct order of draw?

light blue
Red marbled
lavender

c. Are there any additives in the tubes that Julie is using for the blood draw? If so, explain which additives are used (based on the color) and the action of the additive.

NO

2. Fill in the label below according to how Julie should label each of Mr. Olanski's tubes of blood.

Hee Olanski, Hector
11/24/15
10:15 am

7-3-1938

© 2011 Pearson Education, Inc.

☆ LEARNING ACTIVITY: TRUE/FALSE ☆

Indicate whether the statement is true (T) or false (F).

T 1. Partially filled tubes, especially the light-blue-topped tube, can cause erroneous test results, resulting in the patient's blood needing to be redrawn.

T 2. Occasionally, uncontrollable bleeding can occur when the needle is withdrawn.

T 3. Capillary puncture is also called a fingerstick.

F 4. Blood analysis is not considered to be a routine tool of medicine.

F 5. Wait until all of the blood tubes have been collected before asking the patient to release his or her fist.

T 6. The National Committee for Clinical Laboratory Standards (NCCLS) has instituted a recommended order of draw to minimize the effects of additive carryover.

F 7. MCV, MVHV, and MCV are used to differentiate specific types of anemia.

T 8. When drawing blood, you should not promise the patient that the procedure will not hurt.

T 9. The functions of blood are transportation and hydration.

T 10. The liquid component of blood is called plasma.

CRITICAL THINKING

Answer the following questions to the best of your ability. Utilize the textbook as a reference.

1. A patient needs to have blood drawn for an ESR and a glucose level. The patient is extremely nervous and worried about the pain that she will experience with a blood draw and asks if you can "stick her finger" instead. Will that work in this scenario? Why or why not?

_____

_____

_____

2. You have drawn three tubes of blood (gray-topped, lavender-topped, and green-topped). You filled the lavender-topped tube first, the gray-topped tube second, and the green-topped tube last. Is this the correct order of draw? If not, what could possibly happen because of this?

_____

_____

_____

3. A patient has come in today for a blood draw to check her cholesterol level. She is 78 years old, has fragile skin, and her veins are impossible to see. Which method of phlebotomy would you use on this patient and why?

_____

_____

_____

4. Your next patient for phlebotomy today is a 6-year-old child. What special considerations are appropriate for this patient?

_____

_____

_____

_____

RESEARCH ACTIVITY

Utilize Internet search engines to research the following topics and write a brief description of what you find. It is important to utilize reputable websites.

1. Visit the Clinical and Laboratory Standards Institute at www.clsi.org. Navigate through the website and identify reasons why the website would be beneficial for medical assistants working in a clinical or physician's office laboratory.

_____

_____

_____

_____

_____

_____

_____

_____

_____

_____

_____

_____

_____

_____

_____

_____

_____

_____

_____

© 2011 Pearson Education, Inc.

CHAPTER 48
Radiology

CHAPTER OUTLINE

General review of the chapter:

Radiology
Overview of Diagnostic Imaging
Preparing and Positioning the Patient
Diagnostic Imaging Procedures
Radiation Therapy
Nuclear Medicine
Safety Precautions
Radiographic Equipment
Processing X-ray Film
Storage and Records
Ownership of Film

STUDENT STUDY GUIDE

Use the following guide to assist in your learning of the concepts from the chapter.

I. Introduction to Radiology

1. Radiology
   A. Radiology is the branch of medicine that uses _radioactive_ substances, or matter that gives off _radiation_
   B. Uses various techniques for visualizing the _techniques_ structures of the body for the diagnosis and treatment of disease.
   C. Divided into three specialties
      i.   _diagnostic radiology_
      ii. _radiation therapy_
      iii. _nuclear medicine_

2. Radiology Personnel
   A. A _radiologist_ is a physician who specializes in radiology.
   B. A _radiographer_, or _radiologic_ technologist, makes diagnostic radiographs, or X-rays.

3. The Duties of a Radiological Technologist
   A. _Positioning_ patients for radiographic procedures.
   B. Determines the proper _voltage_, _current_, and _exposure_ time for each X-ray.
   C. _Adjusting_ radiographic equipment.
   D. Develops the _film_.
   E. Assists the _radiologist_ with special procedures.

© 2011 Pearson Education, Inc.

4. The Principles of X-rays
   A. Developed in 1895 by Wilhelm Konrad Roentgen
   B. X-rays are produced in a vacum tube when electrons collide.
   C. This collision produces electromagnetic rays.
   D. X-rays coming from the tube form an X-ray cone-shaped X-ray
   E. The radiation field is a cross section of the X-ray beam and the point of use.
   F. The patient is placed between the tube that produces the X-ray beam and the film.

5. Characteristics of X-rays
   A. X-rays penetrate substances of different densities to varying degree.
   B. Cause ionization of the substances through which they pass.
   C. Cause certain substances to flourescence
   D. Travel in a straight line.
   E. Can destory body cells.

6. Diagnostic Imaging
   A. Involves the use of the following
      i. X-rays
      ii. Ultrasound
      iii. radiopharmaceuticals
      iv. radiopaque media
      v. computers

7. The Contrast Medium
   A. The contrast medium is a radiopaque substance.
   B. Does not allow the passage of X-rays.
   liquid C. Include contrast media (barium), powders, air, and gas.
   D. Administered orally, by injections (parenterally), or by enema.
   E. Acts to convert an organ or structure into an opaque area.

8. Contrast Medium Materials
   A. Barium sulfate
      i. Barium sulfate is a positive contraet media
      ii. Consists of a chalky compound mixed with water.
      iii. Used for fluoroscope examination.
   B. Iodine contrast compounds
      i. Used to form radiopraque compounds.
      ii. Cannot be used on patients who are allergic to seafood or iodine.
      iii. Interfere with nuclear medicine.
   C. Negative contrast
      i. Appears black on X-rays.
      ii. Used to visualize the spinalcord

9. The Role of the Medical Assistant During Radiology Exams
   A. Schedules the procedure
   B. educate the patient about the procedure.
   C. Explains to the patient any procedures required.
   D. Ensures that the patient is provided with an ample-size gown and drape.
   E. Requests that the patient remove all metallic materials.
   F. Assists the patient undress and image the procedure.
   G. Provides X-ray instructions.
   H. Informs the patient about procedure to steps the results.

© 2011 Pearson Education, Inc.

10. X-ray Procedures That Require Special Preparation
A. Angiogram: No _breakfast_ if the examination is in the morning or _lunch_ if the examination is in the afternoon.
B. Barium enema (Lower GI)
   i. Enemas are administered until the bowel return is _clear_ on the evening before the examination.
   ii. The doctor may order a rectal _suppository_ in the morning or a _cathortic_ such as 2 oz. of castor oil or citrate of magnesia at 4:00 P.M. the day before the procedure.
   iii. The patient is to have clear liquids and _gelatin_ for dinner.
   iv. Nothing may be taken by mouth (NPO) after _midnight_.
C. Barium meal (Upper GI): NPO after _midnight_.
D. Cholecystogram (GB series)
   i. The patient may have a light supper of non fatty food, such as _fruit_ and _____ without _____ or oil, the evening before the procedure.
   ii. _____ tablets (prescribed by the physician) are taken with water after supper.
   iii. NPO except for water until after the _X ray_ the following day.
E. Computerized tomography (CT): NPO for _4_ hours before the procedure if a _contrast_ medium is used.
F. Intravenous pyelogram (IVP)
   i. Three _Dulcolx_ tablets or 2 oz. of _castor oil_ at 4:00 P.M. the day before the procedure.
   ii. Eat a _light_ supper.
   iii. _NPO_ after midnight.
G. Retrograde pyelogram
   i. Enemas are administered or _____ are taken on the _____ before the procedure.
   ii. NPO for _____ hours before the procedure.
H. Ultrasound: May require a full _____ or _____, depending on the type of ultrasound.

12. Steps for Assisting with a Radiological Procedure
A. Check the X-ray examination _Order_.
B. Check the necessary X-ray _equipment_ as needed.
C. Identify the patient and determine whether the patient has complied with the _Prodceure preparation_
D. Explain the procedure to the patient, and then instruct the patient to remove _____ as necessary for the procedure.
E. Ask the patient to remove all _jewerly_ and _metals_.

13. Anteroposterior (AP)

A. The X-ray beam is directed from _____ to _____.
B. The patient may be standing or _____.
C. The patient's front will face the X-ray _____ and the patient's back will be near the _____ _____.

14. Posterioanterior (PA)

A. The X-ray beam is directed from _____ to _____.
B. The patient will be standing _____.
C. The patient's _____ will face the X-ray equipment and his or her _____ will be near the film plate.

15. The Oblique Position

A. The patient is turned at an angle to the film plate so that the X-ray beam can be directed at an area that would be hidden on an _____, _____, or _____ X-ray.

16. The Lateral Position
    A. The X-ray beam is directed toward _____ _____ of the body.
    B. In the right lateral (RL) position, the patient's right side is near the _____ _____ and the left side is near the _____ _____.
    C. In the left lateral (LL) position, the patient's _____ side is near the film plate.

17. The Axial Position
    A. The X-ray tube is angled to direct the X-ray beam along the _____ of the body or body part.
    B. With _____ angulation, the X-ray beam is directed at an angle from the feet toward the head.
    C. With _____ angulation, the X-ray beam is directed from the head toward the feet.

18. Information Required for Scheduling a Radiological Procedure
    i. _____
    ii. _____
    iii. _____
    iv. _____
    v. _____

19. Beverages that May Be Restricted on an All-Liquid Diet
    i. _____
    ii. _____
    iii. _____
    iv. _____
    v. _____
    vi. _____
    vii. _____
    viii. _____

20. Guidelines for Sequencing Multiple Diagnostic Procedures
    A. Schedule all radiographic examinations and tests that do not require a _____ _____ and iodine intake first.
    B. Do CT scans of the _____ and _____ before performing procedures that require barium.
    C. CT procedures that require an IV contrast medium may be done _____ blood is drawn for the iodine uptake series.

II. Diagnostic Imaging Procedures
    1. General Categories of Diagnostic Imaging
        i. _____
        ii. _____
        iii. _____
        iv. _____

    2. Methods for Administering Contrast Media
        i. _____
        ii. _____
        iii. _____
        iv. _____

    3. Radiological Imaging Procedures That Require Contrast Media
        i. _____
        ii. _____
        iii. _____

© 2011 Pearson Education, Inc.

4. Fluoroscopy Procedures
   A. Fluoroscopy is a _____ examination of a portion of the body or the functioning of an organ using a fluoroscope.
   B. Allows the radiologist to have _____ images.
   C. It is a _____ image that is seen on the fluoroscope and can be filmed using a radiograph (X-ray) to obtain a _____ record.
   D. _____ _____ are often used to better visualize organ functioning and abnormalities.

5. Gastrointestinal Series
   A. A gastrointestinal series is a _____ study of the _____ _____.
   B. Uses a _____ medium.
   C. Can involve an upper or lower _____.

6. Patient Instructions for the Upper GI Series
   A. NPO after _____.
   B. No _____.
   C. Drink _____ _____ during the procedure.
   D. The procedure can last _____ hours.
   E. _____ eating can be resumed after the procedure.
   F. Drinking _____ after the procedure is important.
   G. Stool may be _____ for a few days.

7. Patient Instructions for the Lower GI Series
   A. _____-_____ diet a few days before the procedure
   B. _____-_____ diet the morning before the procedure.
   C. A _____ may be needed the day before the procedure.
   D. An _____ or barium sulfate is given, which the patient retains during the procedure.
   E. Prior to the end of the procedure, the enema is _____ and an X-ray of the _____ _____ is taken.
   F. A regular diet can be resumed, including a lot of _____.
   G. The patient may have _____ stools for 1 or 2 days following the procedure.

8. Intravenous Pyelogram (IVP)
   A. An IVP is an examination of the kidneys, _____, and bladder.
   B. The procedure takes about _____ to _____ hours.
   C. _____ is used.
   D. _____-_____ diet, including a lot of water the day before the procedure.
   E. _____ after midnight.
   F. A _____ with an enema the night before the procedure may be ordered.

9. Cholecystogram
   A. A cholecystogram is an examination of the _____.
   B. Requires a _____ medium.
   C. Utilized when _____ has not provided a definitive diagnosis.
   D. _____-_____ meal the night before the procedure with contrast medium pills.
   E. _____ after midnight.
   F. After the procedure, the patient is asked to eat a _____ meal. _____ hour later, another X-ray is taken.
   G. _____ may occur after the procedure.

10. Myelography
   A. Myelography is a fluoroscopic procedure used to visualize the _____ _____.
   B. Involves a _____ puncture.
   C. Used to detect _____ of the spinal cord or _____ disks.
   D. Typically done if a _____ or an _____ has not provided enough detail.

© 2011 Pearson Education, Inc.

11. Pneumoencephalograph
    A. Performed by injecting _____ instead of a contrast medium after some cerebral spinal fluid has been removed.
    B. Allows visualization of the _____ of the brain.

12. Angiography
    A. Provides a visualization of the _____ _____ of blood vessels after a _____ material has been injected into the blood vessels.
    B. A contrast medium is injected into an _____ or _____ by way of a catheter, which is threaded through the vessel until it reaches the correct site.
    C. Because iodine is used as the contrast medium, the patient should be tested for an _____ to iodine before the procedure begins.
    D. The patient is monitored for a few hours after the procedure for any signs of _____ from the puncture site.

13. Cardiac Catheterization
    A. Cardiac catheterization is a form of _____.
    B. Frequently performed to assess the status of the _____ _____.
    C. The catheter is inserted into the _____ artery and fed through the arteries until it reaches the heart.
    D. If obstructions are discovered, therapeutic interventions such as _____ _____ or stent insertion can take place to relieve a blockage of the coronary arteries.

14. Arthrography
    A. Used to produce an arthrogram, or image, of the inside of a _____.
    B. Helps diagnose abnormalities of the _____, tendons, _____, and cartilage of the knee, hip, or shoulder.
    C. The procedure involves injecting a local _____ followed by a contrast medium or _____, or both, into the joint.
    D. A _____ is used to evaluate the functioning of the joint.
    E. The procedure usually takes about 1 hour, and the patient should be advised to expect some slight _____ and_____ for a day or two.
    F. The patient should be advised to _____ the joint during that time.

15. Procedures That Do Not Require Contrast Media
    Films of the following portions of the anatomy do not require contrast media
       i. _____
      ii. _____
     iii. _____
      iv. _____
       v. _____
      vi. _____
     vii. _____

16. Mammography
    A. Mammography is a radiological examination of the _____ _____ of the breast.
    B. Identifies benign and malignant _____ (tumors).

17. Patient Instructions for Mammography
    A. Because of the effects that these products can have on the clarity of the test, prior to the procedure patients should be instructed not to use the following
       i. Underarm deodorant
      ii. talcom power
     iii. body lotion
      iv. perfume prior

© 2011 Pearson Education, Inc.

18. The Mammography Procedure
    A. The patient stands in _front_ of the X-ray equipment.
    B. The technician positions the patient carefully in order to have all _breast tissue_ examined.
    C. The patient should be instructed to follow the technician's directions regarding the placement of _hands_, _arms_, and _body_ position.
    D. Patients of _child bearing_ are given a lead apron to wear during the procedure.
    E. Each breast is _a hernate_ compressed by the equipment to spread the tissue for better viewing.
    F. X-rays are directed at _____ into the breast tissue.
    G. The procedure takes a _few seconds_ for each view, with the entire procedure lasting about a half hour.
    H. Patients may feel discomfort because of _pressure_ during the breast compression.

19. Addressing Breast Lumps
    A. If a _____ is detected, the patient should follow up immediately with further testing and not wait to see if the _____ disappears over time.
    B. Many abnormalities detected on mammograms are _____ and present no danger to the patient.
    C. Once a mammogram reveals _____ tissue, a breast biopsy should be done to confirm the type of mass detected.

20. Stereotactic Breast Biopsy
    A. Less _____ and less _____ than previous types of biopsies.
    B. The procedure is done with the patient lying _____ _____ with the breast compressed between two _____ with the suspicious mass centered in the window of a paddle.
    C. A computer determines the precise positioning of the _____ _____.
    D. A small sample of _____ is taken and sent for review by a pathologist.

21. Tomography
    A. Allows for the penetration of _____ areas.
    B. Tomography produces _____.
    C. Computed tomography produces _____ scans.

22. Computed Tomography (CT)
    A. Combines radiography with computer analysis of _____ _____.
    B. An X-ray camera _____ completely around the patient, and the computer accumulates _____-_____ slices from each rotation of the camera.
    C. The CT scanner consists of a _____ table with a remote control; the circular structure, or _____, that houses the X-ray equipment; and an _____ _____ with monitor and computer equipment.

23. The CT Procedure
    A. The patient lies on a _____ table that slides into the scanner.
    B. The procedure is painless, is _____, and requires no special preparation.
    C. The computer calculates various factors to detect _____ _____, such as tumors; _____ displacement; and _____ accumulation.

24. Positron Emission Tomography (PET)
    A. Examines the _____ _____ of the body.
    B. The patient is injected with or inhales a _____ substance.
    C. Used to assist in treating the following conditions
        i. _____
        ii. _____
        iii. _____
        iv. _____

© 2011 Pearson Education, Inc.

25. Magnetic Resonance Imaging (MRI)

   A. Provides a visual of internal _____, _____, and structures.
   B. The image is _____-_____.
   C. The hard portion of _____ _____ cannot be viewed.
   D. Cannot be used on patients who have _____ or _____ clips on blood vessels.
   E. No _____ radiation is used.
   F. MRIs allow for the observation of organ _____.

26. Patient Instructions for Magnetic Resonance Imaging

   A. Remove all _____, _____ _____, and metallic objects, such as watches, belts, hearing aids, and hairpins.
   B. Identify which devices, if any, have been inserted into the patient's body, such as the following
      i. _____
      ii. _____
      iii. _____
      iv. _____
   C. Leave _____ _____ or devices that contain metallic or _____ _____ strips outside the MRI chamber.
   D. Use patient gown if patient's clothing has _____ or metal snaps.

27. Digital Radiology

   A. Uses standard _____.
   B. An image is projected onto a TV or _____ _____ screen.
   C. Digital angiography is used for the cardiac and _____ arteries and head and neck angiograms.

28. Ultrasound/Sonography

   A. Used _____-_____ _____ to view internal structures.
   B. Provides _____ monitoring and the detection of abnormalities of the heart, liver, and kidneys.

29. Patient Preparation for the Ultrasound Examination

   A. The patient should wear _____-fitting garments or clothing that is easy to remove because the procedure is performed over bare skin.
   B. During a fetal ultrasound or pelvic ultrasound, the patient is instructed not to _____ right before the test because a full _____ displaces the intestines and allows for a better view of the uterus.
   C. The patient may be asked to drink a _____ or more of water just prior to either of these examinations.
   D. For an ultrasound of the _____ or _____, the patient may be asked not to eat for several hours before the procedure.

30. Radiation Therapy

   A. Uses a specific dose of radiation to kill _____ cells.
   B. Normal cells are altered, but will naturally _____.
   C. Radiation therapy is also known by the following names:
      i. _____
      ii. _____
      iii. _____

31. Types of Rays Used in Radiation Therapy (Briefly explain each type.)

   A. Alpha rays
      i. _____
      ii. _____

© 2011 Pearson Education, Inc.

B. Beta rays

    i. _____

    ii. _____

C. Gamma rays

    i. _____

    ii. _____

32. Conditions That Are Treated with Radiation Therapy

    i. *Cancer*

    ii. *hodgkins disease*

    iii. *wilms tumor*

    iv. *retinoblastoma*

    v. *malignlacies*

    vi. *shrink tumors*

33. Methods for Administering Radiation (Provide the name of each of the methods described.)

A. _____ _____ _____ (ERT): Administering calculated doses of radiation to a specific site.

B. _____ _____ _____ (IRT): Administering radiation through a sealed container that houses radioactive material; administering radiation through a liquid form via the patient's mouth or bloodstream; or administering radiation by instilling it into a body cavity.

34. Nuclear Medicine

A. Nuclear medicine is also known as _____ imaging.

B. Uses radioactive _____ to treat and diagnosis diseases.

C. Involves the use of radioactive isotopes of _____, _____, and other elements.

35. Units of Radiation (Provide the name of each type of unit.)

A. _____: Unit used to measure the amount of ionizing radiation absorbed.

B. _____: Unit used to measure occupational exposure.

C. Units used to measure the effects of radiation

    i. _____

    ii. _____

    iii. _____

36. The Effects of Overexposure to Radiation

    i. *hair loss*

    ii. *skin changes*

    iii. *nausea*

    iv. *diarrhea*

    v. *mucous membranes in the mouth*

    vi. *throat bladder*

    vii. *vagina*

37. Primary Radiation

A. Strikes the patient either for _____ reasons or for an X-ray examination.

B. Once the primary _____ strikes the patient, it can then become _____ radiation as it bounces off the patient.

38. Guidelines for Maintaining the Personal Safety of the Medical Assistant and the Patient

A. Wear a _____ _____ on outer clothing when exposed to any form of radiation.

B. Ensure that the _____ is never covered.

C. Stay behind the _____ _____ in a _____-_____ room when X-ray equipment is being used.

D. Note the _____ or lighted display which indicates that X-ray equipment is in use.

E. Check the _____ on a routine basis.

F. Wear _____ devices if you are in the room when an X-ray is being taken.

G. Have periodic testing to ensure that there are no _____ _____ from radiation exposure.

H. Ask the _____ if he or she has had any recent exposure to X-rays.

I. Place a _____ _____ over the patient's abdominal and reproductive organs for patients who are of childbearing age or are pregnant.

39. The Darkroom

A. Used for _____ film.

B. Contain _____ or _____ safe lights.

C. Should always be _____ when film is being processed.

D. Film can be processed using either _____ or automated methods.

E. Automated processing can take _____ seconds to _____ minutes, depending on the equipment being used.

40. Storage of X-ray Films

A. Kept in containers that protect film from light, heat, _____ _____, and moisture.

B. Stored in a dry, cool place in a _____ _____.

C. Stored on end to prevent _____ _____ and where expiration dates can be viewed.

D. Films should only be _____ with one hand.

E. Processed films should be stored in _____ _____ and filed in film cabinets.

41. Ownership of the Film

A. _____ reports can be sent to other physicians at the patient's request.

B. Films can be loaned to _____ physicians if necessary.

C. Films are a _____ _____ of the patient.

KEY TERMINOLOGY REVIEW

Match the vocabulary term to the correct definition below.

a. Angiography
b. Bucky
c. Claustrophobia
d. Collimator
e. Cumulative
f. Dosimeter
g. Fluoroscopy
h. Gantry
i. Grid
j. Nuclear medicine
k. Radioactive

l. Radiation
m. Radiographs
n. Radiologist
o. Radiology
p. Radiolucent
q. Radiopaque
r. Rem
s. Retrograde pyelography
t. Transducer
u. X-rays

© 2011 Pearson Education, Inc.

1. _____ Procedure using a contrast medium whereby the actual function of a particular organ or structure can be visualized.

2. _____ A branch of medicine which uses radioactive substances or matter that gives off radiation (radiant energy) and various techniques to visualize the internal structures of the body for the diagnosis and treatment of disease.

3. _____ Device that both produces and senses ultrasonic waves.

4. _____ Fear of closed-in spaces.

5. _____ Used to protect patients from secondary or scatter radiation.

6. _____ Produced in a vacuum tube when electrons, traveling at the speed of light (186,000 miles per second), collide with a target made of specific materials such as tungsten.

7. _____ Inserting a catheter into the urinary tract through the bladder and into the ureters. The dye is then sent up the tube into the ureters and kidneys, and X-rays are taken to evaluate the function of the ureters, bladder, and urethra.

8. _____ Permitting greater penetration of X-rays.

9. _____ Radiant energy.

10. _____ A radiological procedure that involves the use of a contrast medium.

11. _____ A circular structure that houses the X-ray equipment.

12. _____ Allows fewer X-rays to pass through.

13. _____ A device that controls the size and shape of the X-ray field coming from the tube.

14. _____ The ability to give off radiation as the result of the disintegration of the nucleus in an atom.

15. _____ A type of grid composed of alternating strips of lead and radiolucent material.

16. _____ X-ray images.

17. _____ A film badge worn on the outer clothing of all personnel who work with or near radiological equipment.

18. _____ The roentgen equivalent in humans.

19. _____ A physician who specializes in radiology.

20. _____ A branch of medicine that uses radioactive isotopes in the diagnosis and treatment of disease.

21. _____ Exposure to radiation is added to the effects of all previous exposures.

APPLIED PRACTICE

Follow the directions as instructed with each question below.

1. Use information from the patient's chart listed below to answer the following questions.

Epley, Marguerite V.
11-24-1941

3/18/20XX, 2:15 P.M.

Ht: 5'5"   Wt: 115 lbs.   T: 98.6°F   P: 90 bpm   BP: 136/88

cc: Pt. presents to office with rt. lower leg pain, after falling while getting out of her bathtub. Pt. rates the pain as a 6 on a scale of 1 to 10. Rt. lower leg appears to be swollen and without bruising at this time.

Jerry Li, CMA (AAMA)

Scenario: Dr. Jefferson wants Jerry, the CMA (AAMA), to perform an X-ray of Ms. Epley's lower rt. leg. The order reads as follows:

> PT: Marguerite Epley DOB: 11/24/1941
>
> Rt. lower leg X-ray. AP and lateral views.
>
> Dx: R/O Fx *(Diagnosis: Rule out fracture)*

A. Dr. Jefferson ordered an AP view. What does this mean?

_____X-ray_____

_____

B. How do you think Jerry should position the patient for the lateral view?

_____Supine or prone position_____

_____Sims_____

C. List some of the protective barriers that Jerry would implement during the X-ray.

_____radiation exposure_____

_____radiation leakage_____

LEARNING ACTIVITY: FILL IN THE BLANK

Using words from the list below, fill in the blanks to complete the following statements.

allergic	front to back	safety precautions
carbon dioxide	high-frequency	sonography
childbearing age	iodine	stomach
contrast medium	liquid	ultrasound
dietary	negative	ultraviolet
education	pregnant	upper GI series

1. In preparation for an _____, the patient should not eat or drink after midnight because the _____ must be empty for this procedure.

2. The field of radiology uses X-rays, radioactive substances, and other forms of radiant energy such as _____ rays.

3. A _____ is a radiopaque substance that facilitates radiographic imaging of internal structures.

4. _____ contrast media include air, _____, and other gases.

5. In the anteroposterior view (AP), the central ray is directed from _____.

6. Before an X-ray, any female of _____ must be asked whether she could be _____.

7. With regard to patient preparation and instructions for an IVP: This procedure should not be performed on a patient who is _____ to _____.

8. _____, or _____, is the use of _____ sound waves to image internal structures.

© 2011 Pearson Education, Inc.

9. Special _____ restrictions in preparation for radiographic procedures often call for an all-_____ diet on the day before the procedure.

10. The medical assistant's role in medical imaging may involve patient preparation and _____, scheduling, and following _____.

CRITICAL THINKING

Answer the following questions to the best of your ability. Utilize the textbook as a reference.

1. You have placed a patient on the table for an X-ray and notice that the lead strip around the table has a few very small cracks in it. What should you do?

   _____

   _____

   _____

   _____

2. Mr. Abdul has come in for a cholecystogram. As you put the patient into the room, you ask him if he has followed the preparation instructions of taking iodine the day before and then NPO this morning. He looks surprised and then admits that he forgot to take the iodine. What would you do?

   _____

   _____

   _____

   _____

3. A patient comes to the front desk and does not have an appointment. She wants to get her original mammogram because she is moving to another state. What can you tell this patient?

   _____

   _____

   _____

   _____

RESEARCH ACTIVITY

Utilize Internet search engines to research the following topics and write a brief description of what you find. It is important to utilize reputable websites.

1. Research your state's laws regarding limited-scope radiography. Would you be allowed to practice limited-scope radiography as a medical assistant with proper training and supervision?

   _____

   _____

   _____

   _____

© 2011 Pearson Education, Inc.

Handwritten answers:
A. "Carbon dioxide"
B. "Superior" and "inferior", "right"
C. "right", "contracts", "ventricle", "tricuspid"
D. "ventricle", "semilunar", "lungs"
E. "oxygenated", "atrium", "Pulmonary"
F. "left", "bicuspid"
G. "left", "aortic", "lungs"
H. "aorta"
I. "coronary artery"
2A. "backward"
3A. "pacemaker"
3B. "60-80"
3C. "40-60"

CHAPTER 49
Electrocardiography

CHAPTER OUTLINE

General review of the chapter:

Heart Structure and Function
The Electrocardiogram
Special Procedures

STUDENT STUDY GUIDE

Use the following guide to assist in your learning of the concepts from the chapter.

I. Heart Structure and Function

1. The Function of the Cardiovascular System
   A. Deoxygenated blood circulates through the body and discharges _Carbon dioxide_, the waste product of cell metabolism, from the lungs.
   B. Blood circulates throughout the body and returns from the general circulation by way of the _Superior_ and _inferior_ vena cava, to the _right_ atrium, moving in one direction from the heart.
   C. When the _right_ atrium is full, the atrium _contracts_ and blood is pumped in the right _ventricle_ through the _tricuspid_ valve.
   D. Upon filling, the blood is pumped by the contraction of the right _ventricle_ through the _semilunar_ valves into the pulmonary artery going to the _lungs_.
   E. Blood is then _oxygenated_ and returned to the left _atrium_ through the four _Pulmonary_ veins.
   F. When that chamber is full, it contracts and blood is squeezed into the _left_ ventricle through the _bicuspid_ valve.
   G. In the _left_ ventricle, blood enters the _aortic_ semilunar valve and moves into all parts of the body except the _lungs_.
   H. Blood travels to all parts of the body via the _aorta_ and then goes into all other arteries.
   I. The heart muscle receives a supply of oxygen and nutrients through the _coronary artery_ system.

2. Heart Valves
   A. Act as gates to prevent the _backward_ flow of blood.
   B. Open and shut in response to the changing _pressure_ brought by cardiac contraction and _relaxation_.

3. The Conduction System of the Heart
   A. The SA node normally serves as the _pacemaker_ of the heart.
   B. The normal rating of the SA node is _60-80_ beats per minute.
   C. The AV node will generate _40-60_ beats per minute.

© 2011 Pearson Education, Inc.

D. The bundle of His will generate less than _40_ beats per minute.

E. The Purkinje system will generate rhythms in an _____.

4. Heart Sounds Associated with Abnormal Conditions

   A. Causes of heart murmurs

     i. _Damaged valves_

     ii. _regurgitation_

     iii. _back-flow of blood through a valve_

II. Performing an Electrocardiogram

1. The Electrocardiogram (EKG, also ECG)

   A. The electrical charges created by the _conduction_ system can be sensed throughout the body.

   B. A normal cardiac cycle is one series of _____ waves.

2. Time and the Cardiac Cycle

   A. The _P_ wave represents the impulse that originated in the _SA_ node and spread through the _atria_.

   B. The _P_-_R_ interval is the time from the beginning of _P_ to the beginning of _QRS_.

   C. A _P_-_R_ interval that is too short means that the impulse has reached the _ventricles_ through a shorter-than-normal pathway.

   D. A _P_-_R_ interval that is too long means that possibly there is a _____ delay in the _____ node.

   E. The _QRS_ complex represents the time necessary for the impulse to travel through the bundle of His, the bundle _branches_, and the _Purkinje_ fibers to complete _ventricular activation_ or contraction.

   F. The ST segment and the T wave represent _repolarization_ of the ventricles.

   G. The ST segment is normally _flat_ or only slightly _elevated_

   H. The T wave represents a part of the recovery of the _ventricle_ after contraction.

3. The EKG Control Panel (Explain and/or provide important information about each part of the control panel.)

   A. Main power switch: _Allow for a warm-up time, specified by_

   B. Record switch: _The switch makes the paper at standard run 25 sp_

   C. Lead selector: _Determines from which sensors the machine will rec_

   D. Standard adjustment screw: _____

   E. Sensitivity control: _Allows the operator to increase/decrease the recording_

   F. Standard button: _Allows verification of calibration to the internal_

   G. Stylus control: _Centers the recording in the middle of the page_

   H. Stylus heat control: _Increases/decreases heat and adjust for the sk_

   I. Marker: _Indicates by a code which lead is being recorded_

_P. 1120_

4. The EKG Paper

   A. Paper is _pressure_ sensitive and must be handled carefully.

   B. If this paper is exposed to light for long periods, the _markings_ will fade with time.

   C. Many newer models use an _ink cartridge_ to supply the stylus and provide a longer-lasting printout.

   D. Paper records both _time_ (horizontally) and _voltage_ (vertically).

5. Time Markers on EKG Paper

   A. Time markers are small _squares_ with a light line and a larger _squares_ with a _darker_ line.

   B. The paper records both time and _voltage_.

© 2011 Pearson Education, Inc.

6. Heart Rate: The 6-Second Method
   A. Begin at one _____-second marker and move to the right for two additional markers.
   B. Count the number of _____ complexes between the first and third markers.
   C. Add a _____.

7. Heart Rate: Count-off Method
   A. Locate a QRS complex close to a 5 -mm line.
   B. Move to the next deflection at the right or the left.
   C. Count how many 5 -mm lines intersect the tracing before the next QRS complex.
   D. Count off at each 5 -mm line.
   E. Stop counting when you reach the next QRS complex.

8. Heart Rate: Exact Calculations
   A. The paper moves at a standard speed of 25 mm/second = 1500 mm/minute.
   B. Count the millimeter boxes between the two QRS complexes.
   C. Divide the number into 1500

9. Sensor Placement
   A. Sensors are placed in the following manner
      i. Over the fleshy part of the inner aspect of both legs lower arms upper or forearms
      ii. Over both upper _____ or _____, avoiding bony prominences
      iii. Chest electrodes are placed in _____ locations.

10. EKG Leads
    A. Each lead will record from a specific combination of _____.
    B. By recording from different combinations of sensors, the _____ activity of the heart is seen from different _____.

11. Patient Preparation for an EKG
    A. Explain to the patient the equipment and procedure as well as what you will expect the patient to do.
    B. The surroundings should be pleasant and the table wide enough for adequate support.
    C. Patients will need to be bare to the waist so privacy should be provided for disrobing.
    D. Position patient in the supine or semi-powlers position.
    E. Jewelry, particularly metal jewelry must be removed so that it does not interfere with the electrical current of the ECG.
    F. Prepare the skin where the sensors will be applied.

12. The EKG Recording
    A. Normally, the EKG recording is made in sensitivity 1 = 10 mm deflection per 1 mV of electricity
    B. If the size is doubled, it is sensitivity _____.
    C. If the size is cut in half, it is sensitivity _____.

13. The Causes of Artifacts
    i. Somatic tremor
    ii. Wandering baseline
    iii. 60 cycle or AC (alternating current) interference
    iv. Erratic stylus

14. Mounting an EKG (List the steps.)
    i. Cut and trim it
    ii. Place it in appropriate area of the folder
    iii. Double check your work
    iv. Repeat the process until all 12 leads have been proper
    v. machine record from 3 leads at once, put in patient Record

© 2011 Pearson Education, Inc.

15. Normal Sinus Rhythm (List the three distinct waves.)
    i. P wave
    ii. T wave
    iii. QRS complex
16. Abnormalities Caused by Cardiac Pathology
    i. Atrial fibrillation
    ii. Atrial flutter
    iii. AV heart block
    iv. Myocardia Infarction (MI)
    v. Paroxysmal atrial tachycardia (PAT)
    vi. Premature atrial contractions (PAC)
    vii. Premature ventricular contractions (PVC)
    viii. Sinus arrhythmia
    ix. Sinus bradycardia
    x. Sinus tachycardia
    xi. Ventricular tachycardia
    xii. Ventricular fibrillation

III. Electrocardiogram-related Diagnostic Procedures

1. Exercise Tolerance Testing

    A. Exercise tolerance testing is also called a _Stress_ test or a _treadmill_ test.
    B. Testing evaluates the heart's response during _moderate_ exercise following a _12_-lead EKG.
    C. May be used for the following reasons
        i. high risk for developing heart disease
        ii. strenuous excersise
        iii. cardic complaints shortness of breath
        iv. rehabilitation following cardic surgery
    D. Patient should be given instructions before test day to wear _comfortable_ exercise or walking _shoes_ and loose-fitting clothes.
    E. The physician evaluates the effect of exercise on the heart rate, _climb contin ues_, and the EKG.
    F. The test may be stopped if the patient experiences _trouble breathing_ or complains of chest pain.

2. Placement of the Sensors for the Stress Test

    A. Sensors are all placed on the _body_.
    B. Arm and leg sensors are put at the _stream_ line on the top of the _chest_ and on the _strenium_ line on the _body_.

3. Guidelines for the Stress Test

    A. The stress test is continued until _85_ % of the maximum target heart rate is achieved or the patient becomes _symptomatic_.
    B. The maximum target heart rate is calculated by using the following formula: _220 min the patient age 220 - 60 = 160 x 8.5 = B.5_
    C. For patients who have had a myocardial infarction, or a heart attack, the target heart rate is set lower at _10_%.

4. The Use of Thallium

    A. Thallium is a _____ used in nuclear medicine that emits _____ rays.
    B. Sometimes it is injected into the patient's _____ during a stress test for a better understanding of perfusion, or blood flow, to the _____.
    C. Normal perfusion of the _____ is indicated by _____ on the pictures.

© 2011 Pearson Education, Inc.

5. Pharmacological Stress Testing
   A. In this test, no _excercise_ is used. Instead, medication is given to the patient that causes the heart rate to climb to the _____ heart rate.
   B. The test is useful for patients with _____ limitations or elderly persons who cannot perform enough exercise to elevate the heart rate.
6. Patient Safety During a Stress Test (List how patient safety may be maintained during the test.)
   i. _____
   ii. _____
   iii. _____
   iv. _____
7. The Holter Monitor
   A. The Holter monitor is used when the _ECG_ is not conclusive or the _cardic_ irregularity was not seen in the EKG.
   B. Patients should carry out all routine daily activities except for _Showering_ and _bathing_.
   C. Patients should avoid high- _Voltage_ areas.
8. Placement of the Holter Monitor (List the placement of each electrode.)
   i. _third intercostal space 2-3 inches to the right sterium_
   ii. _third intercostal space 2-3 inches to the left sterum_
   iii. _fifth intercosteel space at the left_
   iv. _sixth intercostal space at the sterum axillary lin_
   v. _sixth intercostal space at the left anterior axil_
   _li_

KEY TERMINOLOGY REVIEW

Match the vocabulary term to the correct definition below.

a. Artifacts	l. Mediastinum
b. Bradycardia	m. Murmurs
c. Coronary artery disease (CAD)	n. Multiple-gated acquisition (MUGA) scan
d. Einthoven's triangle	o. Pacemakers
e. Electrocardiogram	p. Perfusion
f. Gallops	q. Rhythm
g. Heart rate	r. Stress test
h. Holter monitor	s. Tachycardia
i. Hyperventilating	t. Telemetry
j. Ischemic	u. Thallium
k. Leads	v. Wave

1. _____ The area where the heart is located in the thoracic cavity.
2. _____ A tracing, or recording, of electrical activity as it moves through the heart.
3. _____ The regularity of the occurrence of heartbeats.
4. _____ Movement away from the baseline.
5. _____ Any irregular or erratic markings on an EKG.
6. _____ A radioisotope that emits gamma rays and is used in nuclear medicine.

© 2011 Pearson Education, Inc.

7. _____ Records cardiac activity while the patient is ambulatory for at least a 24-hour period.

8. _____ Blood flow to the myocardium.

9. _____ Blockage of the arteries that supply the heart muscle.

10. _____ Can be caused by damaged valves, regurgitation or backflow of blood through a valve, or high flow rates, all of which cause a kind of turbulence.

11. _____ When the heart is receiving less than the normal amount of blood flow.

12. _____ Involves an evaluation of the heart's response during moderate exercise while a 12-lead EKG is performed.

13. _____ A pictorial guide to placement of the EKG leads.

14. _____ A rapid heart rate.

15. _____ Heartbeats per minute.

16. _____ Electronic devices that help the heart maintain a normal rhythm.

17. _____ Performed to check blood flow in the myocardium.

18. _____ A slow heart rate.

19. _____ Involves using radio waves to transmit the heart's electrical activity to a central monitoring station.

20. _____ A variety of perspectives or angles.

21. _____ Excessively rapid breathing.

22. _____ An abnormal rhythm indicated by three distinct sounds in each heartbeat.

APPLIED PRACTICE

Follow the directions as instructed with each question below.

1. Identify the type of artifact shown in each of the following figures.

somatic tremors artifact

Baseline sway

© 2011 Pearson Education, Inc.

60 - cycle interference

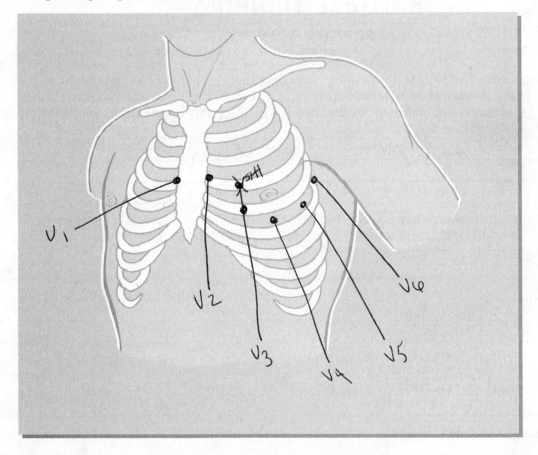

Broken - recording

2. Using the figure provided, identify the placement of chest leads V1–V6.

LEARNING ACTIVITY: TRUE/FALSE

Indicate whether the following statements are true or false by placing a T or an F on the line that precedes each statement.

_____ 1. All patients visiting a physician should have their heart and lungs assessed, regardless of their chief complaint.

_____ 2. The function of the cardiovascular system is to carry oxygen away from the lungs and to all the tissues of the body.

_____ 3. The blood that flows through the heart to the body is used for energy for the heart tissues.

_____ 4. Atrial and ventricular depolarization, plus atrial and ventricular repolarization, make up the cardiac cycle.

_____ 5. When completed, the 12-lead EKG produces a two-dimensional record of cardiac impulses.

_____ 6. Normally, the P–R interval is between 0.12 and 0.20 seconds.

_____ 7. A P–R interval that is too short means that the impulse has reached the ventricles through a longer-than-normal pathway.

_____ 8. The atrial rhythm is determined by measuring the distance between T waves.

_____ 9. The procedure for attaching the sensors will vary slightly, depending on the machine that you are using.

_____ 10. Pharmacological stress testing involves no exercise.

CRITICAL THINKING

Answer the following questions to the best of your ability. Utilize the textbook as a reference.

1. You are performing an EKG. As it is printing, you notice that there is a normal waveform and complex, but the number of beats per minute is more than 100 bpm. What do you think the problem could be? Use the information from your textbook to speculate on what the doctor might diagnose.

_____

_____

_____

_____

2. You are doing a history on a new patient, and she states that she often feels as if her heart has "skipped a beat." Review the information on identifying arrhythmias and dysrhythmias. Name and define this condition.

_____

_____

_____

_____

3. You need to perform an EKG on an elderly female patient, but she seems to be nervous or fearful. What are some of the signs that the patient might exhibit which might lead you to the conclusion that she is fearful of the EKG? How would that fear affect the EKG?

_____

_____

© 2011 Pearson Education, Inc.

RESEARCH ACTIVITY

Utilize Internet search engines to research the following topics and write a brief description of what you find. It is important to utilize reputable websites.

1. Over the past 10 or more years, advancements have been made in addressing heart disease. Conduct research online to find out about some of the procedures and treatments that have been more recently discovered. Write an essay on your findings. Be sure to cite your resources.

CHAPTER 50
Pulmonary Function

CHAPTER OUTLINE

General review of the chapter:

Pulmonary Function
Pulmonary Disorders
Pulmonary Function Tests
Pulmonary Treatments

STUDENT STUDY GUIDE

Use the following guide to assist in your learning of the concepts from the chapter.

I. Pulmonary Functions

1. Pulmonary Functions

   A. Pulmonology is the study and treatment of diseases of the _respiratory_ system.
   B. The primary function of the _respiratory_ system is to transport _oxygen_ to the lungs via the blood stream to all the cells in the body and carry _waste_ products to the outside of the body for elimination.

2. The Purpose of Pulmonary Function Tests

   A. _evaluate_ lung volume and capacity.
   B. Assist in the _different_ diagnosis of patients with suspected obstructive or restrictive pulmonary disease processes.
   C. Assess the _effectiveness_ of drug therapies.

3. Upper Respiratory Conditions

   i. _Acute rihintis common cold_
   ii. _Sinusitis_
   iii. _hayfever_
   iv. _pharyngitis_
   v. _laryngitis_

4. Lower Respiratory Conditions (Name the condition that is described.)

   i. _Obstructive dieases_ : COPD, asthma, acute bronchitis, and emphysema
   ii. _Infectious dieaze_ : Pneumonia, influenza, pleuritis, and Legionnaire's disease
   iii. _malignancies_ : Cancer of the lungs, larynx, and other organs
   iv. _mechanical injuries_ : Pulmonary emboli, pneumothorax, and hemothorax

5. Signs and Symptoms of Respiratory Conditions

   i. _Coughing_
   ii. _Wheezing_
   iii. _____

© 2011 Pearson Education, Inc.

iv. _Rales Crackles_

v. _Sthodor_

vi. _Rhonchus_

vii. _Hemoptysis_

6. Examples of Pulmonary Disorders (Briefly explain each disorder.)

    A. Asthma: _Chronic Inflammatory condition_

    B. Chronic bronchitis: _Chronic obstructive pulmonary diseas_

    C. Cystic fibrosis: _inherited life threatening disorder_

    D. Emphysema: _lung diesease that block airflow_

7. Types of Pulmonary Function Tests

    i. _diagnostic test gas exchange_

    ii. _assessing lungs_

    iii. _Volumes_

    iv. _Capacities_

    v. _rates of flow_

8. Spirometry

    A. Spirometry is a noninvasive test that measures the ability of the lungs to _____.

    B. A diagnostic spirometer is used to evaluate the patient's ability to _____ during a maximum forced exhalation.

    C. The device measures and records the volume exhaled during a _____ length of time.

    D. Air movement is recorded on special paper with a _____ mark for each second and a _____ mark for each liter of oxygen.

    E. The patient must exhale as much air as possible and continue to exhale for _____ seconds for it to have been considered a satisfactory test.

    F. At least _____ efforts at exhalation must be demonstrated.

    G. In patients with healthy lungs, about _____% to _____% of air is exhaled in the first second.

    H. The values are often reported as a ratio: _____/_____.

    I. Patients with normal lungs may have a ratio of _____%.

9. Lung Volumes (briefly explain each type of measurement)

    A. Tidal Volume: _____

    B. Expiratory Reserve Volume: _____

    C. Inspiratory Reserve Volume: _____

    D. Residual Volume: _____

10. Lung Capacities (provide the name of each type of lung capacity explained)

    A. _Total lung Volume_ Volume of the lungs at peak inspiration; equal to the sum of the four volumes.

    B. _Vital Caplaeity_ : Amount of air that can be exhaled following forced inspiration and including maximum expiration.

    C. _Inspiratory_ : Maximum volume that can be inhaled after a normal expiration.

    D. _functional residue capacity_ Volume of air left in the lungs after a normal expiration = ERV and RV

11. Volume Capacity Spirometry

    A. A diagnostic spirometer is used to evaluate the patient's ability to ventilate during a _Maximum forced_ exhalation.

    B. This device measures and records the _volume exhaled_ and the time required to complete the exhalation.

    C. Air movement is recorded on special paper with _Vertical second_ marks and _horizontal liter_ marks.

12. Preparing a Patient for a Spirometry Test
    A. When the procedure is scheduled, a _____ explaining the test should be provided to the patient.
    B. Instruct the patient to refrain from smoking and eating a large meal for _____ to _____ hours and to not use _____ or _____ for 6 hours prior to the test.
    C. On arrival, again explain the test and the steps involved, and determine whether there are any reasons that the test should not be performed, such as _____, _____, or allergy.
    D. Weigh the patient and measure his or her _____ and _____ signs.
    E. _____ and _____ in simple terms what you would like the patient to do.

13. Patient Instructions
    A. If the patient has ill-fitting _____, ask that these be removed.
    B. Have the patient loosen any _____ clothing, ties, girdles, bras, or belts that could impede the test.
    C. The patient should be encouraged to sit because performing the test may cause _____-_____.
    D. The patient's feet should be _____ on the floor, legs _____, and head and chin slightly elevated for the entire procedure.
    E. If the patient prefers to _____ instead of sit, it is acceptable because it will not affect the results and the patient's comfort is important.

14. The Purpose of the Peak Flow Meter
    A. The peak flow meter is a portable, inexpensive handheld device used to measure how _____ _____ from the lungs in _____ _____ breath.
    B. It measures a patient's ability to move air _____ and _____ of the lungs over _____.
    C. It measures the _____ rate at which a patient exhales after taking a maximum breath.
    D. It helps the physician identify patterns of _____ _____ and determine the appropriate treatment.

15. Patient Use of the Peak Flow Meter
    i. _____
    ii. _____
    iii. _____

16. The Role of the Medical Assistant
    A. Teaches the patient and family members the _Use_ for using the peak flow meter.
    B. Helps patients practice in the _Office_ until it is clear that they can perform the procedure correctly.

17. The Purpose of the Oximeter
    i. _____
    ii. _____
    iii. _____

18. General Instructions for Using the Oximeter
    i. _____
    ii. _____
    iii. _____
    iv. _____

19. Arterial Blood Gases
    A. Arterial blood gases measure the amount of oxygen and carbon dioxide, and the _____ of the blood.
    B. They are helpful in evaluating breathing conditions such as _____ and _____.
    C. Provide information on the effectiveness of _____ treatment and the pH of the blood.

© 2011 Pearson Education, Inc.

D. The pH of the blood must be stable, between _____ to _____, or the patient will be in a life-threatening situation.

E. The more carbon dioxide in the blood, the more _____ the blood pH becomes.

F. Usually drawn by respiratory specialists or _____ _____.

G. Arterial blood is drawn from the _____, _____, or arm after cleansing the site.

H. The specimen must be kept on _____ and tested immediately.

I. Direct pressure to the area is applied for _____ to _____ minutes to prevent bleeding.

20. Nebulizers

A. Deliver medication directly to _deeper_ areas in the lungs.

B. The _small_-_volume_ nebulizer is sometimes used to treat breathing difficulties.

C. If a handheld nebulizer is used, a small amount of _aerolife liquored_ medication is placed in the chamber.

   i. The patient is asked to put the nebulizer in his or her mouth and breathe deeply for _8_ to _10_ minutes.

   ii. A _high_-_pressure_ stream of air or oxygen passing through an opening creates the aerosol.

   iii. The aerosol is then delivered into the patient through either a _mouthpiece_ or a _mask_.

21. The Procedure for Using a Nebulizer

A. Note the patient's _____ data.

B. Assemble the handheld nebulizer and select a _mouthpiece_ or a _mask_ for delivery.

C. Using a mask can decrease the amount of the drug that reaches the lungs by about _____% to _2_% because of _deposition_ the face.

D. The mask should be used only when the patient is _unable_ to take the treatment with a mouthpiece.

E. Measure the proper dosage of the drug and _diluent_ into the nebulizer.

F. Set the gas flow to the nebulizer at _6_ to _8_ L/min.

G. Position the patient in a _semi_-_flower_ position.

H. Implement the therapy and encourage the patient to _breathe slowly_ through the mouth.

I. Instruct the patient to deeply inspire periodically and to hold a breath for about _4_ to _10_ seconds.

J. When no aerosol is flowing, _discontinue_ treatment.

K. Monitor and evaluate the patient's _response_ to the treatment.

L. Encourage the patient to _cough_ well, quantifying the amount and describing the type of sputum if the cough is productive.

M. Monitor the patient's pulse, breathing sounds, _peak expiratory flow_ rates, and blood oxygenation.

22. Inhalers

A. Used to deliver a measured amount of medication directly into the _absorption_ _medication_ to dilate the airways.

B. One type of inhaler, a _one_-_various type_ (MDI), holds about 200 doses of the prescribed medication in a pressurized container with an attached mouthpiece.

C. Patient _teaching_ is very important because MDIs are frequently misused, resulting in inadequate treatment.

D. _Written backup_ material is provided to the patient as well.

23. The Procedure for Using an Inhaler

A. The patient should put his or her the mouth over the mouthpiece of the inhaler and inhale when the medication container is _intake_ into the inhaler.

B. An extender is used to improve the _airway_ and to facilitate _intake_ of the medication.

C. A _deposition_ of medication will be dispensed.

© 2011 Pearson Education, Inc.

KEY TERMINOLOGY REVIEW

Match the vocabulary term to the correct definition below.

a. Chronic obstructive pulmonary disease (COPD)

b. Expiratory reserve volume (ERV)

c. Forced expiratory volume (FEV)

d. Forced vital capacity (FVC)

e. Functional residual capacity (FRC)

f. Inspiratory capacity (IC)

g. Inspiratory reserve volume (IRV)

h. Maximal midexpiratory flow (MMEF)

i. Oxygen saturation

j. Peak flow meters

k. Pulmonologist

l. Residual volume (RV)

m. Tidal volume (TV)

n. Total lung capacity (TLC)

o. Vital capacity (VC)

1. _____ The amount of air that can be forcibly inspired after a normal inhale.

2. _____ Measure the patient's ability to move air into and out of the lungs.

3. _____ The volume of air in liters that is forcefully exhaled in the first second of exhalation.

4. _____ The amount of air that can be inhaled after normal expiration.

5. _____ The oxygen content of the blood.

6. _____ The amount of air that can be exhaled following forced inspiration and including maximum expiration.

7. _____ The maximum volume of air expelled when the patient exhales as forcibly and quickly as possible following one inhalation.

8. _____ The average flow rate during the middle half of FVC.

9. _____ The volume of air left in the lungs at the end of an exhalation (around 1200 mL).

10. _____ The amount of air that can be forcibly exhaled after a normal exhalation.

11. _____ The amount of air inhaled or exhaled during normal breathing (about 500 mL).

12. _____ A specialist in lung diseases.

13. _____ The volume of the lungs at peak inspiration.

14. _____ A progressive, chronic, usually irreversible condition in which the lungs have diminished capacity for inhalation and exhalation.

15. _____ The amount of air remaining in the lungs after a normal expiration.

APPLIED PRACTICE

Follow the directions as instructed with each question below.

Scenario

It is a slow day at Fairview Family Practice where you are working as a clinical medical assistant. As you return files to the front office for filing, you see a woman rushing through the front door of the reception area. She states that her teenage son is in the car and suddenly began to have an asthma attack as they were driving. Two of your colleagues rush outside with the mother to assist in transporting the boy to an examination room. At the same time, you inform the physician of the situation. He asks that you gather the "necessary" supplies to assist him in assessing and treating the boy.

© 2011 Pearson Education, Inc.

1. What signs and symptoms would the boy exhibit during a severe asthma attack?
   Difficult respiration or dysprea and Cough

2. What "necessary" supplies would you gather?
   Inhaler, beta 2 medication, oxygen

3. What steps might the physician take to assess and treat the boy?
   Giving him a oxygen mask or give him medication

LEARNING ACTIVITY: TRUE/FALSE

Indicate whether the following statements are true or false by placing a T or an F on the line that precedes each statement.

_____ 1. Pulse oximeters are not available in cordless models.

_____ 2. The respiratory system includes the trachea, bronchitis tubes, lungs, and alveoli.

_____ 3. Pharyngitis is a common upper respiratory condition.

_____ 4. The odor of cigarette smoke is possibly dangerous to patients, especially those with pulmonary problems.

_____ 5. Tuberculosis is considered to be an infectious disease of the blood.

_____ 6. Acute rhinitis is the most common URI.

_____ 7. The pulse oximeter uses an infrared light to measure oxygen in the tissues.

_____ 8. The acronym MMEF stands for minimum midexpiratory flow.

_____ 9. A peak flow meter can detect an asthma attack before symptoms occur.

_____ 10. Cyanosis and drumming of the fingertips are common symptoms of cystic fibrosis and are caused by low levels of oxygen in the blood.

CRITICAL THINKING

Answer the following questions to the best of your ability. Utilize the textbook as a reference.

1. A patient needs to start using an inhaler at home on a daily basis. The patient has rheumatoid arthritis and cannot hold the inhaler in the usual manner. What would you do or how would you teach this patient to use the inhaler?

   _____

   _____

   _____

   _____

© 2011 Pearson Education, Inc.

2. You have a patient with obstructive lung disease who wants to know why he has a hard time breathing. This person has a form of COPD that doesn't allow him to exhale very much. Explain briefly here, as if explaining to the patient, why he feels so short of breath.

_____

_____

_____

_____

RESEARCH ACTIVITY

Utilize Internet search engines to research the following topics and write a brief description of what you find. It is important to utilize reputable websites.

1. Visit www.lungusa.org. What information do you think will be most useful with regard to patient education? What is "hidden" asthma and what age group does it commonly effect? How can this information be useful to patients?

_____

_____

_____

_____

_____

_____

_____

_____

_____

_____

_____

_____

_____

_____

_____

_____

_____

_____

_____

_____

© 2011 Pearson Education, Inc.

CHAPTER 51
Physical Therapy and Rehabilitation

CHAPTER OUTLINE

General review of the chapter:

The Therapeutic Team
Rehabilitation
Patient Assessment
Conditions That Require Physical Therapy
Physical Therapy Methods
Adaptive Equipment and Devices
Diagnostic Testing

STUDENT STUDY GUIDE

Use the following guide to assist in your learning of the concepts from the chapter.

I. The Process of Rehabilitation

1. The Members of the Therapeutic Team
    i.   Physical therapy assistant
    ii. Occupational therapist
    iii. Occupational therapist assistant
    iv. recreation specialist
    v.   excrecise physiologist
    vi. Sport medicine therapist
    vii. massage therapist
    viii. prosthetis or ortnotist

2. Places Where Members of the Therapeutic Team Work
    i.   _____
    ii. _____
    iii. _____
    iv. _____
    v.   _____
    vi. _____
    vii. _____
    viii. _____

3. Educational Requirements for Members of the Therapeutic Team

    A. Physiatrist (MD or DO)
        i.   _____ school graduate
        ii. ____-year residency in physical medicine
        iii. State _____

© 2011 Pearson Education, Inc.

B. Physical Therapist (PT):
    i. _____ degree
    ii. _____ is required in all states.
C. Physical Therapy Assistant (PTA)
    i. _____-year accredited program or associate's degree plus _____.
    ii. _____ is required in all states.
D. Occupational Therapist (OT)
    i. _____ or _____ degree and _____
    ii. Certification from the _____
E. Occupational Therapy Assistant (OTA)
    i. _____- to _____-year certificate program or associate's degree and _____.
    ii. Licensure or _____ is required by most states.
F. Massage Therapist
    i. _____-month to _____-year accredited message therapy program
    ii. Registration or _____ is required by most states.
G. Recreational Therapist (RT) or Certified Therapeutic Recreation Specialist (CTRS)
    i. Usually a _____ degree plus an _____
    ii. Can be certified by the _____ or registration by the
    _____.
H. Recreational Therapy Assistant (Activity Director)
    i. _____- to _____-year certificate program or _____ degree.
    ii. Can be certified by the _____.
I. Sports Medicine (Athletic Trainer, ATS)
    i. _____ or _____ degree
    ii. Can be certified by the _____.
J. Prosthetist/Orthotist
    i. _____ years of college
    ii. _____ years of supervised training

4. The Role of the Physical Therapist

A. Receives special training in assisting patients through the use of *exercise* and *equipment* to regain body motion and strength.
B. Skilled at using special equipment for *strength* muscles and at measuring, fitting, and using *assitive devices* such as crutches, walkers, and canes.

5. The Role of the Occupational Therapist

A. Focuses on increasing the patient's ability to function within his or her own *environmen*
B. Assists the patient by addressing areas that deal with *Activities of daily living* (ADLs).

6. The Role of the Medical Assistant on the Therapeutic Team

A. Carries out orders for treatments, such as the application of heat or cold *compressions* and exercise.
B. Instructs the patient on how to appropriately apply heat or cold *compress* at home.
C. Demonstrates the use of assistive devices such as *canes* and *cructhes*

7. The Process of Rehabilitation

A. Assists the patient in regaining a state of health and the _____ _____ of functioning possible.
B. The _____ approach addresses every aspect of a patient's well-being, not just the present disease or injury.
C. _____ are set for each patient by the professionals on the case and are suited to the individual patient's needs.
D. The patient is assisted in resuming activities of _____ _____.

© 2011 Pearson Education, Inc.

E. During rehabilitation, special attention should be paid to psychological problems, such as
_____ and _____, that can occur from a feeling of loss of control over one's life.

8. Reasons for Receiving Rehabilitation
   i. Surgery such as hip and knees, replacement
   ii. Trauma such as broken bones
   iii. Catastrophic illness, such as smoke
   iv. Disease conditions resulting in musle

9. The Physician's Assessment of a Patient for Rehabilitation
   A. _____ and _____ the patient's limbs and joints to evaluate muscle strength and flexibility.
   B. Evaluates the patient's _____ for clues to specific problems.
   C. Evaluates the patient's _____ to assess symmetry.

10. Conditions That May Require Physical Therapy (Provide the name of each condition described.)
    A. Amputation: The removal of an extremity because of injury or disease
    B. Arthritis: The inflammation of a joint that usually causes pain and swelling
    C. Burn: Damage to the skin from first, second, or third degree burns that result in strictures, decreased mobility, and stiffness
    D. 1st degree burn: Damage to the superficial layer of skin or the outer layer of the epidermis with no scarring, but resulting in erythema
    E. 2nd degree burn: Damage that extends through the epidermis and into the dermis, causing vesicles and scarring
    F. 3rd degree burn: Damage to the full thickness (the epidermis and dermis) and into the underlying layers of the skin with scarring
    G. Cardiovascular disease: Diseases of the circulatory and cardiac systems
    H. Cerebral palsy: A nonprogressive paralysis caused by defects in the brain or birth trauma
    I. Cevebrovascular dental (CVA): Hemorrhaging or clotting in the brain that can result in unconsciousness or paralysis (stroke)
    J. Muscular dystrop: An inflammatory disease of the central nervous system, generally strikes adults between the ages of 20 and 40; causes progressive weakness and numbness
    K. multiple sclerosis: A wasting disease of the muscles
    L. Osteopor osis: A disease that results in a reduction of bone mass, which frequently occurs in postmenopausal women; can result in back pain and fractures
    M. Parapegi: Paralysis of the lower portion of the body
    N. Parkinson disease: A chronic nerve disease with fine tremors, a slow gait, muscular weakness, and rigidity
    O. Poliomye: An acute viral disease that causes an inflammation of the gray matter of the spinal cord, resulting in paralysis in some cases; it has been brought under partial control through vaccinations
    P. Quadriplegi: Paralysis of all four extremities of the body
    Q. Rheumatoid arthritis: A form of arthritis with inflammation of the joints, swelling, stiffness, and pain

11. Physical Therapy Methods
    i. massage
    ii. excercise
    iii. heat and application
    iv. electricity
    v. ultraviolet radiation
    vi. ultrasonic diathermy

vii. _hydrotherap_

viii. _excetricity_

12. Massage

    A. Involves using one's hands to _____ or apply _____ to parts of a patient's body.

    B. Performed to promote muscle relaxation, improve _____ _____, and reduce tension.

    C. Can help to restore _____ and decrease pain.

    D. Considered a form of _____ exercise.

13. Categories of Massage Practiced by Massage Therapists (Provide the name of the type of massage described.)

    A. _____ or _____ massage: Most commonly used in the United States, includes stimulating blood circulation through the soft tissues.

    B. _____ _____ massage: Used to release chronic patterns of tension or pain by applying massage and pressure at deeper levels.

    C. _____ _____ massage: Concentrates finger pressure directly to individual muscles to release "trigger points," or knots in the muscles.

14. Exercise Therapy

    A. Conducted to maintain or _____ fitness.

    B. Can help increase or establish lost _____ _____, improve circulation, relieve stress, correct posture issues, and increase _____.

    C. Twenty to thirty minutes, _____ times a week is recommended for healthy adults.

15. Types of Exercises (Provide the name of the type of exercise described.)

    A. _____: Strengthens the cardiopulmonary system.

    B. _____: Maintains uniform (unchanging) tension or tones the muscles upon stimulation.

    C. _____: Involves contractions with muscles fixed in place so that the tension occurs without noticeable movement.

    D. _____: Results in muscle elongation.

16. Range-of-Motion Exercises (Describe each of the following types of exercises.)

    A. Active range of motion (AROM): _____

    B. Passive range of motion (PROM): _____

    C. Active assist range of motion (AAROM): _____

17. Types of Body Movements Used in a Range-of-Motion Assessment

    i. _____

    ii. _____

    iii. _____

    iv. _____

    v. _____

    vi. _____

    vii. _____

    viii. _____

    ix. _____

    x. _____

    xi. _____

    xii. _____

    xiii. _____

    xiv. _____

© 2011 Pearson Education, Inc.

18. Guidelines for Performing Range-of-Motion Exercises

    A. Perform each exercise _____ times unless otherwise ordered by the physician.

    B. The patient should attempt to do as much as he or she is able without _____.

    C. No body part should be forced beyond the _____ range.

    D. No exercise should bring on _____.

    E. If joints are _____ or swollen, the exercise should not be performed.

    F. Limbs should be supported at the _____ when exercising.

19. The Benefits of Applying Heat

    i. _____

    ii. _____

    iii. _____

    iv. _____

    v. _____

20. Methods for Applying Moist Heat

    i. _____

    ii. _____

    iii. _____

    iv. _____

    v. _____

    vi. _____

    vii. _____

21. Methods for Applying Dry Heat

    i. _____

    ii. _____

    iii. _____

    iv. _____

    v. _____

22. Methods for Applying Cold

    i. _____

    ii. _____

    iii. _____

    iv. _____

23. Other Physical Therapy Methods (Explain how both types work.)

    A. Ultraviolet radiation: _____

    B. Ultrasound: _____

II. Adaptive Equipment and Devices

    1. An Overview of Adaptive Equipment and Devices

        A. Equipment is used to assist recovery from physical _____ or _____.

        B. Includes wheelchairs, walkers, canes, crutches, and special furniture, such as _____ chairs and _____ chairs.

        C. _____ aids or _____ assistive devices are designed to enable the patient to ambulate.

        D. Other devices, including braces, casts, traction, prostheses, splints, and slings, are used to manipulate the patient's damaged _____ and _____.

    2. Crutches

        A. Allow the patient to walk without placing weight on the _____ _____.

        B. _____ is transferred to the arms and hands.

        C. Made from _____ or _____ and should have a _____ tip at the end to prevent slipping on a smooth floor surface.

3. The Three Most Common Types of Crutch
    A. Axillary crutch
        i. A tall crutch with a _____ and _____ that reaches from the ground to under the _____.
        ii. Commonly used for patients who have sustained a _____.
    B. Lofstrand (forearm crutch)
        i. A single aluminum tube with an _____ that fits snugly around the patient's forearm and uses a handgrip for weight bearing.
        ii. Allows the patient to release the _____ to use the hand while still having the crutch held in place by the _____ for support.
    C. Canadian or elbow crutch
        i. A variation of the _____ that extends farther up the arm.

4. Axillary Crutch Measurement
    A. Measurement has to be determined carefully to prevent pressure damage to the _____.
    B. If crutches are too long, the patient may develop a condition known as _____ _____, resulting in muscle weakness in the arm, wrist, and hand.
    C. Back pain, nerve damage, and injury to the _____ and palms of the hands can occur if the crutches are improperly fitted.

5. Steps for Measuring Axillary Crutches
    A. Have the patient wear _____ _____ and stand straight.
    B. Place the crutch tips _____ to _____ inches to the side and _____ to _____ inches in front of each foot.
    C. Adjust the crutch, using the bolts and nuts at the sides of the crutch, so that the axillary crutch bars are _____ _____ widths below the axillae.
    D. Next, adjust the handgrips so that the patient can flex his or her elbows at a ____-degree angle when the crutch is in place and the patient's hands are on the hand bars.

6. The Four-Point Gait
    A. The four-point gait is a _____ and _____ gait.
    B. Used when a patient can _____ _____ on both legs.
    C. Considered the safest of all gaits because the patient always has _____ points of support in contact with the ground at all times.
    D. Used for patients who may have muscular _____ and some lack of _____.

7. The Three-Point Gait
    A. Used when one leg is _____ than the other or when there is no weight bearing on one leg.
    B. Patient must have good _____ coordination and _____ strength.
    C. To use this gait, the patient must be able to support his or her _____ _____ on one leg.
    D. Have the patient move both crutches and the _____ leg forward and then move the _____ leg forward while his or her weight is balanced on both crutches.

8. The Two-Point Gait
    A. The two-point gait is _____ than the four-point gait.
    B. Used by the patient who can bear some weight on both _____ and has good _____.
    C. Occurs when a crutch and the opposite foot are moved _____ at the same time.

9. Swing Gaits
    A. Used by patients who have severe leg disabilities such as _____ or _____.
    B. They may use either of the two swing gaits (Name the two swing gaits described.)
        i. _____-___ _____: The patient moves the crutches forward, lifts his or her body, and then swings the legs up to the same point.

© 2011 Pearson Education, Inc.

ii. _____-_____ _____: The patient moves the crutches forward, as in the swing-to gait, and then swings the legs past the crutches.

10. Procedure for Sitting with Crutches
    A. The patient should face _____ and then _____ into a straight-back chair with arm rests until the back of his or her legs touch the chair seat.
    B. Crutches should be placed in the hand on the _____ side of the body, opposite the _____ leg.
    C. The patient should grasp the _____ _____ with the other hand and lower him- or herself gently into the chair.

11. Procedure for Standing with Crutches
    A. The patient should place the crutches in the hand on the _____ side of the body to use as support.
    B. The patient should move or _____ his or her body forward in the chair.
    C. The patient should grasp the chair arm with the free hand on the _____ side.
    D. The patient should push up to a _____ position.

12. Canes
    A. Used by patients who have muscle or bone weakness on _____ _____ or need assistance with balance.
    B. Two common types of canes are the _____ cane and the _____-_____ cane.
    C. All canes should have _____ tips to prevent slipping.

13. Walkers
    A. Walkers are assistive devices made of _____.
    B. Provide a base of support for patients who need help with _____ and _____.
    C. Should be adjusted to the patient's height and reach just below the patient's _____.
    D. A stationary walker must be picked up by the patient, moved forward, and then used as a base of support while the patient walks into it. This requires strong _____ _____ development.
    E. A walker with wheels can be used by patients who have good _____ and _____.

14. Wheelchairs
    A. Wheelchairs are hand manipulated or _____ _____.
    B. Many patients _____ their own wheelchairs.

15. Considerations When Transferring a Patient from a Wheelchair
    A. Always think of moving a patient as the process of _____ him or her from one place to another.
    B. In many cases, the patient is _____ with the techniques necessary for the transfer and will be able to assist the medical assistant.
    C. A patient who is paralyzed on one side of the body (hemiplegia) or who has a general weakness can be moved from a wheelchair by _____ the patient so that he or she can use the _____ leg to assist you.
    D. Explain to the patient that this _____ technique is used to prevent _____ to the patient and to the individual assisting with the transfer.

16. Braces
    A. Braces are one type of _____ used to support weakened body parts, correct deformities, and prevent joint movement.
    B. May be made out of metal, plastic, or _____ and are customized to the patient's needs and anatomy.

C. To wear this type of assistive leg device, the brace is placed in the patient's _____, the patient's _____ is inserted, and a _____-and-_____ strap is used to hold the brace in place.

D. Any orthotic positioned over a _____ _____ must be padded to avoid skin breakdown.

17. Casts

A. Applied over a _____ to protect the skin.

B. Fiberglass and plastic casts dry quickly, while a _____ of _____ cast may take up to _____ hours to dry.

C. Made from a variety of _____ materials that the physician will mold to fit the body part.

D. A cast can be considered to be a form of _____ bandage.

E. Casts are generally applied using a wet _____-_____ material around a _____ liner and cotton padding over the limb. As the cast dries, it becomes hard.

F. Newer _____ fiberglass materials are being used to form casts that are lighter in weight than a plaster cast.

18. Assisting in Cast Placement

A. Use caution when handling fiberglass materials by wearing protective _____ or an _____ shield.

B. It may be necessary to hold the limb at the _____ areas as the cast is being applied.

C. Remember to handle a damaged limb _____.

D. After the cast has been applied, it must be left _____ during the drying process.

E. The limb may need to be supported on a _____ at this time.

F. The patient should be cautioned against _____ around until the cast is dry.

G. The cast may become _____ or even _____ during the drying process. This is normal.

H. The patient's limb should not become _____ or _____ once the cast has been applied.

I. Check the _____ of the cast and report any changes to the physician.

J. The medical assistant should make frequent checks of the patient's _____.

19. Cast Issues That the Patient Should Report

i. _____
ii. _____
iii. _____
iv. _____
v. _____
vi. _____
vii. _____
viii. _____
ix. _____

20. Traction

A. Traction is a method of _____ or _____ in _____ directions.

B. Used to _____ fractures and correct _____.

C. Reduces _____ of the _____ or other musculoskeletal conditions.

21. Two Types of Traction

A. Skeletal traction
    i. Performed on _____.
    ii. Applied by the physician to the patient's bone by inserting a _____ or _____ through the bone.

B. Skin traction
    i. Done by the physical therapist by attaching _____ and strips of _____ to the skin.

© 2011 Pearson Education, Inc.

ii. _____ are then attached to the material and tension is applied to reduce painful muscle spasms.

iii. This type of traction can be set up in a patient's _____.

22. The Prosthesis

A. A prosthesis is an artificial replacement for a _____ body part.

B. A benefit of immediate fitting is that the patient is able to begin _____ the next day.

C. The decision to select a specific type of fitting rests with the physician and must include an assessment of the patient's overall _____, age, and _____ to learn to use the new limb.

23. The Elements of a Neuromuscular Evaluation

i. _____

ii. _____

iii. _____

iv. _____

v. _____

24. Electromyography (EMG)

A. Consists of using an electromyograph to test the _____ _____ in the muscles.

B. Most often performed when a patient complains of muscle _____ or _____.

C. Consists of electrodes, an _____ to visually produce the waves of muscle activity, an _____, a loudspeaker, an electrical stimulator, and a camera.

D. The patient may receive sedation before this test is conducted, because the stimulation from the _____ _____ can be painful.

E. Consists of inserting a _____-_____ needle electrode through the skin and into a muscle and then sending a small amount of electrical current into the muscle.

F. The procedure permits the physician to examine _____ parts of muscles.

G. Abnormal results are found in conditions such as _____ _____ _____ (ALS), muscular dystrophy, and peripheral nerve damage.

H. The electrical activity of the muscle that is recorded on graph paper or on film is known as an _____ (EMG).

25. Surface Electromyography (SEMG)

A. Involves less _____ for the patient.

B. The results are less _____.

C. In this test, electrodes are attached to the _____ of the body to detect electrical activity.

D. Electrical stimulation with _____-_____ current is helpful to stimulate the nerves that supply muscles.

E. An electrical current is applied using _____ _____ electrodes.

F. This is a passive means of stimulating muscles when a patient cannot _____ because of injury or disease.

26. Transcutaneous Electric Nerve Stimulation (TENS)

A. TENS is another way of using _____ _____ in physical medicine.

B. A TENS unit is attached to the patient at the _____ area, and a _____ dose of current is sent to the muscle to help control intractable pain when medication has not been effective.

C. TENS units may be used at _____.

27. Evoked Potential Studies

A. The study of the responses within the brain to _____ _____ such as light, sound, and touch is called an evoked potential study.

B. The tests are considered _____ because no equipment or needle is inserted into the body.

C. Two types of evoked potential studies (Name the type described.)

    i. _____ _____ _____ _____ (BAER): Used to assess the auditory nerve pathways. Useful in diagnosing auditory tumors and lesions.

    ii. _____ _____ _____ (SEP): Used for diagnosing nerve function defects in peripheral nerves (e.g., in the legs).

KEY TERMINOLOGY REVIEW

Without using your textbook, write a sentence using the selected key terms in the correct context as discussed in material covered in Chapter 51.

1. *ambulation*

2. *atrophy*

3. *contracture*

4. *diathermy*

5. *effleurage*

6. *erythema*

7. *exudate*

8. *friction*

9. *goniometer*

10. *heat hydrotherapy*

© 2011 Pearson Education, Inc.

11. *hemiplegia*

_____

_____

12. *holistic*

_____

_____

13. *massage*

_____

_____

14. *modalities*

_____

_____

15. *orthotist*

_____

_____

16. *petrissage*

_____

_____

17. *physiatrist*

_____

_____

18. *physiatry*

_____

_____

19. *prosthesis*

_____

_____

20. *prosthetist*

_____

_____

21. *range of motion (ROM)*

_____

_____

22. *rehabilitation*

_____

_____

23. *Reiki*

_____

_____

© 2011 Pearson Education, Inc.

24. *suppuration*

_____

_____

25. *tapotement*

_____

_____

APPLIED PRACTICE

Follow the directions as instructed with each question below.

1. Read the following scenario and answer the corresponding questions.

> **Scenario**
>
> It is a busy Monday morning, and you are working as a clinical medical assistant at an orthopedic office. Rachel Dade, an administrative MA, has just informed you that an emergency appointment was just scheduled for Li Chen, a teenager who injured his lower leg while participating in a soccer game during gym class. While he is currently en route to the office, his parents have arrived and are insisting that he be treated using traditional Chinese medicine. Explain how you would address their wishes and traditions.

Ask a person who is higher in position can treat this ~~person~~ patient. If not the other dotors that can help.

_____

_____

_____

2. Create a diagram of the four-point gait as a tool for explaining the use of crutches to an 8-year-old child.

© 2011 Pearson Education, Inc.

LEARNING ACTIVITY: TRUE/FALSE

Indicate whether the following statements are true or false by placing a T or an F on the line that precedes each statement.

_____ 1. Bones are classified according to structure, including flat, round, short, and long.

_____ 2. The three-point gait requires good coordination and muscle strength.

_____ 3. Bursitis is a form of arthritis.

_____ 4. Diathermy is useful in treating muscular disorders, tendonitis, arthritis, and bursitis.

_____ 5. In order to have access to a wheelchair, patients must be able to drive an automobile.

_____ 6. Cryotherapy is using cold for therapeutic purposes.

_____ 7. Prolonged use of a brace may weaken muscles.

_____ 8. Casts are made of plaster, plastic, fiberglass, and metal.

_____ 9. The immediate fitting of a prosthesis involves fitting the patient immediately after the limb is removed, sometimes before leaving the operating room.

_____ 10. There are four types of crutches: axillary, Lofstrand or forearm, Canadian or elbow, and bipedal crutches.

CRITICAL THINKING

Answer the following questions to the best of your ability. Utilize the textbook as a reference.

1. Review the case study at the beginning of this chapter in the textbook. Explain why it is important that Samra wheel Sylvia to the examination room rather than have Sylvia wheel herself.

   _____

   _____

   _____

   _____

2. Without looking back at the material, imagine that you are working in an orthopedic office and a 19-year-old college football player has been brought into the clinic by his coach. He has been seen by the doctor, and X-rays have been taken and looked at by the doctor. He was diagnosed with a strain and you are preparing him for application of a cast by the technician. The patient insists that he has a sprain, not a strain, and asks that you explain to him the difference between the two. From your memory of the material, write your answer. Then check the book and write a correct answer if yours differs.

   _____

   _____

   _____

   _____

3. A patient calls in and has questions after reading her cast care written instructions. She asks how she is supposed to bathe or take a shower. What patient education/instructions would you give her?

   _____

   _____

   _____

   _____

RESEARCH ACTIVITY

Utilize Internet search engines to research the following topics and write a brief description of what you find. It is important to utilize reputable websites.

1. Research new materials and advances being made in prosthetics. What information do you find most interesting and why?

_____

_____

_____

_____

_____

_____

_____

_____

_____

_____

_____

_____

_____

_____

_____

_____

_____

_____

_____

_____

_____

_____

_____

© 2011 Pearson Education, Inc.

CHAPTER 52

Math for Pharmacology

CHAPTER OUTLINE

General review of the chapter:

Mathematics Review
Weights and Measures
Drug Calculations
Rules for Conversion
Calculating Pediatric Dosages

STUDENT STUDY GUIDE

Use the following guide to assist in your learning of the concepts from the chapter.

I. Math for Pharmacology

1. Weights and Measures Used to Calculate Medication Doses

    A. Most physician and facilities have moved to the _____ system when calculating medication doses.

    B. The medical assistant must be familiar with both the apothecary and metric systems because occasionally, medications do appear in the _____ system.

2. The Apothecary System

    A. The dry weight measurement is based on the _____.

    B. _____ numerals are used when numbering in the apothecary system.

    C. It is important to note that the unit of measurement in the apothecary system is placed before the _____ number.

3. Rules for Writing an Apothecary Notation

    A. The unit or _____ comes before the _____.

    B. Use fractions to designate amounts less than _____.

4. The Metric System

    A. Metric system prefixes (Indicate the value of each.)
        i. Kilo = _____
        ii. Hecto = _____
        iii. Deka = _____
        iv. Deci = _____
        v. Centi = _____
        vi. Milli = _____
        vii. Micro = _____

5. Guidelines for Converting Within the Metric System

    A. No change is required to change milliliters into _____ _____ because they are equal to each other.

© 2011 Pearson Education, Inc.

B. To convert liters to milliliters, _____ the liters by _____ or move the decimal point _____ places to the _____.

C. To convert milliliters to liters, _____ the milliliters by _____ or move the decimal point _____ places to the _____.

6. Metric System Dosages

   A. In the metric system, the dosage is written as a _____ number first, followed by the unit of measurement.

   B. Commonly used equivalents for the apothecary and metric systems include the following
      i. Apothecary 1 gr = Metric _____
      ii. Apothecary 5 gr = Metric _____
      iii. Apothecary 10 gr = Metric _____
      iv. Apothecary 15 or 16 gr = Metric _____
      v. Apothecary 15 or 16 m = Metric _____

7. The Ratio Method of Calculating Dosages

   A. A ratio establishes a relationship between two _____.

   B. The proportion resulting from the fraction ½—or the ratio—could be _____ = ½, or _____.

   C. The symbol _____ is used for the unknown quantity.

8. Cross Multiplying

   A. Multiply the _____ number on the _____ side of the equals (=) sign by the _____ number on the _____ side of the equals sign.

   B. The _____ number on the _____ is multiplied by the _____ number on the _____.

   C. Then divide both sides by the number with the _____.

9. The Formula Method

   A. The calculation formula
      i. Available _____ is the _____ of the drug in stock.
      ii. Available _____ is the _____ of the drug in the container.
      iii. Ordered _____ is the physician's order.
      iv. The amount to be given is the _____ quantity.

10. D/H × Q Formula

   A. D = _____
   B. H = _____
   C. Q = _____

11. Guidelines for Conversion

   A. To change grains to grams, divide by _____.
   B. To change ounces to cubic centimeters or milliliters, multiply by _____.
   C. To change grains to milligrams, multiply by _____.
   D. To change kilograms to pounds, multiply by _____.
   E. To change cubic centimeters or milliliters to ounces, divide by _____.
   F. To change drams to milliliters, multiply by _____.
   G. To change cubic centimeters or milliliters to minims, multiply by _____ or _____.
   H. To change minims to cubic centimeters or milliliters, divide by _____ or _____.
   I. To convert drams to grams, multiply by _____.

12. Clark's Rule for Calculating Pediatric Doses

   A. Doses are based on the _____ of the child.
   B. This rule is followed by dividing the child's _____ by _____ _____ and then multiplying that number by the adult dose.

 © 2011 Pearson Education, Inc.

13. Fried's Rule for Calculating Pediatric Doses

   A. Fried's assumption is that a _____-year-old child could take an adult dose.
   B. The formula uses _____ months in the denominator as the equivalent for _____ years.

14. Young's Rule for Calculating Pediatric Doses

   A. To use this formula, divide the child's age in years by the age plus _____.
   B. Multiply this number by the _____ dose to determine the correct pediatric dosage.

15. West's Nomogram Method of Drug Calculation

   A. This method can be used for both _____ and children.
   B. The chart is frequently found in _____ offices, medical textbooks, and dictionaries.

16. The Body Weight Method for Calculating Pediatric Doses

   A. Uses calculations based on the patient's weight in _____.
   B. This is done by calculating the safe drug dosage in _____ and then multiplying that amount by the child's weight in _____.

KEY TERMINOLOGY REVIEW

Use the key terms found at the beginning of the chapter to finish the sentences below.

1. The bottom number in a fraction is called the _____.

2. _____ is the study of medications and drugs, including their forms, intentions for use, and effects.

3. A _____ is a comparison between two numbers.

4. When writing a decimal number less than 1, you must apply the _____.

5. _____ is the preferred method for calculating pediatric dosages, particularly for oncology and critical care patients and underweight children.

6. The top number in a fraction is called the _____.

7. The _____ is based on a calculation of the child's height and weight, and is expressed in square meters (m^2).

8. The _____ states that it is never appropriate to include a zero after a whole number.

9. The _____ is the most commonly used conversion system for dosage calculations.

10. _____ is the method used to calculate dosages for children who are over 1 year of age.

11. The _____ is considered to be the oldest system of measurement.

12. An _____ occurs when not enough medication is given to achieve the desired effect.

13. The two numbers in a fraction are separated by a _____.

14. Taking too much medication could result in an _____.

15. _____ is used to calculate medications for children under the age of 1.

16. When there are two ratios to compare, they may be set up as a _____.

17. A _____ is made up of both a whole number and a fraction.

18. _____ is the most common law used in the calculation of drug dosages for children.

APPLIED PRACTICE

Complete the following exercises.

1. Basic Math Review: *Do not use a calculator.*

    a. Addition
       1. 18 + 49 = _____
       2. 142 + 730 = _____
       3. 1799 + 283 = _____
       4. 7839 + 943 + 41 = _____
       5. 28845 + 83 = _____

    b. Subtraction
       1. 75 − 52 = _____
       2. 429 − 81 = _____
       3. 1648 − 379 = _____
       4. 612 − 419 = _____
       5. 3527 − 274 = _____

    c. Multiplication
       1. 9 × 3 = _____
       2. 32 × 5 = _____
       3. 815 × 4 = _____
       4. 711 × 30 = _____
       5. 3780 × 210 = _____

    d. Division
       1. 150/15 = _____
       2. 1152/12 = _____
       3. 450/60 = _____
       4. 327/6 = _____
       5. 825/50 = _____

2. Dosage Calculations

    A. The physician orders digoxin 0.125 mg to be given to a patient. On hand is a vial of digoxin marked 250 mcg/mL. How much should the medical assistant administer?

    _____

    _____

    B. The physician orders 500 mg of metformin to be given to a patient. On hand is a bottle of metformin that reads 1000 mg/tablet. How much should the medical assistant administer?

    _____

    _____

    C. The physician orders 125 mg of a medication. On hand is a bottle of the same medication that reads 500 mg/5 mL. How much should the medical assistant administer?

    _____

    _____

    D. The medication that the physician ordered reads 20 mg/kg/day. Your patient weighs 220 lbs. The physician wants the patient to take the medication BID in equal doses. How much will the patient be given for each dose?

    _____

    _____

    E. The physician orders 40 mg of furosemide to be given to a patient. On hand is a bottle of furosemide that reads 20 mg/tablet. How much should the medical assistant administer?

    _____

    _____

© 2011 Pearson Education, Inc.

LEARNING ACTIVITY: MULTIPLE CHOICE

Circle the correct answer to each of the questions below.

1. If the doctor orders 4 mg of a certain medication, and the vial states that there are 2 mg in 1 cc, how many cc's would you give to deliver 4 mg?

    a. 2 cc
    b. 4 cc
    c. 6 cc
    d. ½ cc

2. If the doctor orders 1 dram of medication to be given and the vial states that there is 1 mg in 1 cc, you must _____.

    a. give 1 cc
    b. ask the doctor how to determine the number of cc's
    c. ask the pharmacy
    d. convert from the apothecary system to the metric system and then calculate the dosage

3. When adding and subtracting fractions _____.

    a. you do not always need to have a common denominator
    b. to obtain the common denominator, you must multiply the entire fraction by the correct multiplier
    c. subtract the numerators; the denominator remains the same
    d. All of the above

4. When converting an improper fraction to a mixed number _____.

    a. divide the numerator by the denominator
    b. the remainder, if any, is then placed over the denominator to form the fractional component of the mixed number
    c. reduce the fractional component to its simplest form
    d. All of the above

5. To accurately write an apothecary notation, the following rules should be applied:

    a. The unit or abbreviation comes after the amount.
    b. Use lowercase Roman numerals to express whole numbers 1 through 10, 15, 20, and 30.
    c. Use fractions to designate amounts greater than 1.
    d. The symbol *ss* is used to designate the fraction ¾.

6. Metric conversions are simply accomplished by multiplying or dividing by _____.

    a. 100
    b. 500
    c. 1000
    d. None of the above

7. The apothecary measurement of 5 gr is equivalent to _____ using the metric system.

    a. 65 mg, or 0.065 g
    b. 325 mg, or 0.33 g
    c. 650 mg, or 0.67 g
    d. 4 mL

© 2011 Pearson Education, Inc.

8. The apothecary measurement of 3.5 fl oz is equivalent to _____ using the metric system.

   a. 100 mL
   b. 200 mL
   c. 500 mL
   d. 15 mL

9. The measurement of 60 gtts (drops) is equivalent to the common household measurement of _____.

   a. 1 teaspoon (tsp)
   b. 1 tablespoon (T)
   c. 1 oz.
   d. 2 oz.

10. Which of the following factors should be considered when calculating the correct dose of a drug?

   a. Patient's age
   b. Patient's weight
   c. Patient's current health
   d. All of the above

CRITICAL THINKING

Answer the following questions to the best of your ability. Utilize the textbook as a reference.

1. You have received a physician's order to administer 1 mg of a medication to a patient. It is a medication that is injected into the muscle. As soon as you have given the medication, you realize you measured 1 mL instead of calculating 1 mg. What would you do?

   _____

   _____

   _____

2. An established patient has come in to ask for a new prescription for a medication that she has taken for many years because she is out of refills. The physician is not in the office today, but after checking the medical record and noting that it is the patient's usual medication, the medical assistant calls in a new prescription to the pharmacy and makes a note to have the doctor write the order in the chart when she returns. Is this an appropriate action for the MA, since she used critical thinking to check the chart and felt sure that the physician would approve it? Explain your answer.

   _____

   _____

   _____

RESEARCH ACTIVITY

Utilize Internet search engines to research the following topics and write a brief description of what is found. It is important to utilize reputable websites.

© 2011 Pearson Education, Inc.

1. Visit www.rxlist.com. Navigate through the site and determine how the information on this site could be best used by patients. How could a patient benefit from this website?

_____

_____

_____

_____

_____

_____

_____

_____

_____

_____

_____

_____

_____

_____

_____

_____

_____

_____

_____

_____

_____

_____

© 2011 Pearson Education, Inc.

CHAPTER 53
Pharmacology

CHAPTER OUTLINE

General review of the chapter:

Drug Names
Regulations and Standards
References
Legal Classifications of Drugs
Drug Abuse
General Classes of Drugs
Routes and Drug Administration
Frequently Administered Drugs
Side Effects of Medications
Drug Interactions
Drug Use During Pregnancy
Reading and Writing a Prescription
Abbreviations Used in Pharmacology

STUDENT STUDY GUIDE

Use the following guide to assist in your learning of the concepts from the chapter.

I. Pharmacology

1. The Generic Name

    A. The generic name is typically noted in _____ letters.
    B. Considered to be the drug's _____ name.
    C. A generic drug must meet the requirements of the corresponding _____ name drug.
    D. Typically priced _____ than _____ name drugs.

2. The Brand Name

    A. The brand name is typically noted in _____ letters.
    B. It is also called the _____ name.
    C. It is often a drug's most _____ name.

3. Drug Resources (List the available resources.)

    i. _____
    ii. _____
    iii. _____
    iv. _____
    v. _____

© 2011 Pearson Education, Inc.

4. Drug Classifications (List the three classifications.)

    i. _____

    ii. _____

    iii. _____

5. Controlled Substances

    A. Must always be kept in a _____ cabinet.

    B. Must be labeled according to _____ specifications.

    C. All narcotics should be tracked on a _____ log.

6. Commonly Stocked Injectables Drugs (List the injectable drugs that are typically stocked.)

    i. _____

    ii. _____

    iii. _____

    iv. _____

    v. _____

    vi. _____

    vii. _____

    viii. _____

    ix. _____

    x. _____

    xi. _____

    xii. _____

    xiii. _____

    xiv. _____

    xv. _____

    xvi. _____

    xvii. _____

    xviii. _____

7. The Medication Logbook

    A. Contains a complete list of all _____ medications, including sample products.

    B. Contains the name of each medication, the _____ on hand, and the _____ date.

    C. Contains a section for the patient's name, the _____, the date and time of _____, and the medical assistant's initials.

8. Form DEA 224

    A. Used by physicians to register with the _____.

    B. Allows physicians to _____, _____, or _____ controlled substances.

    C. Renewal is required every _____ years.

9. Commonly Abused Drugs

    i. _____

    ii. _____

    iii. _____

    iv. _____

    v. _____

10. Steps to Take When Drug Abuse Is Suspected
     i. _____
    ii. _____
   iii. _____

II. Routes and Drug Administration

1. Methods for Drug Administration: Parenteral
     i. _____
    ii. _____
   iii. _____
   iv. _____
    v. _____
   vi. _____

2. Methods for Drug Administration: Nonparenteral
     i. _____
    ii. _____
   iii. _____
   iv. _____
    v. _____
   vi. _____
   vii. _____
  viii. _____

3. Checklist for Administering Medication
  A. Be sure that you have the correct _____.
  B. Check and _____ that you have the correct _____ as ordered.
  C. Check that you are giving the correct _____.
  D. Make sure that you are using the correct _____.
  E. Make sure that you are giving it at the right _____.
  F. Be sure that the correct _____ is provided.

4. Examples of Side Effects of Medications: Anaphylactic Shock
  A. Anaphylactic shock is a Life-_____ reaction to a drug, food, or insect bite.
  B. Symptoms of anaphylactic shock
     i. _____
    ii. _____
   iii. _____
   iv. _____
    v. _____

5. Drug Interactions
  A. Factors that contribute to a patient's reaction
     i. _____
    ii. _____
   iii. _____
   iv. _____
    v. _____
   vi. _____

© 2011 Pearson Education, Inc.

6. Method of Administration
   A. The method of administration affects the rate at which the body _____ the medication.
   B. The method is chosen according to the _____ _____.

7. Intolerance to Medication
   A. Common symptoms
      i. _____
      ii. _____
      iii. _____

8. Drug Use During Breast Feeding
   A. Contraindicated medications
      i. _____
      ii. _____
      iii. _____
      iv. _____
      v. _____
      vi. _____

9. Guidelines for the Administration of Medications
   A. Medications/drugs can only be administered to a patient under the supervision of a _____ physician.
   B. The order must be written and _____ on the patient's medical record by the _____.
   C. Medications must be checked _____ times before administration.
   D. All narcotics must be _____ in a record maintained for that purpose.
   E. Medication labels should be clean and _____.

KEY TERMINOLOGY REVIEW

Match the correct medical term with the definition listed below.

a. Adverse effects
b. Bioequivalent
c. Brand name
d. Broad-spectrum
e. Contraindicated
f. Drug abuse
g. Drug dependency
h. Drug Enforcement Administration (DEA)
i. Drug tolerance
j. Generic name
k. Habituation
l. Idiosyncratic
m. Inscription

n. Lethal
o. Over-the-counter (OTC)
p. Pharmacists
q. Pharmacology
r. Prophylactically
s. Proprietary name
t. Side effects
u. Signa (sig.)
v. Subscription
w. Superscription
x. Synthetic
y. Toxic

1. _____ The use of a drug improperly or wrongly.

2. _____ Nonprescription drugs.

3. _____ Dependence on a drug.

4. _____ Equivalent to what is sometimes called the "official" or "nonproprietary" name of a drug.

5. _____ Adverse effects that may cause death.

6. _____ The Latin term for label.

7. _____ Having the same strength and action.

8. _____ This name is often the most familiar name for a specific drug.

9. _____ A decrease in the effectiveness of a drug as the body gets used to having the drug in the system.

10. _____ One who relies on the medication or uses the medication for psychological support has a _____.

11. _____ Contains the patient's name, address, age, and date on the top line.

12. _____ Drugs used to prevent the onset of a condition.

13. _____ The name given to a drug by a specific manufacturer.

14. _____ Undesirable effects from a drug.

15. _____ Medications that are so dangerous for the infant that the mother must stop breastfeeding while she is taking them.

16. _____ Specially trained and licensed professionals who prepare and dispense drugs.

17. _____ The dose cannot always be increased because some drugs can become harmful or _____ in excessive amounts.

18. _____ Require the patient to discontinue the medication because the negative effects outweigh the benefit of taking the medication.

19. _____ Side effects or adverse effects that are specific to the individual.

20. _____ Medications created in a laboratory by artificial means.

21. _____ The agency of the federal government responsible for enforcing drug control.

22. _____ Tells the pharmacist how to mix the drug and how much to provide to the patient.

23. _____ The study of medications and drugs, including their forms, intentions for use, and effects.

24. _____ Antibiotics are effective against a wide range of microorganisms.

25. _____ Gives the name of the medication, the actual ingredients, and the dosage.

APPLIED PRACTICE

Complete the following exercises.

1. It is important for patients to understand the instructions when taking medications. If a patient has a difficult time understanding the English language, it is important to overcome this communication barrier. List the various methods that you might use to overcome this barrier.

_____

_____

_____

_____

© 2011 Pearson Education, Inc.

2. On the right-hand side of the table below, explain the use for each drug listed.

Name	Use
Adrenergic	
Adrenergic blocking agent	
Analgesic	
Anesthetic	
Antacid	
Antianxiety	
Antiarrhythmic	
Antibiotic	
Anticoagulant	
Anticonvulsant	
Antidepressant	
Antidiabetic	
Antidiarrheal	
Antidote	
Antiemetic	
Antifungal	
Antihelminthic	
Antihistamine	
Antihypertensive	
Anti-inflammatory	
Antineoplastic	
Antipruritic	
Antipyretic	

(continued)

© 2011 Pearson Education, Inc.

(Continued)

Name	Use
Antiseptic	
Antitussive	
Astringent	
Bronchodilator	
Cardiogenic	
Cathartic	
Contraceptive	
Decongestant	
Diuretic	
Emetic	
Expectorant	
Hemostatic	
Hypnotic	
Hypoglycemic	
Immunosuppressant	
Laxative	
Miotic	
Muscle relaxant	
Mydriatic	
Narcotic	
Purgative	
Psychedelic	
Sedative	
Stimulant	
Tranquilizer	
Vaccine	
Vasodilator	
Vasopressor	
Vitamin	

© 2011 Pearson Education, Inc.

LEARNING ACTIVITY: MULTIPLE CHOICE

Circle the correct answer to each of the questions below.

1. Which of the following is not included in Schedule II drugs?

   a. marijuana
   b. morphine
   c. cocaine
   d. Dilaudid

2. An injection into the fatty tissue under the skin is a(n) _____ _____ injection.

   a. intramuscular
   b. Z-track
   c. subcutaneous
   d. intradermal

3. The medication abbreviation for twice a day is _____.

   a. b.i.d.
   b. t.i.d.
   c. prn
   d. q2h

4. The drug acetaminophen is also known as _____.

   a. Tylenol
   b. Motrin
   c. iso-butyl-propanoic phenolic acid
   d. All of the above

5. The PDR is divided into six sections. The first white section _____.

   a. contains an alphabetical listing of the generic and brand names of each product
   b. contains an alphabetical listing by category or classification of generic and brand names
   c. contains current information regarding pharmaceutical manufacturers
   d. provides product identification and color photos of tablets and capsules listed alphabetically by the manufacturer

6. OTC medications are regulated by the _____.

   a. AMA
   b. FDA
   c. CSA
   d. CMS

7. Schedule III drugs have _____.

   a. the highest potential for addiction and abuse
   b. moderate to low potential for addiction and abuse
   c. lower potential for addiction and abuse
   d. the lowest potential for addiction and abuse

8. Which of the following are common controlled substances?

   a. anabolic steroids
   b. butabarbital
   c. chloral hydrate
   d. All of the above

© 2011 Pearson Education, Inc.

9. How often should the medical assistant review the inventory to ensure that a sufficient supply of all drugs is available and that no medication has expired?

    a. once a day
    b. once a week
    c. every other week
    d. once a month

10. Which of the following is the abbreviation meaning "before meals".

    a. Aa
    b. Ac
    c. ba
    d. ante

CRITICAL THINKING

Answer the following questions to the best of your ability. Utilize the textbook as a reference.

1. A patient has finished seeing the doctor, and on her way out she asks the medical assistant for a sample of Motrin, which is an OTC medication. The MA gives her two packages but does not document this and does not ask the doctor, because the MA felt that, since Motrin is an OTC medication, getting it without an order would be appropriate. Is this appropriate and if not, why?

   _____

   _____

   _____

   _____

2. When administering medications to children, what considerations should be given?

   _____

   _____

   _____

   _____

RESEARCH ACTIVITY

Utilize Internet search engines to research the following topics and write a brief description of what you find. It is important to utilize reputable websites.

1. Visit the FDA website at http://www.fda.gov/. Navigate through the site to learn more about this organization and the information provided on this site. Write an essay on what you learned by visiting the site.

   _____

   _____

   _____

   _____

   _____

   _____

© 2011 Pearson Education, Inc.

© 2011 Pearson Education, Inc.

CHAPTER 54
Administering Medications

CHAPTER OUTLINE

General review of the chapter:

Medication Administration
Equipment Used for Medication Administration
Administration Procedures: OSHA Standards
Charting Medication Administration
Sites for Intramuscular Injections
Subcutaneous Injections
Intradermal Injections
Intravenous Therapy
Immunizations
Reconstituting a Powdered Medication for Administration

STUDENT STUDY GUIDE

Use the following guide to assist in your learning of the concepts from the chapter.

I. The Administration of Medication

1. Nonparenteral Methods (Name and briefly explain each of the nonparenteral routes that can be used to provide medication to patients.)

   i.   _____ : _____
   ii. _____ : _____
   iii. _____ : _____
   iv. _____ : _____
   v.   _____ : _____
   vi. _____ : _____
   vii. _____ : _____
   viii. _____ : _____

2. The Tuberculin Syringe

   A. _____- to _____-gauge needle.
   B. Used to perform tuberculosis and _____ testing.

3. The Insulin Syringe

   A. _____- to _____-gauge syringe
   B. Injected into the _____, _____, or thigh.

4. Needles

   A. The larger the needle, the _____ is the gauge.
   B. Needle length varies from _____ to _____ inches.
   C. Larges needles are _____- to _____-gauge and are used in _____ care.
   D. Needle length varies, depending on the _____ used and the area to be injected.

© 2011 Pearson Education, Inc.

5. Considerations Regarding Syringes and Needles

   A. There is a puncture-proof _____, or cover, on the needle.
   B. Never handle an un_____ needle.
   C. Any dirty or used needles should never be handled or _____.

6. Single-dose or Multiple-dose Vials

   A. These are the most common forms for _____ medications.
   B. They are glass vials with _____ stoppers to protect the medication inside.

7. Withdrawing Medication from an Ampule

   A. Snap _____ and _____ finger gently against tip of ampule.
   B. _____ neck of ampule.
   C. Use _____ between ampule and thumbs when breaking ampule.
   D. Insert the _____ and withdraw fluid.

8. Prefilled Cartridge Injection Systems

   A. Uses a prefilled, _____-dose cartridge that fits in a special cartridge holder.
   B. The system is convenient because medications do not have to be _____ up prior to injection.
   C. The cartridge holders are _____ and long lasting.

9. OSHA

   A. Stands for _____.
   B. Provides guidelines for the _____ of contaminated needles and syringes.
   C. Outlines follow-up procedures for health care workers who are stuck with _____ needles.

10. The Biohazard Sharps Container

   A. All medical offices must have a _____ proof, rigid, _____ container labeled with an _____ biohazard sticker for the disposal of sharps.
   B. These containers should be replaced and disposed of properly when _____ full.

11. Charting Medications

   A. Parenteral medications and oral medications are charted using the same documentation (List the information that should be provided.)
      i. _____
      ii. _____
      iii. _____
      iv. _____
      v. _____
      vi. _____

II. Injection Methods

   1. The Deltoid Muscle

      A. Works well for _Small_ -volume injections only.
      B. The muscle is found by measuring _two_ finger widths _below_ the _acromin_ process of the shoulder.
      C. Do not give shots in the _back_ of the arm.
      D. Use a _23_ -gauge needle.
      E. For smaller arms, use a _25_ -gauge, _5/8_ -inch needle.

   2. The Vastus Lateralis Muscle

      A. In infants, the vastus lateralis muscle lies _below_ the greater _trochanter_ of the _femur_.
      B. In adults, the vastus lateralis muscle extends from the _middle_ of the anterior _front_ to the middle of the lateral _thigh_ one handbreadth above the _knee_.

   3. The Dorosgluteal Muscle

      A. Patient should lie _prone_ and point toes _inward_.
      B. Draw an imaginary line from the greater trochanter of the _femur_ to the posterior superior _iliac_ spine.

4. The Ventrogluteal Muscle

   A. Place the palm of the **right** hand on the greater trochanter and the **index** finger on the superior **iliac** crest.

   B. Inject in the space between the **index** and **middle** fingers.

   C. Give the injection at a _____-degree angle.

5. Subcutaneous Injections

   A. Used for **small** doses of **nonirritating** medications.

   B. Used in the **deltoid**, the upper back, the **abdomen**, and the thighs.

   C. Given at a **45**-degree angle.

6. Intradermal Injections

   A. Common sites for giving an intradermal injection include the **upper** chest and **upper** back, as well as the **anterior** forearm.

   B. Because just the top level of skin is entered, a small **wheal**, or bubble, that contains the injection fluid appears on the skin.

   C. Do not **rub** the area after giving the injection.

7. The Tuberculin Skin Test

   A. Administered **intraderally**

   B. Performed to determine whether a patient has developed an immune response to the bacterium that causes **tuberculosis**

   C. The test cannot tell if the infection is **active** or **inactive**

8. Tuberculin Skin Test Results

   A. Redness alone at the skin test site is a **expected** reaction.

   B. A firm **bump** is a **positive** reaction to the skin test.

9. Intravenous (IV) Therapy

   A. This process involves administering fluids and solutions directly into a patient's **IV**.

   B. Medical assistants must consult their state **practice** act before attempting any IV procedure.

10. How to Prepare an IV Tray (list the steps)

   i. **Perform hand hygiene**

   ii. **Apply gloves**

   iii. **Prepare IV fluid admistration set**

   iv. **Place the absorbent disposable sheet on the tray**

   v. **Assemble equipment and supplies on tray in ord**

   vi. **If using an IV pole/pump hang the IV solution bag on pol**

   vii. **Notify the appropriate personal tray spread**

   viii. **Remove and discard gloves and perfor hygein**

   ix. **Document procedure**

   x. **Clean the area and equipment according to osh**

III. Immunization

  1. Antibodies and Immunity

   A. Antibodies are **protein** substances that are produced by **lymphoctes** in the spleen, lymph nodes, and tissues.

   B. Can react in response to **antigens** or foreign substances.

   C. Produced **antibody** by the human body when one becomes ill.

  2. Childhood and Adolescent Immunizations

   A. Every year, a new recommended childhood and adolescent immunization schedule is produced by the **American Academy of Pediatric** the CDC's **CDC**, and the American Academy of Family Physicians.

   B. Indicates the recommended **age** for immunizations.

The Advisor committee of Immun

© 2011 Pearson Education, Inc.

3. The Hepatitis B Vaccine

   A. Hepatitis B is spread by the ___HBV___ virus.

   B. Transmitted by contaminated ___serum___ in blood.

   C. A child will receive a total of ___4___ doses before he or she is 24 weeks old.

4. The Diphtheria Vaccine

   A. Given to children in ___5___ doses.

   B. The ___fifth___ dose is given between ___4___ and ___6___ years of age.

   C. Diphtheria is diagnosed through a ___throat___ culture.

   D. The symptoms are ___headache___ ___fever___, and ___sore___ ___throat___.

5. The Pertussis Vaccine

   A. Pertussis is caused by ___whooping cough___, directly and indirectly transmitted.

   B. Only ___pertussis is___ vaccination is needed before the child is immune to the disease.

6. The *Haemophilus influenzae* Type B Conjugate Vaccine

   A. ___1___ out of ___200___ children in the United States under 5 years of age gets Hib disease.

   B. Caused by a ___bacterium___ that is spread through the ___air___.

7. The Hepatitis A Vaccine

   A. Hepatitis A affects the ___liver___.

   B. Spreads through personal contact or by eating ___contaminated___ food or drinking water.

   C. The vaccine is given to children over ___2___ years old.

8. The Poliovirus Vaccine

   A. Has been available since ___1955___.

   B. Polio is caused by a ___virus___.

   C. Spreads through contact with ___feces___

9. Reconstituting a Powdered Medication for Administration

   A. Medications supplied in a powdered form generally have a ___longer___ shelf life.

   B. In order to be injected, these powdered medications must be reconstituted with diluents, usually ___sterile water___

10. Steps for Reconstituting a Powdered Medication for Administration (List the steps.)

   i. Gather supplies perform hand hygiene apply

   ii. Select the correct medication ein diluent 3be

     verfiy the dosage against the physician order

   iii. Remove the top from the poduder medication and the top from the dilbent then wipe the tops of both vials

   iv. Insert a sterile needle through the rubber stopp

   v. Withdraw the apprate amount of diluent add po

   vi. Remove the needle from the vial and discard

   vii. To ensure that the medication is mixed well roll well

   viii. _____

KEY TERMINOLOGY REVIEW

Complete the following sentences using the key terms found at the beginning of the chapter.

1. The _____ site is most commonly used for large volume, deep intramuscular injections or irritating, viscous (thick) medications.

2. _____ are used for dispensing oral medication into the respiratory tract.

3. Meningitis is a result of _____.

4. _____ administration means administering a medication through an injection.

5. An alcohol pad or cotton pad must be used to hold the vial to prevent glass cuts when opening _____.

6. The _____ vaccine, until very recently, was not licensed for children under the age of 2 years.

7. There are two types of polio vaccines: _____ and _____.

8. The _____ injection is commonly used for allergy skin tests in which a minute amount of material is injected within the top layer of skin to determine a patient's sensitivity.

9. _____ is a disease of the nervous system and is caused by a bacterium that enters the body through a break in the skin.

10. Hepatitis _____ is the most common type of hepatitis in the United States.

11. _____, also known as whooping cough, is a respiratory disease that is most common in children under age 4.

12. _____ are given to humans to decrease the susceptibility to disease.

13. _____, or chickenpox, is one of the most common childhood diseases.

14. The _____ site is considered safer than the dorsogluteal site because there are no major nerves or blood vessels in this muscle.

15. A _____ injection is given just under the skin in the fat (adipose) tissue.

16. The _____, or thickness, of the medication being given also determines the gauge of the needle.

APPLIED PRACTICE

Complete the following exercises.

1. On the figure below, label each part of the syringe.

Lumen   Hilt   Hub   Flange

Shaft   1/2 1 1/22CC   Barrel   plunger

2. To demonstrate your knowledge regarding the angle of insertion for intramuscular, subcutaneous, and interdermal injections, indicate on the figure provided which angles represent each type of injection. In addition, provide the names of each of the layers of the skin.

Intramusclur   90°   Sub Stutaneas   45°   Intradermea   10-15°

Epidermis
Dermis
Subcutaneas
Tissue
Muske

© 2011 Pearson Education, Inc.

LEARNING ACTIVITY: TRUE/FALSE

Indicate whether the following statements are true or false by placing a T or an F on the line that precedes each statement.

_____ 1. Artificially acquired active immunity develops in response to receiving vaccinations with active organisms.

_____ 2. The deltoid muscle is located on the lower outer surface of the upper arm.

_____ 3. Transmission of diphtheria is by direct and indirect contact.

_____ 4. Hepatitis B, a form of viral hepatitis, is highly contagious and can be fatal.

_____ 5. Immunity can be either genetic or acquired.

_____ 6. Intramuscular injections are usually given with 25- or 26-gauge needles.

_____ 7. Many liquid medications are prescribed for the pediatric patient because of the ease of administration.

_____ 8. The MMR is given in three doses.

_____ 9. Oral medication is swallowed; it enters the body through the tissues of the gastrointestinal system and is then slowly absorbed into the body.

_____ 10. The vastus lateralis muscle is on the outer portion of the upper thigh and is part of the quadriceps.

_____ 11. When giving a medication using the Z-track method, you need to pull the skin upwards prior to inserting the needle.

CRITICAL THINKING

Answer the following questions to the best of your ability. Utilize the textbook as a reference.

1. Explain why IV infusion of medication is the most dangerous method to administer medication and MUST be the right medication, strength, and amount. Errors with this route can cause serious problems. All routes of medication administration MUST be done accurately, but there are specific reasons why this route is riskier than the others.

   Always check the amount and dosage because each patient medication dosage is difference you don't want to make the patient sick or Allergy reaction

2. Although a very small of amount of bubbles or air injected into the muscle or the subcutaneous tissue would not be harmful, *the medical assistant must never let this happen*. Explain why it is not acceptable to have even tiny bubbles within the medication inside the syringe.

   The patient will not get correct medication you are not giving them all

© 2011 Pearson Education, Inc.

RESEARCH ACTIVITY

Utilize Internet search engines to research the following topic. It is important to utilize reputable websites.

1. Some parents believe that it is not necessary to immunize their children. To learn more about this issue, conduct research online and then write an essay on your findings. Conclude with a synopsis of what you believe about the necessity of immunizations for children. Be sure to cite your sources.

_____

_____

_____

_____

_____

_____

_____

_____

_____

_____

_____

_____

_____

_____

_____

_____

_____

_____

_____

_____

_____

_____

_____

_____

© 2011 Pearson Education, Inc.

CHAPTER 55
Patient Education

CHAPTER OUTLINE

General review of the chapter:

Patient Education
How Adults Learn
Teaching Methods and Strategies
Developing a Teaching Plan
Learning Environment
Teaching Resources
Patient Issues
Health and Wellness
Mind–Body Connection
Teaching the Patient

STUDENT STUDY GUIDE

Use the following guide to assist in your learning of the concepts from the chapter.

I. Teaching Methods and Strategies

  1. The Responsibilities of the Medical Assistant When Teaching the Patient

    A. Be prepared to educate the patient on behaviors that might _____ the health of the patient.

    B. Prepare the patient for a _____.

    C. Improve _____ with therapy or medication.

    D. Educate the patient about his or her own _____ behaviors.

  2. Activities and Techniques for Teaching

    i. _____

    ii. _____

    iii. _____

    iv. _____

    v. _____

  3. Guidelines for Creating a Community Resource Brochure

    A. Identify _____ _____ that are available to help patients with disease prevention or health promotion, such as smoking cessation or weight loss.

    B. Research information found in a _____ _____, newspaper, or website.

    C. Create an attractive _____ for distribution to patients that includes the name, location, telephone number, and services offered by the resources.

    D. After the brochure has been polished, obtain approval from the _____ _____ or physician before distributing the brochure to patients.

4. Information to be Included in a Public Relations Brochure

    i. _____

    ii. _____

    iii. _____

    iv. _____

    v. _____

    vi. _____

    vii. _____

    viii. _____

5. Motivational Incentives for Adult Patients

    i. _____

    ii. _____

    iii. _____

    iv. _____

    v. _____

6. Roadblocks to Effective Patient Learning

    i. _____

    ii. _____

    iii. _____

7. Communications and Language Roadblocks

    i. _____

    ii. _____

    iii. _____

    iv. _____

    v. _____

    vi. _____

    vii. _____

    viii. _____

    ix. _____

    x. _____

    xi. _____

8. The Effects of Cultural Influences

    i. _____

    ii. _____

    iii. _____

    iv. _____

    v. _____

    vi. _____

9. The Effects of the Patient's Stage of Development

    A. Attitudes and _____ have a powerful impact on learning readiness.

    B. Some patients may _____ education because of previous negative experiences.

    C. In addition, illness affects people in different ways; _____ and _____ can be obstacles to learning.

10. Ways to Overcome Roadblocks

    A. Create a learning _____ that encourages patient readiness.

    B. Consider _____ the session if the patient is not feeling well at the time.

11. Lecture

    A. The advantages of lecturing include efficiency and the absence of limits on the _____ of patients.

© 2011 Pearson Education, Inc.

B. The disadvantage of lecturing is that there is no _____ in which to handle an individual patient's confusion.

12. Role-Playing
   A. Definition: The patient participates in a _____ _____ in which he or she acts out a story.
   B. Advantages
      i. _____
      ii. _____
   C. Disadvantages
      i. _____
      ii. _____

13. Case Problems
   A. Definition: Apply _____ to real situations.
   B. Advantages: They are believable and concrete instead of _____.
   C. Disadvantages: Significant _____ may be missing, and effectiveness depends on the _____.

14. Demonstration/Return Demonstration
   A. Definition: _____ patients how to do something, and then _____ has them do the same procedure.
   B. Advantages
      i. _____
      ii. _____
   C. Disadvantages
      i. _____
      ii. _____
   D. Usefulness
      i. _____
      ii. _____

15. Contracting
   A. Definition: Sets up goals with clear _____ and _____ for the patient.
   B. Advantages
      i. _____
      ii. _____
      iii. _____
   C. Disadvantages
      i. _____
      ii. _____
      iii. _____
   D. Usefulness
      i. _____
      ii. _____

16. The Use of a Significant Other
   A. Definition: Teaches a close _____/_____ the same information that the patient is being taught.
   B. Advantages
      i. _____
      ii. _____
   C. Disadvantages
      i. _____
      ii. _____
      iii. _____

D. Usefulness
    i. _____
    ii. _____
    iii. _____

17. Past Experiences

  A. Definition: Build on what has been _____ in the past instead of creating a new set of knowledge.

  B. Advantages
    i. _____
    ii. _____

  C. Disadvantages
    i. _____
    ii. _____

  D. Usefulness
    i. _____
    ii. _____

18. Group Teaching

  A. Definition: Brings together patients who have common _____ needs.

  B. Advantages
    i. _____
    ii. _____
    iii. _____

  C. Disadvantages
    i. _____
    ii. _____
    iii. _____
    iv. _____

  D. Usefulness
    i. _____

19. Programmed Instruction

  A. Definition: _____

  B. Advantages
    i. _____
    ii. _____
    iii. _____
    iv. _____

  C. Disadvantages
    i. _____
    ii. _____
    iii. _____
    iv. _____

  D. Usefulness
    i. _____
    ii. _____

20. Simulations (Games)

  A. Definition: Create a _____ _____ for learning purposes.

  B. Advantages
    i. _____
    ii. _____
    iii. _____

© 2011 Pearson Education, Inc.

C. Disadvantages

    i. _____

    ii. _____

    iii. _____

21. Tests of Knowledge

A. Definition: The patient is given _____ _____ that are related to his or her knowledge of the subject.

B. Advantages

    i. _____

    ii. _____

    iii. _____

C. Disadvantages

    i. _____

    ii. _____

    iii. _____

22. Printed Handouts

A. Definition: Brochures or instruction sheets are printed for the purpose of _____ knowledge to the patient.

B. Advantages

    i. _____

    ii. _____

C. Disadvantages

    i. _____

    ii. _____

23. Diagrams

A. Definition: Diagrams are _____ of concepts in _____ form.

B. Advantages

    i. _____

    ii. _____

    iii. _____

C. Disadvantages

    i. _____

    ii. _____

24. Models

A. Definition: Models are _____ _____ of an object that is produced in a substance such as clay or plaster.

B. Advantages

    i. _____

    ii. _____

C. Disadvantage: _____

25. Film

A. Definition: In this context, a film is considered to be a video, _____ _____, or moving picture.

B. Advantages

    i. _____

    ii. _____

C. Disadvantages

    i. _____

    ii. _____

    iii. _____

© 2011 Pearson Education, Inc.

26. Helpful Materials to Use When Teaching Children

    A. Children may need to see a treatment or procedure performed on a _____ before tolerating it well.

    B. Many children like to _____ equipment that will be used on them, such as a _____ or a blood pressure cuff.

    C. Older children may wish to see videos about their upcoming _____ or other treatments.

27. Considerations for Teaching the Visually Impaired

    A. Visually impaired patients may not be able to read written instructions unless the type is _____ _____, and some may not be able to read it at all.

    B. The medical assistant may need to make _____-_____ instructions of information that is usually written.

    C. Be sure to clear _____ from the office that might impede the patient, and make sure to hold the patient's hand to lead him or her to examinations and procedures.

28. Considerations for Teaching Non–English-Speaking Patients

    A. When the appointment is made, ask the patient if he or she would like to have an _____ present.

    B. The patient may prefer to bring a relative who _____ _____.

    C. Be sure to get the patient's permission to discuss _____ _____ with relatives.

    D. Send _____ _____ home with the patient.

    E. If a large percentage of patients in the office speaks a particular language other than English, it may be helpful to create brochures in _____ _____.

    F. Consider _____ and _____, as well as the patient's likes and dislikes, to promote compliance.

29. Changes That Affect the Elderly Learner

    i. _____

    ii. _____

    iii. _____

    iv. _____

30. Methods to Be Considered When Teaching the Elderly

    A. Use handouts with _____ _____, and use video and audiovisual displays.

    B. _____-_____ slides are preferable to a fast video or movie because the slide can be stopped to reinforce learning.

    C. _____-_____ can be useful as long as the patient's energy level can be maintained.

    D. _____ _____ should be included in the teaching process whenever possible.

    E. The elderly person is accustomed to being in _____ and may not wish to learn anything new if he or she does not see the _____ of doing so.

31. Considerations for Creating a Teaching Plan

    A. Patients may not be honest and open in a busy place where they lack _____.

    B. It is ideal if patient education can take place in a _____-_____ room with privacy.

    C. Sometimes placing patient education materials in racks in examining rooms allows patients to take brochures _____.

    D. If a medical assistant is teaching a patient how to use equipment, then that equipment should be _____ for the patient.

    E. If the patient asks a question that the medical assistant cannot answer, the MA should admit that he or she does not know the answer and _____ _____ to the patient with the answer to the question.

    F. Teaching resources are available for _____, or the MA can develop _____ for the office.

    G. Patients have different _____ styles, and the teaching should match the patient's preferred style.

© 2011 Pearson Education, Inc.

32. Ways to Help Patients Be More Compliant
    A. Ensure a _____ relationship is formed between the patient and the health care provider, physician and other staff such as the medical assistant.
    B. Convey to the patient the knowledge that he or she needs to make _____ decisions about health care.
    C. Reinforce learning and reduce _____ by working out a _____-_____ plan with regular evaluation of progress.
    D. This plan should include an _____ stating what the patient should be able to do, as well as a _____ indicating when the objective should be accomplished.

II Patient Education

  1. The Mind–Body Connection
    A. _____are released when patients are happy.
    B. Characteristics of these proteins
        i. They have _____ properties.
       ii. The benefit _____ functioning.
      iii. They boost _____ to disease.
    C. Negative feelings such as fear, anger, and grief can cause certain symptoms (List these symptoms.)
        i. Increase in _____
       ii. Tightening of the _____
      iii. _____ response

  2. The Reality of Pain
    A. Pain is an unpleasant _____ and _____ experience.
    B. Patients respond differently to pain, depending on their tolerance and _____ _____.
    C. It is important for the medical assistant not to put a _____ value on the patient's pain.
    D. Pain can be _____ and _____.
    E. Sometimes pain is _____, meaning that it is felt in an area other than where it actually occurred.
    F. It is important for the medical assistant to assure the patient that pain _____ is possible.

  3. Considerations for the Various Aspects of Pain
    A. Pain is a _____ experience for the patient.
    B. Pain is what the patient _____ it as.

  4. The Long-Term Effects of Chronic Pain
        i. _____
       ii. _____
      iii. _____
       iv. _____
        v. _____
       vi. _____
      vii. _____
     viii. _____
       ix. _____
        x. _____
       xi. _____
      xii. _____

  5. Teaching about Nutrition (list the elements contained in MyPyramid, developed by the United States Department of Agriculture)
        i. _____
       ii. _____

© 2011 Pearson Education, Inc.

iii. _____

iv. _____

v. _____

6. Teaching about Exercise

A. Before starting any exercise program, a patient should consult the _____ to confirm that it is safe for the patient to exercise.

B. Some patients with heart or respiratory problems may need to have a _____ exercise plan.

C. Patients need to be taught to _____ and _____ _____ properly, and how to exercise without becoming injured.

7. Ways to Reduce Stress

i. _____

ii. _____

iii. _____

iv. _____

v. _____

vi. _____

8. Methods for Stopping Smoking

A. Use nicotine or _____ therapy.

B. Utilize various _____ substitutes.

C. Choose the right _____ to quit smoking.

D. Seek _____ support to help stop smoking.

E. _____ in support groups.

F. Receive information about _____ rates.

9. Preparing a Patient for a Cast Application

A. Explain that casts are applied for the purpose of _____ a broken bone or muscle strain and sprain.

B. A cast may be applied after a _____ _____ on a limb to immobilize the area until healing takes place.

10. Supplies Used for Cast Application

i. _____

ii. _____

iii. _____

iv. _____

v. _____

vi. _____

vii. _____

11. Assisting the Physician with Cast Application

A. It may be necessary to hold the limb at the _____ _____ as the cast is being applied.

B. Remember to handle a _____ _____ gently

C. After the cast has been applied, it must be left _____ during the drying process.

D. The limb may need to be supported on a _____ at this time.

E. The patient should be cautioned against moving around until the cast is _____.

F. The cast may feel _____ or even _____ during the drying process.

12. Observations That Patients Should Report

A. _____ that is restricted by the cast.

B. Pain as a result of the cast _____ the skin.

© 2011 Pearson Education, Inc.

C. Excessive _____ under the cast

D. _____ or _____ in the fingers or toes.

E. Discolored _____ or _____

F. _____ of the limb around the edge of the cast

G. _____ soaking through the cast

H. A _____ _____ coming from the cast

13. Types of Casts (Describe each type.)

    A. Short arm cast (SAC): _____

    B. Long arm cast (LAC): _____

    C. Long and short leg casts: _____

14. Patient Cast Care

    A. Clean the cast with a _____ _____.

    B. Do not _____ or _____ the cast. If the edge seems sharp, apply _____ _____ to the sharp edge or use a nail file to trim it down.

    C. Elevate the extremity with the cast on it to reduce _____ and _____.

    D. Observe the fingers and toes for _____ _____, temperature changes, pain, tingling, or decreased sensation.

    E. Allow the cast material to _____ by exposing it to the air and keeping it uncovered, even during the night. If you apply pressure to the cast before it is dry, you can damage the _____ underneath.

    F. Do not try to _____ under the cast by putting objects into the cast. This will result in broken skin that can lead to infection.

    G. When decorating a cast, use only _____-_____ paints or marking pens; otherwise, the cast will not be able to _____.

    H. Call the physician's office if you smell a _____ odor coming from the cast, lose _____ or blood flow beyond the cast, feel a burning sensation, or notice blood coming from the cast.

    I. After being sure that the patient understands the _____ of cast care, the medical assistant must document the teaching in the patient's chart.

15. Equipment Needed for Cast Removal

    i. _____

    ii. _____

    iii. _____

    iv. _____

    v. _____

16. Procedure for Cast Removal

    A. After performing hand hygiene and draping the patient, explain the process to the patient.

        i. The _____ vibrates and does not _____.

        ii. The patient may feel some _____ and _____.

        iii. The patient may be shocked to see that the skin under the cast has become _____ and the muscle tone has decreased, and may need some reassurance that physical therapy will improve the functioning and appearance of the limb.

    B. The medical assistant should stand near the _____ and hand him or her the necessary equipment as requested.

    C. After the cast is removed, the medical assistant should do the following

        i. _____

        ii. _____

        iii. _____

        iv. _____

KEY TERMINOLOGY REVIEW

Complete the sentence by selecting the correct key term, as found in Chapter 55 of your textbook. A few of the sentences will use one or more key terms.

1. The education process begins with _____, or _____ of the patient's needs.

2. _____ pain is pain that continues over time; _____ pain can occur after surgery.

3. Some patients with heart or respiratory problems may need to have a modified exercise _____.

4. _____—not following a physician's orders—can seriously jeopardize a patient's health and recovery.

5. If a patient is unable to complete a teaching plan, be sure to _____ this in the patient's chart.

6. _____ the plan involves actually teaching the patient what to do.

7. Some procedures that require small-muscle _____, such as flossing the teeth and opening medication bottles, are almost impossible for elderly persons with arthritis.

8. _____ are the goals of patient education.

APPLIED PRACTICE

Explain how you would handle the following scenario.

> **Scenario**
>
> Ethan is an RMA working at a pain management clinic. He often conducts patient education seminars on proper medication administration and methods of pain management. Today, Ethan is working with Aidan Baker, a child who had a below-the-knee right leg amputation, and who is also deaf. Explain how you would approach a child with special needs.

_____

_____

_____

_____

LEARNING ACTIVITY: MULTIPLE CHOICE

Circle the correct answer to each of the questions below.

1. What is the main difference between adult and child learning?
   a. The child expects milk and cookies afterward.
   b. The adult needs self-directed learning.
   c. The adult is stubborn and will tend to refuse most new knowledge.
   d. The child is likely to cry throughout most of the teaching session.

2. Which of the following is essential to an exercise program?
   a. Attractive warm-up clothes
   b. Stretching

© 2011 Pearson Education, Inc.

c. Health club membership
d. A running partner

3. Which of the following is not part of a prevention program?

   a. Meditating
   b. Routine immunizations
   c. Smoking cigars instead of cigarettes
   d. Jogging

4. Which of the following should be part of an effective teaching plan?

   a. Understanding desired outcomes.
   b. Behaving in a commanding, authoritative way.
   c. Using sarcasm and ironic comments when the patient is slow.
   d. Offering private lessons.

5. Which of the following should *not* be an aspect of teaching older adults?

   a. Understanding that older adults may take longer to process new information.
   b. Keeping instructions to the point and providing clear written materials.
   c. Not talking down to an adult.
   d. Keeping a bowl of favorite candies nearby for reinforcement.

6. Which of the following is conducive to a proper learning environment?

   a. The reception area
   b. A private examination room
   c. The hallway
   d. The front desk

7. Which of the following is *not* an appropriate teaching resource?

   a. Audiocassette
   b. Videos
   c. Pamphlets
   d. Personal websites

8. The long-term effects of chronic pain can include _____.

   a. a feeling of helplessness
   b. decreased sleep
   c. lowered self-esteem
   d. All of the above

9. When educating patients with regard to dieting and weight loss, what information should *not* be included?

   a. Successful fad diets
   b. Information regarding how to read food labels
   c. Copies of MyPyramid
   d. All of the above should be given.

10. Which of the following is *not* a phase of patient education?

    a. Implementation
    b. Documentation
    c. Production
    d. Planning

© 2011 Pearson Education, Inc.

CRITICAL THINKING

Answer the following questions to the best of your ability. Utilize the textbook as a reference.

1. **Scenario**

   a. Imagine that you are a family member of a patient with chronic pain and are going with him or her to an office visit. You know that the patient is truly in pain and is not a drug seeker. What do you think you would say or do if the medical assistant or any staff member gave the impression, through body language only, that he or she did not believe that the patient had as much pain as the patient indicated?

   _____
   _____
   _____
   _____
   _____

   b. What do you think you would say or do if the medical assistant did not make eye contact, was not warm and caring, and did not chat at all, except to ask the required questions, and then hurried out when the patient started to ask a question?

   _____
   _____
   _____
   _____
   _____

   c. What do you think you would say or do if the medical assistant would talk over the medication treatment, not with you, but only with the patient, stating that the patient alone needs to be able to handle his or her medications?

   _____
   _____
   _____
   _____
   _____

2. **Scenario**

   You are a new medical assistant, and the physician has asked you to go into the examination room and give patient teaching to Mrs. McCarty about her rheumatoid arthritis pain management plan. The physician has written in the chart what the plan is but you are not very familiar with rheumatoid arthritis. Would you (a) try to do the best you can, (b) ask another MA to tell you what to do or how to do it, or (c) ask the patient to wait while you research office policy manuals and the Internet to figure it out? Choose one of the options and then explain your reasoning.

   _____
   _____
   _____
   _____

3. **Scenario**

   You are a medical assistant at an OB/GYN office. The physician has recently put you in charge of creating a list of resources and materials to be used in a patient education library. What patient

© 2011 Pearson Education, Inc.

education topics would you include in an OB/GYN resource library? List at least three topics and explain why you chose them.

_____

_____

_____

_____

_____

RESEARCH ACTIVITY

Utilize Internet search engines to research the following topics and write a brief description of what you find. It is important to utilize reputable websites.

1. Choose a topic for patient education and search the Internet for reputable information. List at least five reputable websites that could be used for patient education. Also, list at least five items of special interest that you learned.

_____

_____

_____

_____

_____

_____

_____

_____

_____

_____

_____

_____

_____

_____

_____

_____

_____

_____

_____

_____

_____

_____

_____

_____

CHAPTER 56
Nutrition

CHAPTER OUTLINE

General review of the chapter:

Nutrition
Dietary Guidelines

STUDENT STUDY GUIDE

Use the following guide to assist in your learning of the concepts from the chapter.

1. Nutrition

1. Diet and Nutrition (Provide the name of the professional who is described.)
   A. _____: A professional who provides information on foods and nutrition
   B. _____: A professional who promotes good health through proper diet and the use of diet in the treatment of disease

2. Digestion
   A. The actual process the body undergoes when it converts food into _____ _____ that can be absorbed into the blood and used by the body tissues and organs.
   B. The actual digestive process is accomplished by physically breaking down, diluting, dissolving, and chemically splitting into _____ _____, the food substance we consume.

3. Major Nutrient Classes
   i. _____
   ii. _____
   iii. _____
   iv. _____
   v. _____
   vi. _____

4. Carbohydrates
   A. Carbohydrates include the following
      i. _____
      ii. _____
      iii. _____
   B. Carbohydrates are stored in the body as _____.

5. Carbohydrates for Health
   A. _____ carbohydrates are ideal foods for a healthy diet.
   B. They are generally low in _____, high in _____, and a good source of vitamins and minerals.
   C. Excess carbohydrates are stored as _____ (after the small amount of glycogen stores fill up).

© 2011 Pearson Education, Inc.

6. Carbohydrate Consumption Recommendations
   A. Only _____ of calories from refined sugar
   B. Approximately _____ to _____ of calories from carbohydrates
7. Sources of Carbohydrates
   i. _____
   ii. _____
8. Fats
   A. Fats are also called _____.
   B. They do not dissolve in _____.
   C. Some fat is needed in the diet for _____ _____.
   D. Fats are a major _____ source for the body.
   E. Found in animal and _____ food products.
   F. Provide taste, consistency, and _____ to foods.
9. Saturated Fats
   A. Produced by _____ sources.
   B. They have many _____ effects on the body.
   C. No more than _____ of the daily caloric intake should come from saturated fat.
   D. Reducing these fats can help _____ the risk of disease.
10. Unsaturated Fats
   A. Polyunsaturated fat is found in _____ and fish oils.
   B. Monounsaturated fat can lower _____ levels and _____.
11. How Fats Benefit the Body
   A. Serve as a _____ energy source.
   B. Help _____ fat-soluble vitamins.
   C. Provide some _____ to foods.
   D. Satisfy the _____.
   E. _____ the skin and internal tissues.
   F. Are _____ for energy use after the meal.
12. Fat Consumption Recommendations
   A. Only _____ of calories should come from saturated fat.
   B. Less than _____ of total calories should come from fat.
13. Sources of Fats (List the sources for each of the following fats.)
   A. Saturated Fats: _____
   B. Polyunsaturated Fats: _____
   C. Monounsaturated Fats: _____
14. Protein
   A. Forms the _____ of every cell.
   B. Formed from _____ of amino acids.
   C. Protein is needed by the body to accomplish the following
      i. _____
      ii. _____
      iii. _____
15. Reading Food Labels
   A. _____ products are the only foods that provide complete proteins (all nine essential amino acids).
   B. Combining certain _____ proteins can add up to a complete protein.

© 2011 Pearson Education, Inc.

16. Water
    A. Water has no _____ value.
    B. The human body is _____ to _____ water.
    C. _____ holds more water.
    D. _____ holds less water.
    E. The water content is _____ in males than in females and _____ with age.

17. Sources of Water
    i. _____
    ii. _____
    iii. _____

18. The Functions of Water
    A. Carries _____ and nutrients to cells.
    B. Regulates body _____.
    C. Prevents _____.
    D. Replaces water lost through perspiration, respiration, _____, and _____.
    E. Removes waste products from _____.
    F. Protects _____ and tissues.

19. The Amount of Water Needed Varies Because of the Following Factors
    i. _____
    ii. _____
    iii. _____
    iv. _____
    v. _____
    vi. _____
    vii. _____

20. Vitamin Classifications
    A. Water-soluble vitamins (Provide examples of water-soluble vitamins.)
        i. _____
        ii. _____
        iii. _____
        iv. _____
        v. _____
        vi. _____
        vii. _____
        viii. _____
        ix. _____
    B. Fat-soluble vitamins (Provide examples of fat-soluble vitamins.)
        i. _____
        ii. _____
        iii. _____
        iv. _____

21. Requirements for Vitamins
    A. Several conditions increase the requirement for vitamins beyond the usual recommended amounts.
        i. _____
        ii. _____
        iii. _____
        iv. _____

© 2011 Pearson Education, Inc.

22. Sources of Vitamins: Vitamin B1 (thiamine)

    i. _____

    ii. _____

    iii. _____

    iv. _____

    v. _____

    vi. _____

23. Sources of Vitamins: Vitamin B2 (riboflavin)

    i. _____

    ii. _____

    iii. _____

    iv. _____

    v. _____

    vi. _____

24. Sources of Vitamins: Vitamin B6

    i. _____

    ii. _____

    iii. _____

    iv. _____

    v. _____

    vi. _____

25. Sources of Vitamins: Vitamin B12

    i. _____

    ii. _____

    iii. _____

    iv. _____

    v. _____

26. Sources of Vitamins: Niacin

    i. _____

    ii. _____

    iii. _____

    iv. _____

    v. _____

27. Sources of Vitamins: Biotin

    i. _____

    ii. _____

    iii. _____

28. Sources of Vitamins: Folacin (folic acid)

    i. _____

    ii. _____

29. Sources of Vitamins: Pantothenic acid

    i. _____

    ii. _____

30. Sources of Vitamins: Vitamin C

    i. _____

    ii. _____

    iii. _____

© 2011 Pearson Education, Inc.

31. Sources of Vitamins: Vitamin A

    i. _____

    ii. _____

    iii. _____

    iv. _____

32. Sources of Vitamins: Vitamin D

    i. _____

    ii. _____

    iii. _____

    iv. _____

    v. _____

    vi. _____

33. Sources of Vitamins: Vitamin E

    i. _____

    ii. _____

    iii. _____

34. Sources of Vitamins: Vitamin K

    i. _____

    ii. _____

    iii. _____

    iv. _____

35. Minerals

    A. Minerals are _____ substances that are of neither plant nor animal origin.

    B. They are found throughout the body, but mainly in _____ and _____.

36. Mineral Classifications

    A. Macrominerals (List the minerals that are classified as macrominerals.)

        i. _____

        ii. _____

        iii. _____

        iv. _____

        v. _____

        vi. _____

        vii. _____

    B. Microminerals (List the minerals that are classified as microminerals.)

        i. _____

        ii. _____

        iii. _____

        iv. _____

        v. _____

        vi. _____

        vii. _____

        viii. _____

        ix. _____

        x. _____

        xi. _____

        xii. _____

37. Sources of Minerals: Calcium

    i. _____

    ii. _____

    iii. _____

© 2011 Pearson Education, Inc.

iv. _____

v. _____

vi. _____

38. Sources of Minerals: Copper

i. _____

ii. _____

iii. _____

iv. _____

v. _____

39. Sources of Minerals: Fluorine

i. _____

ii. _____

iii. _____

40. Sources of Minerals: Iodine

i. _____

ii. _____

iii. _____

41. Sources of Minerals: Iron

i. _____

ii. _____

iii. _____

iv. _____

v. _____

vi. _____

42. Sources of Minerals: Magnesium

i. _____

ii. _____

iii. _____

iv. _____

v. _____

vi. _____

vii. _____

43. Sources of Minerals: Phosphorus

i. _____

ii. _____

iii. _____

iv. _____

v. _____

vi. _____

44. Sources of Minerals: Potassium

i. _____

ii. _____

iii. _____

iv. _____

v. _____

45. Sources of Minerals: Sodium

i. _____

ii. _____

iii. _____

iv. _____

v. _____

vi. _____

46. Cholesterol

   A. Cholesterol is normally found in and is _____ by the body.
   B. It is _____ for the _____ of bodily systems, such as the nervous system, and for the formation of cell membranes and many hormones.

47. Sources of Cholesterol

   A. The _____ body.
   B. Animal _____.
   C. Your _____ produces most of the cholesterol in your body (1000 mg/day).

48. Cholesterol in the Body

   A. Cholesterol moves into and out of the body cells within _____.
   B. _____-_____ _____ (HDLs) carry cholesterol away from the bloodstream.
   C. _____-_____ _____ (LDLs) carry most of the cholesterol into the bloodstream.

49. Cholesterol and Disease

   A. An increase in cholesterol is linked to an increase in the following diseases
      i. _____
      ii. _____

50. Dietary Guidelines for Americans

      i. _____
      ii. _____
      iii. _____
      iv. _____
      v. _____

51. Calories

   A. Food intake is measured in terms of the _____ that food produces.
   B. Calorie: A measurement of a unit of _____ that provides _____.

52. Caloric Requirements

   A. All food (except water) generates _____ in the body.
   B. The daily caloric requirement is based on the following
      i. _____
      ii. _____
      iii. _____
      iv. _____
   C. Men generally need more _____ than women.
   D. Women require more calories during _____ and _____.

53. Dietary Modification

   A. Common conditions that necessitate dietary modification
      i. _____
      ii. _____
      iii. _____
      iv. _____
      v. _____
   B. Common dietary modifications
      i. _____
      ii. _____

© 2011 Pearson Education, Inc

iii. _____

iv. _____

v. _____

vi. _____

vii. _____

viii. _____

ix. _____

x. _____

xi. _____

xii. _____

54. Patient Education

A. Diet _____ should be carefully explained to the patient.

B. Patients are often referred to a _____ _____ (RD) who will discuss the therapeutic diet with the patient.

C. The medical assistant will often provide _____ education for patients in the medical office.

D. _____ _____ are often associated with dietary modification and should be included in patient education.

55. The Clear Liquid Diet

A. Contains no _____ _____ or milk products.

B. Frequently required before certain _____ _____, examinations, or surgery.

C. The patient must not remain on a clear liquid diet for _____ periods.

D. Foods included in a clear liquid diet

i. _____

ii. _____

iii. _____

iv. _____

v. _____

56. The Full Liquid Diet

A. Prescribed for patients who are unable to chew and/or digest solid food because of the following conditions

i. _____

ii. _____

iii. _____

B. Often prescribed as the next step after a _____ _____ diet.

C. Foods included in a full liquid diet

i. _____

ii. _____

iii. _____

iv. _____

v. _____

vi. _____

57. The Mechanical Soft Diet

A. Recommended for patients who have _____ _____ or difficulty swallowing.

B. Recommended for patients who are recovering from _____.

C. Foods included in a mechanical soft diet

i. _____

ii. _____

iii. _____

iv. _____

v. _____

vi. _____
vii. _____

58. The Bland Diet
    A. Contains no seasonings or _____ that are irritating.
    B. Prescribed for patients who have _____ problems or allergies.
    C. Eliminates foods that are _____ _____ (e.g., cabbage).
    D. Eliminates _____ and spices.
    E. Eliminates foods that are high in _____.
    F. Foods included in a bland diet
        i. _____
        ii. _____
        iii. _____
        iv. _____
        v. _____

59. The BRAT Diet
    A. BRAT stands for _____, _____, _____, and _____.
    B. Prescribed for _____ _____ who are experiencing vomiting, nausea, and diarrhea.

60. The High-Protein Diet
    A. Recommended for patients who are recovering from _____ _____.
    B. Aids in _____.

61. The Diabetic Diet
    A. Considerations for placing a patient on a diabetic diet
        i. _____
        ii. _____
        iii. _____
        iv. _____
        v. _____
    B. Often uses a _____ _____ system to allow patients to select preferred foods.
    C. Foods are grouped into the Food Pyramid categories (List the categories.)
        i. _____
        ii. _____
        iii. _____
        iv. _____
        v. _____
        vi. _____

62. The High-Residue/Fiber Diet
    A. Used to treat patients with _____ _____.
    B. Dietary fiber may provide protection against the following diseases or conditions
        i. _____
        ii. _____
        iii. _____
        iv. _____
        v. _____
        vi. _____
        vii. _____
        viii. _____
    C. May _____ cholesterol.
    D. The recommended daily intake of fiber is _____ to _____ grams per day.
    E. Fiber is not found in _____ products or _____ products.

© 2011 Pearson Education, Inc.

63. The Low-Residue Diet
   A. The low-residue diet is often called a _____-_____ diet.
   B. It is useful for patients with the following conditions
      i. _____
      ii. _____
      iii. _____
      iv. _____
   C. Foods included in a low-residue diet
      i. _____
      ii. _____
      iii. _____
      iv. _____
      v. _____
      vi. _____
      vii. _____

64. The Low-Fat/Cholesterol Diet
   A. Aimed at keeping fat content between _____ and _____ grams of fat per day.
   B. The average American diet contains between _____ and _____ grams of fat per day.
   C. May reduce the risk of colon, breast, and _____ cancer; _____ _____;
      and _____.
   D. Foods included in a low-fat/cholesterol diet
      i. _____
      ii. _____
      iii. _____
      iv. _____
      v. _____

65. The Low-Sodium/Salt Diet
   A. Used for patients with _____ and heart or kidney disease.
   B. Recommended for patients on _____-_____ diets in order to reduce
      water retention.

66. Guidelines for a Low-Sodium/Salt Diet
   A. Mild Restriction: _____ to _____ mg of sodium per day
      i. Allow _____ _____ of table salt per day.
      ii. Limit foods that contain salt, including _____ foods.
   B. Moderate Restriction: _____ to _____ mg of sodium per day
      i. Allow _____ _____ of table salt per day.
      ii. No processed and _____ foods with salt.
      iii. No salt in food _____.
      iv. This is the most _____ low-sodium/salt diet.
   C. Severe Restriction: _____ mg of sodium per day
      i. Limit _____ _____ _____, including salt in cooking.
      ii. Use only _____-_____ products.
      iii. Increase the intake of _____ _____ and _____.
      iv. Read _____ carefully.

67. The Caloric Content Diet
   A. Often prescribed as a _____-_____ _____ for persons affected by
      excess weight.
   B. Helps to prevent and control the following diseases or conditions
      i. _____
      ii. _____
      iii. _____

© 2011 Pearson Education, Inc.

C. The _____-_____ diet uses a balance of the five food groups and low-fat foods.

D. Guidelines for a low-calorie content diet

   i. _____

  ii. _____

 iii. _____

 iv. _____

  v. _____

 vi. _____

E. Caloric intake should total _____ calories.

F. Keep a _____ _____.

68. Healthy Food Choices: Eat Less Fat

A. Eat _____ and fish more often.

B. Prepare all meats by roasting, broiling, or _____.

C. Trim off all _____ fat.

D. Remove the _____ from all poultry.

E. Avoid adding _____ during cooking.

F. Eat fewer _____-_____ foods.

G. Drink skim or _____-_____ milk.

69. Healthy Food Choices: Eat More High-Fiber Foods

A. Choose dried beans, _____, and _____ more often.

B. Eat whole-_____ _____, cereals, and crackers.

C. Eat more _____, both raw and cooked.

D. Try _____-_____ foods such as oat bran, barley, brown rice, bulgur, and wild rice.

70. Healthy Food Choices: Use Less Salt

A. Reduce the amount of _____ that you use in cooking.

B. Try not to put _____ on food at the table.

C. Eat fewer _____-_____ foods such as canned soups, ham, hot dogs, pickles, sauerkraut, and foods that taste salty.

71. Healthy Food Choices: Eat Less Sugar

A. Avoid _____ _____, syrup, honey, jam, jelly, candy, sweet rolls, fruit canned in syrup, regular gelatin, desserts, pie, cake with icing, and other sweets.

B. Avoid _____ soft drinks.

C. Choose fresh fruit or fruit canned in _____ _____ or water.

D. If desired, use non-caloric _____ instead of sugar.

72. Exercise

A. Activity helps to _____ the fat in the diet so that it is not stored in the body.

B. Patients should be cleared by a _____ before exercising.

C. Keep exercise programs _____.

KEY TERMINOLOGY REVIEW

Match the vocabulary term to the correct definition below.

a. Calorie

b. Cholesterol

c. Digestion

d. Hydrogenation

e. Lactating

f. Lactose

g. Lipids

h. Macrominerals

i. Metabolism

j. Minerals

© 2011 Pearson Education, Inc.

k. Monosaccharides

l. Nutrients

m. Polysaccharides

n. Recommended Dietary Allowances (RDAs)

o. Refined sugars

p. Vitamins

1. _____ Process whereby unsaturated (liquid) fat can be converted into a solid fat.

2. _____ The sum of all physical and chemical changes that take place within the human body.

3. _____ Recommendations for the amount of protein, vitamins, and minerals that Americans should try to eat for good nutrition (developed by the Food and Nutrition Board of the National Academy of Sciences).

4. _____ Simple sugars.

5. _____ Producing milk.

6. _____ Fatlike material that is essential for the function of bodily systems.

7. _____ Trace minerals, including calcium, magnesium, phosphorus, sodium, potassium, chlorine, and sulfur.

8. _____ Starches that are reduced to glucose during the digestive process and transported into the blood.

9. _____ Processed sugars that have been extracted and concentrated from natural sources.

10. _____ The process the body undertakes when it converts food into chemical substances that can be absorbed into the blood and used by the body tissues and organs.

11. _____ Fatty acids that can be chemically classified as saturated or unsaturated.

12. _____ Organic substances that are essential for metabolism, growth, and development of the body.

13. _____ Organic and inorganic chemical substances found in foods that supply the body with the elements necessary for the process of metabolization.

14. _____ Inorganic elements that are of neither animal nor plant origin.

15. _____ A measurement of a unit of heat that provides energy.

16. _____ The combination of glucose and galactose that is found in animal milk.

APPLIED PRACTICE

Follow the directions as instructed with each question below.

Scenario

Emily is a medical assistant working for Dr. Wynn. Melody Hoffstetler is the first patient of the day. Melody has been unable to control her eating for most of her life and has come for help with this issue. Dr. Wynn suggests that Emily begin by explaining the revised Food Guide Pyramid as a way to begin the conversation.

1. Pretend that you are Emily and write as if you were talking to Melody.

_____

_____

_____

_____

_____

_____

2. Draw and explain MyPyramid in such a way that Emily will understand and feel encouraged and confident.

LEARNING ACTIVITY: TRUE/FALSE

Indicate whether the following statements are true or false by placing a T or an F on the line that precedes each statement.

_____ 1. Energy released from the metabolization of proteins, fats, and carbohydrates is measured in units of kilograms.

_____ 2. The key to a balanced diet is to eat a variety of foods in the correct amount.

_____ 3. Reducing the intake of fat can also reduce the risk of certain types of cancer.

_____ 4. A good postoperative diet is the full liquid diet.

_____ 5. Children are placed on the BRAT diet when they behave like one.

_____ 6. A person's religion can play a role in his or her nutrition.

_____ 7. In a heart-healthy diet, avoid tuna packed in oil.

_____ 8. Carbohydrates are the body's primary source of energy and are found primarily in breads, cereals, pasta products, rice, fruit, and potatoes.

_____ 9. Vitamins are not sources of energy, but they are required for good health.

_____ 10. Minerals constitute 11% percent of the body.

CRITICAL THINKING

Answer the following questions to the best of your ability. Utilize the textbook as a reference.

1. Mr. McNeill is experiencing constipation and has called for advice on how to deal with this. Recall what you have read in this chapter of your textbook and use your common sense to list a few things that might help. After you have done this, check the book and review any items that you may not have learned yet.

_____

_____

_____

_____

© 2011 Pearson Education, Inc.

2. The patient, Millie Stewart, is chatting while you are getting her ready for an examination. She tells you that she has tried every kind of diet and many have worked well and rapidly, but the weight always comes back. Ms. Stewart explains that she has decided that she is just supposed to be 20 pounds overweight and she is not going to diet any more; she is going to enjoy her food and her life. How would you respond to her?

_____

_____

_____

_____

RESEARCH ACTIVITY

Utilize Internet search engines to research the following topics and write a brief description of what you find. It is important to utilize reputable websites.

1. Visit www.mypyramid.gov. Using the information that you find on the website, develop a diet plan for yourself or for one of your patients.

_____

_____

_____

_____

_____

_____

_____

_____

_____

_____

_____

_____

_____

_____

_____

_____

_____

_____

_____

_____

_____

© 2011 Pearson Education, Inc.

Chapter 57
Mental Health

CHAPTER OUTLINE

General review of the chapter:

Psychology
Psychological Disorders
Substance Abuse Disorders
Treatments
Developmental Stages of the Life Cycle
Mind–Body Connection
Maslow's Hierarchy of Needs
Heredity, Environmental, and Cultural Influences on Behavior
Emotions
Motivation
Stress
Assisting the Patient with a Terminal Illness

STUDENT STUDY GUIDE

Use the following guide to assist in your learning of the concepts from the chapter.

I. Psychological Disorders and Treatments

    1. The Psychologist

        A. Usually has a _____ in psychology.
        B. Usually administers psychological tests, performs _____, or does research.
        C. Cannot _____ medication

    2. The Psychiatrist

        A. Can order and perform _____ _____ (ECT) and perform psychotherapy as well.
        B. Can _____ medications.

    3. Abnormal Psychology

        A. Abnormal psychology is the study of behavior that _____ from the normal.
        B. Manifestations of abnormal psychology.
            i. _____
            ii. _____
            iii. _____
            iv. _____
            v. _____

© 2011 Pearson Education, Inc

4. Mental Disorders

    A. Caused by _____ changes to the brain, such as those suffered in depression, but exclude substance abuse and other disorders that are primarily behavioral.

    B. Defined as any behavior or emotional state that causes the following

        i. _____

        ii. _____

        iii. _____

5. Anxiety and Cognitive Disorders (Provide examples of each type of disorder.)

    A. Anxiety disorders

        i. _____

        ii. _____

        iii. _____

    B. Cognitive disorders

        i. _____

        ii. _____

        iii. _____

        iv. _____

6. Disorders Diagnosed in Infancy and Childhood

        i. _____

        ii. _____

        iii. _____

7. Dissociative Disorders

    A. Dissociative _____ is a condition in which important events cannot be remembered after a traumatic event.

    B. Dissociative _____ _____ (multiple personality disorder) is a condition in which two or more personalities or identities are present in one person.

8. Eating Disorder

    A. Abnormal eating _____.

    B. Distorted body _____.

    C. Fear, _____, and _____ characterize these disorders.

9. Factitious Disorders

    A. These are characterized by physical and/or psychological symptoms that are _____ _____ by the patient, which the patient knows are not real.

    B. Patients _____ to be sick (or sicken others) to get attention.

10. Impulse Control Disorder

    A. An impulse control disorder is an inability to _____ an impulse to perform some act that is _____ to the individual or others.

    B. These may include _____ gambling, stealing (kleptomania), _____ _____ (pyromania), or having violent rages.

11. Personality and Mood Disorders

    A. Personality disorders

        i. Personality disorders are inflexible _____ _____ that cause distress or the inability to function.

        ii. These include paranoid, _____, and _____ disorders.

    B. Mood disorders (Provide examples of this type of disorder.)

        i. _____

        ii. _____

        iii. _____

12. Schizophrenia and Other Psychotic Disorders

    A. Characteristics of psychotic disorders

    B.   i. _____

         ii. _____

         iii. _____

13. Sexual and Gender Identity Disorders (List these types of disorders.)

        i. _____

        ii. _____

        iii. _____

14. Anxiety Disorders

    A. Anxiety disorders are mild emotional disturbances that impair _____.

    B. Patients suffering from anxiety disorders are able to tell the difference between _____ and _____.

    C. Anxiety is a _____ feeling of apprehension, worry, uneasiness, or dread.

    D. A certain amount of anxiety is normal, but when it impairs _____, it is an anxiety disorder.

    E. Anxiety disorders are treated with _____, which decrease anxiety.

15. Phobias

    A. The fear of leaving the home and going out is called _____.

    B. _____ is the fear of spiders.

    C. _____ is the fear of enclosed spaces.

16. Cognitive Disorders

    A. Impair the ability of a patient to think _____.

    B. Delirium, particularly if related to _____ _____, can be transient and usually is treated by easing the person into _____ from substances, or treating the _____ cause.

    C. Dementia is a progressive disease that robs the patient of _____-_____ memory, while frequently leaving _____-_____ memory intact.

    D. New medications have been developed to treat dementia, but _____ must be early to be successful.

17. Developmental Disorders

    A. Sometimes disorders appear before age _____.

    B. Include _____ _____ (such as Down syndrome) and _____ disorders (such as antisocial behavior).

    C. Developmental delays are usually treated by _____ the potential of the patient with rehabilitation.

    D. Rehabilitation is usually successful at improving the quality of life for the patient with developmental delays, but will not usually increase the _____ quotient.

    E. Autism, also called _____ _____, has a range of symptoms.

    F. Some patients with _____ _____ (a milder form of autism) may be highly intelligent, but may not seek social contact.

    G. Other patients may be totally absorbed in their own world, hypersensitive to outside stimuli, and engage in _____-_____ behaviors such as rocking back and forth.

18. Dissociative Disorders

    A. Cause a person to withdraw from reality and dissociate, at least temporarily, from the life issues that cause him or her _____.

    B. If the person attempts to flee the life that he or she is living to assume another identity in another place, it is called _____ _____.

    C. _____, or forgetting events, is frequently present with dissociative disorders.

© 2011 Pearson Education, Inc.

D. Dissociative identity disorder, formerly called _____ _____ _____, is a severe dissociative disorder in which the patient assumes multiple personalities.

E. Contrary to frequent depictions of patients with this disorder in the media, these patients have usually been severely _____ and assume multiple personalities as a defense mechanism to protect themselves.

19. Eating Disorders

A. _____ _____ is a psychiatric disorder in which the patient, starved for affection, starves literally as well, while believing that he or she is overweight.

B. _____ _____ is usually found in slightly overweight persons who seek to control their lives by overeating, then purging with laxatives or vomiting.

C. Medications to increase the appetite can be used, but _____ _____ therapy is usually indicated.

20. Hypochondriasis

A. Hypochondriasis is a disorder in which the patient is preoccupied with fears of having, or the idea that one has, a _____ _____, based on a misinterpretation of one of more bodily signs or symptoms.

B. With this disorder, it is important to rule out _____ _____.

C. Therapy would then be directed toward improving the patient's _____ and decreasing anxiety.

21. Impulse Control Disorders

A. Attention-deficit/hyperactivity disorder, an impulse-control disorder, is thought to be a problem with either the _____-_____ _____ or dopamine processing.

B. Although controversial, it is currently treated with _____ that help the patient to focus better.

C. Other impulse control disorders include _____ _____, stealing, and setting fires.

22. Mood Disorders

A. Mood disorders are _____ _____ or _____, including a pervasively negative world view.

B. Depression
   i. Depression is a mood disorder that is characterized by a _____ of _____ in life's pleasures.
   ii. Can be life-threatening when accompanied by _____ thoughts.
   iii. It is a serious mental illness that affects _____ million people in the United States.
   iv. One out of _____ women and one out of _____ men will be diagnosed with depression in their lifetime.

23. Symptoms of Depression

   i. _____
   ii. _____
   iii. _____
   iv. _____
   v. _____
   vi. _____
   vii. _____
   viii. _____

24. Bipolar Disorder

A. Patients with _____ may not stop to eat, rest, relate to others, or sleep.

B. Bipolar disorder is characterized by periods of _____ _____ from excessive mania to profound depression.

© 2011 Pearson Education, Inc.

C. Mania is characterized by _____ _____, flight of ideas, weight loss, and cognitive lack of focus.
D. Medication therapy is targeted usually at the _____ _____, but antidepressants can sometimes be helpful with the depression phase caused by _____ following the manic phase.

25. Personality Disorders

A. Usually treated with _____ _____ with a psychologist.
B. Unlike the other disorders, which may necessitate _____ therapy, talk therapy is the treatment of choice for entrenched personality disorders.

26. Psychotic Disorders

A. Psychotic disorders are severe mental disorders that interfere with a patient's _____ of _____ and his or her ability to cope with the demands of daily living.
B. Psychoses must be treated with _____ medications.

27. Somatoform Disorders

A. Occur when _____ mental illness is displaced into bodily complaints.
B. _____ can be used to decrease anxiety and improve the effectiveness of talk therapy.

28. Factitious Disorders

A. The patient creates _____ to seek attention.
B. Sometimes a patient with a factitious disorder might _____ another person, such as a spouse or child, in order to get attention.
C. If the person injures him- or herself, the disorder is _____ syndrome.
D. If another person is injured by the patient in order to get attention, the condition is known as _____ _____ _____ _____.
E. _____ _____ therapy is preferred over medication for this group of disorders.

29. Dealing with Substance Abuse Patients

A. Carefully document visits to the physician's office so that _____ _____ can be traced.
B. Notify the physician if _____ _____ is suspected.
C. Never give a patient _____ access to medications in the medical office.

30. Psychotherapy

A. Psychotherapy is a method for treating _____ _____ by cognitive rather than physical means.
B. Includes psychoanalysis, humanistic therapies, and _____ and _____ therapy.
C. _____ _____ therapy helps the patient to change the way that he or she both thinks and acts.
D. For some impulse behaviors, the therapist extracts a _____ from the patient, using a contract in order to stop the behavior.
E. The goal of psychotherapy is to help the patient _____ with life.

31. Psychoanalysis

A. Psychoanalysis is a method for obtaining a _____ account of the past and present emotional and mental experiences from the patient in order to determine the source of the problem and to eliminate the effects.
B. It is a system developed by _____ _____ that encourages the patient to discuss repressed, painful, or hidden experiences with the hope of eliminating or minimizing the current problem.
C. Because psychotherapy can be lengthy, _____-_____ payers frequently limit the number of visits that a patient can have with a psychoanalyst.

© 2011 Pearson Education, Inc.

32. Humanistic Therapies

   A. Humanistic therapies are also called _____-_____ or nondirective therapies.
   B. The therapist does not _____ into the patient's past when using these methods.
   C. The patient is helped to feel better by building _____-_____ and a feeling that he or she is respected.
   D. This therapy was pioneered by _____ _____.

33. Family and Group Therapy

   A. Family and group therapy is _____ focused.
   B. The therapist places _____ _____ on the patient's past history and places a strong emphasis on having the patient state his or her goals and then finding a way to achieve them.
   C. Usually led by a specialist in this kind of therapy, and frequently led by someone who has _____ substance abuse.

34. Electroconvulsive Therapy (ECT)

   A. ECT is a controversial treatment in which _____ are placed on one or both sides of the patient's head and a brief electrical current is administered, causing a seizure.
   B. A low level of _____ is used in modern ECT.
   C. The patient is given a _____ _____ and anesthesia prior to administration of the current. This helps prevent violent _____ _____.
   D. Advocates of this treatment say that it is a more effective way to treat _____ _____ than the use of drugs.

35. Antipsychotic Drugs (List the major antipsychotics that can be used.)

   i. _____
   ii. _____
   iii. _____
   iv. _____

36. Antidepressant Drugs

   A. _____ _____ inhibitors, such as Prozac, Effexor, Paxil, and Zoloft, are frequently prescribed because they have fewer side effects.
   B. _____ _____ inhibitors (MAO inhibitors) require a special diet and are thus infrequently prescribed.
   C. _____ antidepressants are nonaddictive, but they can produce unpleasant side effects such as dry mouth, weight gain, blurred vision, and nausea.

37. "Minor" Tranquilizers

   A. Minor tranquilizers include _____ and _____.
   B. They are classified as _____ and are prescribed for anxiety.
   C. They are the _____ effective methods for treating emotional disorders.
   D. Patients may develop a problem with _____ after taking these drugs for an extended time. (They begin to need larger doses.)
   E. In general, antidepressants are preferred to tranquilizers for treating _____ disorders.

38. Lithium

   A. Used successfully to calm patients who suffer from _____ _____ (depression alternating with manic excitement).
   B. Patients on lithium need to be carefully monitored because too much of this drug is _____ and too little is _____.
   C. _____ levels should be regularly monitored to prevent overdosing or underdosing.

II. Understanding Patients and Their Needs

1. The Developmental Stages of the Life Cycle
   i. _____
   ii. _____
   iii. _____
   iv. _____
   v. _____

2. The Prenatal Period
   A. Throughout this period, the _____ of the body, as well as the organs, are formed.
   B. At this time, development is influenced by the _____ and _____.

3. The Infancy Period
   A. This period of vast changes occurs from childbirth until _____.
   B. During this time, an infant gains _____ ability, along with coordination.
   C. The infant will also develop _____ and sensory skills.
   D. During this period, the infant will express basic emotions and feelings, develop _____ or _____, and become attached to caregivers.

4. The Childhood Period
   A. Ages _____ to _____ are considered to be early childhood.
      i. During a child's preschool years, his or her _____, physical, and _____ capabilities will grow rapidly.
      ii. The concept of _____ begins to develop, as does socialization.
   B. Ages _____ to _____ are considered to be middle childhood.
      i. During middle childhood, a child starts to know his or her world, think _____, and make major advances in reading and writing.
      ii. Moral and _____ development progress rapidly.

5. The Adolescence Period
   A. Ages _____ to _____ are considered to be early adolescence.
      i. During this time, the beginning of _____ _____ thinking and sexual maturation take place.
      ii. The early adolescent wants more _____ from his or her parents and, as a result, starts to form companionships with friends.
   B. Late adolescence occurs from ages _____ to _____.
      i. The psychosocial task of _____ identity is achieved.

6. The Adulthood Period
   A. Early adulthood
      i. Occurs during a person's _____ and _____.
      ii. During this time, there are the challenges of making a _____ _____, achieving intimacy, and accomplishing vocational success.
   B. Middle adulthood
      i. Occurs during a person's _____ and _____.
      ii. Achieving vocational success, plus social and _____ responsibility, occurs during this period.
      iii. At some point during this period, a person's _____ changes, as does his or her emotional status.
   C. Late adulthood
      i. Occurs from age _____ until death.
      ii. During this period, many _____ are made.
      iii. A person's _____ capabilities change, as do his or her relationships with others.
      iv. Life _____ and _____ are reported by many during this life stage.

© 2011 Pearson Education, Inc.

7. Maslow's Hierarchy of Needs

   A. Developed by _____ _____.

   B. Maslow believed that a person could not move to a _____ _____ until his or her basic, lower level needs were met.

8. Levels of Maslow's Hierarchy of Needs

   A. Level I: _____ needs such as food, water, and shelter

   B. Level II: _____ needs, which include physical safety, as well as security related to employment

   C. Level III: _____ needs, which include having a sense of belonging to a group and the need for social interaction

   D. Level IV: _____-_____, which includes having a sense of self-worth and pride

   E. Level V: _____-_____, which occurs when the individual achieves all that he or she is capable of achieving and experiences a sense of accomplishment

9. The Role of Heredity and Environmental and Cultural Influences on Behavior

   A. Some people believe that _____ influences behavior more than the environment.

   B. Others believe that the _____ influences behavior more than heredity.

   C. Each one of these factors has been determined to be essential for _____, because each factor can interact with the other.

   D. Before you can _____ effectively with a patient from another culture, you should understand the terms "bias," "prejudice," and "stereotyping."

10. How to Communicate When a Language Barrier Exists

   A. Avoid using _____ _____ if possible.

   B. Determine whether the patient _____ you.

   C. Never use _____.

   D. Be aware of your _____ communication, as well as that of the patient.

   E. Determine whether _____ _____ should be direct or indirect.

   F. _____ _____ can show a variety of emotions, such as sadness, anger, confusion, and happiness.

11. Predisposing Factors for Stress

   i. _____

   ii. _____

   iii. _____

   iv. _____

   v. _____

12. Stress

   A. Can be emotional, _____, or physical.

   B. It can also be _____, economical, or social.

   C. Can be energizing, _____, or exhausting.

   D. Medical research has shown that a certain amount of stress is not a _____ _____.

   E. The body's reaction to stress determines whether it is good stress or bad stress (_____).

   F. Stress has also been implicated in various _____.

13. Methods for Coping with Stress

   A. Develop a strong _____ _____, including family and friends.

   B. Find a balance between _____ and the fear of failure.

   C. Eat _____ meals.

   D. Avoid _____ _____ such as smoking and drinking.

   E. Engage in _____ exercise such as walking, jogging, dancing, biking, and swimming.

F. Look outward to develop a social interest by understanding other people's _____ and needs.

G. Try to see the _____ in situations.

H. Limit the number of activities to a _____ few.

14. Encountering a Patient with Stress

A. After allowing the patient to discuss the stress and stressors, assess the patient's _____ of the topic of stress.

B. Next, determine the appropriate reading, language, and educational level of the patient so that you can select and prepare _____ for use in teaching the patient about stress.

C. After you gather all of your _____ and _____, you will be ready to provide the patient with information about stress.

D. When you have completed _____ the patient, you will need to document it in the patient's medical record.

15. Defense Mechanisms

A. Operate at a _____ _____ to manage anxiety by denying, misinterpreting, or distorting reality.

B. Often hinder _____-_____ by preventing a person from being sensitive to anxiety.

C. Can be helpful in dealing with _____.

D. The consistent use of certain defenses leads to the _____ of either good or self-destructive behavior patterns.

16. Compensation and Denial

A. Compensation
   i. Definition: _____
   ii. Purpose: _____
B. Denial
   i. Definition: _____
   ii. Purpose: _____

17. Displacement and Identification

A. Displacement
   i. Definition: _____
   ii. Purpose: _____
B. Identification
   i. Definition: _____
   ii. Purpose: _____

18. Intellectualization

A. Definition: _____
B. Purpose: _____

19. Introjection

A. Definition: _____
B. Purpose: _____

20. Minimization and Projection

A. Minimization
   i. Definition: _____
   ii. Purpose: _____
B. Projection
   i. Definition: _____
   ii. Purpose: _____

© 2011 Pearson Education, Inc.

21. Rationalization and Reaction Formation

A. Rationalization
    i. Definition: _____
    ii. Purpose: _____

B. Reaction formation
    i. Definition: _____
    ii. Purpose: _____

22. Repression

A. Definition: Resorting to an earlier, more _____ level of functioning that is characteristically less demanding and responsible.

B. Purpose: Allows a person to return to a point in development when _____ and dependency were needed and accepted with comfort. Protects a person from a _____ _____ until he or she has the resources to cope with it.

C. An unconscious mechanism by which _____ _____, feelings, and desires are kept from becoming conscious; the _____ material is denied entry into consciousness.

23. Sublimation and Substitution

A. Sublimation
    i. Definition: _____
    ii. Purpose: _____

B. Substitution
    i. Definition: _____
    ii. Purpose: _____

24. Undoing

A. Definition: An action or words designed to cancel some _____ _____, impulses, or acts in which the person relieves guilt by making reparation.

B. Purpose: Allows a person to appease _____ _____ and atone for _____.

25. Dealing with Patients Who Have a Terminal Illness

A. Listen to the patient express his or her fears and concerns rather than offer _____ _____ for recovery.

B. Death is a _____ process that everyone must face.

C. People have various ways of coping with their own death based on a variety of influences, including culture, religion, _____ _____, and age.

D. The terminally ill patient and his or her family may have already established a very personal approach or method for handling _____ and _____.

E. If the patient wishes to discuss his or her approaching death, the medical assistant should be ready to _____.

26. Stages of Grief

A. Denial
    i. Denial is a _____ to believe that dying is taking place.
    ii. In this stage, the patient (or family member) may need time to _____ to the _____ of the approaching death.
    iii. This stage cannot be _____.

B. Anger
    i. At this stage, the patient may be angry at everyone and may express this intense anger at God, his or her own family, and even _____ _____ _____.
    ii. The patient may take this anger out on the person _____ to him or her.

C. Bargaining
    i. The third stage of grief involves attempting to _____ _____ by making promises in return.

    ii. The patient may bargain with _____.

    iii. The patient may also indicate a need to _____ at this stage.

  D. Depression

    i. This stage is marked by a _____ _____ over the loss of health, independence, and eventually life.

    ii. There is the additional sadness of leaving loved ones _____.

    iii. The grieving patient may become _____.

  E. Acceptance

    i. In the acceptance stage, there is a sense of _____ and _____.

    ii. The patient may make comments such as "_____."

KEY TERMINOLOGY REVIEW

Match the vocabulary term to the correct definition below.

a. Adolescence

b. Adulthood

c. Bias

d. Childhood

e. Compulsions

f. Electroconvulsive therapy (ECT)

g. Hierarchy of needs

h. Infancy

i. Motivation

j. Obsessions

k. Personality disorders

l. Prejudice

m. Psychiatrist

n. Psychiatry

o. Psychologist

p. Psychology

q. Psychopathic disorders

r. Psychotherapy

s. Stress

t. Stressor

u. Terminal illness

v. Tolerance

1. _____ Procedure occasionally used in cases of prolonged major depression.

2. _____ Include narcissistic (self-centered), paranoid (abnormally concerned that people will hurt the patient), antisocial (not concerned with laws and other people), histrionic (dramatic), and borderline (impulsive) behaviors.

3. _____ A branch of medicine that deals with the diagnosis, treatment, and prevention of mental disorders.

4. _____ When a person favors a certain belief or attitude.

5. _____ The science of behavior and the human thought process.

6. _____ An illness expected to end in death.

7. _____ A theory that people have special needs and move through various levels in achieving satisfaction in life.

8. _____ Occurs between childhood and adulthood.

9. _____ A preformed and unfavorable belief or attitude toward a certain culture or group with little or no information about the culture or group.

10. _____ One who is trained in the methods of psychological analysis, therapy, and research.

11. _____ A stimulus that drives us to act.

12. _____ A method for treating mental disorders by cognitive rather than physical means.

© 2011 Pearson Education, Inc.

13. _____ A medical doctor who has chosen to specialize in psychiatry.

14. _____ Divided into early, middle, and late.

15. _____ The body's reaction to the world around it.

16. _____ The second period of childhood development.

17. _____ Repetitive acts performed to relieve anxiety.

18. _____ A real or imaginary event that causes stress.

19. _____ Persistent thoughts.

20. _____ Disorders that affect about 1% of the population and that are characterized by a lack of empathy, narcissism, impulsivity, and antisocial reactions, such as breaking the law and manipulating others.

21. _____ The last period of childhood development.

22. _____ A condition that creates a need for larger and larger doses of medication.

APPLIED PRACTICE

Follow the directions as instructed with each question below.

Scenario

As a medical assistant working in a medical office, you will encounter patients who are frightened, depressed, and angry. On this particular day, Timothy Smither seems to be quite angry about the procedure that he is to undergo, especially because the doctor is late in keeping the appointment.

1. How should you act when you encounter a patient that is experiencing anger?

_____

_____

2. How can you help that patient?

_____

_____

LEARNING ACTIVITY: FILL IN THE BLANK

Using words from the list below, fill in the blanks to complete the following statements.

absence   delusions   reality

addiction   diagnose   schizophrenia

antidepressants   hallucinations   statistical

bipolar   neurotransmitters   stereotyping

capacity to cope   prenatal period   withdrawal symptoms

characteristics   psychopharmacology

conception   psychotic

1. A _____ disorder has two poles: depression and mania.

2. _____ is a physiological need for a substance, which in its absence causes _____.

3. _____ is a psychotic disorder marked by a variety of symptoms, including _____ (fixed false beliefs), _____ (false sensory perceptions), disorganized and incoherent speech, severe emotional abnormalities, and withdrawal into an inner world.

4. _____ is the study of the effects of drugs on the mind and brain, particularly the use of drugs in treating mental disorders.

5. The Diagnostic and _____ Manual of _____ IV (DSM-IV) is the reference manual used by mental health providers to diagnose a wide range of mental disorders.

6. _____ is the formation of negative beliefs or attitudes concerning the specific _____ of a person or group and then their unfair application to an entire population.

7. The first period of childhood development is the _____, which covers the process from _____ until birth.

8. Mental wellness is not necessarily a(n) _____ of mental problems but instead a _____ in healthy ways with the pressures of daily living.

9. _____ alter the patient's mood by affecting the levels of _____ in the brain.

10. _____ disorders are severe mental disorders that interfere with a patient's perception of _____ and his or her ability to cope with the demands of daily living.

CRITICAL THINKING

Answer the following questions to the best of your ability. Utilize the textbook as a reference.

1. If a patient mentions to you that she has been thinking about suicide recently and asks you not to tell the doctor because she would "never really do it," what would you say or do? The answer is not in the book, but use knowledge from what you have learned in your program so far and your thoughts to formulate a few sentences for your answer.

   _____

   _____

   _____

   _____

2. You have a female patient who is 4 months old, and the mother has come in today for test results on the infant. The infant was diagnosed with mental retardation and the mother was told by the physician that there is no treatment that will help the child. The mother is upset and wants to know why there is no treatment available when modern medicine can transplant hearts and do brain surgery. What will you tell her?

   _____

   _____

   _____

   _____

RESEARCH ACTIVITY

Utilize Internet search engines to research the following topics and write a brief description of what you find. It is important to utilize reputable websites.

1. Visit the Mental Health America website at www.nmha.org.
   a. What information do you find to be most helpful on this website?
   b. How could patients with mental health issues benefit from this website?
   c. In what ways could you become involved with Mental Health America?

© 2011 Pearson Education, Inc.

CHAPTER 58
Professionalism

CHAPTER OUTLINE

General review of the chapter:

Professional Skills in the Workplace
Workplace Communication
Critical Thinking
Teamwork
Managing Priorities
Persistence
Professional Image
Lifelong Learning

STUDENT STUDY GUIDE

Use the following guide to assist in your learning of the concepts from the chapter.

I. Professionalism

1. Office Systems

   A. A system is a _____ interacting group of people who function with an organized set of doctrines and _____ typically recorded in a formal policy and procedures manual.
   B. Having a clear understanding of managers' expectations makes the system function _____.
   C. If a medical assistant does not know how to perform a procedure, an admission must be made to his or her _____ in order that the medical assistant can receive the needed training.

2. Communication

   A. Communication is perhaps the most important _____ skill.
   B. Many problems can be solved by having effective communication _____ among team members.

3. Active Listening

   A. While a patient is speaking, if the medical assistant is already beginning to formulate an answer instead of listening, some _____ information may not be heard.
   B. If the physician is giving an order and the medical assistant is thinking of something else, the results can be _____.
   C. Instead of making _____ about what is being said, a medical assistant with good professional skills will focus on the _____ and will ask for clarification if needed.

4. The Key to Presenting Difficult Concepts

   A. Seek _____ from the listener to make sure that he or she understands.
   B. When communicating with a patient, always take into account the _____ and _____ of the patient.
   C. Use a different _____ depending on the age and mental capacity of the patient.

© 2011 Pearson Education, Inc.

5. Critical Thinking

   A. For proper decision making, the medical assistant needs to retrieve _____ facts and events, add _____ to the thinking process, and act in the appropriate manner.
   B. Involves differentiating _____ from _____ or opinion.

6. Insurance Billing and Critical Thinking

   A. The medical assistant must advocate for the patient with the patient's _____ company through a maze of complicated rules for _____.
   B. Thinking critically can improve _____ from the _____ company to the medical practice and greatly relieve the burden on the patient.

7. Laboratory Results and Critical Thinking

   A. Although the medical assistant should never diagnose a patient, it is the medical assistant's responsibility to bring _____ results to the physician's attention.
   B. A critically thinking medical assistant will take in all information before forming a _____.

8. Value Judgments

   A. A medical assistant must make value judgments on a _____ basis.
   B. Critical thinking should become so _____ that the medical assistant is comfortable with value judgments.

9. Teamwork in the Medical Setting

   A. Teamwork is a critical workplace _____.
   B. All medical assistants need to understand how the team functions and be prepared to share _____.
   C. The medical assistant should practice only within his or her own _____ of practice.

10. Diversity in the Medical Office

    A. It is in everyone's best interest that _____, stereotypes, and prejudices be put aside.
    B. Holding grudges or _____ beliefs can prevent the team from functioning smoothly.

11. Managing Priorities

    A. Patient priorities may be managed by a combination of an efficient _____ and a _____ system.
    B. Because the medical assistant is versatile, he or she may be asked to do _____ tasks over a short length of time.
    C. If a medical assistant is distracted by family issues or other personal problems, it can be detrimental and have a _____ impact on job performance.

12. Stress Management (Explain how each of the following techniques help with stress management.)

    A. Aromatherapy: _____
    B. Biofeedback: _____
    C. Deep breathing: _____
    D. Distraction: _____
    E. Exercise: _____
    F. Guided imagery: _____
    G. Hypnosis: _____
    H. Humor: _____
    I. Meditation and prayer: _____
    J. Music: _____
    K. Relaxation: _____
    L. Slow breath counting: _____
    M. Water therapy: _____
    N. Heat: _____

 O. Cold: _____

 P. Pressure: _____

13. Time Management

 A. Requires the ability to _____ what the important tasks are and to complete them on _____.

 B. One of the main responsibilities of the office manager or medical assistant is to manage all of the _____ office functions.

 C. Before establishing a time management system, it is important to define office _____ with the physician.

14. Professional Dress (List what constitutes professional attire.)

 i. _____

 ii. _____

 iii. _____

 iv. _____

 v. _____

 vi. _____

 vii. _____

 viii. _____

KEY TERMINOLOGY REVIEW

Match the vocabulary term to the correct definition below.

a. Affective

b. Aromatherapy

c. Biofeedback

d. Cognitive

e. Diversity

f. Encounter note

g. Guided imagery

h. Lifelong learning

i. Persistence

j. Psychomotor

k. Soft skills

l. System

1. _____ means "variety".

2. _____ is a type of therapy that utilizes biological information in order to relieve stress.

3. _____ involves taking a few minutes to imagine being in some relaxing place, which can cause your body to relax in response to that stimulus.

4. _____, which utilizes pleasant smells such as lavender, has been shown to decrease stress.

5. Although _____ knowledge is important, using facts learned is the goal of learning.

6. _____ is the quality of being able to stay on task longer than the usual time when necessary, even after others might have given up.

7. _____ skills are behaviors that come from feelings and emotions and are truly important in the medical office.

8. _____ refers to coordination of mind and body.

9. An _____ is documentation of the patient's visit to the physician's office.

10. A _____ is a regularly interacting group of people who function with an organized set of doctrines and principles.

11. _____ is the process of continuing to learn throughout one's life.

12. _____ are those skills necessary for the smooth functioning of the workplace.

© 2011 Pearson Education, Inc.

APPLIED PRACTICE

Scenario

John Summers is an office manager at Hillcrest Family Medicine. The physicians at the office have voiced concern to John regarding the lack of professionalism among the office staff. They have asked John to conduct a staff meeting to focus on the importance of professionalism. The physicians have asked that John highlight five qualities of a professional in a health care setting.

---

1. What five qualities do you think John should choose to discuss during the staff meeting? Explain why. The physicians have also asked John to decide upon appropriate consequences for unprofessional behavior.

   ① Listening - Engage with patient not assumptions make clarification

   ② Communication - the impression on how the patient perceives the level of efficiency from the office

   ③ prioritize - make and do what is important take care of the patient

   ④ Speaking - conversation with staff and patient talk where they can understand.

   ⑤ Solving problems appropriately

2. How do you think John should handle this request by the physicians? What consequences do you think would be appropriate for unprofessional behavior?

   John should a meeting with the office staff. How to work with the physicens and the patient on being profession and having training some consequences that would be appropriate for uprofessional behavior is give them a warning talk to them about the problem. Second have that person suspend. Finally, terimated the staff member.

LEARNING ACTIVITY: TRUE/FALSE

_____ 1. It is very important that the medical assistant always engage in passive listening.

_____ 2. When communicating in the health care environment, accuracy is more important than brevity.

_____ 3. Critical thinking involves differentiating fact from fiction or opinion.

_____ 4. The first step in resolving conflicts is to seek to understand the situation.

_____ 5. If two workers are in conflict, it may be wise to ask a peer to resolve the conflict.

_____ 6. The office manager generally has most of the control over the tasks presented in the office.

_____ 7. Urgent tasks are not necessarily important tasks.

_____ 8. Stress can be caused by pain.

_____ 9. In the busy medical office, many tasks may have to be deferred to a later time.

_____ 10. It is not the medical assistant's job to question laboratory results that do not seem to be consistent with the patient's presentation.

CRITICAL THINKING

Answer the following questions to the best of your ability. Utilize the textbook as a reference.

1. In preparation for his externship, Stefan Marquise has been assigned to write an essay on barriers to professionalism in the health care setting. What information should Stefan include in his essay?

   _____

   _____

   _____

   _____

2. A very angry patient asks to talk with the office manager. The patient explains to the office manager that she overheard two staff members discussing the test results of another patient, who happens to be her sister-in-law. How should the office manager handle this situation?

   _____

   _____

   _____

   _____

3. Karen, the office manager, has noticed that a medical assistant, Charles, has been answering his cell phone while at work; as well as checking his e-mail between patients. Today, Charles's wife came to the office to talk with Charles during the busy morning hours. How should Karen address Charles's unprofessional behavior?

   _____

   _____

   _____

   _____

   _____

© 2011 Pearson Education, Inc.

RESEARCH ACTIVITY

Utilize Internet search engines to research the following topics and write a brief description of what you find. It is important to utilize reputable websites.

1. Type the word "professionalism" into an Internet search engine. What are some of the most interesting and helpful results that are returned with your search?

_____

_____

_____

_____

_____

_____

_____

_____

_____

_____

_____

_____

_____

_____

_____

_____

_____

_____

_____

_____

_____

_____

© 2011 Pearson Education, Inc.

CHAPTER 59
Externship and Career Opportunities

CHAPTER OUTLINE

General review of the chapter:

What Is an Externship or Practicum?
Preparing for the Certification Examination
The Job Search
The Résumé
The Cover Letter
The Interview
Follow-up After the Interview
What Does the Employer Want?

STUDENT STUDY GUIDE

Use the following guide to assist in your learning of the concepts from the chapter.

I. Preparing for the Externship and Certification Examination

1. The Externship Experience

   A. Refers to a situation in which one leaves the classroom and works, without _____, in a health care setting under the supervision of someone at the site.
   B. Offers the student an opportunity to get _____-_____-_____experience.
   C. Can be as short as _____ weeks or as long as one semester of school.
   D. Schools that are accredited by the Council on Accreditation of Allied Health Education Programs (CAAHEP) in conjunction with the AAMA require an externship of a minimum of _____ hours.
   E. The American Medical Technologists require a similar experience, which is known as a _____.
   F. Both professional organizations expect the graduates to have had actual _____ experiences in a real-world medical office in order to be certified.
   G. The externship experience should provide the medical assistant with ample experience in both _____ and _____ skills.
   H. Ideally, the practicum or externship experience is carefully monitored by the clinical instructor or _____/_____ coordinator so that any problems that may arise can be addressed.

2. Employer Expectations of Externs

   i. _____.
   ii. _____.
   iii. _____.
   iv. _____.
   v. _____.

© 2011 Pearson Education, Inc.

3. The Benefits of Participating in an Externship

   A. Having the opportunity to see how a physician's office, _____
      _____, or clinic operates on a day-to-day basis.

   B. Being exposed to a variety of different _____ in a work setting.

   C. Gaining additional experience using skills (List the skills that you might use.)

      i. _____

      ii. _____

      iii. _____

   D. Learning how to budget your _____ and _____ your workday, school day, and home life.

4. Areas Evaluated in the Externship

      i. _____

      ii. _____

      iii. _____

      iv. _____

      v. _____

      vi. _____

      vii. _____

      viii. _____

5. Possible Requirements for the Externship

   A. _____ insurance.

   B. A physical examination and immunizations, including immunizations for _____ and _____.

   C. A _____ skin test.

   D. Consideration of _____ and _____ issues.

   E. Errors are to be reported _____ to the supervisor without alarming the patient.

   F. _____ must be maintained.

6. The Role of the Preceptor

   A. Provides additional _____ and _____ for the student by observing the performance of particular skills.

   B. Provides a _____, _____ _____ for the student, usually at the midpoint and end point.

   C. Looks for continual _____ in skills as the student gains confidence.

   D. The student should make every attempt to establish a _____, or a comfortable working relationship, with the preceptor.

7. Areas Covered on a Typical Evaluation Form

      i. _____

      ii. _____

      iii. _____

      iv. _____

      v. _____

      vi. _____

      vii. _____

      viii. _____

      ix. _____

      x. _____

      xi. _____

      xii. _____

      xiii. _____

      xiv. _____

      xv. _____

8. Evaluating of the Externship Experience (What questions could you ask yourself in order to evaluate your externship experience?)

    i. _____

    ii. _____

    iii. _____

    iv. _____

9. The AAMA Certification Exam

    A. Given at numerous _____ _____ throughout the United States.

    B. Available only to medical assistants who have completed a _____-_____ program in medical assisting.

    C. The Certified Medical Assistant (CMA) examination is a comprehensive test that includes the following

        i. _____

        ii. _____

        iii. _____

10. Major Areas Tested on the CMA (AAMA) Examination

    A. General

        i. _____

        ii. _____

        iii. _____

        iv. _____

    B. Administrative

        i. _____

        ii. _____

        iii. _____

        iv. _____

        v. _____

    C. Clinical

        i. _____

        ii. _____

        iii. _____

        iv. _____

        v. _____

11. The Registered Medical Assistant (RMA) (AMT) Certification Exam

    A. Given as a computer-based test or a _____-_____-_____ test at various times throughout the year.

    B. Eligibility to take this examination is based on having either _____ _____ of work experience or a combination of training and work experience.

II. Getting Hired

1. Preparing for Your Job Search

    i. _____

    ii. _____

    iii. _____

    iv. _____

2. The Six Most Common Job Search Mistakes

    i. _____

    ii. _____

    iii. _____

    iv. _____

© 2011 Pearson Education, Inc.

v. _____

　　vi. _____

3. Where to Search for Jobs

　　i. _____

　　ii. _____

　　iii. _____

　　iv. _____

　　v. _____

　　vi. _____

　　vii. _____

　　viii. _____

　　ix. _____

　　x. _____

　　xi. _____

4. Writing a Résumé

　　A. Typed on 8½" × 11", good-quality _____ or off-_____ paper.

　　B. Do not use _____ colored paper.

　　C. Should be neatly typed and _____ free.

　　D. Always use a _____ _____ to prepare your résumé so that you can easily update it.

　　E. Always have a backup copy of your résumé stored on a disk, _____ _____, or other type of storage device.

　　F. _____ your résumé to make sure that it is error free.

5. Standard Items on a Résumé

　　i. _____

　　ii. _____

　　iii. _____

　　iv. _____

　　v. _____

　　vi. _____

　　vii. _____

6. The Heading

　　A. Your name, address, and telephone number are prepared as a _____ _____ at the top of the page.

　　B. If you have a cellular phone number and an _____ _____, this information can also be included.

　　C. When this information is printed in slightly _____ type than the rest of the text, it stands out and provides an easy reference for the reader.

7. The Objective

　　A. Listing an objective lets the reader know your _____ goals.

　　B. When you write your objective, it should be _____ and to the point with regard to what you want in a career.

　　C. Your objective may need to be _____, depending on where you are sending your résumé.

8. Education

　　A. If you are still a student or are a recent graduate with limited work experience, list your education first, in _____ _____ order, beginning with the most recent school/program.

　　B. Add any educational experiences that you have had, such as _____, _____, and courses.

© 2011 Pearson Education, Inc.

9. Employment

    A. List your work experience in the _____ chronological order.

    B. Include externship or practicum experience with a brief description of your _____.

10. Professional Organizations and Memberships

    A. Belonging to a professional organization can be a wonderful experience. It helps you to stay _____ on topics related to your career.

    B. Being a member and participating in an _____ shows your dedication, commitment, and loyalty to your chosen career field.

    C. Many schools have organized a _____ _____ _____.

    D. For a yearly fee, students or graduates can also obtain membership in the _____ or the _____ _____ _____.

11. Credentials

    A. Include information about your professional credentials, such as _____ (AAMA) certification or _____ (AMT) registration.

    B. If you do not have any credentials, _____ _____ include this section on your résumé.

12. References

    A. The references section should never include the name, address, and phone number of the _____ you will be using.

    B. You need to indicate only that references are _____ _____ _____.

13. Items NOT to Be Included on a Résumé

    i. _____

    ii. _____

    iii. _____

    iv. _____

    v. _____

    vi. _____

    vii. _____

    viii. _____

14. Considerations Regarding Your References

    A. State at the _____ of your résumé that references will be furnished upon request.

    B. Type on a separate piece of paper a list of at least _____ references with their addresses and phone numbers.

    C. Names of references are generally not included on the _____ _____.

    D. Obtain permission to use a _____ as a reference.

    E. It is wise to include the names of _____, as well as personal references.

15. Characteristics of the Cover Letter

    A. The cover letter should be _____.

    B. It is not a _____ of everything that is in your résumé.

    C. Explain what you can do for the employer and why your qualifications are a good _____ for their requirements.

    D. Be sure to include an address and _____ _____ where you can be reached.

    E. Do not add _____ comments or additional information to your cover letter.

    F. Always review the _____ of the employer's name and address carefully for accuracy.

    G. If you have word-processing capability, you may wish to _____ several _____ cover letters that you can then access from your computer and add the appropriate heading.

© 2011 Pearson Education, Inc.

16. Common Mistakes to Avoid When Writing a Cover Letter
    A. Failing to _____ the letter to a specific person in the organization.
    B. Failing to clearly state the _____ for which you are applying.
    C. Sending a cover letter that is too long. _____ _____ works best.
    D. Sending a letter that is poorly _____ or has spelling or typographical errors.
    E. Always send the _____ cover letter, never a copy.

17. Reference Materials for Interviewing (List some reference materials that you can use to prepare for an interview.)
    i. _____
    ii. _____
    iii. _____
    iv. _____

18. Dressing for the Interview: What to Avoid
    i. _____
    ii. _____
    iii. _____
    iv. _____
    v. _____
    vi. _____
    vii. _____
    viii. _____
    ix. _____
    x. _____
    xi. _____

19. Dressing for the Interview: What to Wear
    i. _____
    ii. _____
    iii. _____
    iv. _____
    v. _____
    vi. _____
    vii. _____
    viii. _____

20. Guidelines for the Interview
    A. Provide a copy of your résumé and references to the _____.
    B. Never give dishonest or _____ answers.
    C. Know what questions are _____ from being asked in an interview.
    D. Do not make _____ or _____ the focus of the first interview.
    E. Be _____ when the interview is over.

21. The Ten Most Common Errors Committed When Interviewing
    i. _____
    ii. _____
    iii. _____
    iv. _____
    v. _____
    vi. _____
    vii. _____
    viii. _____
    ix. _____
    x. _____

22. Documentation for Completing an Application
    i. _____
    ii. _____
    iii. _____
    iv. _____
    v. _____

23. After the Interview
    A. Always send a letter thanking the interviewer for his or her _____.
       i. It is a good opportunity to again express your _____ in the position.
       ii. Be meticulous about proofreading your letter for mistakes. It may be your final _____ _____ with the interviewer before the decision to hire is made.
    B. You may wish to call the office a few days later to ask about the _____ made on filling the position.
    C. If you are offered a position and decide not to accept it, you would use the same _____ when turning down an offer as you would use when accepting one.

24. Six Basic Skills That Employers Want
    i. _____
    ii. _____
    iii. _____
    iv. _____
    v. _____
    vi. _____

25. Characteristics That Employers Want to See in a Medical Assistant
    i. _____
    ii. _____
    iii. _____
    iv. _____
    v. _____

KEY TERMINOLOGY REVIEW

Match the vocabulary term to the correct definition below.

a. Application
b. Blind ad
c. Certification examination
d. Cover letter
e. Externship
f. Personal assessment

g. Practicum
h. Preceptor
i. Professional reference
j. Proofread
k. Résumé

1. _____ A summary of your credentials, including your employment history, experience, training, and education.

2. _____ An examination needed to become a Certified Medical Assistant and that is offered by the AAMA throughout the year.

3. _____ Does not identify the institution or facility that placed the ad.

© 2011 Pearson Education, Inc.

4. _____ An opportunity that provides the medical assistant with ample experience in both administrative and clinical skills.

5. _____ Refers to a situation in which one leaves the confines of the classroom and works, without payment, in a physician's office, hospital, or other health care setting.

6. _____ Statement of someone who has either worked with you or has known you for a period of time.

7. _____ Making sure that your résumé and cover letter are error free in content and typing.

8. _____ Includes personal information and previous work experience.

9. _____ Self-evaluation of strengths and weaknesses.

10. _____ Provides additional instruction and guidance for a student by observing the performance of particular skills.

11. _____ Intended to introduce you and your résumé to the recipient.

APPLIED PRACTICE

Assume that you are a recent medical assisting graduate preparing to enter the workforce.

1. You have recently received a phone call for an interview for Mountain View Health Care Center. How will you research the medical facility prior to your interview and why is this important?

   _____

   _____

   _____

   _____

2. Considering your current wardrobe, which outfit would you choose to wear to your interview and why?

   _____

   _____

   _____

   _____

3. Practice writing a cover letter to go along with your application. Submit your letter with your completed workbook materials.

LEARNING ACTIVITY: MULTIPLE CHOICE

Circle the correct answer to each of the questions below.

1. The _____ is a fellow medical assistant who will serve as a resource for the student medical assistant during the externship.
   a. office manager
   b. mentor
   c. physician
   d. None of the above

2. Which of the following is a responsibility of the student medical assistant during the externship?
   a. Be on time
   b. Dress appropriately
   c. Act in a professional manner
   d. All of the above

3. Circle the answer that should not be part of an interview.
   a. Have a specific job in mind when you interview so that you project self-assurance.
   b. Prepare responses should the interviewer ask you difficult questions or ask you to describe yourself.
   c. Show off your legs.
   d. Carry extra copies of your résumé.

4. When a student medical assistant has a concern about something at the externship site, to whom should the student bring the problem?
   a. The medical assisting program director
   b. A coworker
   c. The student's spouse
   d. The dean of the college

5. Which of the following may be a reason that a medical assistant may not be called for an interview?
   a. The résumé contains typographical errors.
   b. The résumé contains grammatical errors.
   c. The résumé contains crossed-out words and handwritten corrections.
   d. All of the above.

6. A résumé should ideally be _____ pages in length.
   a. 2–3
   b. 1–2
   c. 3–4
   d. 4–5

7. A thank you note should be sent to the potential employer after an interview within _____ days.
   a. 1–2
   b. 2–3
   c. 3–5
   d. 6–8

8. Which of the following are places that a medical assistant might look for employment?
   a. The newspaper
   b. The local medical assisting program
   c. An employment agency
   d. All of the above

9. Which of the following is an interview "don't"?
   a. Requesting parking validation.
   b. Arriving a bit early.

© 2011 Pearson Education, Inc.

c. Taking notes.
d. All of the above.

10. Which of the following is an appropriate dress code for an applicant going to a job interview?
    a. Casual attire
    b. Business suit
    c. Scrubs
    d. Any of the above

CRITICAL THINKING

Answer the following questions to the best of your ability. Utilize the textbook as a reference.

1. Willie Harrison is finishing his medical assisting training and is preparing for his externship experience. Willie's wife asks him what he will be doing during his externship. How might Willie answer her question?

_____

_____

_____

_____

2. Joann Felmer is a student in an administrative medical assisting course. She has been given an assignment to describe the benefits of the externship experience for the student medical assistant. How might Joann answer this question?

_____

_____

_____

_____

3. Corey Rubatino, CMA (AAMA), has recently been hired to work for Dr. Joe Cresanti. On Corey's first day, he has been asked by Dr. Cresanti to describe what is meant by practicing within his scope of practice. How might Corey answer this question?

_____

_____

_____

_____

4. Maggie Levinski, RMA, is the program director in an accredited medical assisting program. She is attempting to add new externship sites to the program roster. When Maggie meets with someone from a potential site, she is asked to explain the benefits of the externship to the site. How might Maggie answer this question?

_____

_____

_____

_____

RESEARCH ACTIVITY

Utilize Internet search engines to research the following topics and write a brief description of what you find. It is important to utilize reputable websites.

1. Using the Internet and other sources, locate prospective job opportunities for medical assistants in your area. Which jobs interest you most? Explain why.

_____

_____

_____

_____

_____

_____

_____

_____

_____

_____

_____

_____

_____

_____

_____

_____

_____

_____

© 2011 Pearson Education, Inc.

Administering an Intradermal Injection

Objective: Administer an intradermal injection.

Supplies: Gloves, hazardous waste container, alcohol sponges, sterile needle, sterile syringe, vial of medication, medication order, pen, patient record

Affective Behaviors: Affective behaviors provide a professional approach to a skill that enhances the patient encounter. These behaviors may also display sensitivity to a patient's rights and enhance communication. Pay close attention to these skills, which will be in **_bold, italicized_** font.

Steps:
I. Preparation
1. Perform proper hand hygiene. (1 point)
2. Apply gloves, and follow universal blood and body fluid precautions. (1 point)
3. Select the correct medication using the "three befores" technique. (2 points)
4. Gently roll the medication between your hands to mix any medication that may have settled. Refrigerated medication can be rolled between your hands to warm it slightly. (1 point)
5. Prepare the syringe using the correct technique. Carefully carry the covered needle and syringe to the patient. (2 points)
6. **_Identify and warmly greet the patient. Introduce yourself and ask the patient if he or she has any allergies._** (1 point)
7. **_Tell the patient the name of the medication and dosage ordered by the physician. Explain the process of the PPD skin test. Ask the patient if he or she has any questions prior to receiving the medication._** (1 point)
8. Select the proper site (center of forearm, upper chest, or upper back) for an intradermal skin injection. (1 point)
9. Using a circular motion, clean the patient's skin with an alcohol sponge. Wipe the skin with a sweeping motion from the center of the area outward. (1 point)
10. Allow the antiseptic to dry. (1 point)
11. Check the medication dosage against the patient's order. (2 points)
12. Remove the protective covering from the needle, using care not to touch the needle.
    Note: If you accidentally touch the needle, excuse yourself to the patient. Return to your preparation area and change the needle on the syringe. If you are using a self-contained syringe and needle unit that does not come apart, you will have to discard the entire syringe with the medication and start the process over again. (1 point)

II. Injection

13. Hold the syringe between the first two fingers and thumb of your dominant hand with the palm down and the bevel of the needle up. (2 points)
14. Hold the skin taut with the fingers of your nondominant hand. If you are using the center of the forearm, place the nondominant hand under the patient's arm and pull the skin taut. This will allow the needle to slip into the skin more easily. (1 point)
15. Using a 15-degree angle, insert the needle through the skin to about one-eighth of an inch. The bevel of the needle will be facing upward and covered with skin. The needle will still show through the skin. Do not aspirate. (2 points)
16. Slowly inject the medication beneath the surface of the skin. A small elevation of skin, or wheal, will occur where you have injected the medication. (1 point)
17. Withdraw the needle. With the other hand, discard the needle into the biohazard sharps container. (2 points)

III. Patient Followup

18. Do not massage the area. (1 point)
19. *Make sure the patient is safe before leaving him or her unattended. Observe the patient for at least 20–30 minutes for any negative reactions to the medication. Tell the patient not to rub the area.*
   Instruct the patient to return to the office within 48–72 hours for the reading of the skin test. Make certain that the patient understands the directions and does not have any questions. (2 points)
20. Correctly dispose of all materials. (1 point)
21. Remove and discard gloves, and perform proper hand hygiene. (1 point)
22. Document the procedure in the patient's record. (2 points)

Notes:

Administering Parenteral, Subcutaneous, or Intramuscular Injections

Objective: Administer subcutaneous (SubQ) and intramuscular (IM) injections.

Supplies: Medication order; vial of medication; gloves; alcohol sponges; biohazard sharps container; biohazard waste container; appropriate needle and syringe, depending on type of injection; pen; patient record

Affective Behaviors: Affective behaviors provide a professional approach to a skill that enhances the patient encounter. These behaviors may also display sensitivity to a patient's rights and enhance communication. Pay close attention to these skills, which will be in **_bold, italicized_** font.

Steps:
1. Perform proper hand hygiene. (1 point)
2. Apply gloves, and follow universal blood and body fluid precautions. (1 point)
3. Gather supplies. Use the "three befores" technique.
   Note: If you are not familiar with the medication, look it up in a reference book, read the package insert, and/or consult the physician. (1 point)
4. Gently roll the medication between your hands to mix any medication that may have settled. Refrigerated medication can be rolled between your hands to warm it slightly. (1 point)
5. Prepare the syringe using the correct technique. Carefully carry the covered needle and syringe to the patient. (2 points)
6. **_Identify and warmly greet the patient. Introduce yourself, and ask the patient if he or she has any allergies._** (1 point)
7. **_Tell the patient the name of the medication and dosage. Ask the patient if he or she has any questions prior to receiving the medication._** (1 point)
8. Position the patient depending on the site you are using. (1 point)
9. Using a circular motion, cleanse the patient's skin with an alcohol sponge. Wipe the skin with a sweeping motion from the center of the area outward. (1 point)
10. Again check the medication dosage against the order. (2 points)
11. Remove the protective cover from the needle, taking care not to touch the needle.
    Note: If you accidentally touch the needle, excuse yourself to the patient. Then, return to the preparation area and change the needle on the syringe. If you are using a self-contained syringe and needle unit that does not come apart, discard the entire syringe with the medication and start the process over again. (1 point)
12. When you are prepared to administer the injection, place a new alcohol sponge between two fingers of your nondominant hand so that you can easily grasp it when you are finished with the injection. (1 point)

627

13. Firmly grasp the syringe in your dominant hand, similar to holding a pencil. (1 point)

14. **Subcutaneous injection:**
    Pick up a small mass of tissue with your nondominant hand.
    Intramuscular injection:
    With your nondominant hand, stretch the skin tightly at the intersection site. (1 point)

15. Grasp the syringe in a dart-like fashion and insert the entire needle quickly with one swift movement. (1 point)

16. Be sure to insert the needle at the correct angle based on the type of injection:
    Subcutaneous: 45-degree angle
    Intramuscular: 90-degree angle (2 points)

17. Once the needle is inserted, do not move it. (1 point)

18. Aspirate to make sure that you have not punctured a blood vessel. If blood appears, discard the syringe and start over. (2 points)

19. If there is no blood return, slowly inject the medication without moving the needle.
    Note: Insert and withdraw the needle quickly to minimize pain, but administer the medication slowly. (1 point)

20. Taking the alcohol sponge (or cotton ball) from between the last two fingers of your nondominant hand, place it over the area containing the needle. Withdraw the needle at the same angle you used for insertion, using care not to stick yourself with the needle. (1 point)

21. With one hand, place the sponge firmly over the injection site. With the other hand, discard the needle in a biohazard sharps container. (1 point)

22. ***You may gently massage the injection site to assist absorption and ease the patient's pain.*** (1 point)

23. ***Make sure the patient is safe before leaving him or her unattended. Observe the patient for any adverse effect of the medication for at least 15 minutes.*** (2 points)

24. Correctly dispose of all materials. (1 point)

25. Remove gloves and discard them into a biohazard waste bag. Perform proper hand hygiene. (1 point)

26. Record the procedure in the patient's record. (2 points)

Notes:

Applying a Holter Monitor

Objective: Apply a Holter monitor, properly instruct the patient, and obtain a satisfactory recording.

Supplies: Holter monitor with sensors, patient cable, patient activity diary, fresh batteries, blank recording tape, adhesive tape, razor, alcohol

Affective Behaviors: Affective behaviors provide a professional approach to a skill that enhances the patient encounter. These behaviors may also display sensitivity to a patient's rights and enhance communication. Pay close attention to these skills, which will be in ***bold, italicized*** font.

Steps:
1. Assemble all necessary equipment. (1 point)
2. Install new batteries and a blank tape in the monitor. (2 points)
3. Verify that the machine is operational. (1 point)
4. ***Identify, interview, and instruct the patient.*** (2 points)
5. ***Ask the patient to undress from the waist up,*** put on a gown opened in the front, and sit on the examination table. (1 point)
6. Perform proper hand hygiene. (1 point)
7. Prepare the electrode sites and attach the electrodes. Remember to attach the sensors in the proper locations (third intercostal space 2 or 3 inches to the right of the sternum, third intercostal space 2 or 3 inches to the left of the sternum, fifth intercostal space, sixth intercostal space at the right, and sixth intercostal space at the left). (1 point)
8. Attach the wires so that they point toward the feet and connect the patient cable. (1 point)
9. Secure each sensor with adhesive tape. (1 point)
10. Connect the patient cable. (1 point)
11. ***Assist the patient with dressing.*** Extend the cable between the buttons or under the hem. (1 point)
12. Place the recorder in the carrying case, or attach it to the patient's belt or shoulder strap. Be sure that there is no tension on the wires. (1 point)
13. Plug the cable into the recorder. (1 point)
14. Record the start time in the patient's diary. (2 points)
15. ***Ensure that the patient understands the instructions completely.*** (1 point)
16. ***Confirm the time for the patient's*** return to the clinic for removal of the Holter monitor. Instruct the patient that he or she may leave. (1 point)
17. Document the information in the patient's record. Sign and initial your work. (2 points)

Notes:

Assigning a CPT Code

Objective: Accurately assign a CPT code.

Supplies: Patient's medical record, computer, medical billing software, current CPT coding book, superbill with procedure marked

Affective Behaviors: Affective behaviors provide a professional approach to a skill that enhances the patient encounter. These behaviors may also display sensitivity to a patient's rights and enhance communication. Pay close attention to these skills, which will be in ***bold, italicized*** font.

Steps:
1. Locate the complete procedure on the superbill. (1 point)
2. If the only procedure done was a physician visit, locate the CPT E/M codes section of the CPT book. (1 point)
3. Determine by the patient's medical record whether this office visit was a first-time or follow-up visit. (1 point)
4. Also determine by the patient's medical record whether this visit involved the patient's attending physician or a consulting physician. (1 point)
5. Note where the visit took place. (1 point)
6. Locate the level of visit within the place of service codes. (2 points)
7. If there was a surgical procedure, locate the code for it. (1 point)
8. Locate the code for any necessary equipment used in surgery. (1 point)
9. Code any radiologic procedures. (1 point)
10. Locate the procedure done in Sections 7000 to 7999. (2 points)
11. Locate, in the appropriate section, the part of the body on which the procedure was done. (2 points)
12. Locate the correct procedure, being careful to note if the test was bilateral, unilateral, etc. (1 point)
13. Code a laboratory test if done in Sections 80000 to 89999. (1 point)
14. Code any injected medication(s). (1 point)
15. Compare the CPT codes with the ICD codes before finalizing the bill. (2 points)

Notes:

Cleaning the Examination Room

Objective: Prepare and clean the examination room.

Supplies: Disinfectant, paper towels, disposable gloves, examination table, pillow, gown

Affective Behaviors: Affective behaviors provide a professional approach to a skill that enhances the patient encounter. These behaviors may also display sensitivity to a patient's rights and enhance communication. Pay close attention to these skills, which will be in **_bold, italicized_** font.

Steps:
1. Perform proper hand hygiene. (1 point)
2. Put on a clean pair of gloves. (2 points)
3. Roll the soiled disposable gown up and dispose of it in the appropriate waste container. (1 point)
4. Roll the soiled examination table paper covering into a ball and dispose of it in the appropriate waste container. (1 point)
5. Remove the soiled pillow case and place it in the appropriate container. (1 point)
6. Remove any other soiled items or equipment from the examination room. (1 point)
7. Clean the examination table and counter surfaces with disinfectant and paper towels. (2 points)
8. Dispose of cleaning materials in the appropriate container. (1 point)
9. Remove soiled gloves and dispose of them in the proper container. (1 point)
10. Perform proper hand hygiene. (1 point)
11. Put a clean paper covering on the examination table. (1 point)
12. Put a new pillow covering on the pillow. (1 point)
13. Be sure that the examination room is clean, clutter-free, and odor-free. Note: The examination room should be cleaner than when you found it. (2 points)

Notes:

ICD-9-CM Coding

Objective: Accurately assign an ICD-9-CM code.

Supplies: Patient's medical record; patient's insurance card; computer with printer or typewriter; medical reference material; superbill with the doctor's diagnosis.

Affective Behaviors: Affective behaviors provide a professional approach to a skill that enhances the patient encounter. These behaviors may also display sensitivity to a patient's rights and enhance communication. Pay close attention to these skills, which will be in **_bold, italicized_** font.

Steps:
1. Locate the condition or diagnosis on the superbill or in the patient's medical record. (1 point)
2. In _Volume II: Alphabetic Index_ of the ICD-9-CM, locate the condition or diagnosis. (1 point)
3. Examine the diagnostic statements to determine if the main term specifically describes that disease. If it does not, look at the modifiers listed under that main term to find a more specific code. (1 point)
4. Locate the code in _Volume I: Tabular Index._ (1 point)
5. Match the code description in the _Tabular Index_ with the diagnosis in the patient's medical record. (1 point)
6. Use the codes from 0021.0 through V82.9 in the ICD-9-CM to describe the main reason for the patient's office visit. (1 point)
7. First, list the ICD-9-CM code for the condition, problem, or diagnosis that is the main reason for the visit. Then, list coexisting conditions under additional codes. (1 point)
8. Use codes at their highest level of specificity—fifth-digit codes first, followed by fourth-digit codes, then third-digit codes, and so on. (1 point)
9. Do not code questionable, probable, or ruled-out diagnoses. (1 point)
10. V codes describe factors that influence the health status of the patient, such as pregnancy test or vaccination, and are not used to code current illnesses. (1 point)
11. E codes are used for identifying external environmental events or conditions such as the course of injury, some adverse effect, or poisoning. E codes (E930–E949) are mandatory when coding the use of drugs. (1 point)
12. M codes, in Appendix A of _Volume I_, relate to the morphology of neoplasm. Morphology codes are used only by tumor registries for reporting proposes. (1 point)
13. List all diagnosis codes (up to four) on the insurance claim form, with the primary diagnosis listed first. (2 points)
14. Always double-check your coding and ensure proper use of abbreviations and symbols prior to assigning the final code. (2 points)

Notes:

Interviewing a New Patient to Obtain Medical History Information and Preparing for a Physical Examination

Objective: Obtain pertinent patient information for the medical history to assist the physician in establishing the cause and treatment of the present illness (PI) by interview. Include the chief complaint (CC), past history (PH), social or personal history (SH), and family history (FH).

Supplies: Medical history form; clipboard; pen; scale; equipment for vital signs; urine container; gown and drape

Affective Behaviors: Affective behaviors provide a professional approach to a skill that enhances the patient encounter. These behaviors may also display sensitivity to a patient's rights and enhance communication. Pay close attention to these skills, which will be in ***bold, italicized*** font.

Steps:
1. ***Identify the patient, greet the patient warmly, and identify yourself.*** (2 points)
2. Explain the procedure. (1 point)
3. Provide a private area to conduct the interview. (1 point)
4. If not already complete, ask the patient to fill out the required demographic information on the registration form. ***Assist the patient in completing the form if necessary.*** (1 point)
5. Review the patient data portion; ***ask for any additional information necessary.*** (2 points)
6. ***Ask why the patient is being seen by the physician today (CC).*** (1 point)
7. Record the CC in the patient's own words (as appropriate). (2 points)
8. ***Using observations skills, ask the patient other open-ended questions to gather necessary information about the CC. Record this information under PI.*** (1 point)
9. Gather other information about PH, FH, and SH; document in patient's record. (1 point)
10. ***Ask the patient if he or she has any allergies.*** Document according to facility protocol (red ink/ specific area for recording allergy information). (2 points)
11. Document any other relevant observations or information. (1 point)
12. Record all information using correct charting guidelines. (1 point)
13. Correct any charting errors, drawing one line through error and adding the date and your initials. Record the correct information. (2 points)
14. If required or appropriate, ask patient to provide urine specimen or to empty his or her bladder. (1 point)
15. Obtain a complete set of vital signs (temperature, pulse, respirations, blood pressure, height, and weight). Immediately document this data in the patient's record. (2 points)

16. ***Explain what clothes the patient needs to remove, proper donning of the exam gown, and where the patient should sit and wait.*** (1 point)
17. ***Explain what procedures will follow;*** tell the patient that the physician will be in shortly. (1 point)
18. Place the patient's record with the history and complaint in the designated place for the physician. (1 point)

Notes:

Measuring Blood Pressure

Objective: Obtain an accurate systolic and diastolic reading.

Supplies: Sphygmomanometer; stethoscope; 70 percent isopropyl alcohol; alcohol sponges or cotton balls; paper and pen; patient's record

Affective Behaviors: Affective behaviors provide a professional approach to a skill that enhances the patient encounter. These behaviors may also display sensitivity to a patient's rights and enhance communication. Pay close attention to these skills, which will be in **bold, *italicized*** font.

Steps:
1. Perform proper hand hygiene. (1 point)
2. Assemble the equipment. Use a sponge or cotton ball with alcohol to thoroughly cleanse the earpieces, bell, and diaphragm pieces of the stethoscope. Allow the alcohol to dry. (2 points)
3. ***Identify the patient and explain the procedure.*** (1 point)
4. ***Assist the patient into a comfortable position. BP may be taken with the patient in a sitting or lying position. The patient's arm should be at heart level. Ask the patient not to cross his or her legs or talk during the procedure.*** (1 point)
   Note: If the patient's arm is below heart level, the BP reading will be higher than normal; if the arm is higher than heart level, the BP will be lower than normal.
5. Place the sphygmomanometer on a solid surface with the gauge within 3 feet for easy viewing. (1 point)
6. ***Uncover the patient's arm by asking the patient to roll back his or her sleeve 5 inches above the elbow. If the sleeve becomes constricting when rolled back, ask the patient to slip his or her arm out of the sleeve.*** (2 points)
   Note: Never take a BP reading through clothing.
7. Have the patient straighten his or her arm with palms up. Apply a proper-size cuff over the brachial artery 1 to 2 inches above the antecubital space (bend in the elbow). Many cuffs are marked with arrows or circles to be placed over the artery. Hold the edge of the cuff in place as you wrap the remainder of the cuff tightly around the arm securing the Velcro closure. (1 point)
8. Palpate with your fingertips to locate the brachial artery in the antecubital space. (1 point)
9. Pump air into the cuff quickly and evenly until the level of mercury is 20 to 30 mmHg above the point at which the radial pulse is no longer palpable.
   Note the level, rapidly deflate, and wait 60 seconds. (2 points)
10. Place the earpieces in your ears and the diaphragm (or bell) of the stethoscope over the area where you feel the brachial artery pulsing. Hold the diaphragm in place with one hand on the chest piece without placing your thumb over the diaphragm. The stethoscope tubing should hang freely and not touch any object or the patient during the reading. (1 point)

11. Close the thumbscrew on the hand bulb by turning clockwise with your dominant hand. Close the thumbscrew just enough so that no air can leak out. Do not close so tightly that you will have difficulty reopening it with one hand. (1 point)

12. Slowly turn the thumbscrew counterclockwise with your dominant hand. Allow the pressure reading to fall only 2 to 3 mmHg at a time. (2 points)

13. Listen for the point at which the first clear sound is heard. Note where this occurred on the manometer. This is the systolic pressure. (1 point)

14. Slowly continue to allow the cuff to deflate. The sounds will change from loud to murmur and then fade away.
Read the mercury column (or spring gauge scale) at the point where the sound is no longer heard. This is the diastolic pressure. (2 points)

15. Quickly open the thumbscrew all the way to release the air and deflate the cuff completely. (1 point)

16. If you are unsure about the BP reading, wait at least a minute or two before taking a second reading. (1 point)
Note: Never take more than two readings in one arm.

17. Immediately write the BP as a fraction on paper. You may inform the patient of the reading if this is the policy in your office. (2 points)

18. Remove the cuff. (1 point)

19. Clean the earpieces of the stethoscope with an alcohol sponge. (1 point)

20. Perform proper hand hygiene. (1 point)

21. Document results, including the date, time, BP reading, and your name, in the patient's record. (2 points)

Notes:

Measuring Oral Temperature Using an Electronic or Digital Thermometer

Objective: Provide an accurate temperature reading and document it properly.

Supplies: Electronic or digital thermometer (rechargeable); probe cover; waste container; pen; patient record

Affective Behaviors: Affective behaviors provide a professional approach to a skill that enhances the patient encounter. These behaviors may also display sensitivity to a patient's rights and enhance communication. Pay close attention to these skills, which will be in **bold, italicized** font.

Steps:
1. Perform proper hand hygiene. (1 point)
2. Assemble equipment. (1 point)
3. ***Identify the patient and explain the procedure.*** (2 points)
4. Remove the thermometer unit from the base and attach the probe (blue for oral). (1 point)
5. Remove the thermometer probe from the holder. (1 point)
6. Insert the thermometer probe into the disposable tip box to secure the tip. (2 points)
7. Insert into the patient's mouth on either side of the lingual frenulum and ***instruct the patient to close his or her mouth***. (2 points)
8. When temperature signal is seen or heard, remove the thermometer from the patient's mouth and read the result in the LED window. (2 points)
9. Dispose of the thermometer tip in the waste container. (2 points)
10. Return the thermometer probe to the storage place. (1 point)
11. Replace the unit on the rechargeable base. (1 point)
12. Perform proper hand hygiene. (1 point)
13. Document the results. (2 points)

Notes:

Measuring Radial Pulse

Objective: Provide an accurate radial pulse reading and document it properly.

Supplies: Paper and pen; patient's record; watch with second hand

Affective Behaviors: Affective behaviors provide a professional approach to a skill that enhances the patient encounter. These behaviors may also display sensitivity to a patient's rights and enhance communication. Pay close attention to these skills, which will be in ***bold, italicized*** font.

Steps:
1. Perform proper hand hygiene. (1 point)
2. Identify the patient and ***explain the procedure.*** (2 points)
3. Ask the patient about any recent physical activity or smoking. (1 point)
4. Ask the patient to sit down and place his or her arm in a comfortable, supported position. Note: The hand should be at chest level with the palm down. (1 point)
5. Place your finger tips on the radial artery on the thumb side of the wrist. (2 points)
6. Check the quality of the pulse. (1 point)
7. Start counting pulse beats when the second hand on your watch is at 3, 6, 9, or 12. (1 point)
8. Count the pulse for 30 seconds or one full minute. (2 points)
9. Immediately write the number of pulse beats per minute on a piece of paper. (1 point)
10. Perform proper hand hygiene. (1 point)
11. Correctly document the results in the patient's record, describing any abnormalities in pulse rate. (2 points)

Notes:

Measuring Respirations

Objective: Accurately measure respiration and document it properly.

Supplies: Watch with sweep second hand

Affective Behaviors: Affective behaviors provide a professional approach to a skill that enhances the patient encounter. These behaviors may also display sensitivity to a patient's rights and enhance communication. Pay close attention to these skills, which will be in **_bold, italicized_** font.

Steps:
1. Perform proper hand hygiene. (1 point)
2. Identify the patient and **_explain the procedure._** (2 points)
3. Assist the patient into a comfortable position. (1 point)
4. Place your hand on the patient's wrist in position to take the pulse, or place your hand on the patient's back. (1 point)
5. Count each breathing cycle by observing and/or feeling the rise and fall of the patient's chest or upper abdomen. (2 points)
6. Count for 30 seconds or for 1 minute using a watch with a sweep second hand. If the rate is atypical or unusual in any way, take it for another minute. (2 points)
7. Document the respiratory rate in the patient's record, noting the date, time, and any abnormality in rate, rhythm, and depth. Be sure to include your signature. (2 points)

Notes:

Measuring Temperature Using an Aural (Tympanic Membrane) Thermometer

Objective: Provide an accurate temperature reading and document it properly.

Supplies: Tympanic membrane thermometer; disposable protective probe cover; paper and pen; patient record; biohazard waste container

Affective Behaviors: Affective behaviors provide a professional approach to a skill that enhances the patient encounter. These behaviors may also display sensitivity to a patient's rights and enhance communication. Pay close attention to these skills, which will be in **_bold, italicized_** font.

Steps:
1. Perform proper hand hygiene. (1 point)
2. **_Identify the patient and explain the procedure._** (2 points)
   Note: To avoid error, call the patient by name and check against the name on the patient's record.
3. Remove the thermometer unit from its base. The display will read "Ready." (1 point)
4. Attach the disposable cover to the earpiece probe. (1 point)
5. With one hand, gently pull upward on the adult patient's ear or pull back and downward if the patient is a child or infant. (2 points)
6. Gently insert the plastic-covered tip of the probe into the ear canal. (1 point)
7. Press the button that activates the thermometer. (1 point)
8. Observe the temperature reading on the display window. (1 point)
9. Gently withdraw the thermometer. (1 point)
10. Eject the used probe cover into a biohazard waste container. (1 point)
11. Document the results in the patient's record using "T" to indicate tympanic temperature. (2 points)
12. Replace the unit on the rechargeable base. (1 point)
13. Perform proper hand hygiene. (1 point)

Notes:

Performing a Capillary Puncture (Manual)

Objective: Perform a capillary stick using a lancet or spring-loaded lancet following correct aseptic technique and obtaining an adequate sample without error.

Supplies: Biohazard sharps container; gloves; alcohol sponge; 2 x 2 gauze squares or cotton balls; lancet or spring-loaded lancet; capillary tubes; sealing clay; ammonia ampules; bandage; lab coat

Affective Behaviors: Affective behaviors provide a professional approach to a skill that enhances the patient encounter. These behaviors may also display sensitivity to a patient's rights and enhance communication. Pay close attention to these skills, which will be in *bold, italicized* font.

Steps:
1.   Assemble all equipment and supplies. (1 point)
2.   Perform proper hand hygiene. (1 point)
3.   ***Identify the patient and explain the procedure. Position the patient either sitting or lying down.*** (2 points)
4.   Apply gloves. (1 point)
5.   ***Select either the ring or great finger of the patient's nondominant hand.*** Cleanse the site with an alcohol sponge. Allow the alcohol to dry. (1 point)
6.   Remove the plastic cover from the lancet. (1 point)
7.   Grasp the patient's hand and gently squeeze the finger 1 inch below the puncture site. (1 point)
8.   Select the puncture site:
     a. Middle or ring finger of the non-dominant hand.
     b. Lateral curved surface of the heel, or the great toe of an infant.
     c. Make sure that the site chosen is warm and not cyanotic or edematous.
     d. Gently massage the finger from the base to the tip.
     e. Identify the exact location to make the puncture.
     Puncture the finger with a quick jabbing motion (or release the spring- loaded lancet). Do not puncture the site in the direct center of the finger pad. (2 points)
9.   Immediately discard the lancet. (1 point)
10. Wipe away the first drop of blood with a gauze square or cotton ball. (2 points)
11. Obtain the sample using a capillary tube. Seal one end of the tube in a clay sealer. Note: The finger may be gently massaged to increase blood flow. (1 point)
12. Apply clean gauze over the site and instruct the patient to apply firm pressure until the bleeding stops. (1 point)
13. ***Assess the patent.*** Apply a bandage to the site, if needed. (1 point)

14. Remove and dispose of gloves. Perform proper hand hygiene. (1 point)
15. Document the procedure in the patient's record. When documenting, use proper medical terms for right, left, or both. (2 points)

Notes:

Performing a Venipuncture Using the Vacutainer Method

Objective: Perform venipuncture by correctly assembling, locating, and entering a vein, and withdrawing a blood sample.

Supplies: Biohazard sharps container, Vacutainer tubes, multisample needle, gauze squares, alcohol pads, gloves, Vacutainer sleeve, tourniquet, bandage, cotton balls, adhesive, pen, lab coat, patient record, ammonia ampules

Affective Behaviors: Affective behaviors provide a professional approach to a skill that enhances the patient encounter. These behaviors may also display sensitivity to a patient's rights and enhance communication. Pay close attention to these skills, which will be in **bold, *italicized*** font.

Steps:
1. Assemble all equipment and materials. (1 point)
2. Perform proper hand hygiene. (1 point)
3. ***Identify the patient and explain the procedure. Position the patient either sitting or lying down.*** (2 points)
4. Apply gloves. (1 point)
5. Screw the Vacutainer needle into the plastic sleeve. Insert the tube into the other end of the sleeve; be sure not to puncture the tube. (1 point)
6. Apply the tourniquet 2 inches above the antecubital space tight enough to engorge the vein with blood. (1 point)
7. ***Place the patient's arm in an extended position with the palm facing up and comfortably resting.*** (1 point)
8. Palpate the vein with your fingertips. (1 point)
9. Cleanse the chosen venipuncture site with an alcohol sponge in a circular pattern. Allow alcohol to dry. (2 points)
10. Anchor the vein properly. (1 point)
11. Bevel up, line up the needle with the vein approximately 1/4–1/2 inch below the site where the vein is to be entered. (2 points)
    a. At a 15°–30° angle, rapidly and smoothly insert the needle through the skin.
    b. Remove your non-dominant hand, slowly pull back the plunger of the syringe or place two fingers on the flanges of the adapter, and, with the thumb, push the tube onto the needle inside the adapter.
    c. When the blood flow begins in the tube or syringe, allow the patient to release the fist.
    d. Release the tourniquet.
    e. Allow the syringe or tube(s) to fill to capacity.
    f. When the blood flow ceases, remove the tube from the adapter by gripping the tube with the nondominant hand, placing the thumb against the flange during the removal.

        1) Twist and gently pull out the tube. Steady the needle in the vein.

        2) Try not to pull up or press down on the needle while it is in the vein.

    g. Insert any other necessary tubes into adapter and allow each to fill to capacity.

12. Remove the tube from adapter. (2 points)

    a. Place a sterile gauze pad over the puncture site during needle withdrawal.

    b. Do not apply any pressure to the site until the needle is completely removed.

    c. After needle is removed, apply pressure or have patient apply direct pressure for 3–5 minutes.

    d. Do not bend the arm at the elbow

13. Transfer the blood from a syringe into tubes via the transfer device. (2 points)

    a. In the proper order of draw, allow the vacuum to fill the tubes.

    b. Place the tubes in tube rack and carefully insert the device through the stopper.

    c. If the vacuum tubes contain an anticoagulant.

        1) Mix immediately by gently inverting the tube 8–10 times.

        2) Do not shake the tube.

    d. Label the tubes with the proper information.

14. Check the puncture site for bleeding. (1 point)

    a. Apply a bandage, a clean 2 × 2 gauze pad folded in quarters.

    b. Hold in place by a Band-Aid or 3-inch strip of tape.

15. ***Thank the patient.*** (1 point)

16. ***Tell the patient to leave the bandage in place at least 15 minutes and not to carry a heavy object (such as a purse) or lift heavy objects with that arm for an hour.*** (1 point)

12. Remove and dispose of gloves. Perform proper hand hygiene. (1 point)

13. Document the procedure in the patient's record. (2 points)

Notes:

Preparing Injections

Objective: Prepare an injection

Supplies: Medication order, medication, needle, syringe, ampule, gauze, biohazard sharps container, antiseptic wipe

Affective Behaviors: Affective behaviors provide a professional approach to a skill that enhances the patient encounter. These behaviors may also display sensitivity to a patient's rights and enhance communication. Pay close attention to these skills, which will be in ***bold, italicized*** font.

Steps:
1. Wash your hands. (1 point)
2. Review the physician's medication order and select the correct medication. (2 points)
   a. Compare the label with the physician's instructions. Note the expiration date.
   b. Check the label three times: when taking it from the shelf, while drawing it up into the syringe, and when returning to the shelf.
3. Calculate the correct dosage to be given, if necessary. (1 point)
4. Choose the needle and syringe according to the route of administration, type of medication, and size of the patient. (1 point)
5. Open the needle and syringe package. Assemble if necessary. Secure the needle to the syringe. (1 point)
6. Withdraw the correct amount of medication: (2 points)
   a. From an ampule:
   1) Tap the stem of the ampule lightly.
   2) Place a piece of gauze around the ampule neck.
   3) Grasp the gauze and ampule firmly. Snap the stem off the ampule.
   4) Dispose of the ampule top in a biohazard sharps container.
   5) Insert the needle lumen below the level of the medication.
   6) Withdraw the medication.
   7) Dispose of the ampule in a biohazard sharps container.
   8) Remove any air bubbles in the syringe.
   9) Draw back on the plunger to add a small amount of air; then gently push the plunger forward to eject the air out of the syringe.
   b. From a vial:
   1) Using the antiseptic wipe, cleanse the rubber stopper of the vial.
   2) Pull air into the syringe with the amount equivalent to the amount of medication to be removed from the vial.
   3) Insert the needle into the vial top. Inject the air from the syringe.
   4) With the needle inside the vial, invert the vial.
   5) Hold the syringe at eye level.
   6) Aspirate the desired amount of medication into the syringe.

7) Displace any air bubbles in the syringe by gently tapping the barrel.
8) Remove the air by pushing the plunger slowly and forcing the air into the vial.
9) Revert vial and place on the counter; remove needle from vial.
7. Carefully recap the needle using one-hand technique. (1 point)

Notes:

Recording a 12-Lead Electrocardiograph

Objective: Perform an ECG, obtaining a satisfactory tracing without assistance.

Supplies: ECG machine with sensors; patient cable and power cord; ECG paper; electrolyte gel (if needed); alcohol; patient gown

Affective Behaviors: Affective behaviors provide a professional approach to a skill that enhances the patient encounter. These behaviors may also display sensitivity to a patient's rights and enhance communication. Pay close attention to these skills, which will be in ***bold, italicized*** font.

Steps:
1. Perform proper hand hygiene. (1 point)
2. Assemble all necessary equipment and supplies. (1 point)
3. Attach and plug in the power cord. (1 point)
4. Verify that the machine is operational and positioned properly. (2 points)
5. ***Identify and interview the patient, and explain the procedure to him or her.*** (1 point)
6. ***Offer patients gowns with the opening in the front.*** (1 point)
7. ***Position the patient flat on the table with a pillow under head and one under knees (if needed).*** (1 point)
8. Prepare the electrode sites and attach the electrodes. (2 points)
9. Connect the patient cable. (1 point)
10. ***Instruct the patient to relax, breathe normally, and refrain from speaking.*** (2 points)
11. Apply the electrodes snugly against the fleshy, muscular parts of upper arms and lower legs according to the manufacturer's directions. Apply the chest electrodes, V1 through V6. (2 points)
12. Connect the lead wires securely according to the color codes. (2 points)
    a. Untangle the wires before applying them to prevent electrical artifacts.
    b. Each lead must lie unencumbered along the contours of the patient's body to decrease the incidence of artifacts.
    c. Double-check the placement.
13. Determine the sensitivity and paper speed settings on the ECG machine. (1 point)
14. Depress the automatic button on the ECG machine to obtain the 12-lead ECG. (2 points)
15. Remove the electrodes from the patient's skin. (1 point)
16. ***Assist the patient in getting up, if necessary. Instruct the patient to dress.*** (1 point)
17. Perform proper hand hygiene. (1 point)
18. Clean the machine, straps, and sensors. Note: Always follow manufacturer's directions for cleaning. (1 point)

19. Mount the ECG, if necessary, and transfer patient information. (1 point)
20. Document in the patient record. Initial the work. (2 points)

Notes:

Competency Procedures

Directions: For each competency, read and familiarize yourself with the objective, supplies, and procedure steps. Pay particular attention to steps in **_bold, italicized_** font – these refer to affective behaviors that will allow you to demonstrate professionalism, communication skills, and sensitivity to the patient's rights.

You will be given time to practice each competency, and then you will be given an opportunity to pass the competency by earning a minimum score of 75%. Your score on each competency will be determined by a rubric that your instructor will provide that shows the value of each step. If you attain 75% on your first attempt, further attempts are not required. Each competency must be completed within a reasonable amount of time, as determined by your instructor.

Page #	Procedure Title	Date Performed	Instructor's Signature
651	Answering the Telephone and Placing Calls on Hold		
653	Arranging a Referral Appointment		
654	Assigning a CPT Code		
655	Closing the Office		
656	Collating Records		
657	Completing a CMS-1500 Claim Form		
658	Developing a Patient Information Booklet		
659	ICD-9-CM Coding		
660	Opening the Office		
661	Performing an Inventory of Supplies and Equipment		
662	Preparing a Deposit Slip		
663	Recognizing and Responding to Nonverbal Communications		
664	Recognizing and Responding to Verbal Communications		
665	Scheduling a New Patient Appointment		
666	Scheduling Established Patients		
668	Taking a Prescription Refill Message		
669	Taking a Telephone Message		

Answering the Telephone and Placing Calls on Hold

Objective: Ensure that the telephone is answered in a professional manner and, if necessary, that patients are placed on hold appropriately.

Supplies: Message pad, pen, notepad

Affective Behaviors: Affective behaviors provide a professional approach to a skill that enhances the patient encounter. These behaviors may also display sensitivity to a patient's rights and enhance communication. Pay close attention to these skills, which will be in **_bold, italicized_** font.

Steps:
1. Answer the telephone by at least the third ring, with the mouthpiece 1 to 2 inches from your mouth. (2 points)
2. **_Smile and speak clearly, using inflection, a pleasant tone, and a moderate rate of speech._** (1 point)
3. Answer using the greeting your office prefers (e.g., "Thank you for calling Dr. Smith's office. This is Carlos. How may I help you?"). (1 point)
4. At this point, callers will typically identify themselves. If not, ask callers to identify themselves and then verify the information against the patient's medical record. (2 points)
5. Listen to the caller closely to identify the reason for the call. Act accordingly while providing excellent customer service. (2 points)
6. While speaking with one caller, another incoming line may ring. When this occurs, notify the current caller that another line is ringing and ask if he or she can hold. Wait for the caller's response, and then place the call on hold. (1 point)
7. Answer the second call following the procedures described, ask the second caller if he or she can hold, wait for a response, and then place the second call on hold.
   (If the second call is an emergency, do not ask the person to hold and assist the caller immediately.) (1 point)
8. Return to the first call, **_thank the caller for holding_**, and continue assisting the person. (1 point)
9. Once the first call is completed, return to the second call, **_thank the person for holding_**, and continue assisting that caller. (1 point)

10. If the caller asks to speak with another employee who is not readily available and it is necessary to place the call on hold, check back with the caller approximately every 30 seconds. (1 point)
11. Once the first call is completed, return to the second call, thank the person for holding, and continue assisting that caller. (1 point)
12. If the caller asks to speak with another employee who is not readily available and it is necessary to place the call on hold, be sure to check back with the caller approximately about every 30 seconds. (1 point)

Notes:

Arranging a Referral Appointment

Objective: Schedule a referral appointment for a patient.

Supplies: Patient chart; telephone; paper; pen; Rolodex or physician directory; physician request for referral information

Affective Behaviors: Affective behaviors provide a professional approach to a skill that enhances the patient encounter. These behaviors may also display sensitivity to a patient's rights and enhance communication. Pay close attention to these skills, which will be in **_bold, italicized_** font.

Steps:
1. Gather supplies. (1 point)
2. Open patient chart for insurance information and physician request for referral. (1 point)
3. Place call to physician's office to whom the patient is being referred. (1 point)
4. **_Identify yourself and the physician on whose behalf you are calling._** Let the office know you are calling to schedule a referral appointment. (1 point)
5. Before providing the patient's name and so on, verify that the practice accepts the patient's medical insurance. If so, continue with the call. If the office does not accept the patient's insurance, **_thank the practice for its time_** and notify the physician. The physician will then recommend another physician for the patient referral. (1 point)
6. Once it has been determined that the office accepts the patient's insurance, provide the following information: patient's name, address, telephone number, and reason for referral. (2 points)

Notes:

Assigning a CPT Code

Objective: Accurately assign a CPT code.

Supplies: Patient's medical record, computer, medical billing software, current CPT coding book, superbill with procedure marked

Affective Behaviors: Affective behaviors provide a professional approach to a skill that enhances the patient encounter. These behaviors may also display sensitivity to a patient's rights and enhance communication. Pay close attention to these skills, which will be in ***bold, italicized*** font.

Steps:
1. Locate the complete procedure on the superbill. (1 point)
2. If the only procedure done was a physician visit, locate the CPT E/M codes section of the CPT book. (1 point)
3. Determine by the patient's medical record whether this office visit was a first-time or follow-up visit. (1 point)
4. Also determine by the patient's medical record whether this visit involved the patient's attending physician or a consulting physician. (1 point)
5. Note where the visit took place. (1 point)
6. Locate the level of visit within the place of service codes. (2 points)
7. If there was a surgical procedure, locate the code for it. (1 point)
8. Locate the code for any necessary equipment used in surgery. (1 point)
9. Code any radiologic procedures. (1 point)
10. Locate the procedure done in Sections 7000 to 7999. (2 points)
11. Locate, in the appropriate section, the part of the body on which the procedure was done. (2 points)
12. Locate the correct procedure, being careful to note if the test was bilateral, unilateral, etc. (1 point)
13. Code a laboratory test if done in Sections 80000 to 89999. (1 point)
14. Code any injected medication(s). (1 point)
15. Compare the CPT codes with the ICD codes before finalizing the bill. (2 points)

Notes:

Closing the Office

Objective: Secure the office properly during nonoperating hours.

Supplies: Checklist of office closing procedures; blank deposit forms and envelope/ pouch; office keys for rooms and files

Affective Behaviors: Affective behaviors provide a professional approach to a skill that enhances the patient encounter. These behaviors may also display sensitivity to a patient's rights and enhance communication. Pay close attention to these skills, which will be in **_bold, italicized_** font.

Steps:
1. Leave at least 15–30 minutes at the end of the day to close the office. (1 point)
2. Check all records used during the day for any orders that may have been missed. In addition, make sure that every visit is posted and billed. (1 point)
3. Pull, review, and collate records for patients who will be seen during the next day. Place the collated records with the charge slips attached and the master list of the next day's scheduled patients together in the appropriate place. Also, make a copy of the master list of patients for each physician. (2 points)
4. Either deposit in a bank or lock in the office safe all money received from patient payments. It is wise to have the person designated to make the daily bank deposit vary the time of deposit. Many offices now use a courier for this task. For purposes of quality control, the person completing the bank deposit and the person making the deposit should not be the same. Both people should be bonded. (1 point)
5. Lock all files and file rooms, physician offices, and other individual offices within the medical practice. (1 point)
6. Turn off electrical equipment and appliances. Note: Some equipment such as an incubator, fax machine, and computer may require 24-hour operation. (1 point)
7. Check all examination rooms to make sure they are clean and supplied for the next day. Note: This step may be done by the medical assistant who was in charge of rooming patients that day. (1 point)
8. Straighten the reception room. Put away all magazines and pick up toys. (1 point)
9. Activate the answering service before leaving. Know the name of the physician who is accepting emergency calls, or is on call, until morning. Remind the physician who is on call. (1 point)
10. Activate the security system if there is one. Always double-check to make sure the door is locked. (2 points)

Notes:

Collating Records

Objective: Prepare medical records of scheduled patients for review by the physician.

Supplies: Master lists of scheduled patients; charts and records of scheduled patients

Affective Behaviors: Affective behaviors provide a professional approach to a skill that enhances the patient encounter. These behaviors may also display sensitivity to a patient's rights and enhance communication. Pay close attention to these skills, which will be in **_bold, italicized_** font.

Steps:
1. Print or copy the day's appointment schedule. (1 point)
2. Pull all of the medical records of patients who are scheduled to be seen. (1 point)
3. In each record, review the patient's last appointment and make note of any results that should have been received, including laboratory tests, x-ray results, consultation notes, and other tests. (1 point)
4. If any of the results are not in the patient's chart, call the appropriate places to retrieve the results. You may take oral results, but request that the results be faxed to the office as soon as possible. (2 points)
5. Make a list of all results that have been received by phone and any that are outstanding. Let the physician know what remains outstanding. (1 point)
6. Add all received information to each chart for the physician to review and sign off on. (1 point)

Notes:

Completing a CMS-1500 Claim Form

Objective: Complete a CMS-1500 Claim Form

Supplies: Pen or computer, patient and provider information, CPT and ICD-9-CM coding manuals, CMS-1500 claim form

Affective Behaviors: Affective behaviors provide a professional approach to a skill that enhances the patient encounter. These behaviors may also display sensitivity to a patient's rights and enhance communication. Pay close attention to these skills, which will be in ***bold, italicized*** font.

Steps:
1. Enter type of insurance. (1 point)
2. Enter insured's ID number. (1 point)
3. Enter patient's relationship to insured. (1 point)
4. Enter patient's name. (1 point)
5. Enter patient's marital status. (1 point)
6. Enter patient's date of birth. (1 point)
7. Enter patient's address. (1 point)
8. Enter patient's telephone number. (1 point)
9. Enter other health coverage. (1 point)
10. Enter date of onset. (1 point)
11. Enter name of referring provider. (1 point)
12. Enter referring provider's NPI. (1 point)
13. Enter hospitalization dates. (1 point)
14. Enter outside lab work information. (1 point)
15. Enter ICD-9-CM code for primary diagnosis. (1 point)
16. Enter date(s) of service. (1 point)
17. Enter condition related to employment or injury. (1 point)
18. Enter patient signature on file. (1 point)
19. Enter place of service code. (1 point)
20. Enter procedure code. (1 point)
21. Enter modifier. (1 point)
22. Enter charges. (1 point)
23. Enter days/units. (1 point)
24. Enter rendering provider's NPI. (1 point)
25. Enter total charges. (1 point)
26. Enter signature of physician. (1 point)
27. Enter service facility location information. (1 point)
28. Enter service facility NPI. (1 point)
29. Enter billing provider's information and telephone number. (1 point)
30. Enter billing provider's NPI. (1 point)

Notes:

Developing a Patient Information Booklet

Objective: Develop a booklet to inform patients about the services provided by your medical office.

Supplies: Computer, design software (if including images), high-quality paper, printer (or an independent printing service)

Affective Behaviors: Affective behaviors provide a professional approach to a skill that enhances the patient encounter. These behaviors may also display sensitivity to a patient's rights and enhance communication. Pay close attention to these skills, which will be in ***bold, italicized*** font.

Steps:

1. Write the booklet with the reader in mind and at a reading level appropriate for the target audience. (1 point)
2. Avoid long paragraphs of explanation. Keep the sentences short and concise, and use as many bulleted points as possible. (1 point)
3. Proofread the booklet for grammatical and content errors. (2 points)
4. Provide a list of the regular office hours. (1 point)
5. List any special services offered by the practice or clinic, such as patient education classes or blood pressure testing programs. (1 point)
6. Explain the procedure for having a prescription refilled. (1 point)
7. Explain the procedure for processing medical insurance forms. (1 point)
8. Include a general statement about payment of fees, especially if payment is expected at the time of delivery of services. Do not discuss specific fees in patient brochures. (1 point)
9. Provide information about the physician and the staff. Include the name and telephone number of the office manager, the personnel responsible for insurance processing, and the patient educator. (1 point)
10. State what procedure to follow in case of an emergency. Ask the patient to keep this number near his or her telephone. (1 point)
11. Include a telephone number at the end of the brochure to use when additional information is needed. (1 point)
12. ***End the brochure by thanking the patient for taking the time to read the literature.*** (1 point)

Notes:

ICD-9-CM Coding

Objective: Accurately assign an ICD-9-CM code.

Supplies: Patient's medical record; patient's insurance card; computer with printer or typewriter; medical reference material; superbill with the doctor's diagnosis.

Affective Behaviors: Affective behaviors provide a professional approach to a skill that enhances the patient encounter. These behaviors may also display sensitivity to a patient's rights and enhance communication. Pay close attention to these skills, which will be in **_bold, italicized_** font.

Steps:

1. Locate the condition or diagnosis on the superbill or in the patient's medical record. (1 point)
2. In _Volume II: Alphabetic Index_ of the ICD-9-CM, locate the condition or diagnosis. (1 point)
3. Examine the diagnostic statements to determine if the main term specifically describes that disease. If it does not, look at the modifiers listed under that main term to find a more specific code. (1 point)
4. Locate the code in _Volume I: Tabular Index._ (1 point)
5. Match the code description in the _Tabular Index_ with the diagnosis in the patient's medical record. (1 point)
6. Use the codes from 0021.0 through V82.9 in the ICD-9-CM to describe the main reason for the patient's office visit. (1 point)
7. First, list the ICD-9-CM code for the condition, problem, or diagnosis that is the main reason for the visit. Then, list coexisting conditions under additional codes. (1 point)
8. Use codes at their highest level of specificity—fifth-digit codes first, followed by fourth-digit codes, then third-digit codes, and so on. (1 point)
9. Do not code questionable, probable, or ruled-out diagnoses. (1 point)
10. V codes describe factors that influence the health status of the patient, such as pregnancy test or vaccination, and are not used to code current illnesses. (1 point)
11. E codes are used for identifying external environmental events or conditions such as the course of injury, some adverse effect, or poisoning. E codes (E930–E949) are mandatory when coding the use of drugs. (1 point)
12. M codes, in Appendix A of _Volume I_, relate to the morphology of neoplasm. Morphology codes are used only by tumor registries for reporting proposes. (1 point)
13. List all diagnosis codes (up to four) on the insurance claim form, with the primary diagnosis listed first. (2 points)
14. Always double-check your coding and ensure proper use of abbreviations and symbols prior to assigning the final code. (2 points)

Notes:

Opening the Office

Objective: Prepare and set up the office to receive patients and operate efficiently.

Supplies: Checklist of opening office procedures; office keys for rooms and files; message form or pad; master list of scheduled patients

Affective Behaviors: Affective behaviors provide a professional approach to a skill that enhances the patient encounter. These behaviors may also display sensitivity to a patient's rights and enhance communication. Pay close attention to these skills, which will be in ***bold, italicized*** font.

Steps:

1. Arrive at least 30 minutes prior to the first scheduled appointment. (1 point)
2. Turn on the lights in the patient reception area before the first patient arrives. (1 point)
3. Check that the heating or air conditioning and computers are working properly. (1 point)
4. Observe overall reception room for safety hazards such as frayed electrical cords, slippery floor, or torn carpeting. Place a warning sign near any safety hazard and report it immediately to the office manager. (2 points)
5. Check magazines and recycle or discard any that are torn, damaged, or outdated. (1 point)
6. Check for level of cleanliness of housekeeping services and report inadequate services. (1 point)
7. Unlock file rooms or cabinets where records are kept. (1 point)
8. Take calls from the answering machine or answering service. Handle any that need immediate attention. (2 points)
9. Unlock any money that may be used for the day. Count and balance the money to make sure that the amount is the same as it was the day before, when the office was being closed. (1 point)
10. Unlock the outer office door. (1 point)
11. Compare the master list of all patients who will be seen during the day against the patient records that were pulled during the previous office hours.
    Make phone calls to gather any laboratory test information that is missing from the record. Provide the physician(s) and nurse(s) with a copy of the list of any laboratory test information that you have called for but that has not yet been received. (2 points)
12. Type and place a list of all patients who will be seen that day on the physician's desk or other designated area. (1 point)

Notes:

Performing an Inventory of Supplies and Equipment

Objective: Perform an inventory of supplies and equipment.

Supplies: Computer, monitor, printer

Affective Behaviors: Affective behaviors provide a professional approach to a skill that enhances the patient encounter. These behaviors may also display sensitivity to a patient's rights and enhance communication. Pay close attention to these skills, which will be in **_bold, italicized_** font.

Steps:
1. Turn on the computer, monitor, and printer. (1 point)
2. Open the spreadsheet software program. (1 point)
3. Create a file called Supply Inventory. (1 point)
4. Type the title of the spreadsheet (e.g., Medical Office Supplies for Inventory) in the appropriate cell. (1 point)
5. Create a row for each type of supply, and columns to indicate the number of each supply available, the amount of each supply on hand during the month of the year (January through December) and how many supplies must be reordered each month. (2 points)
6. Create formulas in the appropriate cell that will allow automatic calculations for the amount on hand each month. Also create formulas to automatically calculate how many supplies will need to be ordered each month. (2 points)
7. Create a "total" amount column at the end of the spreadsheet and create a formula to automatically calculate the yearly total amount reordered. (2 points)
8. Input the inventory numbers for all supplies and equipment in the appropriate cells. (1 point)
9. Save all work. (1 point)
10. Print the finished spreadsheet. (1 point)

Notes:

Preparing a Deposit Slip

Objective: Correctly complete a deposit slip.

Supplies: Pen; deposit slip; checks and currency to be deposited; endorsing stamp; calculator

Affective Behaviors: Affective behaviors provide a professional approach to a skill that enhances the patient encounter. These behaviors may also display sensitivity to a patient's rights and enhance communication. Pay close attention to these skills, which will be in ***bold, italicized*** font.

Steps:
1. Using the endorsing stamp, endorse all the checks to be deposited. (1 point)
2. Complete the information on the front of the deposit slip. (1 point)
3. If there is cash to be deposited, enter the amount in the upper-right box on the deposit slip beside the "Cash" indicator. In the boxes that list "Currency," list the total amount of all cash paper money to be deposited. In the "Coin" boxes, list the total amount of all coin money to be deposited. (2 points)
4. List each check to be deposited on a different line. If you have more checks than will fit on the front, list each additional check on the reverse side of the deposit slip. (1 point)
5. List each check in a different numbered box. (1 point)
6. Use a calculator to add all the checks and enter the total of all checks in the space labeled "Total" at the bottom of the reverse side of the deposit slip. Place this amount on the front of the deposit slip in the space labeled "Total from Side." (2 points)
7. Use the calculator to add the total amount of the cash and checks being deposited. List this amount in the space labeled "Total" and the space labeled "Net Deposit" on the front of the deposit slip. (2 points)
8. Place the deposit slip along with the cash and checks listed on the slip in an envelope for deposit at the bank. (1 point)

Notes:

Recognizing and Responding to Nonverbal Communications

Objective: Recognize and respond to nonverbal communications.

Supplies: Paper and pen

Affective Behaviors: Affective behaviors provide a professional approach to a skill that enhances the patient encounter. These behaviors may also display sensitivity to a patient's rights and enhance communication. Pay close attention to these skills, which will be in ***bold, italicized*** font.

Steps:
1. Be aware of the nonverbal cues that you are conveying to the patient. ***Use your body language and facial expressions to show care and concern for the patient.*** (1 point)
2. Identify the nonverbal communication cues that the patient is conveying. (2 points)
3. Ask appropriate questions to help verify your assumption. (1 point)
4. If the nonverbal cues do not correspond with the verbal message, convey your concern to the physician. (1 point)
5. Document the interaction with the patient. (1 point)

Notes:

Recognizing and Responding to Verbal Communications

Objective: Recognize and respond to verbal communications.

Supplies: Paper and pen

Affective Behaviors: Affective behaviors provide a professional approach to a skill that enhances the patient encounter. These behaviors may also display sensitivity to a patient's rights and enhance communication. Pay close attention to these skills, which will be in **_bold, italicized_** font.

Steps:
1. Identify possible communication barriers, and obtain resources to help overcome those barriers. (1 point)
2. Begin the interview by properly greeting and addressing the patient. (1 point)
3. Begin the conversation with an open-ended question. (2 points)
4. Ask for clarification or examples as needed. (1 point)
5. Allow time for thought formation (for yourself and the patient). (1 point)
6. Paraphrase what the patient is saying and to help clarify their message. (1 point)
7. Watch for and identify any paralanguage and nonverbal cues that may indicate incongruence with the verbal message. (2 points)
8. Ask closed-ended questions to get specific information. (1 point)
9. Summarize the interview for the patient and ask if there is anything else you need to discuss. (1 point)
10. Terminate the interview once you have satisfactorily discussed all of the patient's concerns. (1 point)
11. Document the patient's concerns as discussed. (1 point)

Notes:

Scheduling a New Patient Appointment

Objective: Schedule the first visit for a new patient.

Supplies: Pencil or pen (if preferred by office management); appointment schedule book or computerized scheduling system

Affective Behaviors: Affective behaviors provide a professional approach to a skill that enhances the patient encounter. These behaviors may also display sensitivity to a patient's rights and enhance communication. Pay close attention to these skills, which will be in **_bold, italicized_** font.

Steps:
1. Assemble necessary appointment scheduling equipment. (1 point)
2. Obtain the patient's full legal name and correct spelling, birth date, full address, telephone contacts (home, office, cell), and e-mail address. (2 points)
3. **_To avoid violating confidentiality, ask the patient whether it is permissible to call at home or at work._** (1 point)
4. Record the patient's chief complaint and symptoms. (1 point)
5. Request the name of the patient's insurance carrier and insurance policy number. (2 points)
6. Ask how the patient was referred to the medical office (physician referral, friend, colleague, insurance company, etc.) (1 point)
7. Ask the patient if he or she has a preference for morning or afternoon appointments. (1 point)
8. Attempt to accommodate the new patient's request for a preferred appointment time. (1 point)
9. Confirm the day, date, and time of the appointment, and **_have the new patient repeat the information for verification and mutual understanding._** (1 point)
10. Inform patients that they need to arrive 15 to 30 minutes prior to their scheduled appointment time to allow them ample time to enter the data requested on the initial history form. (1 point)
11. Provide the new patient with directions to the office. (1 point)
12. Inform the new patient of all materials to bring for the first visit (i.e., insurance verification, photo identification, list of current medications, past medical records, current lab, x-rays, and other medical reports, as necessary). (2 points)
13. **_Welcome and thank the new patient by name for selecting your medical office._** (1 point)
14. Forward all information as discussed with the new patient by mail if there will be enough time between the day the appointment was made and the actual appointment date. (1 point)
15. Document new patient information in a new medical record. (1 point)

Notes:

Scheduling Established Patients

Objective: Use an appointment scheduling system to efficiently schedule patients.

Supplies: Pencil or pen (if preferred by office management); appointment schedule book or computerized scheduling system

Affective Behaviors: Affective behaviors provide a professional approach to a skill that enhances the patient encounter. These behaviors may also display sensitivity to a patient's rights and enhance communication. Pay close attention to these skills, which will be in ***bold, italicized*** font.

Steps:
1. Understand the scheduling system used in your office. (1 point)
2. When scheduling manually, use a pencil so that appointments can be erased to make changes as needed. *Note:* Some offices prefer the use of black or blue ink instead of pencil. If using computerized scheduling, be sure the scheduling system is open. (1 point)
3. Before scheduling patients, set up a matrix by blocking out all time periods when the physician is not available for appointments (due to hospital rounds, vacations, etc.). Ideally, matrix setup or appointment blocking on the computer is done three months ahead of time. (2 points)
4. Schedule appointments by beginning with the first empty appointment in the morning or early in the afternoon, and then fill in the day. Do not schedule appointments at the end of the day with large open gaps in between. (1 point)
5. When scheduling manually, print the patient's full first and last name next to the appropriate time on the schedule. Add Jr. for Junior and Sr. for Senior if two patients in a family have the same name. If using computerized scheduling, search for the correct patient. Some systems allow searching by the patient's Social Security number or medical record number. This decreases the chances of pulling up the wrong patient if you have more than one patient with the same name. (1 point)
6. When scheduling manually, ask the patient for a current work and home telephone number, including area code. Write these numbers next to the patient's name. If using computerized scheduling, verify that the telephone numbers in the system are correct. If they are incorrect, immediately take the time right to update them. Correct contact information is necessary if the office needs to contact the patient prior to the appointment. (1 point)
7. Record the reason for the visit on the schedule using accepted medical abbreviations only. (1 point)
8. Allow the correct amount of time for the appointment. If an appointment will take more than the minimum time allotted on the schedule, use an arrow to indicate that the patient will be using

two or three blocks of time. In some offices a line is drawn across the time blocks. (2 points)

9. ***Once the appointment is recorded, repeat to the patient the date, time, and any special instructions.*** If the patient is in the office while you are scheduling the appointment, ***record the appointment on a reminder card and hand the card to the patient.*** (2 points)

10. ***End your conversation with a pleasant word and a smile.*** (1 point)

Notes:

Taking a Prescription Refill Message

Objective: Ensure that correct information is acquired when refilling a patient's prescription.

Supplies: Message form, pad, or paper; pen

Affective Behaviors: Affective behaviors provide a professional approach to a skill that enhances the patient encounter. These behaviors may also display sensitivity to a patient's rights and enhance communication. Pay close attention to these skills, which will be in **_bold, italicized_** font.

Steps:
1. Document the patient's name. (2 points)
2. Document the patient's telephone number. (1 point)
3. Document the name and dosage of the medication. Ask the caller to spell the name of the medication if you are unclear about what the caller is saying. (2 points)
4. Document how long the patient has been on the medication. (1 point)
5. Document the patient's symptoms and why the prescription is still needed. (1 point)
6. Ask for the patient's date of birth and weight (if the patient is a child). (2 points)
7. Ask for the name and telephone number of the pharmacy and the prescription number. (1 point)
8. Let the caller know you will give the message to the physician and you will call back if the prescription cannot be refilled. (1 point)
9. Attach the telephone message to the patient's medical record and give both to the physician to review. (1 point)

Notes:

Taking a Telephone Message

Objective: Ensure that the correct and relevant information is retrieved when taking a telephone message.

Supplies: Message form or pad with carbon or carbonless for duplicates; pen

Affective Behaviors: Affective behaviors provide a professional approach to a skill that enhances the patient encounter. These behaviors may also display sensitivity to a patient's rights and enhance communication. Pay close attention to these skills, which will be in **bold, italicized** font.

Steps:
1. ***Smile prior to answering the telephone and, in a warm voice, properly answer the telephone.*** (1 point)
2. Use a message form or pad with a carbon copy to keep a record of the message. (1 point)
3. Record the date and time of the call. (1 point)
4. Record the caller's full name, date of birth, and telephone number. (Always ask the caller to spell his or her name.) (2 points)
5. Document for whom the message is intended. (1 point)
6. Document the complete message. Avoid using abbreviations, other than accepted medical abbreviations. Include symptoms, such as temperature, rash, emesis, as well as duration of symptoms. (2 points)
7. Triage the call according to the office policy. (1 point)
8. ***Thank the patient for calling and, prior to hanging up the telephone, ask if he or she has any other questions.*** (1 point)
9. Write your initials to indicate that you took the message. (1 point)

Notes:

Competency Procedures

Directions: For each competency, read and familiarize yourself with the objective, supplies, and procedure steps. Pay particular attention to steps in *__bold, italicized__* font – these refer to affective behaviors that will allow you to demonstrate professionalism, communication skills, and sensitivity to the patient's rights.

You will be given time to practice each competency, and then you will be given an opportunity to pass the competency by earning a minimum score of 75%. Your score on each competency will be determined by a rubric that your instructor will provide that shows the value of each step. If you attain 75% on your first attempt, further attempts are not required. Each competency must be completed within a reasonable amount of time, as determined by your instructor.

Page #	Procedure Title	Date Performed	Instructor's Signature
673	Administering a Rectal or Vaginal Suppository		
675	Administering an Intradermal Injection		
677	Administering Oral Medications		
679	Administering Parenteral, Subcutaneous, or Intramuscular Injections		
681	Application of a Cold Compress		
682	Application of a Heating Pad		
683	Application of a Hot Compress		
684	Application of a Hot Soak		
686	Application of an Ice Bag		
687	Assigning a CPT Code		
688	Assisting with a Sigmoidoscopy		
690	ICD-9-CM Coding		
691	Instructing a Patient to Use a Cane or Single Crutch Correctly		
692	Instructing a Patient to Use Crutches Correctly		
694	Interviewing a New Patient to Obtain Medical History Information and Preparing for a Physical Examination		
696	Measuring Blood Pressure		
698	Measuring Oxygen Saturation		
699	Obtaining a Sputum Specimen for Culture		
700	Obtaining a Stool Specimen for Culture and Sensitivity		
701	Obtaining a Stool Specimen for Examination for Pinworms		
702	Obtaining a Stool Specimen for Ova and Parasites		
703	Obtaining a Throat Culture		
704	Performing a Group A Rapid Strep Test		
706	Performing a Mononucleosis Test		
708	Performing a Nebulized Breathing Treatment		
709	Performing a Pulmonary Function Test (PFT)		
710	Performing a Spirometry Test to Measure Forced Vital Capacity		
712	Performing a Venipuncture Using the Vacutainer Method		
714	Preparing Injections		
716	Sanitizing Instruments		
717	Sterilizing Instruments in an Autoclave		
718	Teaching a Patient to Correctly Use a Walker		
719	Teaching Peak Flow Measurement		
720	Testing for Occult Blood		
721	Wheelchair Transfer to Chair or Examination Table		
723	Wrapping Instruments for Sterilization in an Autoclave		

Administering a Rectal or Vaginal Suppository

Objective: Insert a suppository as ordered by the physician.

Supplies: Medication order; lubricant; biohazard waste container; patient instructions; vaginal suppository or cream; gloves; sanitary napkin; rectal suppository; 4 x 4 gauze square; pen; patient record

Affective Behaviors: Affective behaviors provide a professional approach to a skill that enhances the patient encounter. These behaviors may also display sensitivity to a patient's rights and enhance communication. Pay close attention to these skills, which will be in ***bold, italicized*** font.

Steps:
1. Assemble equipment. (1 point)
2. Perform proper hand hygiene. (1 point)
3. Select the medication using the "three befores."
   Note: If you are not familiar with the medication, look it up in a reference book, read the package insert, and/or consult the physician. (1 point)
4. Double-check the suppository label. Check the drug and its strength. (2 points)
5. Correctly calculate the dosage in writing. Double-check your calculations with someone else. (1 point)
6. Check the dosage again against the medication order. (2 points)
7. Replace the cap on the medication bottle and return the bottle to the storage shelf or refrigerator after reading the label again. (1 point)
8. ***Identify and warmly greet the patient. Introduce yourself, and ask the patient if he or she has any allergies.*** (1 point)
9. Give the patient a gown or sheet. Have the patient remove all clothing from the waist down. Assist the patient, as necessary, ***and provide reassurance if the patient seems uncomfortable with the administration of a suppository.*** (1 point)
10. Tell the patient the name of the medication and dosage that you are administering, per the physician's order. ***Ask the patient if he or she has any questions prior to receiving the medication.*** (1 point)
11. **Rectal suppository administration:**
    Have the patient lie on the left side, with the top leg bent. ***Drape the patient with a sheet.*** Apply gloves. Open the suppository and place it on a gauze square. Moisten the suppository with lubricant or a small amount of water. With one hand, separate the buttocks. Pick up the suppository with the other hand. ***Ask the patient to breathe slowly as you insert the suppository.*** Insert the suppository 1 to 1-and-one-half inches past the rectal sphincter. Hold the buttocks together and instruct the patient not to bear down. Wipe the anal area with the gauze square and discard the square in a biohazard waste container. Have the

patient remain in the side-lying position for approximately 20 minutes.

Vaginal suppository administration:

Have the patient lie in the dorsal recumbent position with the legs apart. ***Drape the patient with a sheet.*** With a gloved hand, open the suppository. If an applicator is provided, drop it on the clean surface. With a gloved hand, separate the labia minora and hold them in place. Using the other hand, insert the suppository one finger length into the vagina. If an applicator was provided, place the suppository in the applicator and insert it in the vagina in a downward direction. Instruct the patient to remain in this position for 10 minutes. Dispose of the applicator. Remove your gloves. Dispose of the items in the biohazard waste container. ***Give the patient wipes to clean with and provide the patient with a sanitary napkin.*** (2 points)

12. ***Remain with the patient until the medication has dissolved.*** (2 points)

13. ***Provide the patient with written followup instructions if further medication is to be taken.*** (1 point)

14. Document the medication administration in the patient's record. (2 points)

Notes:

Administering an Intradermal Injection

Objective: Administer an intradermal injection.

Supplies: Gloves, hazardous waste container, alcohol sponges, sterile needle, sterile syringe, vial of medication, medication order, pen, patient record

Affective Behaviors: Affective behaviors provide a professional approach to a skill that enhances the patient encounter. These behaviors may also display sensitivity to a patient's rights and enhance communication. Pay close attention to these skills, which will be in **_bold, italicized_** font.

Steps:
I. Preparation
1. Perform proper hand hygiene. (1 point)
2. Apply gloves, and follow universal blood and body fluid precautions. (1 point)
3. Select the correct medication using the "three befores" technique. (2 points)
4. Gently roll the medication between your hands to mix any medication that may have settled. Refrigerated medication can be rolled between your hands to warm it slightly. (1 point)
5. Prepare the syringe using the correct technique. Carefully carry the covered needle and syringe to the patient. (2 points)
6. **_Identify and warmly greet the patient. Introduce yourself and ask the patient if he or she has any allergies._** (1 point)
7. **_Tell the patient the name of the medication and dosage ordered by the physician. Explain the process of the PPD skin test. Ask the patient if he or she has any questions prior to receiving the medication._** (1 point)
8. Select the proper site (center of forearm, upper chest, or upper back) for an intradermal skin injection. (1 point)
9. Using a circular motion, clean the patient's skin with an alcohol sponge. Wipe the skin with a sweeping motion from the center of the area outward. (1 point)
10. Allow the antiseptic to dry. (1 point)
11. Check the medication dosage against the patient's order. (2 points)
12. Remove the protective covering from the needle, using care not to touch the needle.
    Note: If you accidentally touch the needle, excuse yourself to the patient. Return to your preparation area and change the needle on the syringe. If you are using a self-contained syringe and needle unit that does not come apart, you will have to discard the entire syringe with the medication and start the process over again. (1 point)

II. Injection

13. Hold the syringe between the first two fingers and thumb of your dominant hand with the palm down and the bevel of the needle up. (2 points)
14. Hold the skin taut with the fingers of your nondominant hand. If you are using the center of the forearm, place the nondominant hand under the patient's arm and pull the skin taut. This will allow the needle to slip into the skin more easily. (1 point)
15. Using a 15-degree angle, insert the needle through the skin to about one-eighth of an inch. The bevel of the needle will be facing upward and covered with skin. The needle will still show through the skin. Do not aspirate. (2 points)
16. Slowly inject the medication beneath the surface of the skin. A small elevation of skin, or wheal, will occur where you have injected the medication. (1 point)
17. Withdraw the needle. With the other hand, discard the needle into the biohazard sharps container. (2 points)

III. Patient Followup

18. Do not massage the area. (1 point)
19. ***Make sure the patient is safe before leaving him or her unattended. Observe the patient for at least 20–30 minutes for any negative reactions to the medication. Tell the patient not to rub the area.***
Instruct the patient to return to the office within 48–72 hours for the reading of the skin test. Make certain that the patient understands the directions and does not have any questions. (2 points)
20. Correctly dispose of all materials. (1 point)
21. Remove and discard gloves, and perform proper hand hygiene. (1 point)
22. Document the procedure in the patient's record. (2 points)

Notes:

Administering Oral Medications

Objective: Administer oral medication.

Supplies: Medication order signed by physician; oral medication; calibrated paper cup or receptacle for medication; water in glass; patient instruction sheet; biohazard waste container; pen

Affective Behaviors: Affective behaviors provide a professional approach to a skill that enhances the patient encounter. These behaviors may also display sensitivity to a patient's rights and enhance communication. Pay close attention to these skills, which will be in ***bold, italicized*** font.

Steps:
1. Assemble equipment. (1 point)
2. Perform proper hand hygiene. (1 point)
3. Select the correct medication using the "three befores" technique. *Note:* If you are not familiar with the medication, look it up in a reference book, read the package insert, and/or consult the physician. (2 points)
4. Always double-check the label to make sure the strength is correct. (2 points)
5. Correctly calculate the dosage in writing. Double-check your calculations with someone else. (1 point)
6. Place a medicine cup or container on a flat surface. (1 point)
7. Gently shake the medication if it is in liquid form. (1 point)
8. Hold the bottle so that the label is in the palm of your hand to prevent damaging the label with liquid medication. (2 points)
9. Recheck the label. (2 points)
10. Remove the cap from the medicine container and place it upside down on a clean surface. (2 points)
11. **Liquid Medication:**
    Hold the calibrated medicine cup at eye level and pour the medication into the cup, stopping at the correct dosage line. Pour the medication away from the label side of the bottle. If too much medication is poured into the calibrated cup, do not return it to the bottle. Discard it into a sink.
    Tablet or Capsule Medication:
    Shake out the correct number of tablets or pills into the bottle cap. Then, place the tablets or pills in the medicine cup. If you accidentally pour out an extra tablet, do not return it to the medication bottle; discard it. (1 point)
12. Check the medication again to make sure the dosage is the same as the medication order. (1 point)
13. Replace the cap on the medication bottle and return the bottle to the storage shelf. (1 point)
14. Take the prepared medication and a glass of water to the patient. (2 points)

15. ***Identify the patient and warmly greet the patient. Introduce yourself to the patient and ask the patient if he or she has any allergies.*** (1 point)

16. Tell the patient the name of the medication and dosage that you are administering per the physician's order. ***Ask the patient if he or she has any questions prior to taking the medication.*** (1 point)

17. ***Remain with the patient until the medication has been swallowed.***

    Note: After giving the medication to the patient, it is best to have the patient wait in the office for 30 minutes. (1 point)

18. ***Provide the patient with written followup instructions if further medication is to be taken.*** (1 point)

19. Document the medication administration, noting in the patient's record the time, medication name, dosage route, and your name. (2 points)

Notes:

Administering Parenteral, Subcutaneous, or Intramuscular Injections

Objective: Administer subcutaneous (SubQ) and intramuscular (IM) injections.

Supplies: Medication order; vial of medication; gloves; alcohol sponges; biohazard sharps container; biohazard waste container; appropriate needle and syringe, depending on type of injection; pen; patient record

Affective Behaviors: Affective behaviors provide a professional approach to a skill that enhances the patient encounter. These behaviors may also display sensitivity to a patient's rights and enhance communication. Pay close attention to these skills, which will be in **bold, italicized** font.

Steps:
1. Perform proper hand hygiene. (1 point)
2. Apply gloves, and follow universal blood and body fluid precautions. (1 point)
3. Gather supplies. Use the "three befores" technique.
   Note: If you are not familiar with the medication, look it up in a reference book, read the package insert, and/or consult the physician. (1 point)
4. Gently roll the medication between your hands to mix any medication that may have settled. Refrigerated medication can be rolled between your hands to warm it slightly. (1 point)
5. Prepare the syringe using the correct technique. Carefully carry the covered needle and syringe to the patient. (2 points)
6. ***Identify and warmly greet the patient. Introduce yourself, and ask the patient if he or she has any allergies.*** (1 point)
7. ***Tell the patient the name of the medication and dosage. Ask the patient if he or she has any questions prior to receiving the medication.*** (1 point)
8. Position the patient depending on the site you are using. (1 point)
9. Using a circular motion, cleanse the patient's skin with an alcohol sponge. Wipe the skin with a sweeping motion from the center of the area outward. (1 point)
10. Again check the medication dosage against the order. (2 points)
11. Remove the protective cover from the needle, taking care not to touch the needle.
    Note: If you accidentally touch the needle, excuse yourself to the patient. Then, return to the preparation area and change the needle on the syringe. If you are using a self-contained syringe and needle unit that does not come apart, discard the entire syringe with the medication and start the process over again. (1 point)
12. When you are prepared to administer the injection, place a new alcohol sponge between two fingers of your nondominant hand so that you can easily grasp it when you are finished with the injection. (1 point)

13. Firmly grasp the syringe in your dominant hand, similar to holding a pencil. (1 point)

14. **Subcutaneous injection:**
Pick up a small mass of tissue with your nondominant hand.
Intramuscular injection:
With your nondominant hand, stretch the skin tightly at the intersection site. (1 point)

15. Grasp the syringe in a dart-like fashion and insert the entire needle quickly with one swift movement. (1 point)

16. Be sure to insert the needle at the correct angle based on the type of injection:
Subcutaneous: 45-degree angle
Intramuscular: 90-degree angle (2 points)

17. Once the needle is inserted, do not move it. (1 point)

18. Aspirate to make sure that you have not punctured a blood vessel. If blood appears, discard the syringe and start over. (2 points)

19. If there is no blood return, slowly inject the medication without moving the needle.
Note: Insert and withdraw the needle quickly to minimize pain, but administer the medication slowly. (1 point)

20. Taking the alcohol sponge (or cotton ball) from between the last two fingers of your nondominant hand, place it over the area containing the needle. Withdraw the needle at the same angle you used for insertion, using care not to stick yourself with the needle. (1 point)

21. With one hand, place the sponge firmly over the injection site. With the other hand, discard the needle in a biohazard sharps container. (1 point)

22. ***You may gently massage the injection site to assist absorption and ease the patient's pain.*** (1 point)

23. ***Make sure the patient is safe before leaving him or her unattended. Observe the patient for any adverse effect of the medication for at least 15 minutes.*** (2 points)

24. Correctly dispose of all materials. (1 point)

25. Remove gloves and discard them into a biohazard waste bag. Perform proper hand hygiene. (1 point)

26. Record the procedure in the patient's record. (2 points)

Notes:

Application of a Cold Compress

Objective: Perform a cold compress application and document the procedure without error.

Supplies: Water; absorbent cloths or gauze squares; waterproof cover or plastic wrap; basin; ice

Affective Behaviors: Affective behaviors provide a professional approach to a skill that enhances the patient encounter. These behaviors may also display sensitivity to a patient's rights and enhance communication. Pay close attention to these skills, which will be in **bold, italicized** font.

Steps:
1. Perform proper hand hygiene. (1 point)
2. Assemble all equipment.
   Note: If an open wound is present, use sterile equipment and standard precautions. (1 point)
3. ***Identify and instruct the patient regarding the procedure.*** (1 point)
4. Fill the basin half full of cold water. Add ice cubes and compress. (1 point)
5. Wring out the compress until it is wet but not dripping. Wrap the compress in a plastic or waterproof covering to prevent dripping. Gently place the compress on the patient's affected body part. (2 points)
6. Check the compress every 3–5 minutes and replace it with another cold compress when it is no longer cool. Add more ice as the water warms. (1 point)
7. Leave the compress in place for the time specified by the ordering physician (usually 15–20 minutes). (1 point)
8. Gently dry the affected body part. (1 point)
9. Place the linens in the proper container. Clean all the equipment. (1 point)
10. Perform proper hand hygiene and return all equipment. (1 point)
11. Document the procedure in the patient's record. (2 points)

Notes:

Application of a Heating Pad

Objective: Perform a heating pad application and document the procedure without error.

Supplies: Heating pad with protective covering or pillowcase. Note: Perform a preliminary check of the heating pad without bending it to determine that the wires are in good condition.

Affective Behaviors: Affective behaviors provide a professional approach to a skill that enhances the patient encounter. These behaviors may also display sensitivity to a patient's rights and enhance communication. Pay close attention to these skills, which will be in **_bold, italicized_** font.

Steps:
1. Assemble and test the equipment. (1 point)
2. Perform proper hand hygiene. (1 point)
3. **_Identify the patient and explain the procedure. Caution against using pins, bending the heating elements within the pad, or lying on the heating pad._** (2 points)
4. Place the heating pad in a protective covering or pillow case. (1 point)
5. Connect the heating pad cord to an electrical outlet. Set the temperature at the ordered setting (low or medium). (1 point)
6. **_Place the heating pad over the patient's affected area. Ask the patient how it feels._** (1 point)
7. **_Instruct the patient regarding the proper temperature setting._** (1 point)
8. Leave the heating pad in place for the ordered amount of time (15 to 20 minutes). **_Check the patient periodically for any signs of redness, swelling, or pain._** (2 points)
9. Remove the heating pad when the procedure is complete. **_Instruct the patient on any after-care procedures such as further home treatment._** (1 point)
10. Place the protective covering in the laundry. (1 point)
11. Use proper hand hygiene and return all used equipment. (1 point)
12. Document the procedure in the patient's record. (2 points)

Notes:

Application of a Hot Compress

Objective: Perform application of a hot compress and document the procedure without error.

Supplies: Sink; basin of warm water or soaking solution. as directed by the physician; bath thermometer; absorbent cloths or gauze squares; waterproof cover; pencil or pen

Affective Behaviors: Affective behaviors provide a professional approach to a skill that enhances the patient encounter. These behaviors may also display sensitivity to a patient's rights and enhance communication. Pay close attention to these skills, which will be in **bold, *italicized*** font.

Steps:
1. Perform proper hand hygiene. (1 point)
2. Assemble all equipment and materials. Use sterile equipment and standard precautions if open wound is present. (1 point)
3. Identify the patient and explain the procedure. (2 points)
4. Fill the basin half full of warm water or medicated solution prepared according to the physician's directions. (1 point)
5. Request that the patient remove any clothing; compresses must be on bare skin. ***Assist the patient, if necessary.*** (1 point)
6. Check the temperature of the solution with a bath thermometer. (1 point)
7. Position the patient comfortably and in a well-supported position. (1 point)
8. Place the cloths in the basin of hot water solution. Wring out one cloth until it is wet but not dripping. (1 point)
9. Gradually place the compress on the patient's body part; ***ask the patient how the temperature feels.*** (1 point)
10. Frequently test the temperature of the solution. Replace the water as the solution cools with warm water. (1 point)
11. Time the procedure according to the physician's order, usually 15–30 minutes. Check the patient periodically for signs of increased redness, swelling, or pain. (2 points)
12. Gently dry the affected body part. (1 point)
13. ***Instruct the patient on any further care, such as continuing the soaks at home.*** (1 point)
14. Place towels in the laundry and clean all equipment. (1 point)
15. Perform proper hand hygiene. (1 point)
16. Document the procedure in the patient's record. (2 points)

Notes:

Application of a Hot Soak

Objective: Perform hot soak application and document the procedure without error.

Supplies: Soaking solution or water; basin or tub; bath thermometer; towels

Affective Behaviors: Affective behaviors provide a professional approach to a skill that enhances the patient encounter. These behaviors may also display sensitivity to a patient's rights and enhance communication. Pay close attention to these skills, which will be in ***bold, italicized*** font.

Steps:
1. Assemble all equipment and materials.
   Note: If an open wound is present, use sterile equipment and standard precautions. (1 point)
2. Perform proper hand hygiene. (1 point)
3. ***Identify the patient and explain the procedure.*** (1 point)
4. Fill the basin or tub half full of water or solution as directed by the physician. (1 point)
5. The soaks should be applied to bare skin. ***Request that the patient remove any clothing and assist, if necessary.*** (1 point)
6. Check water temperature with bath thermometer.
   Note: The temperature range for an adult should be between 105° F and 107° F (41° C and 44° C). (2 points)
7. ***Position the patient in a comfortable, well-supported position.*** (1 point)
8. ***Pad the side of the basin or tub with a towel to prevent the patient's body from rubbing on the edge.*** (1 point)
9. ***Gradually place the patient's body part in the solution. Ask the patient to tell you how the temperature feels.*** (1 point)
10. Frequently test the temperature of the solution. Using a pitcher, remove part of the liquid every 5 minutes and replace it with hot water. Pour the hot water at the edge of the basin and protect the patient by placing your hand between the patient's body part and the hot water. Swirl the water while pouring to mix the water. (1 point)
11. Time the procedure according to the physician's order, usually 15–30 minutes. ***Check the patient periodically for signs of increased redness, swelling, or pain.*** (2 points)
12. Gently dry the affected body part. (1 point)
13. Instruct the patient on any further care, or on further soaks at home. (1 point)
14. Place towels in the laundry. (1 point)
    Note: If an open wound is present, handle linens according to standard precautions.

15. Clean all equipment. (1 point)
16. Perform proper hand hygiene and return equipment. (1 point)
17. Document procedure in patient's record. (2 points)

Notes:

Application of an Ice Bag

Objective: Perform application of an ice bag and document the procedure without error.

Supplies: Ice bag with protective cover; ice chips or crushed ice

Affective Behaviors: Affective behaviors provide a professional approach to a skill that enhances the patient encounter. These behaviors may also display sensitivity to a patient's rights and enhance communication. Pay close attention to these skills, which will be in **bold, *italicized*** font.

Steps:
1. Perform proper hand hygiene. (1 point)
2. Assemble and test equipment. (1 point)
3. ***Identify the patient and instruct the patient about the procedure.*** (1 point)
4. Fill the ice bag one-half to two-thirds full of ice. Expel air by squeezing the empty portion of the ice bag. Replace the cap. (1 point)
5. Dry the bag, and place it in a protective cover or small hand towel. (1 point)
6. Place the ice bag over the patient's affected body part. ***Ask the patient how it feels.*** (1 point)
7. Leave the bag in place for the time specified by the physician's order (15–20 minutes). (2 points)
8. Refill the bag with ice, as needed. (1 point)
9. Clean the equipment. Allow the bag to air dry. (1 point)
10. Perform proper hand hygiene. (1 point)
11. Document the procedure in the patient's record. (2 points)

Notes:

Assigning a CPT Code

Objective: Accurately assign a CPT code.

Supplies: Patient's medical record, computer, medical billing software, current CPT coding book, superbill with procedure marked

Affective Behaviors: Affective behaviors provide a professional approach to a skill that enhances the patient encounter. These behaviors may also display sensitivity to a patient's rights and enhance communication. Pay close attention to these skills, which will be in **_bold, italicized_** font.

Steps:
1. Locate the complete procedure on the superbill. (1 point)
2. If the only procedure done was a physician visit, locate the CPT E/M codes section of the CPT book. (1 point)
3. Determine by the patient's medical record whether this office visit was a first-time or follow-up visit. (1 point)
4. Also determine by the patient's medical record whether this visit involved the patient's attending physician or a consulting physician. (1 point)
5. Note where the visit took place. (1 point)
6. Locate the level of visit within the place of service codes. (2 points)
7. If there was a surgical procedure, locate the code for it. (1 point)
8. Locate the code for any necessary equipment used in surgery. (1 point)
9. Code any radiologic procedures. (1 point)
10. Locate the procedure done in Sections 7000 to 7999. (2 points)
11. Locate, in the appropriate section, the part of the body on which the procedure was done. (2 points)
12. Locate the correct procedure, being careful to note if the test was bilateral, unilateral, etc. (1 point)
13. Code a laboratory test if done in Sections 80000 to 89999. (1 point)
14. Code any injected medication(s). (1 point)
15. Compare the CPT codes with the ICD codes before finalizing the bill. (2 points)

Notes:

Assisting with a Sigmoidoscopy

Objective: Assist the physician during a sigmoidoscopy examination; provide comfort and support for the patient during the exam.

Supplies: Sigmoidoscope with obturator; flexible or inflexible (metal or plastic) anoscope; rectal speculum; insufflator; suction equipment; sterile specimen container with preservative; sterile biopsy forceps; long cotton tip applications; lubricating jelly; basin of warm water; patient drape; gloves; patient gown; examination table pad; tissue; biohazard waste container

Affective Behaviors: Affective behaviors provide a professional approach to a skill that enhances the patient encounter. These behaviors may also display sensitivity to a patient's rights and enhance communication. Pay close attention to these skills, which will be in **_bold, italicized_** font.

Steps:
1. Perform proper hand hygiene. (1 point)
2. Assemble equipment and supplies, check light bulbs on all equipment, and prepare basin of warm water to receive used instruments. Test suction equipment; place obturator within the sigmoidoscope. (2 points)
3. **_Identify patient and explain procedure. Verify that the patient has followed the enema and diet instructions. Check to make sure the consent form has been signed._** (1 point)
4. **_Ask the patient to undress, put on a gown, and empty the bladder._** (1 point)
5. **_Assist patient into the Sims', lateral, or knee-chest position, or onto the proctology table._** (1 point)
6. **_Drape patient, and place a towel or disposable examination pad under the perineal area._** (1 point)
7. Apply gloves. (1 point)
8. Place lubricant on the physician's gloved fingers for a digital examination. (1 point)
9. Place metal scope in a basin of warm water to warm it before insertion into patient. (2 points)
10. Lubricate the tip of the scope. (1 point)
11. Attach both the inflation bulb (for air inflation during the procedure) and the light source. Turn on scope immediately before physician use. (1 point)
12. **_Remind the patient to take deep breaths and relax abdominal muscles. Observe patient for undue reactions._** (1 point)
13. Assist the physician by handing instruments and equipment, such as suction and cotton-tipped applicators, as they are needed. Place used equipment, including suction tubing, into the basin of water. (1 point)
14. Assist with biopsy by holding open specimen container to receive specimen while maintaining sterility of container. (1 point)
15. Clean around the patient's anal opening with tissue. Discard the tissue in biohazard waste container. (1 point)
16. Remove gloves and perform proper hand hygiene. (1 point)

17. **Assist the patient to slowly sit up.** (1 point)
18. **Ask patient to dress, and provide assistance as needed.** (1 point)
19. Label specimen container with patient's name, address, date, time, source of the specimen, and ID number. (2 points)
20. Apply gloves and clean the equipment. Sterilize and sanitize equipment as needed, and clean the examination room. (2 points)
21. Remove gloves and document the procedure. The physician will document the results of the procedure. (2 points)

Notes:

ICD-9-CM Coding

Objective: Accurately assign an ICD-9-CM code.

Supplies: Patient's medical record; patient's insurance card; computer with printer or typewriter; medical reference material; superbill with the doctor's diagnosis.

Affective Behaviors: Affective behaviors provide a professional approach to a skill that enhances the patient encounter. These behaviors may also display sensitivity to a patient's rights and enhance communication. Pay close attention to these skills, which will be in ***bold, italicized*** font.

Steps:
1. Locate the condition or diagnosis on the superbill or in the patient's medical record. (1 point)
2. In *Volume II: Alphabetic Index* of the ICD-9-CM, locate the condition or diagnosis. (1 point)
3. Examine the diagnostic statements to determine if the main term specifically describes that disease. If it does not, look at the modifiers listed under that main term to find a more specific code. (1 point)
4. Locate the code in *Volume I: Tabular Index.* (1 point)
5. Match the code description in the *Tabular Index* with the diagnosis in the patient's medical record. (1 point)
6. Use the codes from 0021.0 through V82.9 in the ICD-9-CM to describe the main reason for the patient's office visit. (1 point)
7. First, list the ICD-9-CM code for the condition, problem, or diagnosis that is the main reason for the visit. Then, list coexisting conditions under additional codes. (1 point)
8. Use codes at their highest level of specificity—fifth-digit codes first, followed by fourth-digit codes, then third-digit codes, and so on. (1 point)
9. Do not code questionable, probable, or ruled-out diagnoses. (1 point)
10. V codes describe factors that influence the health status of the patient, such as pregnancy test or vaccination, and are not used to code current illnesses. (1 point)
11. E codes are used for identifying external environmental events or conditions such as the course of injury, some adverse effect, or poisoning. E codes (E930–E949) are mandatory when coding the use of drugs. (1 point)
12. M codes, in Appendix A of *Volume I,* relate to the morphology of neoplasm. Morphology codes are used only by tumor registries for reporting proposes. (1 point)
13. List all diagnosis codes (up to four) on the insurance claim form, with the primary diagnosis listed first. (2 points)
14. Always double-check your coding and ensure proper use of abbreviations and symbols prior to assigning the final code. (2 points)

Notes:

Instructing a Patient to Use a Cane or Single Crutch Correctly

Objective: Instruct a patient on the correct use of a cane.

Supplies: Cane suited to the patient's needs, gait belt

Affective Behaviors: Affective behaviors provide a professional approach to a skill that enhances the patient encounter. These behaviors may also display sensitivity to a patient's rights and enhance communication. Pay close attention to these skills, which will be in **_bold, italicized_** font.

Steps:
1. Assemble all equipment as ordered by the physician. (1 point)
2. Check the cane height and condition of the cane tip. (2 points)
3. **_Identify the patient and explain the procedure._** (1 point)
4. Perform proper hand hygiene. (1 point)
5. Be sure that the patient is wearing sturdy, nonskid shoes. (2 points)
6. Demonstrate the correct position. (1 point)
7. Demonstrate the gait requested by the physician. (1 point)
8. **_Instruct the patient_** to hold the cane on the unaffected side. (1 point)
9. **_Instruct the patient_** to place the cane 6 inches in front and slightly to one side of the unaffected side. Make sure the cane tip is firmly on the floor and the weight is supported on the strong leg and cane. The patient's elbow should be slightly flexed during weight bearing. (2 points)
10. **_Instruct the patient_** to hold his or her head up and to stand straight, not looking down at the feet. (1 point)
11. Have the patient move the cane forward 6–12 inches and bring the affected leg forward until it is even with the cane. (1 point)
12. **_Instruct the patient_** to move the strong leg forward past the cane and weaker leg. As the unaffected foot moves forward, the weight is shifted to the weak or affected foot and cane. Thus the cane will provide support for weight bearing. (2 points)
13. Have the patient repeat the walking pattern, and evaluate the patient's balance and endurance. (1 point)
14. Document the procedure in the patient's record. (2 points)

Notes:

Instructing a Patient to Use Crutches Correctly

Objective: Instruct a patient on the correct use of crutches.

Supplies: Crutches, gait belt

Affective Behaviors: Affective behaviors provide a professional approach to a skill that enhances the patient encounter. These behaviors may also display sensitivity to a patient's rights and enhance communication. Pay close attention to these skills, which will be in **bold, italicized** font.

Steps:
1. Assemble all equipment as ordered by the physician. (1 point)
2. Check the crutches to determine that they are in good working order and without defects. (2 points)
3. Perform proper hand hygiene. (1 point)
4. ***Identify the patient and explain the procedure.*** (1 point)
5. ***Be sure that the patient is wearing sturdy, nonskid shoes.*** (2 points)
6. ***Demonstrate the correct positioning.*** (1 point)
7. ***Demonstrate the gait requested by the physician.*** (1 point)
8. ***Have the patient stand against the wall or near a chair for support.*** (1 point)
9. Adjust the crutch length to the appropriate height.
   Note: The distance between the top of the crutch and axilla should be equivalent to three finger widths. (2 points)
10. ***Instruct the patient to hold his or her head up and to stand straight, with the abdomen in and the feet straight, with a slight bend at the knee.*** (1 point)
11. ***Explain to the patient that his or her weight should be supported by the hands, not the underarms.***
    Note: Be sure to instruct the patient to not rest his or her body weight on the axillary bars for more than 1–2 minutes. (2 points)
12. ***Instruct the patient to assume the basic crutch or tripod stance to provide a firm base of support.*** (1 point)
13. Crutches should always be moved forward and to the side so the feet can swing through. (1 point)
14. ***Instruct the patient to take small steps and swing through when first learning to use crutches.***
    Note: The crutches should only move about 12 inches forward with each step. (1 point)
15. ***Have the patient practice the gait.*** (2 points)
16. ***Remind the patient to report any numbness or tingling in the arm. Pad crutch shoulders and hand bars for extra comfort, if necessary.*** (1 point)

17. ***Remind the patient to periodically check the nuts and wing bolts to maintain tightness, and to frequently check the rubber tips for cracks.*** (1 point)
18. Make corrections on the patient's crutches, as needed. (1 point)
19. Document the procedure in the patient's record. (2 points)

Notes:

Interviewing a New Patient to Obtain Medical History Information and Preparing for a Physical Examination

Objective: Obtain pertinent patient information for the medical history to assist the physician in establishing the cause and treatment of the present illness (PI) by interview. Include the chief complaint (CC), past history (PH), social or personal history (SH), and family history (FH).

Supplies: Medical history form; clipboard; pen; scale; equipment for vital signs; urine container; gown and drape

Affective Behaviors: Affective behaviors provide a professional approach to a skill that enhances the patient encounter. These behaviors may also display sensitivity to a patient's rights and enhance communication. Pay close attention to these skills, which will be in ***bold, italicized*** font.

Steps:

1. ***Identify the patient, greet the patient warmly, and identify yourself.*** (2 points)
2. Explain the procedure. (1 point)
3. Provide a private area to conduct the interview. (1 point)
4. If not already complete, ask the patient to fill out the required demographic information on the registration form. ***Assist the patient in completing the form if necessary.*** (1 point)
5. Review the patient data portion; ***ask for any additional information necessary.*** (2 points)
6. ***Ask why the patient is being seen by the physician today (CC).*** (1 point)
7. Record the CC in the patient's own words (as appropriate). (2 points)
8. ***Using observations skills, ask the patient other open-ended questions to gather necessary information about the CC. Record this information under PI.*** (1 point)
9. Gather other information about PH, FH, and SH; document in patient's record. (1 point)
10. ***Ask the patient if he or she has any allergies.*** Document according to facility protocol (red ink/ specific area for recording allergy information). (2 points)
11. Document any other relevant observations or information. (1 point)
12. Record all information using correct charting guidelines. (1 point)
13. Correct any charting errors, drawing one line through error and adding the date and your initials. Record the correct information. (2 points)
14. If required or appropriate, ask patient to provide urine specimen or to empty his or her bladder. (1 point)
15. Obtain a complete set of vital signs (temperature, pulse, respirations, blood pressure, height, and weight). Immediately document this data in the patient's record. (2 points)

16. ***Explain what clothes the patient needs to remove, proper donning of the exam gown, and where the patient should sit and wait.*** (1 point)
17. ***Explain what procedures will follow;*** tell the patient that the physician will be in shortly. (1 point)
18. Place the patient's record with the history and complaint in the designated place for the physician. (1 point)

Notes:

Measuring Blood Pressure

Objective: Obtain an accurate systolic and diastolic reading.

Supplies: Sphygmomanometer; stethoscope; 70 percent isopropyl alcohol; alcohol sponges or cotton balls; paper and pen; patient's record

Affective Behaviors: Affective behaviors provide a professional approach to a skill that enhances the patient encounter. These behaviors may also display sensitivity to a patient's rights and enhance communication. Pay close attention to these skills, which will be in **bold, italicized** font.

Steps:
1. Perform proper hand hygiene. (1 point)
2. Assemble the equipment. Use a sponge or cotton ball with alcohol to thoroughly cleanse the earpieces, bell, and diaphragm pieces of the stethoscope. Allow the alcohol to dry. (2 points)
3. ***Identify the patient and explain the procedure.*** (1 point)
4. ***Assist the patient into a comfortable position. BP may be taken with the patient in a sitting or lying position. The patient's arm should be at heart level. Ask the patient not to cross his or her legs or talk during the procedure.*** (1 point)
    Note: If the patient's arm is below heart level, the BP reading will be higher than normal; if the arm is higher than heart level, the BP will be lower than normal.
5. Place the sphygmomanometer on a solid surface with the gauge within 3 feet for easy viewing. (1 point)
6. ***Uncover the patient's arm by asking the patient to roll back his or her sleeve 5 inches above the elbow. If the sleeve becomes constricting when rolled back, ask the patient to slip his or her arm out of the sleeve.*** (2 points)
    Note: Never take a BP reading through clothing.
7. Have the patient straighten his or her arm with palms up. Apply a proper-size cuff over the brachial artery 1 to 2 inches above the antecubital space (bend in the elbow). Many cuffs are marked with arrows or circles to be placed over the artery. Hold the edge of the cuff in place as you wrap the remainder of the cuff tightly around the arm securing the Velcro closure. (1 point)
8. Palpate with your fingertips to locate the brachial artery in the antecubital space. (1 point)
9. Pump air into the cuff quickly and evenly until the level of mercury is 20 to 30 mmHg above the point at which the radial pulse is no longer palpable.
    Note the level, rapidly deflate, and wait 60 seconds. (2 points)
10. Place the earpieces in your ears and the diaphragm (or bell) of the stethoscope over the area where you feel the brachial artery pulsing. Hold the diaphragm in place with one hand on the chest piece without placing your thumb over the diaphragm. The stethoscope tubing should hang freely and not touch any object or the patient during the reading. (1 point)

11. Close the thumbscrew on the hand bulb by turning clockwise with your dominant hand. Close the thumbscrew just enough so that no air can leak out. Do not close so tightly that you will have difficulty reopening it with one hand. (1 point)

12. Slowly turn the thumbscrew counterclockwise with your dominant hand. Allow the pressure reading to fall only 2 to 3 mmHg at a time. (2 points)

13. Listen for the point at which the first clear sound is heard. Note where this occurred on the manometer. This is the systolic pressure. (1 point)

14. Slowly continue to allow the cuff to deflate. The sounds will change from loud to murmur and then fade away.
    Read the mercury column (or spring gauge scale) at the point where the sound is no longer heard. This is the diastolic pressure. (2 points)

15. Quickly open the thumbscrew all the way to release the air and deflate the cuff completely. (1 point)

16. If you are unsure about the BP reading, wait at least a minute or two before taking a second reading. (1 point)
    Note: Never take more than two readings in one arm.

17. Immediately write the BP as a fraction on paper. You may inform the patient of the reading if this is the policy in your office. (2 points)

18. Remove the cuff. (1 point)

19. Clean the earpieces of the stethoscope with an alcohol sponge. (1 point)

20. Perform proper hand hygiene. (1 point)

21. Document results, including the date, time, BP reading, and your name, in the patient's record. (2 points)

Notes:

Measuring Oxygen Saturation

Objective: Attach and measure the patient's oxygen saturation.

Supplies: Pulse oximeter, nail polish remover, alcohol wipe, patient record, gloves, adhesive tape

Affective Behaviors: Affective behaviors provide a professional approach to a skill that enhances the patient encounter. These behaviors may also display sensitivity to a patient's rights and enhance communication. Pay close attention to these skills, which will be in ***bold, italicized*** font.

Steps:
1. Perform proper hand hygiene. Apply gloves. (1 point)
2. Assemble equipment based on patient's size and condition. (1 point)
3. ***Identify the patient and explain the procedure.*** (1 point)
4. Choose the correct size sensor for the patient. (2 points)
5. ***Ask if the patient is allergic to adhesive tape.*** If so, use a clip on the oximeter. (1 point)
6. Remove nail polish, if needed. (1 point)
7. Assess patient's pulse rate. (1 point)
8. Wipe the site with an alcohol wipe. Attach the sensor. Be sure the sensors are correctly aligned opposite each other. (2 points)
9. Connect the sensor to the pulse oximeter.
    Note: Some oximeters are cordless. (1 point)
10. Turn on the machine and set the alarm as directed. (1 point)
11. Change the position of the oximeter every 4 hours or as directed. (1 point)
12. Compare the pulse previously evaluated with pulse on the oximeter. If there is a large difference between these pulse measurements, check the oximeter function. (2 points)
13. Record the oxygen saturation level in the patient record at the intervals ordered by the physician. (1 point)
14. If oxygen saturation level is abnormal, follow facility protocol for notifying superiors. (1 point)

Notes:

Obtaining a Sputum Specimen for Culture

Objective: Obtain a sputum specimen without contamination.

Supplies: Sterile sputum container with lid, laboratory requisition form, gloves, biohazard waste container

Affective Behaviors: Affective behaviors provide a professional approach to a skill that enhances the patient encounter. These behaviors may also display sensitivity to a patient's rights and enhance communication. Pay close attention to these skills, which will be in **bold, italicized** font.

Steps:
1. Assemble all equipment. (1 point)
2. Perform proper hand hygiene. (1 point)
3. ***Identify the patient and explain the procedure.*** Provide written instructions that the patient can take home if necessary. (2 points)
4. Don gloves. (1 point)
5. ***Instruct the patient to breathe in or out 2 to 4 times and cough deeply to raise sputum.*** Instruct the patient to expel the fluid into the center of the specimen container. A morning specimen is preferable. (2 points)
6. Be sure that no other fluids enter the cup, such as tears, mucus, or saliva. (1 point)
7. Place the lid securely on the container, and write the time and date the specimen was obtained.
   Note: If the patient is collecting the specimen at home, he or she should bring the sample into the office as soon as possible. The sample should not be refrigerated for more than 2 hours. (1 point)
8. Label the envelope with information, seal it shut, and transport it immediately. (2 points)
9. Remove and dispose of gloves. Perform proper hand hygiene. (1 point)
10. Document the procedure in the patient's record. (2 points)

Notes:

Obtaining a Stool Specimen for Culture and Sensitivity

Objective: Clearly instruct a patient on how to collect a stool sample for culture and sensitivity in a sterile container using correct infection control procedures.

Supplies: Sterile stool collection container or bedpan; tongue depressor or sterile applicator sticks; transportation/mailing container; labels; rubber band; laboratory requisition form; gloves; biohazard waste container

Affective Behaviors: Affective behaviors provide a professional approach to a skill that enhances the patient encounter. These behaviors may also display sensitivity to a patient's rights and enhance communication. Pay close attention to these skills, which will be in **_bold, italicized_** font.

Steps:
1. Assemble all equipment. (1 point)
2. Use proper hand hygiene. (1 point)
3. **_Identify the patient and clearly explain the procedure. Provide written instructions if necessary._** (2 points)
4. Instruct the patient to defecate into the container or bed pan. (1 point)
5. When the patient returns with the specimen, don gloves. (1 point)
6. Using a tongue depressor or applicator stick, remove a small amount of stool from different parts of the specimen and place it in the specimen container. (2 points)
   Note: Be sure no other contaminants are included (toilet paper, urine, toilet water, etc.).
7. Correctly fill out the laboratory requisition form. (1 point)
8. Wrap the form around the container, securing it with a rubber band. Place it in the proper container for delivery. (2 points)
9. Clean the area. Remove and dispose of the gloves, and perform proper hand hygiene. (1 point)
10. Document the procedure in the patient's record. (2 points)

Notes:

Obtaining a Stool Specimen for Examination for Pinworms

Objective: Collect a rectal swab using cellulose tape for pinworm examination.

Supplies: Slide; tongue depressor or swab; gauze; microscope; cellulose tape; laboratory requisition form

Affective Behaviors: Affective behaviors provide a professional approach to a skill that enhances the patient encounter. These behaviors may also display sensitivity to a patient's rights and enhance communication. Pay close attention to these skills, which will be in **bold, *italicized*** font.

Steps:
1. Assemble all equipment and supplies. (1 point)
2. Attach the sticky side of a piece of cellulose tape to the slide surface and wrapping tape around one end. Leave room to attach a small square of paper for labeling at the other end.
   Note: Do not use double-sided sticky or Magic tape. (1 point)
3. Perform proper hand hygiene and apply gloves. (1 point)
4. ***Identify the patient and clearly explain the procedure. Prepare the patient on exam table or parent's lap with anal area exposed.*** (1 point)
5. Peel tape off slide by the labeled end and wrap around tongue depressor or swab with the sticky side out. (2 points)
6. Press the tape on both sides of the area around the anus. (2 points)
7. Replace the tape on the slide with the sticky side down. Smooth it with gauze. (1 point)
8. Label the slide with the patient's name and the date. Correctly fill out the laboratory requisition form. (1 point)
9. Clean the area and dispose of all waste. (1 point)
10. Remove and dispose of the gloves, and perform proper hand hygiene. (1 point)
11. Document the procedure in the patient's record. (2 points)

Notes:

Obtaining a Stool Specimen for Ova and Parasites

Objective: Clearly instruct a patient on how to collect a stool sample (fresh and preserved specimens) for ova and parasites and sensitivity in a sterile container using correct infection control procedures.

Supplies: Stool collection kit with containers for fresh and preserved specimens, or bedpan; tongue depressor or sterile applicator sticks; transportation/mailing container; labels; laboratory requisition form; rubber band; gloves; biohazard waste container

Affective Behaviors: Affective behaviors provide a professional approach to a skill that enhances the patient encounter. These behaviors may also display sensitivity to a patient's rights and enhance communication. Pay close attention to these skills, which will be in ***bold, italicized*** font.

Steps:
1. Assemble all equipment. (1 point)
2. Use proper hand hygiene. (1 point)
3. ***Identify the patient and clearly explain the procedure. Provide written instructions if necessary.*** (2 points)
4. Instruct the patient to defecate into the container or bed pan. (1 point)
5. When the patient returns with the specimen, don gloves. (1 point)
6. Using a tongue depressor or applicator stick, remove a small amount of stool from different parts of the specimen and place it in each vial, using a different depressor for each vial.
   Note: Be sure no other contaminants are included (toilet paper, urine, toilet water, etc.). (2 points)
7. Correctly fill out laboratory requisition form. (1 point)
8. Wrap the form around the container, securing it with a rubber band. Place it in the proper container for delivery. (2 points)
9. Clean the area. Remove and dispose of the gloves, and perform proper hand hygiene. (1 point)
10. Document the procedure in the patient's record. (2 points)

Notes:

Obtaining a Throat Culture

Objective: Collect a throat or nasopharyngeal culture without contaminating the specimen.

Supplies: Culturette system, laboratory requisition, tongue depressor, gloves, biohazard waste container

Affective Behaviors: Affective behaviors provide a professional approach to a skill that enhances the patient encounter. These behaviors may also display sensitivity to a patient's rights and enhance communication. Pay close attention to these skills, which will be in **bold, italicized** font.

Steps:
1.   Assemble all equipment. (1 point)
2.   ***Identify the patient and explain the procedure.*** (1 point)
3.   Perform proper hand hygiene and apply gloves. (1 point)
4.   Position the patient facing a light source and instruct the patient to open his or her mouth as wide as possible and say "Aaaaah" (to diminish the gag reflex). (2 points)
5.   Remove sterile swab from the Culturette. (1 point)
6.   Depress the tongue, insert the swab, and roll it firmly across the back of the patient's throat or nasopharyngeal area where infected. Avoid the uvula.
     Note: Be careful not to contaminate the swab on the teeth, lips, tongue, or cheeks. (2 points)
7.   Insert the swab in a plastic vial. Crush an internal vial of transport medium; make sure that the swab is saturated. (2 points)
8.   Place the swab in a labeled mailing/transport envelope and seal it shut or immediately inoculate culture plate if specimen is to be analyzed on site. (1 point)
9.   Remove and dispose of gloves. Perform proper hand hygiene. (1 point)
10. Document the procedure in the patient's record. (2 points)

Notes:

Performing a Group A Rapid Strep Test

Objective: Perform a Group A Rapid Step test

Supplies: Specimen container, specimen label, laboratory form, patient information, Group A strep kit, patient swab, nonsterile disposable gloves, gown, face shield, timer, biohazard waste container, disinfectant, paper towels, pen or black marker

Affective Behaviors: Affective behaviors provide a professional approach to a skill that enhances the patient encounter. These behaviors may also display sensitivity to a patient's rights and enhance communication. Pay close attention to these skills, which will be in **_bold, italicized_** font.

Steps:
1. Wash your hands.1 point)
2. Verify that the names on the specimen container and the laboratory form are the same. (1 point)
3. Label one extraction tube with the patient's name, one with the positive control, and one with the negative control. (1 point)
4. Follow the directions for the kit. Add the appropriate reagents and drops to each of the extraction tubes. Avoid splashing, and use the correct number of drops. (1 point)
5. Insert the patient's swab (one of the two swabs) into the labeled extraction tube. If only one culture swab was submitted, first swab a beta strep agar plate, then use the swab for the rapid strep test. (2 points)
6. Add the appropriate controls to each of the labeled extraction tubes. (2 points)
7. Set the timer for the appropriate time to ensure accuracy. (1 point)
8. Add the appropriate reagent and drops to each of the extraction tubes. (1 point)
9. Use the swab to mix the reagents, then press out any excess fluid on the swab against the inside of the tube. (1 point)
10. Add three drops from the well-mixed extraction tube to the sample window of the strep A test unit labeled with the patient's name. Do the same for each control. (1 point)
11. Set the timer for the appropriate time. (1 point)
12. A positive result appears as a line in the result window within 5 minutes. The strep A test unit has an internal control; if a line appears in the control window, the test is valid. (1 point)
13. Read a negative result at exactly 5 minutes to avoid a false positive. (1 point)
14. Verify results of the controls before recording test results. Log the controls and the patient's information on the worksheet. (1 point)

15.	Depending on the laboratory protocol, you may have to culture all negative rapid strep screens on beta-strep agar. A bacitracin disk may be added to the first quadrant when you set up or after 24 hours if a beta-hemolytic colony appears. A culture is more sensitive than a rapid immunoassay test. (1 point)

16.	Clean the work area and dispose of waste properly. Remove gown, gloves, and shield. Wash your hands. (1 point)

Notes:

Performing a Mononucleosis Test

Objective: Perform a mononucleosis test

Supplies: Mono-Test kit, nonsterile disposable gloves, gown, face shield, blood serum or plasma, disposable capillary tube, laboratory form, patient worksheet, patient information, biohazard waste container, disinfectant, paper towels, bleach, pen or black marker

Affective Behaviors: Affective behaviors provide a professional approach to a skill that enhances the patient encounter. These behaviors may also display sensitivity to a patient's rights and enhance communication. Pay close attention to these skills, which will be in ***bold, italicized*** font.

Steps:
1. Wash your hands and don gown, gloves, and shield. (2 points)
2. Verify that the names on the specimen container and the laboratory form are the same. (1 point)
3. Assemble equipment and ensure that the materials in the kit are at room temperature before beginning the procedure. (1 point)
4. Label the slide or card with the patient's name, positive control, and negative control. One circle or space is provided per patient and control. (1 point)
5. Place the rubber bulb on the capillary tube. (1 point)
6. Aspirate the patient's specimen up to the marked line. (2 points)
7. Dispense the sample in the middle of the circle labeled with the patient's name. (1 point)
8. Avoid air bubbles to ensure accurate results. (1 point)
9. Gently mix the positive control. (1 point)
10. Using a capillary tube, aspirate the positive control up to the marked line. (2 points)
11. Dispense the control in the middle of the circle labeled "negative control." (1 point)
12. Avoid air bubbles. (1 point)
13. Mix the latex reagent. (1 point)
14. Add 1 drop to each circle or space. (1 point)
15. Avoid splashing the reagents. (1 point)
16. Using a clean stirrer for each test, mix reagent with the patient sample and controls. (1 point)
17. Mix only one circle at a time, keeping within each circle. (2 points)
18. Ensure that stirs do not go outside of a circle to prevent cross-contamination and incorrect results. (1 point)
19. Gently rock the slide for 2 minutes. (1 point)
20. Observe for agglutination (clumping). (1 point)
21. Testing time may vary if you are using a disposable card. (1 point)
22. Verify results of controls before documenting the patient's results, then log controls and patient information on the worksheet. (1 point)

23. Read the kit's instructions if titration is required. (1 point)
24. Clean the work area and dispose of waste properly. (1 point)
25. Wash the slide thoroughly with bleach and rinse with water before using again. (1 point)
26. Remove gown, gloves and shield. Wash your hands. (1 point)

Notes:

Performing a Nebulized Breathing Treatment

Objective: Perform a nebulized breathing treatment

Supplies: Compressor, nebulizer with mask and tubing, medication, saline, biohazard container, patient's chart, pen

Affective Behaviors: Affective behaviors provide a professional approach to a skill that enhances the patient encounter. These behaviors may also display sensitivity to a patient's rights and enhance communication. Pay close attention to these skills, which will be in ***bold, italicized*** font.

Steps:
1. Wash your hands. (1 point)
2. Assemble the equipment and medication, checking the medication label three times as indicated when administering any medications. (2 points)
3. ***Greet and identify the patient and explain the procedure.*** (1 point)
4. Remove the nebulizer treatment cup from the setup and add the exact amount of medication ordered by the physician. (1 point)
5. Add 2–3 mL of saline for inhalation therapy to the cup that contains the medication. (1 point)
6. Place the top on the cup securely, attach the "T" piece to the top of the cup, and position the mouthpiece firmly on one end of the "T" piece. (2 points)
7. Attach one end of the tubing securely to the connector on the cup and the other end to the connector on the nebulizer machine. (1 point)
8. Ask the patient to place the mouthpiece into the mouth and make a seal with the lips, without biting the mouthpiece. Instruct the patient to breathe normally during the treatment, occasionally taking a deep breath. (2 points)
9. Turn the machine on using the on/off switch. The medication in the reservoir cup will become a fine mist that is inhaled by the patient breathing through the mouthpiece. (1 point)
10. Before, during, and after the breathing treatment, take and record the patient's pulse. (1 point)
11. When the treatment is over and the medication/saline is gone from the cup, turn the machine off and have the patient remove the mouthpiece. (1 point)
12. Disconnect the disposable treatment setup and dispose of all parts into a biohazard container. Properly put away the machine. (1 point)
13. Wash your hands and document the procedure, including the patient's pulse before, during, and after the treatment. (2 points)

Notes:

Performing a Pulmonary Function Test (PFT)

Objective: Perform a pulmonary function test (PFT)

Supplies: Spirometer, disposable tubing, disposable mouthpiece, disposable nose clips, biohazard container, patient information, patient chart, pen

Affective Behaviors: Affective behaviors provide a professional approach to a skill that enhances the patient encounter. These behaviors may also display sensitivity to a patient's rights and enhance communication. Pay close attention to these skills, which will be in **_bold, italicized_** font.

Steps:
1.   Wash your hands. (1 point)
2.   Assemble the equipment. (1 point)
3.   **_Greet and identify the patient and explain the procedure._** (1 point)
4.   Turn the PFT machine on. If the spirometer has not been calibrated according to the office policy, calibrate the machine using the calibration syringe according to the manufacturer's instructions, and record the calibration in the appropriate log book. (1 point)
5.   With the machine on and calibrated, attach the appropriate cable, tubing, and mouthpiece for the type of machine being used. (1 point)
6.   Using the keyboard on the machine, input patient data into the machine including the patient's name or identification number, age, weight, height, sex, race, and smoking history. (2 points)
7.   Ask the patient to remove any restrictive clothing such as a necktie and instruct the patient in applying the nose clip. (1 point)
8.   Ask the patient to stand, breathe in deeply, and blow into the mouthpiece as hard as possible. He or she should continue to blow into the mouthpiece until the machine indicates that it is appropriate to stop blowing. **_A chair should be available in case the patient becomes dizzy or lightheaded._** (1 point)
9.   During the procedure, **_coach the patient as needed to obtain an adequate reading._** (1 point)
10.   Continue the procedure until three adequate readings or maneuvers are performed. (1 point)
11.   After printing the results, properly care for the equipment and dispose of the mouthpiece into the biohazard container. Wash your hands. (1 point)
12.   Document the procedure and place the printed results in the patient's medical record. (1 point)

Notes:

Performing a Spirometry Test to Measure Forced Vital Capacity

Objective: Perform a spirometer test to accurately measure forced vital capacity.

Supplies: Spirometry machine; nose clip; mouthpiece; disinfectant; biohazard waste container; patient record; scale for height and weight; sphygmomanometer; stethoscope

Affective Behaviors: Affective behaviors provide a professional approach to a skill that enhances the patient encounter. These behaviors may also display sensitivity to a patient's rights and enhance communication. Pay close attention to these skills, which will be in **_bold, italicized_** font.

Steps:
1. Assemble all equipment and materials. Perform proper hand hygiene. (1 point)
2. Calibrate the spirometer, as necessary. (1 point)
3. **_Identify the patient and inquire about his or her present general health._** (2 points)
4. **_Question the patient about proper preparation for the test by not smoking or using bronchodilators for at least 6 hours._** (2 points)
5. **_Explain and demonstrate the procedure._** (1 point)
6. Weigh and measure the patient, obtain vital signs, and document. (1 point)
7. Explain the proper positioning and have the patient loosen any tight clothing. (1 point)
8. Start the machine and enter data, as necessary. (1 point)
9. **_Review the procedure with the patient. Make sure the patient knows to breathe forcibly several times into the spirometer._** (2 points)
10. Instruct the patient to place the mouthpiece in the mouth and tightly seal the lips around it. (1 point)
11. Apply nose clips. (1 point)
12. **_Ask patient to inhale deeply._** (1 point)
13. Push the start button at the same time that you **_instruct the patient._** (1 point)
14. **_Encourage or "coach" the patient to blast breath out hard, quickly, and as long as possible._** (2 points)
15. **_Make recommendations to improve outcome,_** if necessary. (1 point)
16. Obtain the second set of maneuvers. (1 point)
17. Obtain the third set of maneuvers. (1 point)
18. Continue until you have three acceptable outcomes.
    Note: You may facilitate up to eight attempts. Some computerized machines will pick the best attempt and print. (1 point)
19. Remove nose clips. **_Ask the patient to remain until the physician reviews the results._** (1 point)

20. Provide the physician with the trial information for review. (1 point)
21. Record the results in the patient's record. (2 points)
22. Clean tubing and dispose of mouthpieces using standard precautions. (1 point)

Notes:

Performing a Venipuncture Using the Vacutainer Method

Objective: Perform venipuncture by correctly assembling, locating, and entering a vein, and withdrawing a blood sample.

Supplies: Biohazard sharps container, Vacutainer tubes, multisample needle, gauze squares, alcohol pads, gloves, Vacutainer sleeve, tourniquet, bandage, cotton balls, adhesive, pen, lab coat, patient record, ammonia ampules

Affective Behaviors: Affective behaviors provide a professional approach to a skill that enhances the patient encounter. These behaviors may also display sensitivity to a patient's rights and enhance communication. Pay close attention to these skills, which will be in **bold, *italicized*** font.

Steps:
1.   Assemble all equipment and materials. (1 point)
2.   Perform proper hand hygiene. (1 point)
3.   ***Identify the patient and explain the procedure. Position the patient either sitting or lying down.*** (2 points)
4.   Apply gloves. (1 point)
5.   Screw the Vacutainer needle into the plastic sleeve. Insert the tube into the other end of the sleeve; be sure not to puncture the tube. (1 point)
6.   Apply the tourniquet 2 inches above the antecubital space tight enough to engorge the vein with blood. (1 point)
7.   ***Place the patient's arm in an extended position with the palm facing up and comfortably resting.*** (1 point)
8.   Palpate the vein with your fingertips. (1 point)
9.   Cleanse the chosen venipuncture site with an alcohol sponge in a circular pattern. Allow alcohol to dry. (2 points)
10.   Anchor the vein properly. (1 point)
11.   Bevel up, line up the needle with the vein approximately 1/4–1/2 inch below the site where the vein is to be entered. (2 points)
    a. At a 15°–30° angle, rapidly and smoothly insert the needle through the skin.
    b. Remove your non-dominant hand, slowly pull back the plunger of the syringe or place two fingers on the flanges of the adapter, and, with the thumb, push the tube onto the needle inside the adapter.
    c. When the blood flow begins in the tube or syringe, allow the patient to release the fist.
    d. Release the tourniquet.
    e. Allow the syringe or tube(s) to fill to capacity.
    f. When the blood flow ceases, remove the tube from the adapter by gripping the tube with the nondominant hand, placing the thumb against the flange during the removal.

       1) Twist and gently pull out the tube. Steady the needle in the vein.

       2) Try not to pull up or press down on the needle while it is in the vein.

  g. Insert any other necessary tubes into adapter and allow each to fill to capacity.

12. Remove the tube from adapter. (2 points)

  a. Place a sterile gauze pad over the puncture site during needle withdrawal.

  b. Do not apply any pressure to the site until the needle is completely removed.

  c. After needle is removed, apply pressure or have patient apply direct pressure for 3–5 minutes.

  d. Do not bend the arm at the elbow

13. Transfer the blood from a syringe into tubes via the transfer device. (2 points)

  a. In the proper order of draw, allow the vacuum to fill the tubes.

  b. Place the tubes in tube rack and carefully insert the device through the stopper.

  c. If the vacuum tubes contain an anticoagulant.

       1) Mix immediately by gently inverting the tube 8–10 times.

       2) Do not shake the tube.

  d. Label the tubes with the proper information.

14. Check the puncture site for bleeding. (1 point)

  a. Apply a bandage, a clean 2 × 2 gauze pad folded in quarters.

  b. Hold in place by a Band-Aid or 3-inch strip of tape.

15. ***Thank the patient.*** (1 point)

16. ***Tell the patient to leave the bandage in place at least 15 minutes and not to carry a heavy object (such as a purse) or lift heavy objects with that arm for an hour.*** (1 point)

12. Remove and dispose of gloves. Perform proper hand hygiene. (1 point)

13. Document the procedure in the patient's record. (2 points)

Notes:

Preparing Injections

Objective: Prepare an injection

Supplies: Medication order, medication, needle, syringe, ampule, gauze, biohazard sharps container, antiseptic wipe

Affective Behaviors: Affective behaviors provide a professional approach to a skill that enhances the patient encounter. These behaviors may also display sensitivity to a patient's rights and enhance communication. Pay close attention to these skills, which will be in **_bold, italicized_** font.

Steps:
1. Wash your hands. (1 point)
2. Review the physician's medication order and select the correct medication. (2 points)
   a. Compare the label with the physician's instructions. Note the expiration date.
   b. Check the label three times: when taking it from the shelf, while drawing it up into the syringe, and when returning to the shelf.
3. Calculate the correct dosage to be given, if necessary. (1 point)
4. Choose the needle and syringe according to the route of administration, type of medication, and size of the patient. (1 point)
5. Open the needle and syringe package. Assemble if necessary. Secure the needle to the syringe. (1 point)
6. Withdraw the correct amount of medication: (2 points)
   a. From an ampule:
   1) Tap the stem of the ampule lightly.
   2) Place a piece of gauze around the ampule neck.
   3) Grasp the gauze and ampule firmly. Snap the stem off the ampule.
   4) Dispose of the ampule top in a biohazard sharps container.
   5) Insert the needle lumen below the level of the medication.
   6) Withdraw the medication.
   7) Dispose of the ampule in a biohazard sharps container.
   8) Remove any air bubbles in the syringe.
   9) Draw back on the plunger to add a small amount of air; then gently push the plunger forward to eject the air out of the syringe.
   b. From a vial:
   1) Using the antiseptic wipe, cleanse the rubber stopper of the vial.
   2) Pull air into the syringe with the amount equivalent to the amount of medication to be removed from the vial.
   3) Insert the needle into the vial top. Inject the air from the syringe.
   4) With the needle inside the vial, invert the vial.
   5) Hold the syringe at eye level.
   6) Aspirate the desired amount of medication into the syringe.

7) Displace any air bubbles in the syringe by gently tapping the barrel.

8) Remove the air by pushing the plunger slowly and forcing the air into the vial.

9) Revert vial and place on the counter; remove needle from vial.

7.   Carefully recap the needle using one-hand technique. (1 point)

Notes:

Sanitizing Instruments

Objective: Demonstrate the proper cleaning and sanitizing of instruments.

Supplies: Instruments; basin; disposable gloves; rubber gloves; cleaning brush; germicidal agent or low pH detergent; water; towel

Affective Behaviors: Affective behaviors provide a professional approach to a skill that enhances the patient encounter. These behaviors may also display sensitivity to a patient's rights and enhance communication. Pay close attention to these skills, which will be in ***bold, italicized*** font.

Steps:
1. Apply rubber gloves over disposable gloves. (2 points)
2. Fill basin approximately halfway with a low-sudsing detergent or germicidal agent (sanitizing solution). (1 point)
3. Rinse all instruments and place them in the sanitizing solution. (1 point)
4. Scrub each instrument individually with a brush and detergent under running water. Open the instruments and scrub all serrated edges and hinged areas. (2 points)
5. Thoroughly rinse instruments again under hot water. (1 point)
6. After thoroughly rinsing instruments, roll them in a clean, dry towel to finish drying. (1 point)
7. Check the condition of the instruments for defects or remaining soil. (2 points)
8. Wrap instruments for sterilization when dry. (1 point)

Notes:

Sterilizing Instruments in an Autoclave

Objective: Load and operate an autoclave correctly to prevent the spread of pathogens.

Supplies: Autoclave; instruments sanitized and wrapped for autoclaving; distilled water

Affective Behaviors: Affective behaviors provide a professional approach to a skill that enhances the patient encounter. These behaviors may also display sensitivity to a patient's rights and enhance communication. Pay close attention to these skills, which will be in **_bold, italicized_** font.

Steps:
1. Perform proper hand hygiene and assemble materials. (1 point)
2. Check the level of distilled water in the autoclave reservoir and fill as necessary to the fill line. (1 point)
3. Load the autoclave, paying close attention to the following: (2 points)
   - Trays and packs should be loaded on their sides.
   - Containers should be loaded on their sides with lids off or ajar.
   - Mixed loads are loaded with hard objects on bottom racks and softer items on top racks.
   - Large packs are to be placed 2 to 4 inches apart; small packets 1 to 2 inches apart.
4. Read the manufacturer's instructions and follow them exactly. (Most autoclaves follow similar protocols.) (2 points)
5. With the door open, turn the control knob to "Fill" and observe the water reaching the fill line. (1 point)
6. Turn the knob to the autoclave position (this shuts off the water). (1 point)
7. When pressure reaches 15 to 17 pounds per square inch and temperature reaches 250°F to 270°F, set the timer for the required time according to the manufacture's protocol. (1 point)
8. When timing is complete, turn autoclave knob to "Vent." (1 point)
9. When the pressure reaches zero, open the chamber door about 1 inch and allow items to dry completely before removing them. (This takes approximately 30–45 minutes.) (2 points)
10. Remove wrapped items and check the autoclave tape for color change. Store in dry, closed cabinet for use. (1 point)
11. Record date, time, and types of items autoclaved into log and initial. (1 point)

Notes:

Teaching a Patient to Correctly Use a Walker

Objective: Instruct a patient on the correct use of a walker.

Supplies: Walker suited to patient's needs, gait belt

Affective Behaviors: Affective behaviors provide a professional approach to a skill that enhances the patient encounter. These behaviors may also display sensitivity to a patient's rights and enhance communication. Pay close attention to these skills, which will be in ***bold, italicized*** font.

Steps:
1. Assemble all equipment as ordered by the physician. (1 point)
2. Check the condition of the walker. (2 points)
3. Perform proper hand hygiene. (1 point)
4. ***Identify the patient and explain the procedure.*** (1 point)
5. Be sure that the patient is wearing sturdy, nonskid shoes. (2 points)
6. ***Demonstrate the correct stance and gait with the walker.*** (1 point)
7. ***Assist the patient into the walker.*** (1 point)
8. ***Evaluate the walker for proper height and fit.***
    Note: The top of the walker should reach the patient's hipbone and the patient's hands ***should*** be on the handgrip with the elbow flexed at a 30-degree angle. (2 points)
9. Instruct the patient to distribute his or her weight evenly between the walker and both legs. (2 points)
10. Have the patient move the walker 6–8 inches ahead, with all four legs of the walker hitting the floor at the same time. (1 point)
11. Instruct the patient to bring the weaker foot into the walker. (1 point)
12. Instruct the patient to bring the stronger foot forward, even with the weaker foot. (1 point)
13. Have the patient continue walking with the walker while you evaluate the patient's balance and endurance. (1 point)
14. Document the teaching and the patient's response in the patient's record. (2 points)

Notes:

Teaching Peak Flow Measurement

Objective: Instruct the patient to correctly monitor peak flow and to record results.

Supplies: Peak flow meter; documentation diary/chart; diagram of lungs and breathing processes; pen; patient record

Affective Behaviors: Affective behaviors provide a professional approach to a skill that enhances the patient encounter. These behaviors may also display sensitivity to a patient's rights and enhance communication. Pay close attention to these skills, which will be in **bold, italicized** font.

Steps:
1. Perform proper hand hygiene. (1 point)
2. Assemble peak flow meter with disposable mouthpiece or individual peak flow meter for patient use at home. (1 point)
3. ***Identify the patient and explain the procedure: Explain breathing processes and their importance to overall health. Demonstrate how the mouthpiece fits and explain what the numbers mean. The peak flow meter should always be set at zero.*** (2 points)
4. ***Have the patient place the mouthpiece in the mouth and form a tight seal. Explain that better results may be obtained if the patient is standing during the test.*** (1 point)
5. ***Instruct the patient to stand, take deepest breath possible, position mouthpiece without biting down, and exhale completely and as forcefully as possible.*** (2 points)
6. ***Instruct the patient to note the number on the machine where the sliding gauge stopped and to record the results. Reset to zero. Repeat three times.*** (1 point)
7. ***Instruct the patient to follow the physician's orders for when and how often to perform the test each day. The "best" result is documented.*** (1 point)
8. ***Demonstrate how to wash the mouthpiece with soap and water without submerging the peak flow meter.*** (1 point)
9. Document the instruction in the patient's record. (2 points)
10. Perform proper hand hygiene. (1 point)

Notes:

Testing for Occult Blood

Objective: Test feces for occult blood.

Supplies: 3 occult blood slides, applications, envelope, timer, patient's record, pen, gloves, color developer. *Note:* Many test kits are available on the market. Each one has its own set of directions, color developer, slides, and control monitors. The test kit directions should be followed exactly

Affective Behaviors: Affective behaviors provide a professional approach to a skill that enhances the patient encounter. These behaviors may also display sensitivity to a patient's rights and enhance communication. Pay close attention to these skills, which will be in ***bold, italicized*** font.

Steps:
1. Perform proper hand hygiene. (1 point)
2. Apply gloves. Place a paper towel on the area to hold the slides. (1 point)
3. Check the name and date on the occult blood slides. (2 points)
4. Check the expiration date on the color developer. (2 points)
5. Open the window flap on the back of slide and apply 2 drops of the developer to Box A and Box B. (1 point)
6. Interpret the results in 30 to 60 seconds or according to the manufacturer's directions. A positive result will exhibit the color blue around the edge of the specimen; a negative result will not change color. Any amount of blue color is positive. (2 points)
7. For quality control purposes, perform a test on positive and negative controls as required by the manufacturer. (2 points)
8. Test the remaining slides in the same manner. (1 point)
9. Dispose of all materials in a biohazard waste container. Clean the work area. (1 point)
10. Remove gloves. (1 point)
11. Perform proper hand hygiene. (1 point)
12. Document the results in the patient's record. (2 points)

Notes:

Wrapping Instruments for Sterilization in an Autoclave

Objective: Demonstrate the proper procedure for wrapping, packaging, and labeling instruments for autoclaving (sterilization).

Supplies: Instruments, wrapping material, sterilization indicator strip, indelible pen, tape

Affective Behaviors: Affective behaviors provide a professional approach to a skill that enhances the patient encounter. These behaviors may also display sensitivity to a patient's rights and enhance communication. Pay close attention to these skills, which will be in **_bold, italicized_** font.

Steps:
1. Perform proper hand hygiene. (1 point)
2. Place a square of wrapping material on the table so that it appears in a diamond shape when you are facing it. Ensure the wrapping material is large enough to completely cover the entire article you are wrapping for autoclaving. (1 point)
3. Place the item in the center of the wrapping material. If the instrument is hinged, open it so that the hinge is in the open position. If the instrument has a sharp point/tip, cover it with gauze to prevent a puncture through the wrapping material. (2 points)
4. Place the indicator strip in the center of the package. (1 point)
5. Fold the bottom point of the "diamond" up and over the instruments. Fold a small portion of the point back over so that it can be used to pick up the wrapping when it is opened for use. (2 points)
6. Fold right side of the "diamond" up and over the instruments. Again, fold a small portion back, as described above. (2 points)
7. Fold the left side of the "diamond" over until it covers the instruments. Again, fold a small portion back. (2 points)
8. Fold the bottom of the point of the "diamond" up until it reaches the top point. (2 points)
9. Make sure the pack is folded securely. (1 point)
10. Using a piece of autoclave tape, securely tape the pack closed. (1 point)
11. Label the package with the contents (instruments or items inside), your initials, and the date. (2 points)
12. If you are using bags for autoclaving, place the item and indicator strip inside the bag. Seal the bag and label as described above. (1 point)

Notes:

Competency Procedures

Directions: For each competency, read and familiarize yourself with the objective, supplies, and procedure steps. Pay particular attention to steps in **_bold, italicized_** font – these refer to affective behaviors that will allow you to demonstrate professionalism, communication skills, and sensitivity to the patient's rights.

You will be given time to practice each competency, and then you will be given an opportunity to pass the competency by earning a minimum score of 75%. Your score on each competency will be determined by a rubric that your instructor will provide that shows the value of each step. If you attain 75% on your first attempt, further attempts are not required. Each competency must be completed within a reasonable amount of time, as determined by your instructor.

Administering an Intradermal Injection

Objective: Administer an intradermal injection.

Supplies: Gloves, hazardous waste container, alcohol sponges, sterile needle, sterile syringe, vial of medication, medication order, pen, patient record

Affective Behaviors: Affective behaviors provide a professional approach to a skill that enhances the patient encounter. These behaviors may also display sensitivity to a patient's rights and enhance communication. Pay close attention to these skills, which will be in **_bold, italicized_** font.

Steps:
I.   Preparation
1.   Perform proper hand hygiene. (1 point)
2.   Apply gloves, and follow universal blood and body fluid precautions. (1 point)
3.   Select the correct medication using the "three befores" technique. (2 points)
4.   Gently roll the medication between your hands to mix any medication that may have settled. Refrigerated medication can be rolled between your hands to warm it slightly. (1 point)
5.   Prepare the syringe using the correct technique. Carefully carry the covered needle and syringe to the patient. (2 points)
6.   **_Identify and warmly greet the patient. Introduce yourself and ask the patient if he or she has any allergies._** (1 point)
7.   **_Tell the patient the name of the medication and dosage ordered by the physician. Explain the process of the PPD skin test. Ask the patient if he or she has any questions prior to receiving the medication._** (1 point)
8.   Select the proper site (center of forearm, upper chest, or upper back) for an intradermal skin injection. (1 point)
9.   Using a circular motion, clean the patient's skin with an alcohol sponge. Wipe the skin with a sweeping motion from the center of the area outward. (1 point)
10.   Allow the antiseptic to dry. (1 point)
11.   Check the medication dosage against the patient's order. (2 points)
12.   Remove the protective covering from the needle, using care not to touch the needle.
Note: If you accidentally touch the needle, excuse yourself to the patient. Return to your preparation area and change the needle on the syringe. If you are using a self-contained syringe and needle unit that does not come apart, you will have to discard the entire syringe with the medication and start the process over again. (1 point)

II. Injection

13. Hold the syringe between the first two fingers and thumb of your dominant hand with the palm down and the bevel of the needle up. (2 points)
14. Hold the skin taut with the fingers of your nondominant hand. If you are using the center of the forearm, place the nondominant hand under the patient's arm and pull the skin taut. This will allow the needle to slip into the skin more easily. (1 point)
15. Using a 15-degree angle, insert the needle through the skin to about one-eighth of an inch. The bevel of the needle will be facing upward and covered with skin. The needle will still show through the skin. Do not aspirate. (2 points)
16. Slowly inject the medication beneath the surface of the skin. A small elevation of skin, or wheal, will occur where you have injected the medication. (1 point)
17. Withdraw the needle. With the other hand, discard the needle into the biohazard sharps container. (2 points)

III. Patient Followup

18. Do not massage the area. (1 point)
19. *Make sure the patient is safe before leaving him or her unattended. Observe the patient for at least 20–30 minutes for any negative reactions to the medication. Tell the patient not to rub the area.*
Instruct the patient to return to the office within 48–72 hours for the reading of the skin test. Make certain that the patient understands the directions and does not have any questions. (2 points)
20. Correctly dispose of all materials. (1 point)
21. Remove and discard gloves, and perform proper hand hygiene. (1 point)
22. Document the procedure in the patient's record. (2 points)

Notes:

Administering Oral Medications

Objective: Administer oral medication.

Supplies: Medication order signed by physician; oral medication; calibrated paper cup or receptacle for medication; water in glass; patient instruction sheet; biohazard waste container; pen

Affective Behaviors: Affective behaviors provide a professional approach to a skill that enhances the patient encounter. These behaviors may also display sensitivity to a patient's rights and enhance communication. Pay close attention to these skills, which will be in **_bold, italicized_** font.

Steps:
1. Assemble equipment. (1 point)
2. Perform proper hand hygiene. (1 point)
3. Select the correct medication using the "three befores" technique. *Note:* If you are not familiar with the medication, look it up in a reference book, read the package insert, and/or consult the physician. (2 points)
4. Always double-check the label to make sure the strength is correct. (2 points)
5. Correctly calculate the dosage in writing. Double-check your calculations with someone else. (1 point)
6. Place a medicine cup or container on a flat surface. (1 point)
7. Gently shake the medication if it is in liquid form. (1 point)
8. Hold the bottle so that the label is in the palm of your hand to prevent damaging the label with liquid medication. (2 points)
9. Recheck the label. (2 points)
10. Remove the cap from the medicine container and place it upside down on a clean surface. (2 points)
11. **Liquid Medication:**
     Hold the calibrated medicine cup at eye level and pour the medication into the cup, stopping at the correct dosage line. Pour the medication away from the label side of the bottle. If too much medication is poured into the calibrated cup, do not return it to the bottle. Discard it into a sink.
     Tablet or Capsule Medication:
     Shake out the correct number of tablets or pills into the bottle cap. Then, place the tablets or pills in the medicine cup. If you accidentally pour out an extra tablet, do not return it to the medication bottle; discard it. (1 point)
12. Check the medication again to make sure the dosage is the same as the medication order. (1 point)
13. Replace the cap on the medication bottle and return the bottle to the storage shelf. (1 point)
14. Take the prepared medication and a glass of water to the patient. (2 points)

15. ***Identify the patient and warmly greet the patient. Introduce yourself to the patient and ask the patient if he or she has any allergies.*** (1 point)

16. Tell the patient the name of the medication and dosage that you are administering per the physician's order. ***Ask the patient if he or she has any questions prior to taking the medication.*** (1 point)

17. ***Remain with the patient until the medication has been swallowed.***

    Note: After giving the medication to the patient, it is best to have the patient wait in the office for 30 minutes. (1 point)

18. ***Provide the patient with written followup instructions if further medication is to be taken.*** (1 point)

19. Document the medication administration, noting in the patient's record the time, medication name, dosage route, and your name. (2 points)

Notes:

Administering Parenteral, Subcutaneous, or Intramuscular Injections

Objective: Administer subcutaneous (SubQ) and intramuscular (IM) injections.

Supplies: Medication order; vial of medication; gloves; alcohol sponges; biohazard sharps container; biohazard waste container; appropriate needle and syringe, depending on type of injection; pen; patient record

Affective Behaviors: Affective behaviors provide a professional approach to a skill that enhances the patient encounter. These behaviors may also display sensitivity to a patient's rights and enhance communication. Pay close attention to these skills, which will be in **_bold, italicized_** font.

Steps:
1. Perform proper hand hygiene. (1 point)
2. Apply gloves, and follow universal blood and body fluid precautions. (1 point)
3. Gather supplies. Use the "three befores" technique.
   Note: If you are not familiar with the medication, look it up in a reference book, read the package insert, and/or consult the physician. (1 point)
4. Gently roll the medication between your hands to mix any medication that may have settled. Refrigerated medication can be rolled between your hands to warm it slightly. (1 point)
5. Prepare the syringe using the correct technique. Carefully carry the covered needle and syringe to the patient. (2 points)
6. **_Identify and warmly greet the patient. Introduce yourself, and ask the patient if he or she has any allergies._** (1 point)
7. **_Tell the patient the name of the medication and dosage. Ask the patient if he or she has any questions prior to receiving the medication._** (1 point)
8. Position the patient depending on the site you are using. (1 point)
9. Using a circular motion, cleanse the patient's skin with an alcohol sponge. Wipe the skin with a sweeping motion from the center of the area outward. (1 point)
10. Again check the medication dosage against the order. (2 points)
11. Remove the protective cover from the needle, taking care not to touch the needle.
    Note: If you accidentally touch the needle, excuse yourself to the patient. Then, return to the preparation area and change the needle on the syringe. If you are using a self-contained syringe and needle unit that does not come apart, discard the entire syringe with the medication and start the process over again. (1 point)
12. When you are prepared to administer the injection, place a new alcohol sponge between two fingers of your nondominant hand so that you can easily grasp it when you are finished with the injection. (1 point)

13. Firmly grasp the syringe in your dominant hand, similar to holding a pencil. (1 point)
14. **Subcutaneous injection:**
    Pick up a small mass of tissue with your nondominant hand.
    Intramuscular injection:
    With your nondominant hand, stretch the skin tightly at the intersection site. (1 point)
15. Grasp the syringe in a dart-like fashion and insert the entire needle quickly with one swift movement. (1 point)
16. Be sure to insert the needle at the correct angle based on the type of injection:
    Subcutaneous: 45-degree angle
    Intramuscular: 90-degree angle (2 points)
17. Once the needle is inserted, do not move it. (1 point)
18. Aspirate to make sure that you have not punctured a blood vessel. If blood appears, discard the syringe and start over. (2 points)
19. If there is no blood return, slowly inject the medication without moving the needle.
    Note: Insert and withdraw the needle quickly to minimize pain, but administer the medication slowly. (1 point)
20. Taking the alcohol sponge (or cotton ball) from between the last two fingers of your nondominant hand, place it over the area containing the needle. Withdraw the needle at the same angle you used for insertion, using care not to stick yourself with the needle. (1 point)
21. With one hand, place the sponge firmly over the injection site. With the other hand, discard the needle in a biohazard sharps container. (1 point)
22. *You may gently massage the injection site to assist absorption and ease the patient's pain.* (1 point)
23. *Make sure the patient is safe before leaving him or her unattended. Observe the patient for any adverse effect of the medication for at least 15 minutes.* (2 points)
24. Correctly dispose of all materials. (1 point)
25. Remove gloves and discard them into a biohazard waste bag. Perform proper hand hygiene. (1 point)
26. Record the procedure in the patient's record. (2 points)

Notes:

Administering Sublingual or Buccal Medication

Objective: Administer a medication to a patient under the tongue or between the cheek and gum.

Supplies: Medication order; oral medication; paper cup or receptacle for medication; patient instruction sheet; biohazard waste container; pen; patient record

Affective Behaviors: Affective behaviors provide a professional approach to a skill that enhances the patient encounter. These behaviors may also display sensitivity to a patient's rights and enhance communication. Pay close attention to these skills, which will be in ***bold, italicized*** font.

Steps:

1. Assemble equipment. (1 point)
2. Perform proper hand hygiene. (1 point)
3. Select the correct medication using the "three befores" technique. *Note:* If you are not familiar with the medication, look it up in a reference book, read the package insert, and/or consult the physician. (2 points)
4. Always double-check the label to make sure the strength is correct. (2 points)
5. Correctly calculate the dosage in writing. Double-check your calculations with someone else. (1 point)
6. Place a medicine cup/container on a flat surface. (1 point)
7. Shake the tablet ordered into the bottle cap and then into a medication container. (1 point)
8. Check the dosage again against the medication order. (2 points)
9. Replace the cap on the medication bottle, and return the bottle to the storage shelf after reading the label again. (2 points)
10. ***Introduce yourself, identify the patient, and warmly greet the patient. Ask the patient if he or she has any allergies.*** (2 points)
11. ***Tell the patient the name of the medication and dosage you are administering per the physician's order. Ask the patient if he or she has any questions prior to taking the medication.*** (1 point)
12. **Sublingual medication:**
    Have the patient place the tablet under the tongue. ***Instruct the patient not to swallow until the tablet has dissolved.***
    Buccal medication:
    Have the patient place the tablet ***between the cheek and gum area.*** Instruct the patient not to swallow until the tablet is dissolved. (1 point)
13. ***Tell the patient not to take fluids until the tablet is dissolved.*** (1 point)
14. ***Remain with the patient until the medication has dissolved.***
    Note: After administration of the medication, it is best to have the patient wait in the office for 30 minutes. (1 point)

15. ***Provide the patient with written followup instructions if further medication is to be taken.*** (1 point)

16. Document the medication administration in the patient's record. (2 points)

Notes:

Assigning a CPT Code

Objective: Accurately assign a CPT code.

Supplies: Patient's medical record, computer, medical billing software, current CPT coding book, superbill with procedure marked

Affective Behaviors: Affective behaviors provide a professional approach to a skill that enhances the patient encounter. These behaviors may also display sensitivity to a patient's rights and enhance communication. Pay close attention to these skills, which will be in ***bold, italicized*** font.

Steps:
1. Locate the complete procedure on the superbill. (1 point)
2. If the only procedure done was a physician visit, locate the CPT E/M codes section of the CPT book. (1 point)
3. Determine by the patient's medical record whether this office visit was a first-time or follow-up visit. (1 point)
4. Also determine by the patient's medical record whether this visit involved the patient's attending physician or a consulting physician. (1 point)
5. Note where the visit took place. (1 point)
6. Locate the level of visit within the place of service codes. (2 points)
7. If there was a surgical procedure, locate the code for it. (1 point)
8. Locate the code for any necessary equipment used in surgery. (1 point)
9. Code any radiologic procedures. (1 point)
10. Locate the procedure done in Sections 7000 to 7999. (2 points)
11. Locate, in the appropriate section, the part of the body on which the procedure was done. (2 points)
12. Locate the correct procedure, being careful to note if the test was bilateral, unilateral, etc. (1 point)
13. Code a laboratory test if done in Sections 80000 to 89999. (1 point)
14. Code any injected medication(s). (1 point)
15. Compare the CPT codes with the ICD codes before finalizing the bill. (2 points)

Notes:

Assisting with a Neurologic Examination

Objective: Assist the physician with a neurologic screening examination.

Supplies: Percussion hammer; safety pin; tongue depressor; mayo tray; penlight; cotton ball; tuning fork; neurological wheel; ophthalmoscope; otoscope; hot and cold water; materials with different odors

Affective Behaviors: Affective behaviors provide a professional approach to a skill that enhances the patient encounter. These behaviors may also display sensitivity to a patient's rights and enhance communication. Pay close attention to these skills, which will be in ***bold, italicized*** font.

Steps:
1. Perform proper hand hygiene. (1 point)
2. Assemble equipment on the tray and cover the tray. (1 point)
3. Identify patient and ***explain procedure***. (1 point)
4. ***Evaluate the patient's mental status while taking a medical history, paying attention to responses, memory, and coherence of thought, overall mood, and awareness.*** (2 points)
5. If ordered, perform a visual acuity test. (1 point)
6. ***Assist the patient onto the examination table*** and drape as needed for comfort. (1 point)
7. The physician will test reflexes with the percussion hammer. (1 point)
8. Sensory ability and skin sensations are tested using a safety pin, neurological wheel, and cotton ball, and the patient's recognition of simple objects are tested by touch (key, pen, coin). (2 points)
9. The physician will check the cranial nerves by having the patient touch the finger to the nose, touch the heel to the shin, and mover the heel down the opposite shin. (1 point)
10. Assist the physician as needed during the remainder of the examination by handing equipment. (1 point)
11. ***Assist the patient off the table*** if the physician wants to evaluate gait or to have the patient perform the Romberg test successfully (patient closes eyes and stands with feet together without swaying). (1 point)
12. ***Assist the patient off the table and instruct him or her to dress. Assist and provide privacy as needed.*** (1 point)
13. Clean the examination room. (1 point)
14. Perform proper hand hygiene. (1 point)
15. Document the patient's record. (2 points)

Notes:

ICD-9-CM Coding

Objective: Accurately assign an ICD-9-CM code.

Supplies: Patient's medical record; patient's insurance card; computer with printer or typewriter; medical reference material; superbill with the doctor's diagnosis.

Affective Behaviors: Affective behaviors provide a professional approach to a skill that enhances the patient encounter. These behaviors may also display sensitivity to a patient's rights and enhance communication. Pay close attention to these skills, which will be in **_bold, italicized_** font.

Steps:
1. Locate the condition or diagnosis on the superbill or in the patient's medical record. (1 point)
2. In *Volume II: Alphabetic Index* of the ICD-9-CM, locate the condition or diagnosis. (1 point)
3. Examine the diagnostic statements to determine if the main term specifically describes that disease. If it does not, look at the modifiers listed under that main term to find a more specific code. (1 point)
4. Locate the code in *Volume I: Tabular Index*. (1 point)
5. Match the code description in the *Tabular Index* with the diagnosis in the patient's medical record. (1 point)
6. Use the codes from 0021.0 through V82.9 in the ICD-9-CM to describe the main reason for the patient's office visit. (1 point)
7. First, list the ICD-9-CM code for the condition, problem, or diagnosis that is the main reason for the visit. Then, list coexisting conditions under additional codes. (1 point)
8. Use codes at their highest level of specificity—fifth-digit codes first, followed by fourth-digit codes, then third-digit codes, and so on. (1 point)
9. Do not code questionable, probable, or ruled-out diagnoses. (1 point)
10. V codes describe factors that influence the health status of the patient, such as pregnancy test or vaccination, and are not used to code current illnesses. (1 point)
11. E codes are used for identifying external environmental events or conditions such as the course of injury, some adverse effect, or poisoning. E codes (E930–E949) are mandatory when coding the use of drugs. (1 point)
12. M codes, in Appendix A of *Volume I*, relate to the morphology of neoplasm. Morphology codes are used only by tumor registries for reporting proposes. (1 point)
13. List all diagnosis codes (up to four) on the insurance claim form, with the primary diagnosis listed first. (2 points)
14. Always double-check your coding and ensure proper use of abbreviations and symbols prior to assigning the final code. (2 points)

Notes:

Instilling Ear Medication

Objective: Instill ear medication as ordered by physician.

Supplies: Otic drops in dropper bottle, cotton balls, gloves

Affective Behaviors: Affective behaviors provide a professional approach to a skill that enhances the patient encounter. These behaviors may also display sensitivity to a patient's rights and enhance communication. Pay close attention to these skills, which will be in **bold, *italicized*** font.

Steps:
1. Review the physician's order. (1 point)
2. Perform proper hand hygiene. (1 point)
3. Assemble the equipment. (1 point)
4. ***Identify the patient.*** (1 point)
5. Check the medication label for the name, concentration, and expiration date. Note: Be sure to check the label 3 times! (2 points)
6. If the medication is cold, warm it by rolling the bottle between the palms. (1 point)
7. ***Have the patient sit or lie down with the affected ear tilted facing up.*** (2 points)
8. Pull the earlobe down and back for a child, and pull the auricle up and out for an adult, to straighten the ear canal. (1 point)
9. Place the dropper in the ear canal; avoid touching the sides of the ear canal. (2 points)
10. Instill the appropriate number of drops along the sides of the ear canal. (2 points)
11. Instruct the patient to remain in the same position for 3–5 minutes. (1 point)
12. ***Give instructions for home care if needed. Ask the patient if he or she has any questions.*** (1 point)
13. Dispose of equipment and clean the area. (1 point)
14. Perform proper hand hygiene. (1 point)
15. Document the procedure, medication information, and patient reaction in the patient's record. When documenting, use proper medical terms for right, left, or both. (2 points)

Notes:

Instilling Eye Medication

Objective: Instill eye medication as ordered by the physician.

Supplies: Sterile medication; sterile eyedropper; tissues; sterile gauze squares; gloves; drape or towel

Affective Behaviors: Affective behaviors provide a professional approach to a skill that enhances the patient encounter. These behaviors may also display sensitivity to a patient's rights and enhance communication. Pay close attention to these skills, which will be in ***bold, italicized*** font.

Steps:
1. Perform proper hand hygiene. (1 point)
2. Review the physician's order. (1 point)
3. ***Properly identify the patient and explain the procedure.*** (1 point)
4. Check the name, expiration date, and concentration of the solution. Note: Be sure to check medicine 3 times! (2 points)
5. Ask the patient if he or she has any allergies to the medication. (1 point)
6. ***Hand the patient a tissue to blot the cheeks.*** (1 point)
7. Put on gloves. (1 point)
8. Position the patient with the head tilted back and looking upward. (1 point)
9. Pull down the lower eyelid, exposing the conjunctiva. (1 point)
10. Place the dropper about one-half-inch above the eyeball with your dominant hand. Insert the proper number of drops in the center of the conjunctiva or, if ointment is used, apply a thin strip from the inner to the outer canthus. (2 points)
11. Do not touch the dropper or ointment tube to eye. (2 points)
12. Ask the patient to gently close eye and rotate the eyeball. (1 point)
13. Remove excess medication from the inner canthus to the outer canthus using sterile gauze. (2 points)
14. ***Explain to the patient that his or her vision may be blurry.*** (1 point)
15. Cleanse the area and dispose of unused medication. (1 point)
16. Remove gloves and perform proper hand hygiene. (1 point)
17. Document procedure in the patient's record. When documenting, use proper medical terms for right, left, or both. (2 points)

Notes:

Interviewing a New Patient to Obtain Medical History Information and Preparing for a Physical Examination

Objective: Obtain pertinent patient information for the medical history to assist the physician in establishing the cause and treatment of the present illness (PI) by interview. Include the chief complaint (CC), past history (PH), social or personal history (SH), and family history (FH).

Supplies: Medical history form; clipboard; pen; scale; equipment for vital signs; urine container; gown and drape

Affective Behaviors: Affective behaviors provide a professional approach to a skill that enhances the patient encounter. These behaviors may also display sensitivity to a patient's rights and enhance communication. Pay close attention to these skills, which will be in ***bold, italicized*** font.

Steps:
1. ***Identify the patient, greet the patient warmly, and identify yourself.*** (2 points)
2. Explain the procedure. (1 point)
3. Provide a private area to conduct the interview. (1 point)
4. If not already complete, ask the patient to fill out the required demographic information on the registration form. ***Assist the patient in completing the form if necessary.*** (1 point)
5. Review the patient data portion; ***ask for any additional information necessary.*** (2 points)
6. ***Ask why the patient is being seen by the physician today (CC).*** (1 point)
7. Record the CC in the patient's own words (as appropriate). (2 points)
8. ***Using observations skills, ask the patient other open-ended questions to gather necessary information about the CC. Record this information under PI.*** (1 point)
9. Gather other information about PH, FH, and SH; document in patient's record. (1 point)
10. ***Ask the patient if he or she has any allergies.*** Document according to facility protocol (red ink/ specific area for recording allergy information). (2 points)
11. Document any other relevant observations or information. (1 point)
12. Record all information using correct charting guidelines. (1 point)
13. Correct any charting errors, drawing one line through error and adding the date and your initials. Record the correct information. (2 points)
14. If required or appropriate, ask patient to provide urine specimen or to empty his or her bladder. (1 point)
15. Obtain a complete set of vital signs (temperature, pulse, respirations, blood pressure, height, and weight). Immediately document this data in the patient's record. (2 points)

16. ***Explain what clothes the patient needs to remove, proper donning of the exam gown, and where the patient should sit and wait.*** (1 point)
17. ***Explain what procedures will follow;*** tell the patient that the physician will be in shortly. (1 point)
18. Place the patient's record with the history and complaint in the designated place for the physician. (1 point)

Notes:

Irrigation of the Ear

Objective: Irrigate ear as ordered by the physician.

Supplies: Gloves, ear syringe, sterile basin, emesis basin, warm irrigation solution, towels, cotton balls

Affective Behaviors: Affective behaviors provide a professional approach to a skill that enhances the patient encounter. These behaviors may also display sensitivity to a patient's rights and enhance communication. Pay close attention to these skills, which will be in **bold, italicized** font.

Steps:

1. Review the physician's order. (1 point)
2. Perform proper hand hygiene. (1 point)
3. Assemble the equipment. (1 point)
4. Check the name, concentration, and expiration date of solution. Note: Be sure to check solution 3 times! (2 points)
5. ***Properly identify the patient and explain the procedure.*** (2 points)
6. Apply gloves. (1 point)
7. Have the patient sit with the affected ear tilted slightly downward. (1 point)
8. Place a towel over the patient's shoulder and ask the patient to hold the emesis basin. (1 point)
9. Clean the external ear canal with a moistened cotton ball, if necessary. (1 point)
10. Pour warmed solution into a sterile basin and fill the syringe with 50 cc of solution. (2 points)
11. For adults, pull the auricle up and out to straighten the ear canal. Note: For children younger than age three, pull earlobe down and back to straighten ear canal. (2 points)
12. Expel air from the syringe and insert the tip into the ear canal. Aim the stream of flow toward the roof of the canal. (1 point)
13. Repeat until the return from the ear canal is clear or no cerumen is visible upon otoscope examination. (2 points)
14. Remove basin, dry outer ear, and remove towel. (1 point)
15. Give the patient cotton balls to wipe any further external drainage from the ear. (1 point)
16. ***Instruct the patient about home care, if needed. Ask patient if he or she has any questions.*** (1 point)
17. Dispose of waste material properly and clean all equipment used. (1 point)
18. Perform proper hand hygiene. (1 point)
19. Document the procedure and the patient's reaction. Note any drainage, cerumen impaction, or patient symptoms such as vertigo or pain. When documenting, use proper medical terms for right, left, or both. (2 points)

Notes:

Irrigation of the Eye

Objective: Cleanse or irrigate the eye.

Supplies: Gloves, sterile basin, emesis basin, sterile solution, towel, sterile irrigating syringe, sterile gauze, towel, tissues, pen, patient record

Affective Behaviors: Affective behaviors provide a professional approach to a skill that enhances the patient encounter. These behaviors may also display sensitivity to a patient's rights and enhance communication. Pay close attention to these skills, which will be in ***bold, italicized*** font.

Steps:
1. ***Identify the patient and explain the procedure.*** (1 point)
2. Review the physician's order. (1 point)
3. Assemble all equipment and supplies. (1 point)
4. Check the name, expiration date, and concentration of the solution. Bring the solution to room temperature. Note: Be sure to check medicine 3 times! (2 points)
5. ***Place the patient in a comfortable position, either sitting or lying down.*** (1 point)
6. ***Place a towel over the patient's shoulder.*** (1 point)
7. Perform proper hand hygiene. (1 point)
8. Open the irrigating solution and fill the syringe. (1 point)
9. ***Ask the patient to tilt his or her head to the affected side, if seated, and hold the basin.*** (1 point)
10. ***Open the patient's eye using the index finger and thumb of your nondominant hand.*** (1 point)
11. Hold a tissue on the patient's cheekbone below the lower lid, and pull down and expose the conjunctiva. (1 point)
12. Hold the syringe one-half-inch from the eye. (2 points)
13. Gently irrigate from inner to outer canthus, or corner of the eye, aiming at the lower conjunctiva. (2 points)
14. Continue irrigating until all of the solution is used. (1 point)
15. Dry the area around the eye with sterile gauze. (1 point)
16. Dispose of equipment properly. (1 point)
17. Perform proper hand hygiene. (1 point)
18. Document the information, including the name and expiration date of the irrigation solutions, in the patient's record. When documenting, use proper medical terms for right, left, or both. (2 points)

Notes:

Measuring Blood Pressure

Objective: Obtain an accurate systolic and diastolic reading.

Supplies: Sphygmomanometer; stethoscope; 70 percent isopropyl alcohol; alcohol sponges or cotton balls; paper and pen; patient's record

Affective Behaviors: Affective behaviors provide a professional approach to a skill that enhances the patient encounter. These behaviors may also display sensitivity to a patient's rights and enhance communication. Pay close attention to these skills, which will be in ***bold, italicized*** font.

Steps:

1. Perform proper hand hygiene. (1 point)
2. Assemble the equipment. Use a sponge or cotton ball with alcohol to thoroughly cleanse the earpieces, bell, and diaphragm pieces of the stethoscope. Allow the alcohol to dry. (2 points)
3. ***Identify the patient and explain the procedure.*** (1 point)
4. ***Assist the patient into a comfortable position. BP may be taken with the patient in a sitting or lying position. The patient's arm should be at heart level. Ask the patient not to cross his or her legs or talk during the procedure.*** (1 point)
   Note: If the patient's arm is below heart level, the BP reading will be higher than normal; if the arm is higher than heart level, the BP will be lower than normal.
5. Place the sphygmomanometer on a solid surface with the gauge within 3 feet for easy viewing. (1 point)
6. ***Uncover the patient's arm by asking the patient to roll back his or her sleeve 5 inches above the elbow. If the sleeve becomes constricting when rolled back, ask the patient to slip his or her arm out of the sleeve.*** (2 points)
   Note: Never take a BP reading through clothing.
7. Have the patient straighten his or her arm with palms up. Apply a proper-size cuff over the brachial artery 1 to 2 inches above the antecubital space (bend in the elbow). Many cuffs are marked with arrows or circles to be placed over the artery. Hold the edge of the cuff in place as you wrap the remainder of the cuff tightly around the arm securing the Velcro closure. (1 point)
8. Palpate with your fingertips to locate the brachial artery in the antecubital space. (1 point)
9. Pump air into the cuff quickly and evenly until the level of mercury is 20 to 30 mmHg above the point at which the radial pulse is no longer palpable.
   Note the level, rapidly deflate, and wait 60 seconds. (2 points)
10. Place the earpieces in your ears and the diaphragm (or bell) of the stethoscope over the area where you feel the brachial artery pulsing. Hold the diaphragm in place with one hand on the chest piece without placing your thumb over the diaphragm. The stethoscope tubing should hang freely and not touch any object or the patient during the reading. (1 point)

11. Close the thumbscrew on the hand bulb by turning clockwise with your dominant hand. Close the thumbscrew just enough so that no air can leak out. Do not close so tightly that you will have difficulty reopening it with one hand. (1 point)
12. Slowly turn the thumbscrew counterclockwise with your dominant hand. Allow the pressure reading to fall only 2 to 3 mmHg at a time. (2 points)
13. Listen for the point at which the first clear sound is heard. Note where this occurred on the manometer. This is the systolic pressure. (1 point)
14. Slowly continue to allow the cuff to deflate. The sounds will change from loud to murmur and then fade away.
    Read the mercury column (or spring gauge scale) at the point where the sound is no longer heard. This is the diastolic pressure. (2 points)
15. Quickly open the thumbscrew all the way to release the air and deflate the cuff completely. (1 point)
16. If you are unsure about the BP reading, wait at least a minute or two before taking a second reading. (1 point)
    Note: Never take more than two readings in one arm.
17. Immediately write the BP as a fraction on paper. You may inform the patient of the reading if this is the policy in your office. (2 points)
18. Remove the cuff. (1 point)
19. Clean the earpieces of the stethoscope with an alcohol sponge. (1 point)
20. Perform proper hand hygiene. (1 point)
21. Document results, including the date, time, BP reading, and your name, in the patient's record. (2 points)

Notes:

Monitoring Blood Glucose Levels

Objective: Accurately determine blood glucose level using a glucometer.

Supplies: Sterile lancet, testing strips, glucometer, gloves, cotton balls, alcohol sponges, gauze squares, pen lab coat, patient record

Affective Behaviors: Affective behaviors provide a professional approach to a skill that enhances the patient encounter. These behaviors may also display sensitivity to a patient's rights and enhance communication. Pay close attention to these skills, which will be in **bold, italicized** font.

Steps:

1. ***Identify the patient and explain the procedure. Make sure the patient is fasting, if required.*** (1 point)
2. Assemble equipment and supplies. (1 point)
3. Perform proper hand hygiene and apply gloves. (1 point)
4. Be sure that the glucometer is calibrated and ready for use. (2 points)
5. Remove a plastic strip from the container and place it in the designated slot on the glucometer. Ensure the "Apply Blood" message appears on the screen. (1 point)
6. Perform a capillary puncture using a sterile lancet. (1 point)
7. Apply a large drop of blood from the capillary puncture site to the test strip, ensuring that it is completely covered.
   Note: Be sure to wipe away the first drop of blood with cotton or gauze. Touch the test strip to the second drop of blood. The glucometer should automatically start the timer. (2 points)
8. ***Provide the patient with cotton or a gauze square to hold over the puncture site.*** (1 point)
9. When the glucometer alerts you, look at the reading, and immediately remove the test strip and discard all used equipment.
   Note: The blood glucose reading will remain on the glucometer until the unit is turned off. (1 point)
10. Remove and dispose of gloves. Perform proper hand hygiene. (1 point)
11. Record in patient record as number of mg (milligrams) of glucose per deciliter (mg/dL) displayed on glucometer screen. (2 points)

Notes:

Performing a Capillary Puncture (Manual)

Objective: Perform a capillary stick using a lancet or spring-loaded lancet following correct aseptic technique and obtaining an adequate sample without error.

Supplies: Biohazard sharps container; gloves; alcohol sponge; 2 x 2 gauze squares or cotton balls; lancet or spring-loaded lancet; capillary tubes; sealing clay; ammonia ampules; bandage; lab coat

Affective Behaviors: Affective behaviors provide a professional approach to a skill that enhances the patient encounter. These behaviors may also display sensitivity to a patient's rights and enhance communication. Pay close attention to these skills, which will be in **bold, italicized** font.

Steps:
1. Assemble all equipment and supplies. (1 point)
2. Perform proper hand hygiene. (1 point)
3. ***Identify the patient and explain the procedure. Position the patient either sitting or lying down.*** (2 points)
4. Apply gloves. (1 point)
5. ***Select either the ring or great finger of the patient's nondominant hand.*** Cleanse the site with an alcohol sponge. Allow the alcohol to dry. (1 point)
6. Remove the plastic cover from the lancet. (1 point)
7. Grasp the patient's hand and gently squeeze the finger 1 inch below the puncture site. (1 point)
8. Select the puncture site:
   a. Middle or ring finger of the non-dominant hand.
   b. Lateral curved surface of the heel, or the great toe of an infant.
   c. Make sure that the site chosen is warm and not cyanotic or edematous.
   d. Gently massage the finger from the base to the tip.
   e. Identify the exact location to make the puncture.
   Puncture the finger with a quick jabbing motion (or release the spring- loaded lancet). Do not puncture the site in the direct center of the finger pad. (2 points)
9. Immediately discard the lancet. (1 point)
10. Wipe away the first drop of blood with a gauze square or cotton ball. (2 points)
11. Obtain the sample using a capillary tube. Seal one end of the tube in a clay sealer. Note: The finger may be gently massaged to increase blood flow. (1 point)
12. Apply clean gauze over the site and instruct the patient to apply firm pressure until the bleeding stops. (1 point)
13. ***Assess the patent.*** Apply a bandage to the site, if needed. (1 point)

14. Remove and dispose of gloves. Perform proper hand hygiene. (1 point)
15. Document the procedure in the patient's record. When documenting, use proper medical terms for right, left, or both. (2 points)

Notes:

Performing a Glucose Tolerance Testing (GTT)

Objective: Measure blood glucose

Supplies: Biohazard sharps container, Vacutainer tubes, multisample needle, gauze squares, alcohol pads, gloves, Vacutainer sleeve, tourniquet, bandage, cotton balls, adhesive, lab coat, patient record, ammonia ampules, Glucola,

Affective Behaviors: Affective behaviors provide a professional approach to a skill that enhances the patient encounter. These behaviors may also display sensitivity to a patient's rights and enhance communication. Pay close attention to these skills, which will be in **_bold, italicized_** font.

Prior to the patient's test, ensure the patient has adhered to the following instructions:
1. Eat normal, balanced meals for at least three days prior to the test.
2. Fast for 8 to 12 hours prior to the beginning of the test.
3. Do not drink, unsweetened tea, coffee, or any other beverage during fasting or during the procedure.
4. Drink water.
5. Do not smoke, chew tobacco, or chew gum during the fasting time or during the procedure.
6. Do not exercise, even mildly, during the test.
8. Do not have any illness in the last two weeks prior to the test.

Procedure Steps:
1. Assemble all equipment and materials. (1 point)
2. Perform proper hand hygiene. (1 point)
3. **_Identify the patient and explain the procedure. Position the patient either sitting or lying down._** (2 points)
4. Apply gloves. (1 point)
5. Obtain a fasting blood specimen by performing a venipuncture. (2 points)
6. Take the fasting blood specimen to the lab for testing. (1 point)
7. Ensure test results are normal prior to giving the patient Glucola. (1 point)
8. With a normal fasting specimen confirmed, give the patient a standard load of glucose. (1 point)
9. After the liquid has been consumed, note the time. (1 minute)
10. Obtain an additional blood specimen one hour after Glucola has been consumed. (2 minute)
11. Review the physician orders to ensure a 2 hr or 3 hr GTT is not required. (1 point)
12. As specimens are obtained, label the tubes accurately. (Such as 1st hour, and so on). (1 point)
13. Upon collection, send each specimen to the laboratory for immediate testing. (1 point)

15. ***Thank the patient.*** (1 point)
16. Remove and dispose of gloves. Perform proper hand hygiene. (1 point)
14. Document the procedure in the patient's record. (2 points)

Notes:

Performing a Venipuncture Using the Vacutainer Method

Objective: Perform venipuncture by correctly assembling, locating, and entering a vein, and withdrawing a blood sample.

Supplies: Biohazard sharps container, Vacutainer tubes, multisample needle, gauze squares, alcohol pads, gloves, Vacutainer sleeve, tourniquet, bandage, cotton balls, adhesive, pen, lab coat, patient record, ammonia ampules

Affective Behaviors: Affective behaviors provide a professional approach to a skill that enhances the patient encounter. These behaviors may also display sensitivity to a patient's rights and enhance communication. Pay close attention to these skills, which will be in **bold, italicized** font.

Steps:
1. Assemble all equipment and materials. (1 point)
2. Perform proper hand hygiene. (1 point)
3. ***Identify the patient and explain the procedure. Position the patient either sitting or lying down.*** (2 points)
4. Apply gloves. (1 point)
5. Screw the Vacutainer needle into the plastic sleeve. Insert the tube into the other end of the sleeve; be sure not to puncture the tube. (1 point)
6. Apply the tourniquet 2 inches above the antecubital space tight enough to engorge the vein with blood. (1 point)
7. ***Place the patient's arm in an extended position with the palm facing up and comfortably resting.*** (1 point)
8. Palpate the vein with your fingertips. (1 point)
9. Cleanse the chosen venipuncture site with an alcohol sponge in a circular pattern. Allow alcohol to dry. (2 points)
10. Anchor the vein properly. (1 point)
11. Bevel up, line up the needle with the vein approximately 1/4–1/2 inch below the site where the vein is to be entered. (2 points)
    a. At a 15°–30° angle, rapidly and smoothly insert the needle through the skin.
    b. Remove your non-dominant hand, slowly pull back the plunger of the syringe or place two fingers on the flanges of the adapter, and, with the thumb, push the tube onto the needle inside the adapter.
    c. When the blood flow begins in the tube or syringe, allow the patient to release the fist.
    d. Release the tourniquet.
    e. Allow the syringe or tube(s) to fill to capacity.
    f. When the blood flow ceases, remove the tube from the adapter by gripping the tube with the nondominant hand, placing the thumb against the flange during the removal.

       1) Twist and gently pull out the tube. Steady the needle in the vein.

       2) Try not to pull up or press down on the needle while it is in the vein.

   g. Insert any other necessary tubes into adapter and allow each to fill to capacity.

12. Remove the tube from adapter. (2 points)

   a. Place a sterile gauze pad over the puncture site during needle withdrawal.

   b. Do not apply any pressure to the site until the needle is completely removed.

   c. After needle is removed, apply pressure or have patient apply direct pressure for 3–5 minutes.

   d. Do not bend the arm at the elbow

13. Transfer the blood from a syringe into tubes via the transfer device. (2 points)

   a. In the proper order of draw, allow the vacuum to fill the tubes.

   b. Place the tubes in tube rack and carefully insert the device through the stopper.

   c. If the vacuum tubes contain an anticoagulant.

       1) Mix immediately by gently inverting the tube 8–10 times.

       2) Do not shake the tube.

   d. Label the tubes with the proper information.

14. Check the puncture site for bleeding. (1 point)

   a. Apply a bandage, a clean 2 × 2 gauze pad folded in quarters.

   b. Hold in place by a Band-Aid or 3-inch strip of tape.

15. ***Thank the patient.*** (1 point)

16. ***Tell the patient to leave the bandage in place at least 15 minutes and not to carry a heavy object (such as a purse) or lift heavy objects with that arm for an hour.*** (1 point)

12. Remove and dispose of gloves. Perform proper hand hygiene. (1 point)

13. Document the procedure in the patient's record. (2 points)

Notes:

Performing Audiometry Testing

Objective: Perform an audiometry test

Supplies: Audiometer, audiometer tips/speculums, audiometric test report form, patient chart

Affective Behaviors: Affective behaviors provide a professional approach to a skill that enhances the patient encounter. These behaviors may also display sensitivity to a patient's rights and enhance communication. Pay close attention to these skills, which will be in ***bold, italicized*** font.

Steps:
1. Wash your hands. (1 point)
2. ***Greet and identify patient and explain the procedure.*** (1 point)
3. Take patient to a quiet area or room for testing. (1 point)
4. Visually inspect the ear canal and tympanic membrane before the examination. (1 point)
5. Choose the correct-size tip for the end of the audiometer. (2 points)
6. Attach a speculum to fit the patient's external auditory meatus. (1 point)
7. With the specula in the ear canal, retract the pinna: (2 points)
    a. Adults: Gently pull up and back to straighten the auditory canal.
    b. Children: Gently pull slightly down and back to straighten the auditory canal.
8. Follow audiometer instrument directions for use. (1 point)
    a. Screen right ear.
    b. Screen left ear.
9. If the patient fails to respond at any frequency, rescreening is required. (1 point)
10. If the patient fails rescreening, notify the physician. (1 point)
11. Record the results in the medical record. (1 point)

Notes:

Preparing Injections

Objective: Prepare an injection

Supplies: Medication order, medication, needle, syringe, ampule, gauze, biohazard sharps container, antiseptic wipe

Affective Behaviors: Affective behaviors provide a professional approach to a skill that enhances the patient encounter. These behaviors may also display sensitivity to a patient's rights and enhance communication. Pay close attention to these skills, which will be in ***bold, italicized*** font.

Steps:
1. Wash your hands. (1 point)
2. Review the physician's medication order and select the correct medication. (2 points)
   a. Compare the label with the physician's instructions. Note the expiration date.
   b. Check the label three times: when taking it from the shelf, while drawing it up into the syringe, and when returning to the shelf.
3. Calculate the correct dosage to be given, if necessary. (1 point)
4. Choose the needle and syringe according to the route of administration, type of medication, and size of the patient. (1 point)
5. Open the needle and syringe package. Assemble if necessary. Secure the needle to the syringe. (1 point)
6. Withdraw the correct amount of medication: (2 points)
   a. From an ampule:
   1) Tap the stem of the ampule lightly.
   2) Place a piece of gauze around the ampule neck.
   3) Grasp the gauze and ampule firmly. Snap the stem off the ampule.
   4) Dispose of the ampule top in a biohazard sharps container.
   5) Insert the needle lumen below the level of the medication.
   6) Withdraw the medication.
   7) Dispose of the ampule in a biohazard sharps container.
   8) Remove any air bubbles in the syringe.
   9) Draw back on the plunger to add a small amount of air; then gently push the plunger forward to eject the air out of the syringe.
   b. From a vial:
   1) Using the antiseptic wipe, cleanse the rubber stopper of the vial.
   2) Pull air into the syringe with the amount equivalent to the amount of medication to be removed from the vial.
   3) Insert the needle into the vial top. Inject the air from the syringe.
   4) With the needle inside the vial, invert the vial.
   5) Hold the syringe at eye level.
   6) Aspirate the desired amount of medication into the syringe.

7) Displace any air bubbles in the syringe by gently tapping the barrel.

8) Remove the air by pushing the plunger slowly and forcing the air into the vial.

9) Revert vial and place on the counter; remove needle from vial.

7.   Carefully recap the needle using one-hand technique. (1 point)

Notes:

Respond to a Patient Who Has Fainted

Objective: Correctly care for a patient who has fainted, within the time limit set by the instructor.

Supplies: Blanket; footstool or box

Affective Behaviors: Affective behaviors provide a professional approach to a skill that enhances the patient encounter. These behaviors may also display sensitivity to a patient's rights and enhance communication. Pay close attention to these skills, which will be in *bold, italicized* font.

Steps:
1. *If the patient communicates a faint feeling, help the patient sit, bend forward, and place the head on the knees. If the patient collapses with no warning, do not move the patient.* The patient may have sustained a neck or back injury. (1 point)
2. Remain calm and notify the physician. (1 point)
3. *Loosen any tight clothing and cover the patient with the blanket for warmth.* (1 point)
4. *If the physician directs, use the footstool to support the patient's legs in a raised position.* (1 point)
5. If the physician directs, call for EMS. (1 point)
6. Once the emergency passes, Obtain a full set of vital signs and document all activities in the patient's medical record. (2 points)

Notes:

Screening for Color Vision Acuity

Objective: Screen a patient for color vision defects.

Supplies: Ishihara screening book/cards, pen, patient record

Affective Behaviors: Affective behaviors provide a professional approach to a skill that enhances the patient encounter. These behaviors may also display sensitivity to a patient's rights and enhance communication. Pay close attention to these skills, which will be in **_bold, italicized_** font.

Steps:

1. Perform proper hand hygiene. (1 point)
2. Review the physician's order. (1 point)
3. Assemble equipment. (1 point)
4. **_Identify the patient and introduce yourself._** (1 point)
5. **_Explain the procedure._** (1 point)
6. Have the patient assume a comfortable position and ask the patient to keep both eyes open. (1 point)
7. In a well-lit room at a distance of 30 inches, **_ask the patient to identify_** the number that is formed by the colored dots on each card or page within 3 seconds per page or card. (2 points)
8. **_If the patient is unable to identify the numbers, have the patient trace the numbers with his or her finger._** (1 point)
9. Score each plate as it is read. If the patient is able to identify a number, record the number seen after the plate number. If the patient is unable to identify a number on the plate, record the plate number and mark an X next to it. (1 point)
10. Note any unusual symptoms. (2 points)
11. Document the results accurately in the patient's record. (1 point)

Notes:

Testing Visual Acuity Using a Snellen Eye Chart

Objective: Screen a patient for distance acuity using a Snellen eye chart.

Supplies: Snellen eye chart; eye shield or occluder; pointer; pen; patient document; alcohol and gauze

Affective Behaviors: Affective behaviors provide a professional approach to a skill that enhances the patient encounter. These behaviors may also display sensitivity to a patient's rights and enhance communication. Pay close attention to these skills, which will be in **bold, italicized** font.

Steps:

1. Assemble equipment. (1 point)
2. Review the physician's order. (1 point)
3. Perform proper hand hygiene and **identify the patient.** (1 point)
4. **Explain the procedure.** (1 point)
5. **Determine patient's ability to recognize letters.**
   Note: If the patient is unable to read letters, use an alternate chart to accommodate patient's abilities. (2 points)
6. Use pointer, and point to letters or appropriate symbols in random order. (1 point)
7. Place the patient 20 feet from the chart, either seated or standing, with Snellen chart at eye level. (2 points)
8. Follow office policy regarding testing with or without corrective lenses. (1 point)
9. Have patient read the lines with both eyes first at a distance of 20 feet. (1 point)
10. Follow office policies regarding which eye to test first. Have patient cover the other eye with a cup or occluder.
    Note: The occluder should be positioned in such a way that it does not interfere with the position of the patient's glasses. (1 point)
11. Starting with the 20/70 line, **ask the patient to identify** each line and proceed down the chart to the last line the patient can read without error.
    Note: Be sure to che **ny squinting or tilting of the**
    head, which would in **fficulty in identifying letters.** (2 points)
12. Record the ratio numbers adj **error.** If there is an error line the patient can read without error. If there is an error line the patient can read **points)**
13. Repeat the procedure with the othe line the patient can read **rd result.**
    Note: Follow office policy for charting **points)**
14. Clean the occluder with gauze and alcohol. **points)**
15. Remove and dispose of gloves. Perform prop **(2 points)** point)
16. Document results accurately in the patient's cha **points)**
    (1

Notes:

Competency Procedures

Directions: For each competency, read and familiarize yourself with the objective, supplies, and procedure steps. Pay particular attention to steps in ***bold, italicized*** font – these refer to affective behaviors that will allow you to demonstrate professionalism, communication skills, and sensitivity to the patient's rights.

You will be given time to practice each competency, and then you will be given an opportunity to pass the competency by earning a minimum score of 75%. Your score on each competency will be determined by a rubric that your instructor will provide that shows the value of each step. If you attain 75% on your first attempt, further attempts are not required. Each competency must be completed within a reasonable amount of time, as determined by your instructor.

Administering an Intradermal Injection

Objective: Administer an intradermal injection.

Supplies: Gloves, hazardous waste container, alcohol sponges, sterile needle, sterile syringe, vial of medication, medication order, pen, patient record

Affective Behaviors: Affective behaviors provide a professional approach to a skill that enhances the patient encounter. These behaviors may also display sensitivity to a patient's rights and enhance communication. Pay close attention to these skills, which will be in ***bold, italicized*** font.

Steps:
I. Preparation
1. Perform proper hand hygiene. (1 point)
2. Apply gloves, and follow universal blood and body fluid precautions. (1 point)
3. Select the correct medication using the "three befores" technique. (2 points)
4. Gently roll the medication between your hands to mix any medication that may have settled. Refrigerated medication can be rolled between your hands to warm it slightly. (1 point)
5. Prepare the syringe using the correct technique. Carefully carry the covered needle and syringe to the patient. (2 points)
6. ***Identify and warmly greet the patient. Introduce yourself and ask the patient if he or she has any allergies.*** (1 point)
7. ***Tell the patient the name of the medication and dosage ordered by the physician. Explain the process of the PPD skin test. Ask the patient if he or she has any questions prior to receiving the medication.*** (1 point)
8. Select the proper site (center of forearm, upper chest, or upper back) for an intradermal skin injection. (1 point)
9. Using a circular motion, clean the patient's skin with an alcohol sponge. Wipe the skin with a sweeping motion from the center of the area outward. (1 point)
10. Allow the antiseptic to dry. (1 point)
11. Check the medication dosage against the patient's order. (2 points)
12. Remove the protective covering from the needle, using care not to touch the needle.
    Note: If you accidentally touch the needle, excuse yourself to the patient. Return to your preparation area and change the needle on the syringe. If you are using a self-contained syringe and needle unit that does not come apart, you will have to discard the entire syringe with the medication and start the process over again. (1 point)

II. Injection

13. Hold the syringe between the first two fingers and thumb of your dominant hand with the palm down and the bevel of the needle up. (2 points)
14. Hold the skin taut with the fingers of your nondominant hand. If you are using the center of the forearm, place the nondominant hand under the patient's arm and pull the skin taut. This will allow the needle to slip into the skin more easily. (1 point)
15. Using a 15-degree angle, insert the needle through the skin to about one-eighth of an inch. The bevel of the needle will be facing upward and covered with skin. The needle will still show through the skin. Do not aspirate. (2 points)
16. Slowly inject the medication beneath the surface of the skin. A small elevation of skin, or wheal, will occur where you have injected the medication. (1 point)
17. Withdraw the needle. With the other hand, discard the needle into the biohazard sharps container. (2 points)

III. Patient Followup

18. Do not massage the area. (1 point)
19. *Make sure the patient is safe before leaving him or her unattended. Observe the patient for at least 20–30 minutes for any negative reactions to the medication. Tell the patient not to rub the area.*
Instruct the patient to return to the office within 48–72 hours for the reading of the skin test. Make certain that the patient understands the directions and does not have any questions. (2 points)
20. Correctly dispose of all materials. (1 point)
21. Remove and discard gloves, and perform proper hand hygiene. (1 point)
22. Document the procedure in the patient's record. (2 points)

Notes:

Administering Parenteral, Subcutaneous, or Intramuscular Injections

Objective: Administer subcutaneous (SubQ) and intramuscular (IM) injections.

Supplies: Medication order; vial of medication; gloves; alcohol sponges; biohazard sharps container; biohazard waste container; appropriate needle and syringe, depending on type of injection; pen; patient record

Affective Behaviors: Affective behaviors provide a professional approach to a skill that enhances the patient encounter. These behaviors may also display sensitivity to a patient's rights and enhance communication. Pay close attention to these skills, which will be in **_bold, italicized_** font.

Steps:
1. Perform proper hand hygiene. (1 point)
2. Apply gloves, and follow universal blood and body fluid precautions. (1 point)
3. Gather supplies. Use the "three befores" technique.
   Note: If you are not familiar with the medication, look it up in a reference book, read the package insert, and/or consult the physician. (1 point)
4. Gently roll the medication between your hands to mix any medication that may have settled. Refrigerated medication can be rolled between your hands to warm it slightly. (1 point)
5. Prepare the syringe using the correct technique. Carefully carry the covered needle and syringe to the patient. (2 points)
6. **_Identify and warmly greet the patient. Introduce yourself, and ask the patient if he or she has any allergies._** (1 point)
7. **_Tell the patient the name of the medication and dosage. Ask the patient if he or she has any questions prior to receiving the medication._** (1 point)
8. Position the patient depending on the site you are using. (1 point)
9. Using a circular motion, cleanse the patient's skin with an alcohol sponge. Wipe the skin with a sweeping motion from the center of the area outward. (1 point)
10. Again check the medication dosage against the order. (2 points)
11. Remove the protective cover from the needle, taking care not to touch the needle.
    Note: If you accidentally touch the needle, excuse yourself to the patient. Then, return to the preparation area and change the needle on the syringe. If you are using a self-contained syringe and needle unit that does not come apart, discard the entire syringe with the medication and start the process over again. (1 point)
12. When you are prepared to administer the injection, place a new alcohol sponge between two fingers of your nondominant hand so that you can easily grasp it when you are finished with the injection. (1 point)

13. Firmly grasp the syringe in your dominant hand, similar to holding a pencil. (1 point)

14. **Subcutaneous injection:**
Pick up a small mass of tissue with your nondominant hand.
Intramuscular injection:
With your nondominant hand, stretch the skin tightly at the intersection site. (1 point)

15. Grasp the syringe in a dart-like fashion and insert the entire needle quickly with one swift movement. (1 point)

16. Be sure to insert the needle at the correct angle based on the type of injection:
Subcutaneous: 45-degree angle
Intramuscular: 90-degree angle (2 points)

17. Once the needle is inserted, do not move it. (1 point)

18. Aspirate to make sure that you have not punctured a blood vessel. If blood appears, discard the syringe and start over. (2 points)

19. If there is no blood return, slowly inject the medication without moving the needle.
Note: Insert and withdraw the needle quickly to minimize pain, but administer the medication slowly. (1 point)

20. Taking the alcohol sponge (or cotton ball) from between the last two fingers of your nondominant hand, place it over the area containing the needle. Withdraw the needle at the same angle you used for insertion, using care not to stick yourself with the needle. (1 point)

21. With one hand, place the sponge firmly over the injection site. With the other hand, discard the needle in a biohazard sharps container. (1 point)

22. ***You may gently massage the injection site to assist absorption and ease the patient's pain.*** (1 point)

23. ***Make sure the patient is safe before leaving him or her unattended. Observe the patient for any adverse effect of the medication for at least 15 minutes.*** (2 points)

24. Correctly dispose of all materials. (1 point)

25. Remove gloves and discard them into a biohazard waste bag. Perform proper hand hygiene. (1 point)

26. Record the procedure in the patient's record. (2 points)

Notes:

Assigning a CPT Code

Objective: Accurately assign a CPT code.

Supplies: Patient's medical record, computer, medical billing software, current CPT coding book, superbill with procedure marked

Affective Behaviors: Affective behaviors provide a professional approach to a skill that enhances the patient encounter. These behaviors may also display sensitivity to a patient's rights and enhance communication. Pay close attention to these skills, which will be in ***bold, italicized*** font.

Steps:

1. Locate the complete procedure on the superbill. (1 point)
2. If the only procedure done was a physician visit, locate the CPT E/M codes section of the CPT book. (1 point)
3. Determine by the patient's medical record whether this office visit was a first-time or follow-up visit. (1 point)
4. Also determine by the patient's medical record whether this visit involved the patient's attending physician or a consulting physician. (1 point)
5. Note where the visit took place. (1 point)
6. Locate the level of visit within the place of service codes. (2 points)
7. If there was a surgical procedure, locate the code for it. (1 point)
8. Locate the code for any necessary equipment used in surgery. (1 point)
9. Code any radiologic procedures. (1 point)
10. Locate the procedure done in Sections 7000 to 7999. (2 points)
11. Locate, in the appropriate section, the part of the body on which the procedure was done. (2 points)
12. Locate the correct procedure, being careful to note if the test was bilateral, unilateral, etc. (1 point)
13. Code a laboratory test if done in Sections 80000 to 89999. (1 point)
14. Code any injected medication(s). (1 point)
15. Compare the CPT codes with the ICD codes before finalizing the bill. (2 points)

Notes:

Assisting with a Complete Physical Examination

Objective: Assist with the physical examination by preparing the room and the necessary equipment, while observing proper sequencing and ensuring patient safety with limited direction.

Supplies: Examination equipment (varies depending on type and purpose of examination and personal preference of the physician); examination table with clean sheet; pillow with clean cover; Snellen chart; urine specimen container; sphygmomanometer; stethoscope; tape measure; thermometer; probe cover; gown and drape; gloves; waste container; pencil or pen

Affective Behaviors: Affective behaviors provide a professional approach to a skill that enhances the patient encounter. These behaviors may also display sensitivity to a patient's rights and enhance communication. Pay close attention to these skills, which will be in ***bold, italicized*** font.

Steps:

1. Perform proper hand hygiene. (1 point)
2. Assemble all equipment in the examination room. (1 point)
3. ***Identify the patient, escort him or her to the examination room, and explain the procedure.*** (2 points)
4. If a urine specimen is needed for testing, provide the patient with a urine specimen container and give instructions at this time. If no specimen is needed, offer the patient an opportunity to use the restroom before the examination begins. (1 point)
5. Take vital signs and measurements. Properly document this data in the patient's record immediately. (2 points)
6. ***Provide the patient with a gown and drape, and give instructions on undressing. Allow the patient to undress in privacy.*** (1 point)
7. Have the patient sit on the examination table with his or her legs hanging over; ***place a drape sheet over the patient's legs.*** (2 points)
8. Tell the physician that the patient is ready. (1 point)
9. Assist the physician as needed. (1 point)
10. Apply gloves when handling soiled equipment that may contain biohazardous materials, such as body secretions (e.g., laryngeal mirror). (1 point)
11. As the physician progresses from one section of the body to the next, ***reposition the drape to expose only the portion of the patient being examined at that time.*** (1 point)
12. Use gloves when handling specimens. (1 point)
13. Label all specimens as soon as possible. (2 points)
14. When the examination is complete, ***assist the patient in slowly sitting up.*** (1 point)
15. ***Assist the patient off the examination table.*** (1 point)
16. ***Ask the patient if he or she requires help dressing. If no help is needed, allow the patient to dress in privacy.*** (1 point)

17. ***Instruct the patient where to go after dressing.*** (1 point)
18. After the patient leaves the examination room, discard all disposable materials in the appropriate sharps/waste containers. (1 point)
19. Replace supplies in the examination room. (1 point)
20. Clean the examination table, and replace linens and gowns. (2 points)
21. Ensure all documentation of the examination is complete in the patient's record. (1 point)

Notes:

Assisting with a Pelvic Examination and a Pap Test

Objective: Set up and assist with a gynecologic examination, including collection without error of "dry" or "liquid" prep-method Pap smear.

Supplies: Vaginal speculum; water-soluble lubricant; cotton-tipped applicator; patient drape; Pap smear materials—*Dry-prep*: cervical spatula brush; glass slides; fixative spray or liquid slide holder; identification label; *Liquid-based prep*: plastic cervical spatula, broom, or brush; cytology medium transport vial; identification label; laboratory request form; cleansing tissue; gloves; container for contaminated vaginal speculum; gooseneck lamp; biohazard waste container

Affective Behaviors: Affective behaviors provide a professional approach to a skill that enhances the patient encounter. These behaviors may also display sensitivity to a patient's rights and enhance communication. Pay close attention to these skills, which will be in **bold, italicized** font.

Steps:
For "Dry Prep" Collection
1. Assemble equipment. (1 point)
2. Perform proper hand hygiene. (1 point)
3. Label the slides and complete the laboratory form. (1 point)
4. Identify the patient and **explain the procedure.** (2 points)
5. **Direct the patient to the restroom to empty her bladder.** (2 points)
6. **Ask the patient to remove her clothing and put on the gown with the opening in front.** (2 points)
7. **Drape the patient appropriately, and assist her into the supine position for breast and abdominal examination.** (2 points)
8. When the physician is ready to collect the Pap specimen, **assist and instruct the patient to assume the dorsal lithotomy position with her buttocks at the edge of the table and her feet in the stirrups. Knees should be relaxed and rotated outward. Expose the genitalia by moving the drape away from this area while it still covers the legs.** (2 points)
9. Adjust the gooseneck lamp and place the physician's stool in the proper position at the end of examination table. (1 point)
10. Assist the physician with the procedure: (2 points)
    - Apply gloves.
    - Hand gloves and equipment to the physician as needed. Place lubricant onto the speculum as the physician holds it.
    - Hold the microscopic slides as the physician smears the slides. Mark the slides C for cervical, V for vaginal, and E for endocervical.
    - Spray fixative from about 6 inches away from the slide.

- Place the slide into a container with the appropriate label.
11. Hold the receptacle as the physician places the contaminated speculum into it. Set the container into the sink for later cleaning. (1 point)
12. Apply lubricant to the physician's gloved fingers in preparation for the manual examination. (1 point)
13. Properly dispose of gloves in a biohazard waste container and perform proper hygiene. (1 point)
14. Assist the patient to sit up by (a) helping her move back on the table, (b) taking her feet out of the stirrups, and (c) helping her to a sitting position. (2 points)
15. Sanitize and sterilize equipment as needed. (2 points)
16. Perform proper hand hygiene. (2 points)
17. Prepare the Pap specimen to be sent to the laboratory. (2 points)

For "Liquid-Based Prep" Collection
18. Proceed through steps 1–9 above. (2 points)
19. Open the vial of liquid transport medium and hold it so the physician can place both the plastic spatula and either the brush or the broom containing the specimen into the vial. (2 points)
20. Rinse the broom vigorously by pushing it to the bottom of the vial 10 times. (2 points)
21. Use the spatula to scrape cells from the brush, and swirl both the spatula and brush in the vial to mix before removing. (2 points)
22. Label the vial and dispose of hazardous waste appropriately. (2 points)
23. Proceed through steps 1–17 above. (2 points)

Notes:

Calculating Adult Body Mass Index

Objective: Accurately calculate adult body mass index.

Supplies: Patient's record; pen and paper; scale for height and weight; BMI formula or nomogram, or chart for BMI

Affective Behaviors: Affective behaviors provide a professional approach to a skill that enhances the patient encounter. These behaviors may also display sensitivity to a patient's rights and enhance communication. Pay close attention to these skills, which will be in **_bold, italicized_** font.

Steps:
1.   Perform proper hand hygiene. (1 point)
2.   If recent height and weight measurements are not available, follow the steps in Procedure 35-1 for measuring adult height and weight. (1 point)
3.   Insert the patient's height and weight into the formula, using pounds and inches or kilograms and meters, according to facility policy. (1 point)
4.   Formula for pounds and inches:
      BMI = Weight in pounds ÷ (Height in inches x Height in inches) x 703(1 point)
5.   _Example:_ Weight of 175 lbs; Height of 64 inches
      175 ÷ (64 x 64) = 0.0427
      0.0427 x 703 = 30.0 BMI
      A BMI between 19 and 25 is considered a healthy weight, 25–30 is considered overweight, and over 30 is considered obese. (2 points)
6.   Record the results in the patient's record. (2 points)

Notes:

Calculating Growth Percentiles

Objective: Plot the age, weight, and height of a patient, and obtain correct percentiles.

Supplies: Patient's record with weight and height values; pen; growth chart; patient record

Affective Behaviors: Affective behaviors provide a professional approach to a skill that enhances the patient encounter. These behaviors may also display sensitivity to a patient's rights and enhance communication. Pay close attention to these skills, which will be in **bold, *italicized*** font.

Steps:
1. Select the proper growth chart for the patient. (1 point)
2. Locate the child's age in the horizontal axis at the bottom of the chart. Draw an imaginary vertical line on the chart. (2 points)
3. Locate the proper growth value and draw an imaginary horizontal line on the chart. (2 points)
4. Find the point at which the two imaginary lines intersect on the graph and place a dot there. (2 points)
5. Follow the curved line closest to the dot upward, then read the percentile located on the right side of the chart. (2 points)
6. If the dot you placed falls between two curved lines, estimate the percentile that falls between the two closest percentile lines. (2 points)
7. Record the results in the patient's record. (2 points)

Notes:

Changing a Sterile Dressing

Objective: Change a wound dressing using sterile technique.

Supplies: Gloves; antiseptic solution; solution container; prepackaged dressing pack; thumb forceps; sterile cotton balls; sterile gloves; sterile dressing; adhesive tape; scissors (for tape); waste container/plastic bag; biohazard waste container; Mayo stand or side tray

Affective Behaviors: Affective behaviors provide a professional approach to a skill that enhances the patient encounter. These behaviors may also display sensitivity to a patient's rights and enhance communication. Pay close attention to these skills, which will be in **bold, italicized** font.

Steps:
1. Assemble all equipment and supplies needed using the Mayo stand. (1 point)
2. Perform proper hand hygiene. (1 point)
3. Prepare the sterile field using aseptic technique with prepackaged dressing packet. Employ sterile transfer forceps to place additional needed sterile items onto the sterile field. (1 point)
4. ***Identify the patient and explain the procedure.*** (2 points)
5. ***Assist the patient into a comfortable position with the area to be dressed resting on a support, such as an examination table.*** (1 point)
6. Apply nonsterile gloves. (1 point)
7. Remove the soiled dressing from the wound by loosening the tape with gloved hands and/or forceps and pulling it from both sides toward the wound. Without passing the soiled dressing over the sterile field, place it in the soiled waste bag. Do not allow the dressing to touch the outside or edges of the bag. (2 points)
8. Inspect the wound for signs of infection and inflammation, and for signs of healing. Note any discharge by type, amount, color, and odor. (2 points)
9. Remove and discard gloves and forceps properly. Disposable gloves and forceps are placed in the biohazard waste container. Reusable forceps are placed in the basin for later cleaning. (1 point)
10. Drop antiseptic on several gauze sponges until they are moist but not saturated. (1 point)
11. Open sterile gloves and apply them properly, maintaining sterile technique. (1 point)
12. Clean the wound using sterile forceps to hold the sponges. Cleanse the wound by moving from top to bottom once. Use a new sponge with antiseptic for each wipe. Next, cleanse from the inside of the wound to the outside edges, moving in concentric circles. (2 points)
13. Pick up the sterile dressing with gloved hands and place it over the wound. (1 point)
14. Discard your gloves and forceps properly. (1 point)
15. Apply tape or other material as ordered to hold the dressing in place. Do not apply it too tightly, as this will restrict circulation.

The strips of tape should be long enough to hold the dressing in place. Do not wrap the tape entirely around an extremity or completely cover a dressing.

Note: Some facilities require that you add your initials and the date of the dressing. Follow office policy. (2 points)

16. ***Instruct the patient on dressing care and schedule a followup appointment to see the physician.*** (1 point)

17. Document the procedure, including date, time, location, condition of the wound, and instructions given to the patient. (2 points)

Notes:

Collecting a 24-Hour Urine Specimen

Objective: Clearly instruct a patient on how to collect a 24-hour urine specimen.

Supplies: 24-hour specimen container (some patients may require 2 containers); smaller collection container or toilet insert; patient instruction sheet; collection label; patient record; requisition slip; preservation additive and hazardous indicator label (as required); 1 L graduated cylinder; gloves; pen

Affective Behaviors: Affective behaviors provide a professional approach to a skill that enhances the patient encounter. These behaviors may also display sensitivity to a patient's rights and enhance communication. Pay close attention to these skills, which will be in **_bold, italicized_** font.

Steps:
1. Verify orders for specific test in patient record. (1 point)
2. Assemble equipment and supplies.
   Note: Be sure to check laboratory directory for specific instructions (dietary restrictions or preservatives) for tests ordered. (1 point)
3. Perform proper hand hygiene. (1 point)
4. Label container with patient's name, start and end dates, and times for collection.
   Note: If indicated by the lab directory, add preservative to the container and correct chemical hazard label. (1 point)
5. **_Identify the patient and greet the patient. Introduce yourself and guide the patient to the treatment area._** (1 point)
6. **_Clearly instruct the patient on the following procedure for urine collection:_**
   - Wash hands.
   - Void into the toilet upon arising.
   - Record the time and the date (i.e., 7 am, Thursday, xx/xx/xxxx).
   - Collect all voided urine after this time for the next 24 hours until the recorded time is reached the next day (i.e., 7 am, Friday, xx/xx/xxxx).
   - Note on the label the date and time of each urination.
   - All urine will go into the 24-hour collection container. (1 point)
7. DO NOT void directly into the large 24-hour collection container.
   - Void all urine into the smaller collection container or toilet insert, and pour it into the larger container.
   - Each time wash, rinse, and air-dry the smaller container.
   - After each specimen is placed in the larger specimen container, screw the lid tightly.
   - Store the container in the refrigerator or portable cooler unless otherwise indicated by the lab directory for the specific test. (2 points)

8. The first voided specimen of the second morning is the last specimen to be added to the container, ending the collecting period.
   - At the end of the 24-hour period, bring the large container in as soon as possible to ensure accurate results.
   - ***Ask the patient if he or she has any questions prior to leaving the office and beginning the specimen collection.*** (1 point)
9. ***Provide a written copy of these instructions to the patient, along with the prepared container(s).*** (1 point)
10. Document the supplies and instructions given in the patient's record. (1 point)
11. Upon return of the specimen, ***verify the collection dates and times with patient for accuracy.*** (1 point)
12. Perform proper hand hygiene and apply gloves. (1 point)
13. Fill out a lab requisition slip for the specimen. Be sure to check if any other additives need to be included per the laboratory directory for the specific testing. (2 points)
14. Mix the urine sample by swirling carefully. Measure and record total volume of collected urine. (1 point)
15. Pour an aliquot (portion obtained by dividing whole amount into equal portions) of urine into the container for delivery.
    Record the total volume of urine collected and preservative added (if any). Dispose of the remainder of the urine per laboratory directions. (2 points)
16. Clean the area, disposing of urine containers in biohazard waste containers. (1 point)
17. Remove and dispose of gloves. Perform proper hand hygiene. (1 point)
18. Record the date, time, volume of urine, and where specimen was sent in the patient's record. (1 point)

Notes:

Collecting a Clean-Catch Midstream Urine Specimen

Objective: Instruct both male and female patients to correctly obtain a contaminant-free, clean-catch midstream urine specimen.

Supplies: Sterile urine container, antiseptic towelettes, written patient instructions

Affective Behaviors: Affective behaviors provide a professional approach to a skill that enhances the patient encounter. These behaviors may also display sensitivity to a patient's rights and enhance communication. Pay close attention to these skills, which will be in **bold, italicized** font.

Steps:
1. Assemble equipment and supplies. Perform proper hand hygiene. (1 point)
2. ***Identify and greet the patient.*** (1 point)
3. ***Explain procedure to a <u>male</u> patient as follows:*** (2 points)
   - Perform proper hand hygiene.
   - Expose penis. Pull foreskin back if uncircumcised, and hold back until the specimen has been collected.
   - Cleanse each side of the urethral opening from top to bottom using a separate antiseptic wipe, wiping in one direction only. Cleanse across the top of the urethral opening with a third antiseptic wipe, wiping in one direction only.
   - Be certain to avoid having any body part touch the inside of the specimen container.
   - Void a small amount into the toilet. Then, void into the container, taking care not to touch the insides of the container. Remove the container.
   - Continue voiding the remainder of the urine into the toilet.
   - Re-cap container, taking care not to contaminate the inside of the lid.
   - Deliver the specimen as directed.
4. ***Explain procedure to <u>female</u> patient as follows:*** (2 points)
   - Perform proper hand hygiene and remove underwear.
   - Expose urinary meatus by pulling apart labia and hold open with nondominant hand.
   - Use dominant hand to cleanse around one side of the urinary meatus from front to back with one antiseptic wipe. Use a second wipe to cleanse the other side in the same manner. Using a third wipe, cleanse across the opening of the meatus itself. Continue holding the labia apart until the procedure is complete.
   - Begin voiding into the toilet. Place the container into position and void into the container without touching the inside of the container with fingers.
   - Remove container and continue voiding into the toilet.
   - Wipe in usual manner and cover container with lid, avoiding contaminating the inside of the lid.

- Deliver the specimen as directed.
5. Label specimen container appropriately and complete the lab requisition form. (1 point)
6. Perform proper hand hygiene. (1 point)
7. Document chart appropriately. (2 points)

Notes:

Evaluating the Physical Characteristics of Urine

Objective: Evaluate the physical characteristics of urine and properly record the results.

Supplies: Urine specimen, centrifuge tube, laboratory slip, personal protective equipment, as needed

Affective Behaviors: Affective behaviors provide a professional approach to a skill that enhances the patient encounter. These behaviors may also display sensitivity to a patient's rights and enhance communication. Pay close attention to these skills, which will be in **_bold, italicized_** font.

Steps:
1. Assemble all equipment and supplies. (1 point)
2. Perform proper hand hygiene and apply gloves. (1 point)
3. Label a centrifuge tube with the patient's name. (1 point)
4. Mix the urine by carefully swirling it, avoiding spillage. (1 point)
5. Assess the color of the specimen and record it using appropriate terminology. (2 points)
6. Assess the clarity of the urine and record it using proper terminology. (2 points)
7. Clean and sanitize the work area. (1 point)
8. Remove and dispose of gloves properly. (1 point)
9. Perform proper hand hygiene, unless proceeding with complete urinalysis. (1 point)
10. Document your observations in the patient's record using proper terminology. (2 points)

Notes:

ICD-9-CM Coding

Objective: Accurately assign an ICD-9-CM code.

Supplies: Patient's medical record; patient's insurance card; computer with printer or typewriter; medical reference material; superbill with the doctor's diagnosis.

Affective Behaviors: Affective behaviors provide a professional approach to a skill that enhances the patient encounter. These behaviors may also display sensitivity to a patient's rights and enhance communication. Pay close attention to these skills, which will be in **_bold, italicized_** font.

Steps:

. Locate the condition or diagnosis on the superbill or in the patient's medical record. (1 point)
. In *Volume II: Alphabetic Index* of the ICD-9-CM, locate the condition or diagnosis. (1 point)
. Examine the diagnostic statements to determine if the main term specifically describes that disease. If it does not, look at the modifiers listed under that main term to find a more specific code. (1 point)
. Locate the code in *Volume I: Tabular Index*. (1 point)
. Match the code description in the *Tabular Index* with the diagnosis in the patient's medical record. (1 point)
. Use the codes from 0021.0 through V82.9 in the ICD-9-CM to describe the main reason for the patient's office visit. (1 point)
. First, list the ICD-9-CM code for the condition, problem, or diagnosis that is the main reason for the visit. Then, list coexisting conditions under additional codes. (1 point)
. Use codes at their highest level of specificity—fifth-digit codes first, followed by fourth-digit codes, then third-digit codes, and so on. (1 point)
. Do not code questionable, probable, or ruled-out diagnoses. (1 point)
0. V codes describe factors that influence the health status of the patient, such as pregnancy test or vaccination, and are not used to code current illnesses. (1 point)
1. E codes are used for identifying external environmental events or conditions such as the course of injury, some adverse effect, or poisoning. E codes (E930–E949) are mandatory when coding the use of drugs. (1 point)
2. M codes, in Appendix A of *Volume I*, relate to the morphology of neoplasm. Morphology codes are used only by tumor registries for reporting proposes. (1 point)
3. List all diagnosis codes (up to four) on the insurance claim form, with the primary diagnosis listed first. (2 points)
4. Always double-check your coding and ensure proper use of abbreviations and symbols prior to assigning the final code. (2 points)

Notes:

Interviewing a New Patient to Obtain Medical History Information and Preparing for a Physical Examination

Objective: Obtain pertinent patient information for the medical history to assist the physician in establishing the cause and treatment of the present illness (PI) by interview. Include the chief complaint (CC), past history (PH), social or personal history (SH), and family history (FH).

Supplies: Medical history form; clipboard; pen; scale; equipment for vital signs; urine container; gown and drape

Affective Behaviors: Affective behaviors provide a professional approach to a skill that enhances the patient encounter. These behaviors may also display sensitivity to a patient's rights and enhance communication. Pay close attention to these skills, which will be in ***bold, italicized*** font.

Steps:
1. ***Identify the patient, greet the patient warmly, and identify yourself.*** (2 points)
2. Explain the procedure. (1 point)
3. Provide a private area to conduct the interview. (1 point)
4. If not already complete, ask the patient to fill out the required demographic information on the registration form. ***Assist the patient in completing the form if necessary.*** (1 point)
5. Review the patient data portion; ***ask for any additional information necessary.*** (2 points)
6. ***Ask why the patient is being seen by the physician today (CC).*** (1 point)
7. Record the CC in the patient's own words (as appropriate). (2 points)
8. ***Using observations skills, ask the patient other open-ended questions to gather necessary information about the CC. Record this information under PI.*** (1 point)
9. Gather other information about PH, FH, and SH; document in patient's record. (1 point)
10. ***Ask the patient if he or she has any allergies.*** Document according to facility protocol (red ink/ specific area for recording allergy information). (2 points)
11. Document any other relevant observations or information. (1 point)
12. Record all information using correct charting guidelines. (1 point)
13. Correct any charting errors, drawing one line through error and adding the date and your initials. Record the correct information. (2 points)
14. If required or appropriate, ask patient to provide urine specimen or to empty his or her bladder. (1 point)
15. Obtain a complete set of vital signs (temperature, pulse, respirations, blood pressure, height, and weight). Immediately document this data in the patient's record. (2 points)

16. ***Explain what clothes the patient needs to remove, proper donning of the exam gown, and where the patient should sit and wait.*** (1 point)
17. ***Explain what procedures will follow;*** tell the patient that the physician will be in shortly. (1 point)
18. Place the patient's record with the history and complaint in the designated place for the physician. (1 point)

Notes:

Measuring Blood Pressure

Objective: Obtain an accurate systolic and diastolic reading.

Supplies: Sphygmomanometer; stethoscope; 70 percent isopropyl alcohol; alcohol sponges or cotton balls; paper and pen; patient's record

Affective Behaviors: Affective behaviors provide a professional approach to a skill that enhances the patient encounter. These behaviors may also display sensitivity to a patient's rights and enhance communication. Pay close attention to these skills, which will be in **bold, *italicized*** font.

Steps:
1. Perform proper hand hygiene. (1 point)
2. Assemble the equipment. Use a sponge or cotton ball with alcohol to thoroughly cleanse the earpieces, bell, and diaphragm pieces of the stethoscope. Allow the alcohol to dry. (2 points)
3. ***Identify the patient and explain the procedure.*** (1 point)
4. ***Assist the patient into a comfortable position. BP may be taken with the patient in a sitting or lying position. The patient's arm should be at heart level. Ask the patient not to cross his or her legs or talk during the procedure.*** (1 point)
    Note: If the patient's arm is below heart level, the BP reading will be higher than normal; if the arm is higher than heart level, the BP will be lower than normal.
5. Place the sphygmomanometer on a solid surface with the gauge within 3 feet for easy viewing. (1 point)
6. ***Uncover the patient's arm by asking the patient to roll back his or her sleeve 5 inches above the elbow. If the sleeve becomes constricting when rolled back, ask the patient to slip his or her arm out of the sleeve.*** (2 points)
    Note: Never take a BP reading through clothing.
7. Have the patient straighten his or her arm with palms up. Apply a proper-size cuff over the brachial artery 1 to 2 inches above the antecubital space (bend in the elbow). Many cuffs are marked with arrows or circles to be placed over the artery. Hold the edge of the cuff in place as you wrap the remainder of the cuff tightly around the arm securing the Velcro closure. (1 point)
8. Palpate with your fingertips to locate the brachial artery in the antecubital space. (1 point)
9. Pump air into the cuff quickly and evenly until the level of mercury is 20 to 30 mmHg above the point at which the radial pulse is no longer palpable.
    Note the level, rapidly deflate, and wait 60 seconds. (2 points)
10. Place the earpieces in your ears and the diaphragm (or bell) of the stethoscope over the area where you feel the brachial artery pulsing. Hold the diaphragm in place with one hand on the chest piece without placing your thumb over the diaphragm. The stethoscope tubing should hang freely and not touch any object or the patient during the reading. (1 point)

11. Close the thumbscrew on the hand bulb by turning clockwise with your dominant hand. Close the thumbscrew just enough so that no air can leak out. Do not close so tightly that you will have difficulty reopening it with one hand. (1 point)
12. Slowly turn the thumbscrew counterclockwise with your dominant hand. Allow the pressure reading to fall only 2 to 3 mmHg at a time. (2 points)
13. Listen for the point at which the first clear sound is heard. Note where this occurred on the manometer. This is the systolic pressure. (1 point)
14. Slowly continue to allow the cuff to deflate. The sounds will change from loud to murmur and then fade away.
    Read the mercury column (or spring gauge scale) at the point where the sound is no longer heard. This is the diastolic pressure. (2 points)
15. Quickly open the thumbscrew all the way to release the air and deflate the cuff completely. (1 point)
16. If you are unsure about the BP reading, wait at least a minute or two before taking a second reading. (1 point)
    Note: Never take more than two readings in one arm.
17. Immediately write the BP as a fraction on paper. You may inform the patient of the reading if this is the policy in your office. (2 points)
18. Remove the cuff. (1 point)
19. Clean the earpieces of the stethoscope with an alcohol sponge. (1 point)
20. Perform proper hand hygiene. (1 point)
21. Document results, including the date, time, BP reading, and your name, in the patient's record. (2 points)

Notes:

Measuring the Chest Circumference of a Child

Objective: Accurately measure the circumference of a child's chest.

Supplies: Tape measurer, examination table, patient record, pen

Affective Behaviors: Affective behaviors provide a professional approach to a skill that enhances the patient encounter. These behaviors may also display sensitivity to a patient's rights and enhance communication. Pay close attention to these skills, which will be in **bold, italicized** font.

Steps:
1. ***Introduce yourself, identify the patient, and explain the procedure.*** (1 point)
2. ***Talk to the patient soothingly to gain trust.*** (2 points)
3. Perform proper hand hygiene. (1 point)
4. Position the child on the table in the supine position. (2 points)
   Note: If the patient is older than age 2, he or she may sit on the table. (1 point)
5. Place the end of the tape (0) in the center of the child's chest in line with the child's nipples. Slip the tape under the child's body and bring it to meet the other end of the tape.
   Take a measurement in centimeters to the nearest 0.01 or in inches to the nearest one-half-inch. (2 points)
6. ***Place the child in the caregiver's care before recording the results.*** (2 points)
7. Perform proper hand hygiene. (1 point)

Notes:

Measuring the Head Circumference of an Infant or Small Child

Objective: Obtain an accurate measurement of the head circumference of an infant or small child.

Supplies: Flexible tape measure, growth chart

Affective Behaviors: Affective behaviors provide a professional approach to a skill that enhances the patient encounter. These behaviors may also display sensitivity to a patient's rights and enhance communication. Pay close attention to these skills, which will be in *bold, italicized* font.

Steps:
1. *Identify the patient.* (1 point)
2. *Talk to the infant to gain trust.* (2 points)
3. *Explain the procedure to the patient's parent or caregiver.* (1 point)
4. Perform proper hand hygiene. (1 point)
5. Position the patient on the examination table or have the caregiver hold the infant. (1 point)
6. Hold the end of the tape (0) on the forehead, over the patient's eyebrows. (2 points)
7. Bring the tape around the head and over the ears to meet in the front. (1 point)
8. Take the measurement with accuracy to a fraction of an inch or centimeter. (1 point)
9. Repeat procedure if in any doubt about measurements. (1 point)
10. Perform proper hand hygiene. (1 point)
11. Document results in patient's record and on growth chart. (2 points)

Notes:

Measuring the Weight and Height of an Infant

Objective: Obtain the weight and height of an infant.

Supplies: Baby scale; patient record; pen; small towel or protector for scale; tape measure

Affective Behaviors: Affective behaviors provide a professional approach to a skill that enhances the patient encounter. These behaviors may also display sensitivity to a patient's rights and enhance communication. Pay close attention to these skills, which will be in **bold, *italicized*** font.

Steps:
1. ***Introduce yourself and identify the infant by stating infant's name to the parent. Have the infant remain with the parent or caregiver while you prepare the equipment. Explain the procedure.*** (2 points)
2. Place a towel or paper protector on the baby scale. (1 point)
3. Perform proper hand hygiene. (1 point)
4. Balance the scale by placing all weights to the left side and turning the adjustment bolt until the balance bar pointer is in the middle. (2 points)
5. ***Undress the infant. Gently lay the infant on the scale. Remember to always keep one hand on the infant until the weights are adjusted. Do not leave the infant unattended at any time.*** (1 point)
6. ***Keeping one hand over the infant's body as a safety precaution***, move the large pound weight into the groove closest to the weight estimated for the baby. Then move the smaller ounce weight by tapping it gently until the pointer floats in the center of the frame. (2 points)
7. Keep the weights in place while moving the infant to the examination table for height measurement under the caregiver's care while you record the weight. (2 points)
8. Holding the tape measure with one hand, place the tape at the top of the side of the infant's head. Stretch the infant out full-length as you pull the tape measure down to the bottom of the feet. If you are using a table with a measure bar, place the infant's head on one end of the table with the soles of the feet touching the footboard.
   Note: It is best to have two people measure the length of an infant. The parent can assist by keeping the infant's head still. If the child is active, make pencil marks on the examination table paper at the top of the head and at the heel. Remove child and measure area between the marks. (2 points)
9. Note the height in inches and fractions of an inch, and write the measurement on the exam table paper. (1 point)
10. ***Ask the parent to hold the infant while the height and weight are charted in the infant record.*** (2 points)

11. Tell the measurements to the parent. (1 point)
12. Discard the scale cover or place it in the laundry bin. (1 point)
13. Perform proper hand hygiene. (1 point)

Notes:

Performing a Venipuncture Using the Vacutainer Method

Objective: Perform venipuncture by correctly assembling, locating, and entering a vein, and withdrawing a blood sample.

Supplies: Biohazard sharps container, Vacutainer tubes, multisample needle, gauze squares, alcohol pads, gloves, Vacutainer sleeve, tourniquet, bandage, cotton balls, adhesive, pen, lab coat, patient record, ammonia ampules

Affective Behaviors: Affective behaviors provide a professional approach to a skill that enhances the patient encounter. These behaviors may also display sensitivity to a patient's rights and enhance communication. Pay close attention to these skills, which will be in ***bold, italicized*** font.

Steps:
1. Assemble all equipment and materials. (1 point)
2. Perform proper hand hygiene. (1 point)
3. ***Identify the patient and explain the procedure. Position the patient either sitting or lying down.*** (2 points)
4. Apply gloves. (1 point)
5. Screw the Vacutainer needle into the plastic sleeve. Insert the tube into the other end of the sleeve; be sure not to puncture the tube. (1 point)
6. Apply the tourniquet 2 inches above the antecubital space tight enough to engorge the vein with blood. (1 point)
7. ***Place the patient's arm in an extended position with the palm facing up and comfortably resting.*** (1 point)
8. Palpate the vein with your fingertips. (1 point)
9. Cleanse the chosen venipuncture site with an alcohol sponge in a circular pattern. Allow alcohol to dry. (2 points)
10. Anchor the vein properly. (1 point)
11. Bevel up, line up the needle with the vein approximately 1/4–1/2 inch below the site where the vein is to be entered. (2 points)
    a. At a 15°–30° angle, rapidly and smoothly insert the needle through the skin.
    b. Remove your non-dominant hand, slowly pull back the plunger of the syringe or place two fingers on the flanges of the adapter, and, with the thumb, push the tube onto the needle inside the adapter.
    c. When the blood flow begins in the tube or syringe, allow the patient to release the fist.
    d. Release the tourniquet.
    e. Allow the syringe or tube(s) to fill to capacity.
    f. When the blood flow ceases, remove the tube from the adapter by gripping the tube with the nondominant hand, placing the thumb against the flange during the removal.

       1) Twist and gently pull out the tube. Steady the needle in the vein.

       2) Try not to pull up or press down on the needle while it is in the vein.

   g. Insert any other necessary tubes into adapter and allow each to fill to capacity.

12. Remove the tube from adapter. (2 points)

   a. Place a sterile gauze pad over the puncture site during needle withdrawal.

   b. Do not apply any pressure to the site until the needle is completely removed.

   c. After needle is removed, apply pressure or have patient apply direct pressure for 3–5 minutes.

   d. Do not bend the arm at the elbow

13. Transfer the blood from a syringe into tubes via the transfer device. (2 points)

   a. In the proper order of draw, allow the vacuum to fill the tubes.

   b. Place the tubes in tube rack and carefully insert the device through the stopper.

   c. If the vacuum tubes contain an anticoagulant.

      1) Mix immediately by gently inverting the tube 8–10 times.

      2) Do not shake the tube.

   d. Label the tubes with the proper information.

14. Check the puncture site for bleeding. (1 point)

   a. Apply a bandage, a clean 2 × 2 gauze pad folded in quarters.

   b. Hold in place by a Band-Aid or 3-inch strip of tape.

15. ***Thank the patient.*** (1 point)

16. ***Tell the patient to leave the bandage in place at least 15 minutes and not to carry a heavy object (such as a purse) or lift heavy objects with that arm for an hour.*** (1 point)

12. Remove and dispose of gloves. Perform proper hand hygiene. (1 point)

13. Document the procedure in the patient's record. (2 points)

Notes:

Positioning the Patient in the Dorsal Recumbent Position

Objective: Assist the patient into the dorsal recumbent position.

Supplies: Patient gown and drape; examination table

Affective Behaviors: Affective behaviors provide a professional approach to a skill that enhances the patient encounter. These behaviors may also display sensitivity to a patient's rights and enhance communication. Pay close attention to these skills, which will be in **bold, italicized** font.

Steps:
1. ***Greet and identify the patient. Introduce yourself, and escort him or her to the examination room.*** (2 points)
2. Perform proper hand hygiene. (1 point)
3. ***Explain the procedure to the patient.*** Provide a gown and ask the patient to completely undress and to put on the gown. Assist the patient if necessary. (1 point)
4. Instruct the patient to sit on the end of the examination table. ***Assist the patient onto the table.*** If a separate step stool is used, stabilize it with your feet as the patient steps up to prevent the stool from sliding. (1 point)
5. Pull out the foot extension. Ask the patient to lie back on the table. ***Assist the patient by supporting the patient's back.*** (1 point)
6. ***Ask the patient to bend his or her knees and place the feet flat on the table.*** Push in the foot extension. (1 point)
7. ***Cover the patient with the drape from the patient's chest to ankles.*** (1 point)
8. Place a pillow under the patient's head. (1 point)
9. Place the light source and rolling stool in place for the examiner. (1 point)
10. After the examination, ***assist the patient to a sitting position***. Allow the patient to remain seated to prevent dizziness. (1 point)
11. When the patient is stable and the examination is complete, ***assist the patient to a standing position and hold the patient's arm while he or she steps down.*** Stabilize the step stool with your feet again. Give further instructions as needed. ***Prior to leaving the examination room, ask the patient if he or she has any questions***. (1 point)
12. Clean the examination room. (1 point)
13. Perform proper hand hygiene. (1 point)

Notes:

Positioning the Patient in the Fowler's Position

Objective: Assist the patient into the Fowler's position.

Supplies: Patient gown and drape; examination table with stirrups

Affective Behaviors: Affective behaviors provide a professional approach to a skill that enhances the patient encounter. These behaviors may also display sensitivity to a patient's rights and enhance communication. Pay close attention to these skills, which will be in **bold, italicized** font.

Steps:
1. ***Greet and identify the patient. Introduce yourself, and escort him or her to the examination room.*** (2 points)
2. Perform proper hand hygiene. (1 point)
3. ***Explain the procedure to the patient.*** Provide a gown and ask the patient to completely undress and put on the gown. Assist the patient if necessary. (1 point)
4. Instruct the patient to sit on the end of the examination table. ***Assist the patient onto the table.*** If a separate step stool is used, stabilize it with your feet as the patient steps up to prevent the stool from sliding. (1 point)
5. ***Cover the patient's legs with a drape.*** (1 point)
6. ***Assist the patient to slide back and lean on the raised end of the table.*** (1 point)
7. Pull out the foot extension while supporting the patient's feet. (1 point)
8. Raise the head of the table to a 90-degree angle for Fowler's position and to a 45-degree angle for the Semi-Fowler's position. (1 point)
9. ***Place a pillow under the patient's knees to relieve strain on the lower back. Adjust the drape as needed.*** (1 point)
10. When the examination is complete, push in the foot extension. ***Ask the patient to remain seated at the end of the table to prevent dizziness.***
    Note: Inform the patient before lowering the table. Ask the patient to lean forward while you support the patient's back and lower the table. (1 point)
11. When the patient is stable and the examination is complete, ***assist the patient to a standing position and hold the patient's arm while he or she steps down.*** Stabilize the step stool with your feet again. Give further instructions as needed. ***Prior to leaving the examination room, ask the patient if he or she has any questions.*** (1 point)
12. Clean the examination room. (1 point)
13. Perform proper hand hygiene. (1 point)

Notes:

Positioning the Patient in the Knee-Chest Position

Objective: Assist the patient into the Knee-Chest position.

Supplies: Patient gown and drape; examination table

Affective Behaviors: Affective behaviors provide a professional approach to a skill that enhances the patient encounter. These behaviors may also display sensitivity to a patient's rights and enhance communication. Pay close attention to these skills, which will be in **bold, italicized** font.

Steps:
1. ***Greet and identify the patient. Introduce yourself, and escort him or her to the examination room.*** (2 points)
2. Perform proper hand hygiene. (1 point)
3. ***Explain the procedure to the patient.*** Provide a gown and ask the patient to undress and put on the gown. ***Assist the patient if necessary.*** (1 point)
4. Instruct the patient to sit on the examination table. ***Assist the patient onto the table.*** If a separate step stool is used, stabilize it with your feet as the patient steps up to prevent the stool from sliding. (1 point)
5. **Cover the legs with a drape.** (1 point)
6. Pull out the foot extension. Ask the patient to lie back on the table. ***Assist the patient by supporting the patient's back.*** (1 point)
7. ***Ask the patient*** to turn toward you onto his or her abdomen, providing assistance as needed. Position yourself close to the middle of the table to prevent the patient from falling. (1 point)
8. ***Assist the patient*** onto his or her knees, with hips bent and keeping the chest on the table. Buttocks will be raised in the air, arms bent, head turned to the side, and hands next to the head. The patient may rest his or her weight on the elbows if it is more comfortable. Place a pillow under the patient's head for comfort. (1 point)
9. ***Adjust the drape so the point of the drape is between the patient's legs.*** (1 point)
10. When the examination or procedure is complete, help the patient to lie flat on the abdomen. When the patient is ready, ask him or her to turn toward you and onto his or her back. ***Assist the patient to a sitting position.*** Allow the patient to remain seated to prevent dizziness. (1 point)
11. Push the foot extension into place while supporting the patient's feet. (1 point)
12. When the patient is stable and the examination is complete, ***assist the patient to a standing position and hold the patient's arm while he or she steps down.*** Stabilize the step stool with your feet again. Give further instructions as needed. ***Prior to leaving the examination room, ask the patient if he or she has any questions.*** (1 point)

13. Clean the examination room. (1 point)
14. Perform proper hand hygiene. (1 point)

Notes:

Positioning the Patient in the Lithotomy Position

Objective: Assist the patient into the lithotomy position.

Supplies: Patient gown and drape; examination table with stirrups

Affective Behaviors: Affective behaviors provide a professional approach to a skill that enhances the patient encounter. These behaviors may also display sensitivity to a patient's rights and enhance communication. Pay close attention to these skills, which will be in **bold, italicized** font.

Steps:

1. ***Greet and identify the patient. Introduce yourself, and escort him or her to the examination room.*** (2 points)
2. Perform proper hand hygiene. (1 point)
3. ***Explain the procedure to the patient.*** Provide a gown and ask the patient to completely undress and put on the gown. Assist the patient if necessary. (1 point)
4. Instruct the patient to sit on the end of the examination table. ***Assist the patient onto the table.*** If a separate step stool is used, stabilize it with your feet as the patient steps up to prevent the stool from sliding. (1 point)
5. ***Cover the patient's legs with a drape.*** (1 point)
6. Pull out the foot extension. Ask the patient to lie back on the table. ***Assist the patient by supporting the patient's back.*** (1 point)
7. Position the stirrups level with the height of the table, about 1 foot from the side of the table, and lock them in place. (1 point)
8. ***Ask the patient to slide down on the table until the buttocks is on the edge of the table end.*** (1 point)
9. ***Ask the patient to bend his or her knees and place his or her feet in the stirrups.*** Position the drape for privacy with a point between the legs. Push in the foot extension. (1 point)
10. Place the light source and rolling stool in place for the examiner. (1 point)
11. ***Place a pillow under the patient's head.*** (1 point)
12. When the examination is complete, pull out the foot extension and help the patient remove his or her feet from the stirrups and place them on the foot extension. (1 point)
13. ***Ask the patient to slide up on the table, assisting as necessary. Keep the drape in place to ensure privacy.*** (1 point)
14. ***Assist the patient to a sitting position and push in the foot extension.*** Allow the patient to remain seated to prevent dizziness. (1 point)
15. When the patient is stable and the examination is complete, ***assist the patient to a standing position and hold the patient's arm while he or she steps down.*** Stabilize the step stool with your feet again. Give further instructions as needed. ***Prior to leaving the examination room, ask the patient if he or she has any questions.*** (1 point)

16. Clean the examination room. (1 point)
17. Perform proper hand hygiene. (1 point)

Notes:

Positioning the Patient in the Prone Position

Objective: Assist the patient into the prone position.

Supplies: Patient gown and drape; examination table

Affective Behaviors: Affective behaviors provide a professional approach to a skill that enhances the patient encounter. These behaviors may also display sensitivity to a patient's rights and enhance communication. Pay close attention to these skills, which will be in **bold, italicized** font.

Steps:
1. ***Greet and identify the patient. Introduce yourself, and escort him or her to the examination room.*** (2 points)
2. Perform proper hand hygiene. (1 point)
3. ***Explain the procedure to the patient.*** Provide a gown and ask the patient to undress and put on the gown. ***Assist the patient if necessary.*** (1 point)
4. Instruct the patient to sit on the examination table. ***Assist the patient onto the table.*** If a separate step stool is used, stabilize it with your feet as the patient steps up to prevent the stool from sliding. (1 point)
5. Pull out the foot extension. Ask the patient to lie back on the table. ***Assist the patient by supporting the patient's back.*** (1 point)
6. ***Ask the patient to turn toward you onto his or her side, then onto the abdomen. Position yourself close to the middle of the table to prevent the patient from falling.*** (1 point)
7. ***Place a pillow under the patient's head and feet as needed for comfort. Cover with a drape from the patient's shoulders to ankles.*** (1 point)
8. ***Cover the patient with the drape from the patient's chest to ankles.*** (1 point)
9. When the examination is complete, ask the patient to turn toward you and ***assist the patient to a sitting position.*** Allow the patient to remain seated to prevent dizziness. (1 point)
10. Push the foot extension into place while supporting the patient's feet. (1 point)
11. When the patient is stable and the examination is complete, ***assist the patient to a standing position and hold the patient's arm while he or she steps down.*** Stabilize the step stool with your feet again. Give further instructions as needed. ***Prior to leaving the examination room, ask the patient if he or she has any questions.*** (1 point)
12. Clean the examination room. (1 point)
13. Perform proper hand hygiene. (1 point)

Notes:

Positioning the Patient in the Sims' Position

Objective: Assist the patient into the Sims' position.

Supplies: Patient gown and drape; examination table

Affective Behaviors: Affective behaviors provide a professional approach to a skill that enhances the patient encounter. These behaviors may also display sensitivity to a patient's rights and enhance communication. Pay close attention to these skills, which will be in **bold, italicized** font.

Steps:
1. ***Greet and identify the patient. Introduce yourself, and escort him or her to the examination room.*** (2 points)
2. Perform proper hand hygiene. (1 point)
3. ***Explain the procedure to the patient.*** Provide a gown and ask the patient to undress and put on the gown. ***Assist the patient if necessary.*** (1 point)
4. Instruct the patient to sit on the examination table. ***Assist the patient onto the table.*** If a separate step stool is used, stabilize it with your feet as the patient steps up to prevent the stool from sliding. (1 point)
5. Pull out the foot extension. Ask the patient to lie back on the table. ***Assist the patient by supporting the patient's back.*** (1 point)
6. ***Ask the patient to turn toward you*** onto his or her left side, placing the body weight on the chest with the left knee flexed slightly. Position yourself close to the middle of the table to prevent the patient from falling. (1 point)
7. Ask the patient to flex the right knee to a 90-degree angle. Bend the patient's right arm at the elbow with his or her hand toward the head. Place a pillow under the patient's head for comfort. (1 point)
8. ***Cover the patient with the drape from the patient's shoulder to ankles.*** (1 point)
9. When the examination is complete, ask the patient to turn toward you and onto his or her back. ***Assist the patient to a sitting position.*** Allow the patient to remain seated to prevent dizziness. (1 point)
10. Push the foot extension into place while supporting the patient's feet. (1 point)
11. When the patient is stable and the examination is complete, ***assist the patient to a standing position and hold the patient's arm while he or she steps down.*** Stabilize the step stool with your feet again. Give further instructions as needed. ***Prior to leaving the examination room, ask the patient if he or she has any questions.*** (1 point)
12. Clean the examination room. (1 point)
13. Perform proper hand hygiene. (1 point)

Notes:

Positioning the Patient in the Supine Position

Objective: Assist the patient into the supine position.

Supplies: Patient gown and drape; examination table

Affective Behaviors: Affective behaviors provide a professional approach to a skill that enhances the patient encounter. These behaviors may also display sensitivity to a patient's rights and enhance communication. Pay close attention to these skills, which will be in **bold, *italicized*** font.

Steps:
1. ***Greet and identify the patient. Introduce yourself, and escort him or her to the examination room.*** (2 points)
2. Perform proper hand hygiene. (1 point)
3. ***Explain the procedure to the patient.*** Provide a gown and ask the patient to completely undress and put on the gown. Assist the patient if necessary. For a breast examination, instruct the patient to tie the gown in the front. (1 point)
4. ***Ask the patient to sit on the examination table. Assist the patient onto the table.*** If a separate step stool is used, stabilize it with your feet as the patient steps up to prevent the stool from sliding. (1 point)
5. Pull out the foot extension. Ask the patient to lie back on the table. ***Assist the patient by supporting the patient's back.*** (1 point)
6. Place a pillow under the patient's head. (1 point)
7. ***Cover the patient with the drape from his or her chest to ankles.*** (1 point)
8. After the examination, ***assist the patient to a sitting position***. Allow the patient to remain seated to prevent dizziness. (1 point)
9. Push the foot extension into place while supporting the patient's feet. (1 point)
10. When the patient is stable and the examination is complete, ***assist the patient to a standing position and hold the patient's arm while he or she steps down***. Stabilize the step stool with your feet again. Give further instructions as needed. ***Prior to leaving the examination room, ask the patient if he or she has any questions.*** (1 point)
11. Clean the examination room. (1 point)
12. Perform proper hand hygiene. (1 point)

Notes:

Preparing Injections

Objective: Prepare an injection

Supplies: Medication order, medication, needle, syringe, ampule, gauze, biohazard sharps container, antiseptic wipe

Affective Behaviors: Affective behaviors provide a professional approach to a skill that enhances the patient encounter. These behaviors may also display sensitivity to a patient's rights and enhance communication. Pay close attention to these skills, which will be in **_bold, italicized_** font.

Steps:
1. Wash your hands. (1 point)
2. Review the physician's medication order and select the correct medication. (2 points)
   a. Compare the label with the physician's instructions. Note the expiration date.
   b. Check the label three times: when taking it from the shelf, while drawing it up into the syringe, and when returning to the shelf.
3. Calculate the correct dosage to be given, if necessary. (1 point)
4. Choose the needle and syringe according to the route of administration, type of medication, and size of the patient. (1 point)
5. Open the needle and syringe package. Assemble if necessary. Secure the needle to the syringe. (1 point)
6. Withdraw the correct amount of medication: (2 points)
   a. From an ampule:
   1) Tap the stem of the ampule lightly.
   2) Place a piece of gauze around the ampule neck.
   3) Grasp the gauze and ampule firmly. Snap the stem off the ampule.
   4) Dispose of the ampule top in a biohazard sharps container.
   5) Insert the needle lumen below the level of the medication.
   6) Withdraw the medication.
   7) Dispose of the ampule in a biohazard sharps container.
   8) Remove any air bubbles in the syringe.
   9) Draw back on the plunger to add a small amount of air; then gently push the plunger forward to eject the air out of the syringe.
   b. From a vial:
   1) Using the antiseptic wipe, cleanse the rubber stopper of the vial.
   2) Pull air into the syringe with the amount equivalent to the amount of medication to be removed from the vial.
   3) Insert the needle into the vial top. Inject the air from the syringe.
   4) With the needle inside the vial, invert the vial.
   5) Hold the syringe at eye level.
   6) Aspirate the desired amount of medication into the syringe.

7) Displace any air bubbles in the syringe by gently tapping the barrel.

8) Remove the air by pushing the plunger slowly and forcing the air into the vial.

9) Revert vial and place on the counter; remove needle from vial.

7. Carefully recap the needle using one-hand technique. (1 point)

Notes:

Removing Sutures

Objective: Remove sutures using proper sterile technique as ordered by the physician.

Supplies: Suture removal pack

Affective Behaviors: Affective behaviors provide a professional approach to a skill that enhances the patient encounter. These behaviors may also display sensitivity to a patient's rights and enhance communication. Pay close attention to these skills, which will be in **_bold, italicized_** font.

Steps:
1. Assemble all equipment and supplies needed; check expiration dates on all packs. (1 point)
2. Perform proper hand hygiene. (1 point)
3. **_Identify the patient._** (1 point)
4. **_Explain the procedure to the patient and place him or her in a comfortable position._** (2 points)
5. Perform proper hand hygiene. (1 point)
6. Remove the dressing from the site using proper technique and dispose of it in the appropriate waste container. (1 point)
7. Perform proper hand hygiene. (1 point)
8. Open the suture removal pack using proper sterile technique. (2 points)
9. Apply sterile gloves using proper sterile technique. (2 points)
10. Cleanse the wound as needed. (1 point)
11. Place a gauze sponge next to the wound to hold the removed sutures. (1 point)
12. Grasp the knot of the suture with forceps and lift it gently. (1 point)
13. Insert the suture scissors and cut the suture at skin level. Pull out the suture. (1 point)
14. Place the cut suture on the gauze pad and check to see that all the pieces of the suture have been removed. (2 points)
15. Repeat these steps until all sutures have been removed. (1 point)
16. Count the removed sutures, making sure that all sutures have been removed. (2 points)

Removal of staples
1. Follow steps 1–10 of suture removal. (1 point)
2. Place the lower tips of a sterile staple remover under the staple. (1 point)
3. Squeeze the handles together until they are completely closed, thus bending the staple and removing the staple edges from the skin.
   Note: Do not lift the staple remover when squeezing the handles. (2 points)
4. When both ends of the staple are visible, gently move the staple away from the incision site. (1 point)

5. Hold the staple remover over a disposable container, release the handles, and release the staple. (1 point)
6. Repeat these steps until all staples are removed. Count the number of staples to ensure all have been removed. (2 points)

Closing steps for either suture or staple removal

1. Clean the wound with antiseptic and allow it to dry. (2 points)
2. Dress wound as ordered. (1 point)
3. Properly dispose of equipment and supplies. (1 point)
4. Remove and dispose of gloves. Perform proper hand hygiene. (1 point)
5. ***Instruct patient on wound care.*** (1 point)
6. Document the procedure, including condition of the wound, number of staples/sutures removed, and patient wound care instructions, in the patient's record. (2 points)

Notes:

Testing the Chemical Characteristics of Urine with Reagent Strips

Objective: Perform chemical testing on urine using chemical reagent strips.

Supplies: Urine specimen; reagent test strips; timer; paper towels; laboratory slip; pen/pencil; personal protective equipment, as needed

Affective Behaviors: Affective behaviors provide a professional approach to a skill that enhances the patient encounter. These behaviors may also display sensitivity to a patient's rights and enhance communication. Pay close attention to these skills, which will be in **bold, *italicized*** font.

Steps:

1. Assemble all equipment and supplies. (1 point)
2. Perform proper hand hygiene. Apply gloves and personal protective equipment, as needed. (1 point)
3. Check the specimen for the patient identity, date, and time of collection. (2 points)
4. Check the expiration date on reagent strips. (1 point)
5. Allow urine to reach room temperature and swirl gently to mix. (1 point)
6. Dip a chemical reagent strip in urine, making sure that all pads on the strips are moistened. (2 points)
7. Read each pad by comparing it to the chart on the side of the reagent strip container, appropriately timing each test. Ignore any color change after the time has elapsed. (2 points)
8. Record the results on the patient's laboratory slip. (2 points)
9. Clean and sanitize the work area. (1 point)
10. Remove gloves and PPE, and perform proper hand hygiene. (1 point)

Notes: